THE CENTURY EARTH SCIENCE SERIES, Kirtley F. Mather, *Editor*

The Geography of Europe

THE GEOGRAPHY
of EUROPE

George D. Hubbard
Professor Emeritus
Oberlin College

SECOND EDITION

New York

APPLETON-CENTURY-CROFTS, INC.

To

My Students

Active Critics, Yet a Continuous Inspiration

This Book Is Dedicated

Preface to the Second Edition

The first edition of this book appeared in 1937. Not long thereafter a collection of notes of various kinds anticipating revision began to accumulate. Some errors were marked; unfortunate phrases, discrepancies in the descriptions of countries, and omissions were noted. In the discovery of these both students and colleagues were helpful.

As World War II proceeded, need for revision in political and economic geographic fields became very obvious. New discoveries in the prehistory of man and new studies of movements of peoples, studies of resources and of commercial relations, and new development of natural resources and of industries to prepare the resources for use were made known. Many geographic and historic publications added to our knowledge. Dates were set for revision and postponed in order that boundary treaties might be written before final form should be given to the new edition. At last formal revision was deemed wise, and the publishers decreed to the joy and satisfaction of the author that the new edition should of necessity be completely reset, thus opening the way for many changes.

Nature of changes

The general plan of the book has not been changed. The continued use of the first edition for fifteen years, even during the disturbances of the war, seems to indicate the stability of climatic divisions and of grouping of states, as well as the value of large use of physical patterns for subdivisions of the continent and of the national domains for treatment. These cannot be disturbed by wars and power aspirants.

Political boundaries have been drawn on all maps in accord with treaties and agreements so far as they were settled at the close of 1951.

Population and area statistics have been changed extensively; yet we recognize that as yet exact figures, such as were available in 1937, are impossible. *World Almanac, Annual Yearbooks* of Britannica, *Europa, a Year Book,* and national yearbooks, estimates, both within the several nations and from outside, and in rare instances censuses, have been used. Because this book is neither an economic geography nor a commercial geography, and because knowledge of statistics of production, exports, and imports was in far too imperfect a condition at the close of 1951 to make exact figures possible, we have purposely spared the reader statistical tables and have attempted few rigorous comparisons in these fields. What statistics are given have been scrutinized with great care and are the best we can do in this edition. Most countries and areas are believed to be swinging back to the levels of the late 1930's, and some are known to exceed such figures.

The so-called "iron curtain" drawn around the republics of the U.S.S.R. and their satellites prevents much information, especially of a statistical nature, from reaching nations of western Europe and America; and the small amount seeping out has little validity. Such transfer of information is also hampered by Soviet restrictions laid on trade with the west.

Many pages, in some cases whole sections, have been rewritten in order to make necessary deletions and additions. Blocks of material given formerly in one country are necessarily transferred to another because sovereignty has changed. This is most noticeable in Germany, Poland, and adjacent Russia. Many pages have had lines and paragraphs changed and few pages have come through unscathed. Two new chapters have been added; one at the end of Part I describes some of the geographic changes inflicted by the war so as to remove the need of discussing this matter under many individual countries. The other new chapter treats of the geography of the Mediterranean Sea and is placed at the close of the chapters describing the area having Mediterranean climate. It seems to the author that this sea has been as important a factor in European history and geography as any single country on its shores. In modern times there has been considerable interest in the question "Whose sea is it?", a question geographers as well as statesmen do well to study.

The Baltic States incorporated into the U.S.S.R. in 1940 are here treated in a separate chapter before beginning the discussion of European Russia. This is in recognition of the fact that not many governments, particularly our own, have recognized their annexation to the U.S.S.R. The chapter on Poland now follows the chapter on Germany.

Because of the necessity imposed by political changes, scores of maps have been redrawn or revised to show changes in boundaries. Touches of historical geography and economic trends have been worked in because of political changes and new economic activities.

More than 170 new halftone illustrations have been used and as many former ones deleted. These map and picture changes have done more to give this edition a "new look" than anything else, though to the careful reader the new look will be apparent in every chapter.

Credits

Students and colleagues have been very kind in calling attention to ways of improving the book, and of eliminating its "worst" features and have tendered helps and suggestions at many points. This service and helpful coöperation is much appreciated. It is hoped that future users will be as helpful in the years to come.

The author is under deep obligation to many authors and teachers who have written since 1937, as our revised chapter bibliographies will suggest. To the Oberlin College photostat studio and to several draftsmen who have worked over the maps, much credit is due. To the several consular offices and information services of European nations and to our own government bureaus, thanks are due for assistance in obtaining new pictures. In the legends for the illustrations specific credit is given.

To the series editor, Dr. Kirtley F. Mather, thanks and due credit for many pointers and encouragement are given.

My greatest obligation, as in the former edition, is to my wife, Edna Rugg Hubbard, for patience and skill in proofreading, and more for her perspicacity and lucidity of expression and her indefatigable efforts to help produce a readable text.

And so the new edition goes out with the hope that it may be as service-able as its predecessor.

G. D. H.

Preface to the First Edition

The ideal, as phrased before the book was begun, has been to prepare a textbook in the geography of Europe for American colleges and universities: to make a book of interest to students in European history, economics, political science, sociology, and diplomatic service, and to furnish information to the traveler and the general reader. It is hoped the book will develop good citizenship, international-mindedness, and racial and religious sympathies and show the interdependence of nations and peoples, places, and climates. It may even stimulate interest in European travel, literature, music, architecture, and scultpure by showing many relationships between the arts and geographic conditions. The book may serve to develop a broader, more sympathetic culture, a deeper response to the news of the day, a keener appreciation and perception of the problems, difficulties, possibilities, and future of the European nations. How well the ideals have been met may appear in the years ahead as the book makes its way among its fellows.

Approach

First and always comes the relation of man and his activities to the physical conditions in which he finds himself. These conditions include topography, soils, climate, distribution of land and water, and elements of relief; resources, as forests, power, fuels, building materials, ores and other minerals, fisheries, and wild life; neighbors and their social, economic, and religious standards and status. The relation of man to these conditions consists of responses, adjustments of both nature and man, disregard, opposition, and (very rarely) control. Due recognition is given to past history, past races, and past activities.

A balanced book, with space devoted to each country and topic, and to text and illustrations in adequate proportion, has been the author's ambition. Some map shows the situation of every place mentioned in the text. Questions at the end of each chapter are not memory or drill questions but are designed to help teacher and pupil to discuss principles stated or suggested in the text.

Basis for the book

The author taught European geography for twenty years, then determined to see the countries. During a sabbatical year promoted by Oberlin's generous plan, he saw all the countries of Europe, met a few of their geographers, and visited educational institutions. He learned many new items, revised others, and unlearned not a few. On his return he reworked his subject material in a seminar on the geography of Europe, participated in by the departmental staff, all the graduate students in geography, several seniors, and several friends who had traveled in Europe. As the chapters of this book have been written during the past four years, many of them have been tried out with classes, and the general method of the book has been used successfully in the classroom.

Acknowledgments

Grateful thanks are hereby given to Oberlin College for generosity in time, library facilities, photostatic work, and every help possible; to draftsmen, typists, readers of references, and helpers in the making of bibliographies. These persons have all been Oberlin students—Beatrice Winter, Harriet Colburn, D. A. Kaufman, Dorothy Platt, F. H. Horn, Frederick Herschleb, and Herman Thompson; their desire for coöperation and accuracy have been a continual source of joy and strength. Many chapters have been read by residents of the country discussed therein. Special thanks are here expressed in permanent form to Doctor Oscar Jászi, formerly of Hungary; Mrs. Recha Jászi, who has read the sections on Austria and Czechoslovakia; Professor and Mrs. Axel Skjerne, Denmark; Miss Edith Metcalf, Albania; Miss Magdalene Schepp of Germany; Basil Milovsoroff for much help on Russia; to former students, Margaret Stevens, Walter Ristow, Ruth Rockwood, and my daughter Ruth Hubbard who have each read several chapters; to my colleagues Dr. Fred Foreman and Dr. Reuel B. Frost, for reading chapters and for a continued interest and assistance all through the work. My greatest debt is due my wife, Mrs. Edna Rugg Hubbard, whose thorough training in English and whose wide reading and travel have made her a priceless critic, whose accuracy and diligence have discovered many a subtle error and clouded expression, and whose persistent devotion to a long task has done much to make the book what it is. Acknowledgment is also due the wise and sympathetic editor and long-time friend, Dr. Kirtley F. Mather, for many general suggestions, coöperation, and frequent editorial touches.

Acknowledgments for photographs are many and will be found in courtesy lines beneath the pictures. Officials of every nation have shown friendly, helpful solicitude. Many sources have been drawn upon for maps; some have been largely traced from atlases and books, many are compilations from several sources. In each case there appears a credit line. The author thanks his many contributors for the pictures and maps, which he believes add very much to the understanding of the text. Bibliographies follow each chapter and suggest that a book, like many modern buildings, is not built but assembled. The author justly thanks not only the authors and institutions mentioned in the bibliographies but hundreds more whose contribution is, on the part of both giver and receiver, more or less unconscious, but none the less real.

For inadvertent errors the author is responsible. One cannot be an authority in all the related fields upon which such a book as this must border. The author asks the indulgence of those whose special knowledge enables them to find such errors and requests that they be brought to his attention. Errors in or differences of interpretation likewise invite discussion.

If the book is adjudged good, it is largely the recognition of the work of the scores who have assisted; if unworthy, that is in spite of all they could do for it.

To the reader the author has a word. There is back of this piece of work a philosophy. No one should think of taking a thorough course in geography and expect to come out of it the same person. As he meditates and discusses the principles and philosophy underlying, some parts should find permanent lodgment in his own philosophy.

G. D. H.

Contents

Part VII

LOWER DANUBE STATES

Part VIII

CONCLUSION

Part I

INTRODUCTORY SECTION

CHAPTER I

Situation and General Relations

Europe does not stand for quantity but for quality, not for size
but for variety.—PAUL COHEN-PORTHEIM

Two facts alone concerning the continent of Europe, if grasped in their
fullness, are ample reason for launching on a thorough study of the continent, its physique, history, and geography. Europe comprises about one
fifteenth of the land of the earth; yet it contains about one fourth of the
earth's inhabitants. It is doing about four times its quota. Naturally the question arises: Why has Europe thus become the world's dominant continent?

Relations to Asia. Physically, Europe is not clearly marked from Asia;
nor is it climatically, economically, or politically separate. Climatically, it
grades from Atlantic marine types into the severer Continental conditions
of Asia. Long historic separation and geographic isolation have given place
recently to intimate economic and political relations. When the Ephesian
scholar wanted to designate the plains behind the city, he said *Asu* ("sun-
rise"); and for the lands beyond the Ægean Sea, he said *Erib* ("sunset").
There and then the Ægean was specific and exact enough for a boundary.
As in this first differentiation water demarked the limits of Europe, so for
centuries the line continued north along water—Dardanelles, Marmara,
Bosporus, and Black Sea—in a wholly satisfactory way; but when it became desirable to mark off Europe farther north, the problem was beset with
complications.

The boundary does not now follow, and rarely in the past has it followed,
the crest of the Caucasus, nor does it try to follow any ridge in the Urals;
but north of the Caspian Sea it has followed at different times one or the
other of the friendly rivers, Don and Ural, where men have traveled and
met on familiar terms. The difficulty in selecting a boundary is further
shown by the fact that the line has often been put on neither stream but
between them, and east of the Ural, and even west of the Don on the
Dnieper. Instead of laying the line on the unaccommodating Caucasus
Sierras, it has often been placed on the Manych, a channel once carrying
Caspian waters into the Black Sea, at the mouth of the Don. Today the
modern nations of Turkey and the Soviet Union lie across the intercon-

tinental boundary lines of previous ages. All these items are expressions of the intimate physical identity of the Eurasian continents.

Relations to Africa. Not so troublesome and movable has been the southern boundary. The Mediterranean, a great arm of the Atlantic thrust 2,300 miles in between the lands as a most influential climatic and transportational factor, has visibly laid a southern physical limit. But, strangely enough, ethnic, religious, political, and commercial interests have never stopped at this line. The Sahara Desert really marks the limit of Human Europe, and during early centuries of legend and history the Mediterranean was its center. Why?

Latitude relations. Placed on a spinning globe illuminated by one sun, a continent finds its latitude of prime importance in determining the climate, and through climate the vegetation, animals, and general habitability of the place for man. On meridian 25° E. Europe stretches across 36° of latitude or from Crete in the Mediterranean, Lat. 35° N., to Cape North, Norway, just beyond 71° N. On no meridian is the continent wider, but it has islands more than 10° farther north. Europe thus lies almost wholly in the temperate zone and nowhere either reaches the extremes of tropical heat, humidity, and monotony or deeply invades the rigors of arctic ice and snow. Everywhere it has the spur of the seasons and the varying length of day; it has winters and summers, rainy and dry seasons, and the migration of much wild life—all of which changes have meant much in the development of agriculture, in the domestication of stock, and in the evolution of man.

In longitude it lies leeward from the Atlantic, from which the prevailing winds bring noteworthy climatic influences, tempering both heat and cold and generously supplying more moisture than comes to the lands on the opposite side of the sea.

Significant facts in Europe's geography. Although Europe has only about one fourth of the world's people, her population density is about four times the mean for all the lands of the earth, and before 1940 her annual commerce, imports and exports, was about half that of the whole world. Her tangible properties, buildings, roads, mills and factories, educational plants, palaces, art collections, museums, docks and warehouses, farms and farm equipment, fisheries, forests, and shipping, all together, far exceeded those of any other continent. Postwar reports show that Europe now produces about 75 per cent of the world's potash, pyrite, rye, flax and linen; about 50 per cent of the cement, coal, nitrates, steel, rayon, barley, wheat, beet sugar, potatoes, olives, apples, and horses; and about 30 per cent of the aluminum, iron ore, sheep, synthetic dyes, milk, paper and paper-pulp.

For two or three thousand years Europe has been furnishing statesmen, physicians, scientists, jurists, historians, economists, philosophers, poets, and musicians far in excess of its quota. Men from Europe have explored the world from pole to pole, colonized great portions not known anciently to either Asia or Europe, and governed, at least indirectly and often only for development, millions of square miles of other continents. Empires and commonwealths have been built up by European colonists. Over 85 per cent of the land of the earth is controlled by the people of Europe or their descendants, and 55 per cent of the inhabitants of the earth are governed by these same people. Whether it be to their glory or not, Europeans and their descendants control Australia, South America, North America, and all of Africa except Liberia and Ethiopia, as well as great blocks of Asia in both north and south. Egypt is a constitutional monarchy under strong British influence. The citizens of those countries not directly under European administration have been taking lessons of Europe and the West, and have been revising their customs to make them like those of Europe, or as much like them as possible, while endeavoring to avoid some of the mistakes of Western civilization.

There is a European geographic landscape, a characteristic European aspect on the continent; and similar cultural landscapes are appearing the world around. In some instances European influences have been forced upon people; in many cases they have been applied by mutual consent, in some more or less unconsciously. In many instances European styles and appearances have been transplanted by Europeans into new worlds, but in many others natives have desired to copy and adopt European trappings of government, business, education, architecture. So far have these processes gone that every student of such affairs raises the question, "Why?"

The interpretation is not easy, simple, nor all in one field. To say it is historic is to stop short of the ultimate causes. History has been shaped and directed by men as they have responded consciously and unconsciously to situations of climate, resource, highway, or shelter. To say it is inherent in the race obviously raises another question. Why have these people and groups of people done these things that others have not? Would these people, if their lot had been in Australia or in India, have done the same things they have done here; or would Mongolians or Africans have done as Europeans have done, had their home been Europe for 25,000 years and not eastern Asia or Equatorial Africa?

Geographic, racial, or historical interpretation. As men have grappled with this large and penetrating question, many factors, in at least three categories, geographic, racial, and historical, have been set out for study. Probably no interpretation is complete that does not embody most of the suggested factors; and equally probable is it that the answer will be incomplete until additional factors and influences are discovered.

Mediterranean superiority. Discoveries indicate that in southern Europe during the glacial period the people were little differentiated. They could not go far north because of ice and cold. They were privileged to go far south into Africa because Mediterranean land bridges were then available and the Sahara was less a barrier than now. Thus considerable homogeneity existed across the zone from the cold and icy mountain barriers of central Europe south to the desert barriers of torrid heat and climatic uniformity. East to west these people mingled across the inland seas, great plains, varied mountains, stimulating islands, peninsulas, straits, isthmuses, gulfs, and bays from the Persian Gulf to the Gulf of Biscay, from Egypt to Gadis (Cadiz).

As the ice waned and conditions improved northward, the Sahara high-pressure belt became drier and a more effective barrier. People north of it could not well cross to central Africa, and the Equatorial people, easily fed, clothed, and satisfied, never migrated north. They pass out of the picture.

In the north, as men pushed north following the retreating ice, they found alternating seasons, summer with long, warm days succeeding winter with short, cold ones. Foresight and care for provisions became an advantage, and the necessity of this care for food, clothing, and shelter became a great incentive. In the borders of the Mediterranean belt, from Mesopotamia through the Nile and Po valleys on to the Atlas Mountains, extremes of water supply suggested need and methods of irrigation. When the temptation to irrigate was indulged, men were under a new stimulus to responsibility (always a developer of character), to coöperation, and to stability of residence.

Europe was in closer touch with both Asia and north Africa than were the latter two with each other, a linkage which for thousands of years helped develop a strong European life. The cradle of European civilization and culture was built at the corner of these three continents. The locality has no continental unity but a remarkable unity in climate, in the interpenetration of land and water, in native crops and the opportunities to develop them. Much of this unity was the result of the existence of a large body of water, the Mediterranean, in a mild latitude. The attachment of the people for the water is attested by the colonization patterns of many Mediterranean peoples, particularly that of the Greeks.

The sea embodied many of the helps to progress found in this Mediterranean belt. No doubt the lack of any repelling forest greatly helped in the possession of the land; but the frequency of islands and promontories and the narrowness of channels, bays, and gulfs invited men out to sea. The long distance around, and the short distance across, from the coasts of Asia Minor to those of the Peloponnesus tempted men to take the risk of tracing their courses step by step from island to island. Clear skies in the climatic belt of high-pressure calms revealed the stars as guides to the belated navigator and summoned to astronomical and mathematical research. Long after these beginnings the stars furnished bases for mapping. Land and sea breezes, so well developed on islands and peninsulas in response to alternate heating and cooling of lands in day and night, helped the navigator to sail into port in the daytime and prevented him from being forced upon the rocks if obliged to stay at sea at night.

A geologic map of lands about the Ægean strongly suggests a diversity of rock, mineral, and soil resource and the need of navigation and commerce. The topographic pattern is small, commensurate with the power and limited means of communication of the small rulers and peoples of early days. Many of the islands were large enough for political units; scores of small land units, plains among hills, were nearly as well protected and isolated for the evolution of a state as were the islands. The remarkable unity of the land flooded by the Nile or even of Upper and Lower Egypt, of the Mesopotamian plains, and of the lands on the lower middle and upper Po gave little states habitat and security.

It was no accident that forty nations rose and flourished, fought and failed, in this belt of country from Persian Gulf to Atlantic; nor need it seem strange that, during the millenniums as people gained strength, poise, and more adequate adjustment to climate and topography, the star of empire moved west and north from Ur to London.

As the climate in Greece and the Near East induced the building of open temples and even pillared homes, so in central Europe it easily persuaded men to take shelter in caves and then to build houses, dark and thick-walled, planned to shut out the elements. In their caves they contended with the wild denizens, and having vanquished the bear or wolf in the den or the deer in the forest they adopted its skin for clothing and used it for beds. The struggle for sustenance was keen here; the urge was strong to subdue beast and forest, to protect from inclement weather, and to store food for winter; all such tasks arouse mental activity and impel toward higher civilization.

Atlantic supremacy. When Europe began to face west, toward the Atlantic instead of toward the Mediterranean, many geographic factors favored rapid progress in the new direction. Islands, bays, and interior and marginal seas stimulated seafaring as much on the Atlantic as they had on the Mediterranean. More profitable fishing further urged maritime adventure and called for more efficient ships and sailors than the Mediterranean needed. The possibility of plunder from communities in England and Normandy, even from rich Mediterranean coasts, tempted Vikings far afield. Passes through the mountains, and gaps between them, invited invasion, travel, commerce, and exchange of ideas between south and west Europe. With the turn of Europe to the west came great voyages of discovery and exploration. No people on other continents had risen to such heights of commerce, travel, geographical curiosity, and ship-building powers as had Europeans; hence no one really disputed the European advance. Exploration proceeded; then followed colonization, conquest, exploitation, and various policies and practices of selfish or philanthropic development of other peoples and lands.

Position is important in business, whether it be for the crossroads keeper of the general store or for the city department store, for a nation or for a continent. When Europe faced west, the most energetic people of the world were in the midst of the industrial and commercial arena. That central position became more commanding every decade as new lands were discovered, new colonies founded, new resources uncovered, and new markets established; for every place was within striking distance of European enterprise. Coast-line, inland waters, continental trade routes, and stupendous resources all ministered to the augmentation of Europe's opportunity. Subsequent descriptions of individual countries will indicate their relative importance in Europe's growth.

Recent studies have shown that climatic factors have combined to produce what has been called climatic energy, expressed in human health and drive. This commodity is very unevenly distributed over the lands of the earth. The map of the distribution of climatic energy in five degrees of intensity shows Europe almost entirely within the two deeper shadings, and all of west central Europe in the area of maximum strength. No similar area is found elsewhere in the Old World. May this not be one of the more important reasons why Europe is so significant?

QUESTIONS

1. What geographic influences are involved in the northwestward migration of the centers of action and of the great capitals from Babylon to London?

2. Compare, in spirit and culture, the early interior nations with those on the Mediterranean shores.

3. Compare, in quality, reach, and range of life affected, the great "gifts of southern Europe" with those of western Europe.

4. What is involved in the question, Would the Africans or Chinese have made Europe as significant had they been its inhabitants?

5. How would land and sea breezes keep navigators off rocky shores at night?

6. What differences would it have made to the very early people of Europe if there had been no Mediterranean Sea? if there had been a great river flowing west where the Mediterranean is now?

7. What differences would it have made to the people of Europe in later times if there had been no Mediterranean Sea? if there had been a large river where the sea is and no peninsulas on the south?

8. How would the relations with Asian peoples have been different if Europe had been a great island but in about the same situation?

9. Try to think how the history of Europe might have been different had the continent not been so peninsular.

10. In the light of this chapter and any other reading you have done, what relative value would you give to geographic, racial, and historic factors in answering the questions in the paragraph about the middle of page 5?

11. What items now unknown would you think important to know to solve such questions as these?

BIBLIOGRAPHY

BECKETT, Sir W. Eric, *The North Atlantic Treaty, The Brussels Treaty, and The Charter of the United Nations* (London, Stevens, 1950).

BLACK, C. E., and HELMREICH, E. C., *Twentieth Century Europe* (New York, Alfred A. Knopf, Inc., 1950).

BOYD, Andrew, and METSON, William, *Atlantic Pact, Commonwealth and United Nations* (London, Hutchinson, 1949).

CONDLIFFE, J. B., *The Commerce of Nations* (New York, W. W. Norton & Company, Inc., 1950).

EAST, W. Gordon, *Historical Geography of Europe* (New York, E. P. Dutton & Co., Inc., 1935).

FAIRGRIEVE, James, *Geography and World Power* (New York, E. P. Dutton & Co., Inc., 1941).

FEBVRE, Lucien, *A Geographical Introduction to History,* trans. by E. G. Mountford and J. H. Paxton (New York, Alfred A. Knopf, Inc., 1925).

FITZGERALD, Walter, *The New Europe* (New York, Harper and Brothers, 1946).

GOTTMANN, Jean, *A Geography of Europe* (New York, Henry Holt & Company, Inc., 1950).

GEORGE, H. B., *Relations of Geography and History* (Oxford, Clarendon Press, 1924).

HARTSHORNE, Richard, "A Survey of Boundary Problems in Europe," in Charles C. Colby, ed., *Geographical Aspects of International Relations* (Chicago, University of Chicago Press, 1938).

JAMES, Preston E., *An Outline of Geography* (Boston, Ginn and Company, 1943).

LYDE, L. W., *Continent of Europe* (New York, The Macmillan Company, 1924).

MOODIE, A. E., *Geography Behind Politics* (London, Hutchinson, 1949).

NEWMAN, Bernard, *The New Europe* (New York, The Macmillan Company, 1943).

PEARCY, G. Etzel, FIFIELD, Russell H., *et al., World Political Geography* (New York, Thomas Y. Crowell Company, 1948).

PEATTIE, Roderick, *Geography in Human Destiny* (New York, G. W. Stewart, 1940).

PLESSIA, R., *L'Europe Unie: Problèmes et Perspectives Economiques* (Paris, Pedone, 1949).

RENNER, George T., *et al., Global Geography* (New York, Thomas Y. Crowell Company, 1944).

SHACKLETON, Margaret R., *Europe, A Regional Geography* (London, Longmans, Green & Company, 1942).

SPAAK, Paul-Henri, "The Integration of Europe: Dreams and Realities," *Foreign Affairs,* Vol. 29 (October, 1950), pp. 94-100.

STEMBRIDGE, Jasper H., *The World, A General Regional Geography* (Oxford, Clarendon Press, 1941).

TAYLOR, T. Griffith, *Geography in the Twentieth Century* (New York, Philosophical Library, Inc., 1951).

TEAL, John W., Jr., "Europe's Northernmost Frontier," *Foreign Affairs,* Vol. 29 (January, 1951), pp. 263-275.

VAN VALKENBURG, Samuel, *Elements of Political Geography* (New York, Prentice-Hall, Inc., 1939).

WALLIS, B. C., *Stanford's Compendium of Geography and Travel* (London, E. Stanford, Ltd., 1924).

WHITTLESEY, Derwent S., *The Earth and the State* (New York, Henry Holt & Company, Inc., 1939).

————, *Environmental Foundations of European History* (New York, Appleton-Century-Crofts, Inc., 1949).

ATLASES

BARTHOLOMEW, J. G., *Oxford Advanced Atlas* (Edinburgh, H. Milford, 1950).

DENOYER, L. P., *School Atlas* (Chicago, Denoyer-Geppert Co., 1947).

GOODE, J. Paul, *School Atlas* (Chicago, Rand McNally & Company, 1944), or later.

CHAPTER 2

Geology and Physiography

To him who commands time nothing is impossible.
—HESIOD

Introduction. This chapter and the next are written to give readers a background for a better understanding of chapters dealing with individual countries, particularly such readers as have not had the opportunity of pursuing general courses in geology, physiography, and climatology. The chapters are not exposition in their respective fields, but are descriptive of the geology and climatology of Europe with such explanations of terms and processes as are deemed necessary. For more extended systematic studies in these fields one should read standard texts in geology, physiography, meteorology, climatology, and climates of the continents, such as are referred to in the bibliographic references at the close of the chapters.

STRUCTURE OF EUROPE

Much of the structure of the continent is expressed in its relief, some in its outlines or its shape; and both structure and relief show in the patterns displayed on a good map of the distribution of population. Topography may be classified under three headings: (1) old worn-down mountains (including many uplands and plateaus); (2) young rugged mountains; and (3) lowlands and interior plains. In the first and second areas, the layers of rock are generally tilted, folded, and much disturbed. In the third, the strata are usually more nearly horizontal, their position as they were laid down in the sea.

Old worn-down mountains. The largest area of old mountains occupies all of Norway and about three fourths of Sweden, the portion north of Lake Wener. More than three fourths of the rocks in these mountains, the Kiolen Range, are ancient (Pre-Cambrian) [1] schists, gneisses, granites, and other igneous rocks. From Cape North to the southern coast near Stavanger Fiord, in a belt of varying width the rocks are mostly early Paleozoic (Cambrian, Ordovician, Silurian, and Devonian). These rocks were originally deposited as sediments in seas somewhat like the Baltic; then they were

[1] See the Geologic Time Scale on p. 15.

11

folded and uplifted to become a part of the old Kiolen mountain mass. An older part had preceded them by millions of years. They are of only limited value to men, for they have no coal and not much of other mineral wealth, but they do furnish many kinds of building stones, slate, and marble.

The same sort of rocks, structures, and restricted resources are found again in Scotland north of the strath as well as in northern and western Ireland. Evidently an old land mass with complexly folded structure lay northeast-southwest along the edge of the continent in Pre-Cambrian time, and after profound erosion it was warped down along its axis to form the trough which received these early Paleozoic sediments. If this region has ever had later sediments, they have all been removed, and the record thus obliterated. In Finland and southern Sweden, plateau areas with the same old mountain structure and rocks are now found near sea level with relatively much more of mineral wealth.

Another great mountain range, uplifted much later, but still an old structure, lies across central Europe, in the main north of the younger Alps-Carpathians; but it is not continuous as is the Kiolen Range. It is known variously as the Paleozoic Alps, the Variscan, or the Hercynian Range (pertaining to the Harz Mountains of Germany). After its formation near the end of the Paleozoic time, erosion reduced its form to old-age topography; then it was warped down in places so that the sea could partly cover this old-age surface and large sections of what had formerly been the roots of the mountains, while new sediments were being laid over the surface, concealing mountain stumps. Intricate folding, faulting, and metamorphism of the sedimentary rocks and the granite intrusions testify to former mountain grandeur and to the pressure and movement through which they were put. Remnants of these old mountains are found in southern Ireland, Wales, and Cornwall, in Bretagne and the Central Plateau or Massif of France, and in the Meseta, the Central Massif or core of the Iberian Peninsula. These may presumably be interpreted as portions of the former continuous arcs of the Hercynian mountains, one arc running westward from central Europe to Ireland, the other southward through France to central Spain. Study the map below and a good atlas to find other parts of this old mountain system and learn in what countries it occurs. Although all this topography was once mountains, much now appears as plateaus or even plains, covered by much younger rocks.

While in no way significant as a serious mountain barrier at the present time, these remnants bear much rich soil and some of the finest forests of Europe. Their rocks contain the coal, slate, and metalliferous minerals of Wales, the minerals of Cornwall, Auvergne Plateau, and Meseta, the coal and ores of Belgium, France, Germany, Czechoslovakia, Poland, and Russia, not to mention a wealth and variety of building materials. Modern industrial Europe could not be what it is if it were not for this old mountain range and its treasure of coal, iron, and other valuable minerals.

In late Paleozoic time the Ural Mountains were made from marine sediments by much simpler folding accompanied by the intrusion of granite. The minerals of these mountains have also contributed much to Europe's industrial development.

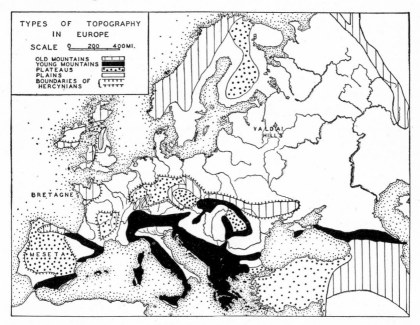

Types of topography in Europe. Some of the Hercynian System of mountains is here classed as old mountains and some as plateau. In Poland and Russia the Hercynians are covered with recent sedimentary rocks and do not look like mountains or plateaus. (Adapted from Atwood's *Regional-Political Europe*)

Young rugged mountains. A much more recent mountain-making episode occurred in Tertiary time. During several geologic periods sediments had been accumulating in inland seas, arms of the ocean, and bays resembling the Caspian, Black, Adriatic, or Tyrrhenian seas, or in alluvial basins like that of the Po or the Danube in the plains of Hungary. Then followed slow folding and mashing of the layers on a grand scale until the magnificent chains of southern Europe raised their heads to the snow line, in some parts to heights adequate for permanent glaciers. The Caucasus, as mountains, extends today only from the Caspian to the Black Sea, but its structure continues east of the Caspian and west into the Crimea and Bulgaria. In the intervening spaces the structure subsequently foundered so as to be covered by the sea. The great crescents of the mountain ranges lead on from Bulgaria and Yugoslavia north to the Iron Gate. In the Carpathians the folds develop breadth without so much height. The structure is low again in Austria, the borders of Hungary, and in eastern Czechoslovakia; and the Danube for the second time crosses the great chain. Then follow Tyrolese Alps and Swiss Alps with their forefolds (the Jura and the French

Alps) to the Mediterranean Sea. Here the folds divide and become lower. One branch continues in Liguria and through the Apennines as far as Sicily. A second branch leaves west of Nice, goes beneath the sea and comes up in the Balearic Islands and in the Sierra Madre of southern Spain; while a third branch springs from the last and emerges in the lofty Pyrenees. In the northwest corner of Yugoslavia, near the place where Carpathians and Tyrolese Alps fuse, come in also the Dinaric Alps, which sprawl southeastward through Yugoslavia, Albania, and Greece, and thence eastward into eastern Greece. The Sierra Nevadas of Spain jump across the Straits and continue in the Atlas Mountains of Northern Africa.

Most of these systems of mountains were uplifted more than once, some of them three or four times. During the intervals erosion continued to carve, remove, and redeposit the waste, as in the Po Valley and Adriatic Sea, thus preparing new beds of rocks for plains of today and for future uplift and mountain structure. The loftiest mountains are the youngest. They are still rugged, steep, and rocky and serve as more effective barriers than any other forms on the continent. These young mountains seem to be comparatively barren of mineral resources.

Lowlands and interior plains. Fully half the continent belongs in this category. Europe is the lowest of the continents. Most of the plains are young (of comparatively recent development) and lie near sea level. Sand and clay laid in the sea or over old land areas make plains. Thus the great deltas of the Scheldt, Meuse, Rhine, Ems, Weser, and Elbe constitute a new plain built since the last young mountains were made. Likewise the Po plains have been made of mountain waste and are still being built forward, filling and replacing the Adriatic. The Rhône-Saône system has a delta-flood-plain extending miles above Lyons. The plains of Hungary were once rough lands, then later were so depressed that they were covered by a large lake, into which sediments were spread until a little uplift allowed the waters to drain out and leave these rich agricultural lands in a marshy condition or easily subject to flood. In southeastern England and the Paris basin, marine sediments accumulated in shallow seas at the same time that the sediments of the Alps and Pyrenees were laid in deepening geosynclines whose depth increased enormously as the sediments accumulated. Then gentle uplift and warping brought the new rocks out of the shallow seas and permitted streams to carve from the hard and soft layers the present cuestas of France and the downs of England, separated by valleys eroded in the weaker rocks. Over the great interior of Russia, which seems to have been a vast peneplain in Tertiary time, the shallow seas spread, and in them a few hundreds of feet of sediments were laid. Then, when in Pleistocene time the Arctic seas spread far over Russia and the lowlands of the great Obi Valley east of the Urals, the youngest layers were deposited in both areas. When these waters withdrew, on account of gentle differential uplift in the closing stages of the ice age, streams began their present cycle; but owing to the shortness of subsequent time they have accomplished little. Valleys are youthful, and many areas are still poorly drained.

GEOLOGIC TIME TABLE AND ROCK SCALE

Eras	Periods of time— systems of rocks		Estimated duration in millions of years		Great events— mountain-making
	Psychozoic or Recent time, post-glacial				
Cenozoic	Pleistocene		1-2		Great Ice Age
	Pliocene		10		Uplift of young
	Miocene,	Tertiary	12	3% of geologic time	mountains of Europe
	Oligocene	time	10		Jura Mountains,
	Eocene		10		Alps, Caucasus, Car-
	Paleocene		12		pathians, Pyrenees
Mesozoic	Cretaceous		80		
	Jurassic		35	7%	
	Triassic		25		
Paleozoic	Permian		40		Hercynian or
	Pennsylvanian * ...		40		Variscan mountains,
	Mississippian		30		Urals
	Devonian		40	17%	
	Silurian		30		
	Ordovician		70		
	Cambrian		90		
	Pre-Cambrian		1,500...... 73%		Early Uplifts of Kiolen Mountains

* The Pennsylvanian and Mississippian periods are often called, together, the Carboniferous.

During the ice age, when large glaciers formed in Scandinavia, Scotland, the Alps, and to a less extent in the Caucasus and Pyrenees, the great ice sheet spread outward from the Scandinavian highlands over lower Sweden, Finland, the three Baltic states, a very large area of west and southwest Russia, over the Baltic plains in Poland, Germany, and Denmark, and, augmented by the glaciers of Scotland, over all the British Isles except the part south of Bristol and London. In the more level land there was little ice erosion, but drift was left in moraines and drumlins, and a till sheet mantled all. Drainage was modified; new ground-up rock waste from the highlands was mixed with the local soils of the plains to complicate agricultural as well as transportational problems. Bogs and peat beds developed in the depressions of poorly drained areas.

Notwithstanding the fact that old mountains, plateaus, and young mountains have conditioned man's activities and contributed much to the geographic landscape, probably glaciation has been as influential as any recent factor, both in its effects upon the plains it reached and in its erosion of the highlands. Glaciation is still going on in many high parts. Streams are still persistently carving and depositing; even uplift and depression of lands, earthquakes, and volcanism are operating locally to play into the problems of human occupations. All belong to present as well as ancient history.

THE GEOLOGIC TIME SCALE

In the above paragraphs and in many places throughout the text geologic time terms are used. Some of these terms are identical with the geologic names for great systems of rocks. The time and rock scale as worked out by the geologists is given here for reference. The table is read from the bottom up; the oldest rocks and time periods are at the bottom, the youngest at the top. When reference is made to a group of time periods, such as early Paleozoic, either the event occurred more or less continuously through the Cambrian, Ordovician, and Silurian periods, or its exact date is not known more closely than as early Paleozoic. The making of the young mountains continued at intervals, through Tertiary time; all except the Juras were started before the middle of the era. The Variscan and Ural mountains were uplifted and their strata folded in late Paleozoic time. They have been disturbed occasionally since by uplift, depression, and warping. Although Pre-Cambrian time is enormously long, is divided by geologists into several eras and periods, and probably includes as complex geologic structures and activities as do later time periods, no details are significant for the subjects we are considering. Hence the broad term *Pre-Cambrian* is used for all time that passed before the first period of the Paleozoic Era began. Periods are longer in earlier times partly because we know less about them and because we find it increasingly difficult as we go back in time to work out the possible subdivisions.

RIVERS AND THEIR PHYSIOGRAPHY

Courses of streams. It is obvious from the preceding paragraphs that not all the rivers of Europe could have begun their work at the same time, and that most rivers have been disturbed by vertical movements of the surface of the earth (diastrophic movements), by glaciation, or by actual submergence beneath the sea. Perhaps the rivers of central Spain have flowed essentially in their present courses for as long a time as any. Streams of this region developed a peneplain across the structures of the Meseta a long time ago; then the region was uplifted, and the streams have had time since to cut only young valleys below the peneplain. That is why Spanish transportation is hampered by gorges and other young valleys.

When the young mountains were uplifted, the Danube must have had a course something like its present one and must have maintained its course across the slowly rising mountains, else it could not now flow across mountain masses. Thus it has been able to make and keep open the Iron Gate at Orsova. It must have flowed into and out of the lake of the Hungarian Plain and thereby furnished much of the sands and clays laid as sediments in the lake. It is probable that most of the Russian rivers found their courses across the late Tertiary and Recent deposits when the sea withdrew in late Pleisto-

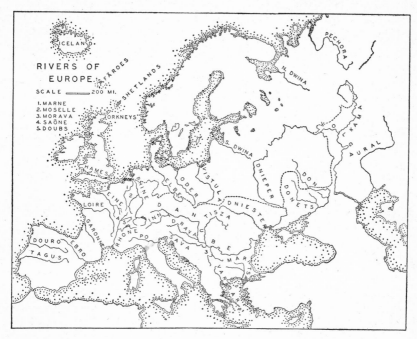

Larger European rivers. Most rivers which drain several countries are named here. Short streams may be found in their respective countries. The dash line indicates the southern and eastern limit of continental glaciation.

cene time and there began to carve their valleys. Since the sea left the Russian plains, the land has not been lifted greatly and hence the streams can cut but little. The short time and the fact that the streams have had only a little fall account for the shallowness of Russian river valleys and their meager obstruction to transportation, also for the easy grades and gentle flow which render them navigable for long distances.

Many rivers have taken, or been given, portions at least of their courses since the Pleistocene glaciers melted. In Norway and Scotland and among the Alps and other young mountains, pre-glacial streams had made valleys before the coming of the ice, which filled them and prevented any stream flow. When the ice melted, some streams were able to occupy pre-glacial valleys; but others were unable to get into the old courses, at least in places, and had to flow across hard rocks from one old valley to another, or search out entirely new courses for many miles. This accounts for many waterfalls with their beauty and power and for many lakes with their attractiveness, navigation possibility, and water-storage values. In other places, as on the central European plains from the Gulf of Finland to the Rhine, streams were obliged to seek their courses across glacial plains. When the Scandinavian glacier was melting from these plains, it built moraines round its edge; streams could not flow directly away from the ice as they could in the United States because the land is higher southward; therefore, streams flowed along the margin of the ice between the moraines as they accumulated. When the moraines were finished as more or less definite ridges east and west across the South Baltic Plains and more nearly north and south on the plains east of the Baltic, and when the ice was gone from the Baltic Sea area, streams at first followed their marginal courses; but the unloading of the land, due to ice melting, allowed lands to rise unevenly enough to aid streams in attaining new courses; so on the South Baltic Plains all the streams have elbows and from the elbows abandoned channels, as from the Oder to the Elbe past the site of Berlin, and from the Vistula below Thorn to the Warthe, and Oder. These abandoned channels, graded by marginal ice drainage, have been of great value as highways for early movements of people and as aids for the later construction of a network of easy-grade canals on the plains. (See Chapter 30.)

Climate and the régime of rivers. Since rivers depend ultimately upon precipitation for their water, there must be a lively relation between the régime of a stream and the rainfall received by its basin. Examine the Danube. Its sources are fed by the winter rain of the Black Forest and by spring melting of snows both in these mountains and much more in the Alps, from whence come many of its tributaries. A part of its waters, especially during the summer drought, disappears in a sink-hole and flows underground for 8 miles, then emerges as a "big spring" 560 feet lower and joins the Rhine system in Lake Constance. Below the sink-hole the Danube receives a tributary larger than itself, direct from glaciers and snow fields— the Inn. Through the next section, therefore, the Danube shows a late spring and summer maximum and provides prime conditions for navigation above and below Vienna. In this vicinity the Danube receives much spring water with a temperature of about 48°, warm enough to add much to the usefulness of the river almost every year by preventing ice. Having passed Vienna and the Alp-Carpathian chains, it finds great extremes of heat and cold and reaches its maximum earlier in spring, as its tributary waters come primarily from winter snows. This is Hungary, with higher summer temperatures, less rainfall, and greater evaporation—a steppe condition—which reduces the usefulness of the river. With these melting snows and ice come the normal summer rain season (but insufficient rainfall) and summer heat, which combine to put the river at minimum flow at Belgrade in September. Once through the Iron Gate at Orsova the river is in true steppe conditions and becomes smaller all the way to its mouth. Winters are sharp and cold, approaching with a rush which often catches a quantity of shipping still on the water. In exceptionally cold winters scores of steamers and barges are thus frozen in. In spring this section frequently suffers from its position, since the river flows into colder winters and later springs as it proceeds eastward and northward. Therefore thawing earlier upstream than down, it floods the delta section with ice, mud, and water before the channels are themselves liberated from winter's chains. No other floods annoy men in the lower section of the Danube.

The spring-flood peculiarity of the lower Danube is especially well marked in north-flowing streams, as the Dwina and Pechora of northern Russia. It would be much more serious in a land with more people and more business for the river. The Volga flows east from its sources 600 miles to the great turn south at Kazan, Russia, into more severe continental climate, and makes the people and their commerce much trouble by thawing upstream two or three weeks before it can at Kazan. With its very easy grade of 600 feet in nearly 2,300 miles, it is remarkably navigable. It is, however, ice-closed over 140 days at Kazan; downstream the time is of course much shorter—107 days at Stalingrad. In this lower section the Volga has little flood trouble, for the lack of rain and the high temperature cause it to decrease in size from Saratov down. Some of the neighboring streams do not reach the sea at all. The Volga's east-flowing section passes through a glaciated plain, where moraines and marshes are the rule. Floods, pouring over the banks upon the low land and marshes, bring disaster to agriculture and navigation, and often destruction to peasant villages.

The Seine and Loire are good examples of streams under the influence of the simple marine type of climate. The Seine has an easier grade and more porous rocks than the Loire; but both streams are under essentially the same climatic conditions over all their respective basins, with the exception of some of the Loire sources on the Auvergne plateau. Both are easily flooded. This condition is augmented where the stream flows over granite instead of pervious sandstones. Floods down the main streams rise slowly enough to be calculated and predicted at Paris a day or two before their arrival. It would be of great help to Seine floods if a canal could be made from Yonne to Loire, so as to divert the waters in flood to the Loire and away from the Seine.

Rivers of Spain rarely have floods because of the limited rainfall; but in the Sierras, where much precipitation is in the form of snow which melts with the return of spring, there is the nearest approach to floods. The Po has high waters in the winter when the rains of the cyclonic westerlies migrate far enough south to bring rains, and it has another flood season when the summer melting of snow occurs in the mountains. The latter flood is extremely beneficial because the summer is the dry season and amply warm to bring forth luxuriant crops where water is available. The northern Po tributaries have been used successfully for a century to irrigate the great alluvial fans which they have built.

Stream work prepares lands for men. Youthful topography as seen in the Alps or the North German Plains is young because streams have only started on their long task. As they carry away the rock and waste, valleys are widened and deepened, tiny flood-plains are prepared for men to work, and room is found for towns in the valleys below the uplands. So men begin to move down from upland surfaces to the streams. In the Black Forest and Vosges, many people still live on the uplands; but there is relatively so much valley space here, as compared with topography in younger stages, that a considerable portion of the population now live in the valleys. In the Bretagne peninsula, streams have accomplished much more, and a larger proportion of the people occupy the broader, more mature valleys. In European Turkey, valleys are being widened below a peneplained upland surface, and the population is concentrated even more in the valleys, although grazing utilizes the uplands. Great portions of the plateau of central Spain constitute an old erosion surface which has been uplifted so recently that the streams have scarcely begun to dissect it. People live everywhere over it, as they would over a surface in youth. As soon as the valleys get started, people will cautiously drop to the bottoms of them for their power mills and small farms, but they will not utilize the steep valley walls for cultivation.

So streams, valleys, and topography in general pass through a cycle of development from youth to maturity and old age; and man's use of the land, his distribution over it, and the distribution of his transportation and other activities are all influenced by the stage of development reached.

GLACIATION

Frequent reference has been made to glaciation and must be made again in many connections. The last glacial or ice age in Europe occupied more or less fully the last million years or more of earth history. It is not expedient here to discuss the causes and the evidences for and against the theories of ice ages, ice movement, and methods of glacial erosion. It is germane that glacier ice accumulated in the loftier, colder parts of the continent and spread several times extensively over lower lands. Habitually, these moving sheets of ice eroded in the higher parts, or in their central portions, and when the ice melted deposited the eroded material in lower warmer areas around the margins. Thus the Highlands of Scotland, of Norway, and of the Alps have lost extensively to Ireland and England, lower Sweden, Denmark, and the Baltic Plains to the plateaus of Switzerland and south Germany, and to the marginal valleys of the young mountains. Where valleys were deep, differential erosion deepened them, widened them by straighten-ing, and thus gave rise to the rugged valleys of Norway, which have been left at such an altitude as to hold deep arms of the sea—fiords—and to the similar valleys in higher Sweden, which contain long, narrow lakes, one or more along a valley. It formed also the similar valleys, some with and some without lakes, in the young mountains. This glaciated topography with its charm and beauty is a rich and attractive resource for countries the people of which would entertain tourist guests.

But nowhere has deep erosion done more for man or served man longer than in the high Alps, where it has carved connecting valleys between the heads of streams on opposite sides of the ridges. Nearly all the Alpine passes of note are through valleys thus carved low enough to be serviceable in summer, and in some places in winter, for travel. Migrating races, armies, colonists, and trains of freight and passengers have used and still use these passes; in modern railroad days, where the pass is too high, a tunnel has been built through underneath.

The glaciers have modified the courses of streams in the Alps, in Sweden, in Scotland and England; they have covered regions of slight relief with drift so thickly that the streams have been obliged to find wholly new places to flow and to make themselves new valleys. This type of stream modifica-tion is particularly common in central England, in Denmark, in the low-lands of Sweden, in Finland, in all the Baltic Plains, and in Ireland. By interfering with the drainage the glaciers have induced or superimposed youthful conditions which streams have not yet overcome, so that thou-sands of square miles, especially in countries bordering the Baltic and in the British Isles, are swampy, marshy, or peaty, and unfit for agriculture.

The time involved in the glacial age is divided into glacial and inter-glacial epochs and a present post-glacial epoch. The interglacial times were probably longer than the glacial times and the post-glacial epoch. The changes in climate implicated in the coming and going of the ice must have been a stimulus to primitive men to care for themselves. Such changes re-quired men to adjust in clothing, shelter, and food habits to the changing environment; every little adjustment made for higher civilization, a closer correlation of life and its activities with the surrounding conditions.

SHORELINES

Marginal and other seas. A continent of peninsulas and islands must have an intricate shoreline. Between peninsulas are bays; between islands, straits. Whatever caused the peninsulas was a factor in making the bays, border seas, and straits. Just how peninsular is Europe? The Spanish penin-sula is the most outstanding one. If the land between the Bay of Biscay and the Gulf of Lyons be called an isthmus, the land between the Adriatic and North seas may likewise be called an isthmus, and all west of it a peninsula. But the line might be drawn from Adriatic to Baltic, or Black to Baltic, or even from Black to White, making most of the continent a peninsula. If the rainfall in the Caspian basin were a little greater, or evaporation a little less, the Caspian Sea would have communication with the Black Sea, and one might sense the connecting neck of land between the Caspian Sea and the Gulf of Obi, making all Europe a peninsula. In each case the isthmus is commensurate with the dimensions of the peninsula. In post-glacial time an embayment of the Arctic flooded the Obi plains so that the neck of land between it and the Caspian was very narrow (in fact, at times the land was wholly submerged). While these changes were in progress, Europe itself was a peninsula or an island. History would have been different if the peninsulas and marginal seas had been different.

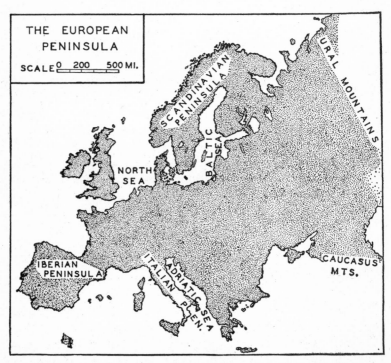

Note the possibility of considering almost any part of Europe, from Iberia to the whole continent, as a peninsula.

Just as the lands of the northern part of the continent in recent periods have been subjected to warping, while those in the southern part have experienced faulting and folding, so the floors of marginal seas reflect similar movements. North Sea, Irish Sea, St. George's Channel, English Channel, Baltic Sea, and White Sea are all flooded former land surfaces; similarly the north part of the Caspian Sea and the Sea of Azov with the bay serving Odessa are characterized by shallow depths with stream-made forms on the bottoms and commonly with gentle slopes from bottoms to adjacent lands. South of the line of young mountain structures, Caucasus-Alps-Pyrenees, the seas are deep, generally with rugged shorelines. The Mediterranean through all historic time has been marked by its many rocky headlands. The Tyrrhenian Sea occupies a depressed area, defined by well-known fault lines. The Ægean and Black seas lie in partly warped and partly down-faulted areas. The southern Caspian Sea and even the Red Sea are of this nature. These characteristics together with climatic factors have made the shallow northern seas, without exception, valuable fishing grounds, but the deep southern ones are of indifferent value, so that much northern fish for hundreds of years has been shipped to Mediterranean lands for human food.

The shallow northern seas are more subject to freezing than would be deeper waters in the same latitude. The Gulf of Finland is closed by ice about five months each year, unless kept open by ice-breakers; the whole Baltic occasionally freezes entirely over. In 1658 King Charles X marched his army across the frozen Belts between Denmark and Sweden. Accumulation of deltas and other silt has shoaled many parts of these northern seas and increased the ice difficulties.

Changes of level. All the evidence of former changes of level is supported by changes that have occurred in historic time. In Italy, north of Naples at the Bay of Baiæ, the stone columns of the temple of Jupiter Serapis have often been cited as evidence of such change. Holes have been bored in them by little marine animals, but the holes are now 15 to 20 feet above the water. These are interpreted to mean that the columns have been lowered below sea level for a time, then raised again to their present height, and this all in the Christian era. Old roads of Sweden near the coast are now under water. Old marine beaches and deltas in many places in Finland, Norway, Sweden, Denmark, and the British Isles are now standing well above sea level. Land around Cherbourg that was formerly above sea level is now beneath the sea. A few centuries ago lands in the Netherlands settled down enough to make the Zuider Zee and other water areas where land had been. Raised beaches and deltas make splendid well-drained level areas for homes, and the new seas make ideal fishing grounds. These features are post-glacial and often historic.

Shoreline erosion and filling. Not only have changes of level modified the shoreline, but waves, currents, and land streams are constantly conducting operations called *changes of normal development*. Chalk cliffs of England and France have been formed by erosion and are being cut back year by year. The shores of Biscay in France have received large additions in beach sands, and the shoreline has been straightened into a beautiful sweeping curve; but it is now useless for harbor purposes. Alternate beaches and headlands characterize most of the British coasts. The processes have not gone far enough to straighten out the shoreline into long, sweeping crescents, but the tendency is in that direction. Beaches for bathing, dan-

gerous, rocky headlands bearing lighthouses, unfilled bays between headlands for harbors are characteristics of such a shoreline. Plymouth Bay,
Torquay, and the Mumbles, with the associated beaches and headlands are
good examples.

Ancient and modern land connections. Since shorelines change and sea
floors rise and sink, it follows that land connections between parts of Europe and between Europe and other continents change also; such changes
modify the migrational possibilities of men, plants, animals together with
the movements of armies, culture, ideas, and goods.

Within the life of primitive man in Europe, the Baltic has been a fresh
sea, enclosed except for a stream outlet and smaller than the present Baltic.
This phase occurred during the closing stages of the ice age, while the ice
was withdrawing from the Baltic region. After the ice was gone from the
British Isles, that portion of Europe stood high enough so that there was
no North Sea, Irish Sea, or English Channel. Wild animals and men could
then move freely from the continent to any part of what is now the British
Isles without bothering about water transportation routes. Men could cross
between Denmark and Scotland without considering any water except the
lower Rhine, which then extended far north across the present North Sea
floor. Submergence seems to have begun in the west and to have separated
Ireland first, then to have proceeded far enough to separate Britain from
the mainland. Not until essentially modern distributions of sea and land
were reached did the Rhine begin to build its present delta.

Earlier than the glacial period—about mid-Tertiary time—there were
land connections from Bretagne Peninsula through England, Ireland, Scotland, and on northwestward, to North America. These broke down before
the glacial period, but the connections between Britain and the continent
served men after the ice age. The water connections between the Black Sea
and the Mediterranean are relatively recent, but there have been many
changes of level of land in the Caspian-Black-Ægean region. A river, draining the Black Sea to the Ægean, carved valleys where now are the Dardanelles, Marmara, and Bosporus; then a change of level warped the land
down unevenly, drowning parts broadly as in Marmara, and other parts
narrowly as straits. This submergence was more extensive than at present,
as is shown by marine beach terraces at several levels above the present
water level. The subsequent uplift of lands has apparently been intermittent, with halts long enough to build obvious beaches.

, All this history of changes of level is of interest in its influence upon
movements of early man and in its relation to present as well as future
commerce and defense. There is little fishing in the Black Sea except on
the shallow banks in the northern embayments, because salt waters, which
destroyed much of the fresh-water life, flowed into it from the Ægean so
recently that it is not yet restocked, and indeed cannot be until the old,
dead organic matter is covered or ceases to emit sulphur compounds detri-

mental to life. Fresh water flows out of the Black Sea today on the surface through the Bosporus, and salt water flows in underneath.

Within the time men have been in Europe the Mediterranean Sea has taken its present shape. Early men found a land bridge at Gibraltar, and probably another from Tunis to Sicily and to Italy.

The evidence is convincing that shorelines, and with them gulfs, bays, peninsulas, islands, straits, and isthmuses, have changed, are changing, and will change. Slight changes of level result in connections or cause disjunctions which may profoundly affect man's movements, wars, and commerce. Shoreline development changes are of more significance in man's short span than river developmental changes.

QUESTIONS

1. Find on the maps the two great divide areas from which many of the streams flow. Compare them as to altitude, distance from Atlantic and from other seas. Note probable grade and pace of the two groups of streams. Consider the uses to which each could best be put.

2. Which group of streams described in Question 1 has heavier rainfall? steadier flow? severer winter? What have these items to do with usefulness of these streams?

3. Compare the development of shorelines with the development of land topography under the action of streams.

4. Compare and contrast man's uses of lands in different stages and of shorelines in different stages of development.

5. How long has it taken to get Europe prepared as well as it is now for human occupation?

BIBLIOGRAPHY

BRANSON, Edwin B., and TARR, W. A., *Introduction to Geology* (New York, McGraw-Hill Book Company, Inc., 1941).

CHAMBERLIN, Rollin T., and McCLINTOCK, Paul, *College Geology*, 2 vols. (New York, Henry Holt & Company, Inc., 1930).

DALY, R. A., *The Changing World of the Ice Age* (New Haven, Yale University Press, 1934).

DUNBAR, Carl O., *Historical Geology* (New York, John Wiley & Sons, Inc., 1949).

HOLMES, Arthur, *Principles of Physical Geology* (New York, The Ronald Press Co., 1945).

HOLMES, Chauncey D., *Introduction to College Geology* (New York, The Macmillan Company, 1949).

KENDREW, W. G., *Climates of the Continents* (Oxford, Clarendon Press, 1942).

LONGWELL, Chester R., KNOPF, A., and FLINT, R. F., *Physical Geology* (New York, John Wiley & Sons, Inc., 1948).

MILLER, William J., *An Introduction to Geology, Physical and Historical* (New York, D. Van Nostrand Company, Inc., 1925).

TARR, Ralph S., and MARTIN, L., *College Physiography* (New York, The Macmillan Company, 1921).

VON ENGELN, Oscar D., *Geomorphology* (New York, The Macmillan Company, 1942).

ZON, Raphael, and SPARHAWK, William N., *Forest Reserves of the World* (New York, McGraw-Hill Book Company, Inc., 1923).

CHAPTER 3

Climate

To talk of the weather it's nothing but folly
For when it rains on the hill, it shines in the valley.
—DENHAM

INTRODUCTION; GENERAL RELATIONS OF CLIMATE

To Asia and to the sea. The climate of Europe is determined in large measure by the fact that Europe is a peninsula of Asia, the largest continent, and by its location on the leeward side of the Atlantic Ocean. In winter the large land area cools more than the sea and is covered by a cold anticyclonic area in which the air moves in general downward and outward; likewise, in summer the same land warms more readily than the water and is then covered by a warm cyclonic area in which the air moves in general inward on the ground and upward. Asia is so large compared with Europe that this circulation dominates the climate of the peninsula.

The Atlantic Ocean is warmer than the land in winter and cooler in summer; hence, with onshore winds it acts as an equalizer of the climate of adjacent land, giving to the people of Europe the largest area of equable climate in the world. Moreover, the ocean has in it the North Atlantic drift, formerly called the Gulf Stream, a broad, shallow expanse of water, warmed near the tropics, which moves northeast from the intertropical part of the sea to the shores of Britain, Norway, and on into the Arctic Ocean. This together with the westerly winds brings into north temperate and arctic latitudes a great amount of heat in addition to the normal insolation (sun radiation).

To the general circulation of air. Between latitudes approximately 30° or 35° N. and 30° or 35° S. the prevailing wind direction is westward and equatorward. These great masses of air are called north and south trade winds and, until the invention of steam power, were of inestimable value to water commerce. Air thus transferred toward the equator becomes warm as it goes, and ascends in a broad low-pressure belt in the equatorial zone. Poleward from the belts of trade winds the air moves eastward and gently poleward. These last two belts of moving air are known respectively as the northern and southern prevailing westerlies. They are not as steady as the trades, but have greatly assisted men in the Low Countries to pump the water out of their polders and in Ukrainia to grind their wheat. Most of Europe lies within the northern westerlies, winds that move on the average from the west and west-southwest toward the interior of Asia.

Between the westerlies and the trades of each hemisphere is a belt, or zone, of relatively high pressure, where air from aloft descends and divides, some becoming the westerlies, some the trades. In a general way this high-pressure belt lies over the Mediterranean region; as it extends eastward it bears a little northward into central Asia, where it is 10° farther north, or about 45° N. It is one of the factors that give to the Great Sea its clear skies and dry summers. Outward from the polar area blow winds, fed by air that has descended in polar areas. These are even less constant than the westerlies. Europe is so placed that its northern extremities are frequently influenced by these polar winds. The southern edges are always more or less dominated by the high-pressure belt, or alternately by the fringes of westerlies and trades.

In the westerlies are a succession of great eddies of air 1,000 miles or more across, called *highs* and *lows*. The former are cool and contain descending outflowing air; the latter are warm and contain inflowing and ascending air. These eddies, also called *anticyclones* and *cyclones,* move with the westerlies in general toward the east and bring the chief variations in wind direction, temperature, and moisture that Europe experiences. They are of great benefit also in providing the frequent and sudden changes of weather conditions which are so stimulating and valuable to health and activity.

To the Azores high and Icelandic low. Off the Azores on the Atlantic Ocean the belt of high pressure becomes more marked, especially in summer when it directs and pushes the winds farther north than in winter. In the Icelandic region a great permanent low, stronger in winter than in summer, gives birth to some of the cyclones that bring weather changes to central Europe. Other cyclones start in America and drift across the ocean and Europe, becoming lost in the winter high of central Asia.

In addition to lows and highs, and often associated with them, are great masses of air moving from place to place. From high latitudes over the lands, U.S.S.R. and Asiatic interior, continental or arctic cold masses move toward the south and southwest; from high latitudes over the sea between Spitsbergen and Nova Zembla, marine polar masses move southwest and south invading the lands. Warm or tropical marine masses from the tropical North Atlantic move northeast and slip over the lands where they may meet the colder masses from high latitudes; then they contribute to the formation of cyclones and to precipitation.

To migration of great wind belts. Just as these great wind belts and their correlated pressure belts arise from unequal heating by the sun of different parts of the earth, so the migration of the sun, bringing vertical rays in the course of six months to all intertropical areas, forces the wind and pressure belts to migrate northward in summer and southward in winter. This change permits the westerlies with their strong marine influence and moisture-bearing cyclones to enter Europe so far south as to bless the Mediterranean region with winter rains, while it brings the rainless high-pressure belt and even the moisture-absorbing trades across the Mediterranean in summer, making rain and even clouds, impossible and contributing the dry, clear, hot summer characteristic of all true Mediterranean lands. This migration, aided by the warm low pressure of central Asia, permits the oceanic influence and cyclones to travel far inland and bring needed summer rain to the plains of Russia. It also permits the polar winds and the cold, piercing winds from central Asia to get into northern and even eastern Europe in winter, bringing very little precipitation even in the form of snow.

All this helps to explain the notable transitional character of European climate. A narrow seagirt strip is oceanic; most of Russia is continental; but the Baltic states and central Europe as far as the Black Sea have a transitional climate, neither continental nor oceanic, the largest transitional area on the earth—an excellent situation for the development of an active people.

To the topographic pattern of Europe. Not only is Europe peninsular with reference to Asia, but it has itself many peninsular forms which permit sea influences to reach far into the land. Its great mountain and plain areas have an east-west distribution further assisting marine influences in a long, free sweep 1,000 to 1,500 miles into the very heart of the continent. This circumstance can be contrasted with similar temperate zones in North and South America. Perhaps as beneficial is the long Mediterranean Sea, extending 2,000 miles between the lands. Because it is so large and warm, it develops a local, low-pressure belt, widening and splitting the normal high of the latitude so that an axis of high pressure lies over North Africa most of the time, and a stronger, more persistent one over Europe north of the sea. In winter a small, subsidiary low lies in each large basin of the Mediterranean. In summer the split is less noticeable. Since winds move from highs to lows, these local differences of pressure bring local winds to many parts of the Mediterranean region. The Iberian Peninsula is large enough to carry its own low in summer and high in winter, and it seems probable that Italy and Greece may to a less extent do likewise.

DESCRIPTION OF CONDITIONS

Pressure and winds. We have noted the general distribution of winds and pressure belts, the Icelandic and Azores centers, the great Asiatic cold, high-pressure area with radiating winds in winter, and the great Asiatic warm, low-pressure area with inblowing winds in summer. Europe lies between the four great centers and is affected by all of them. North of the

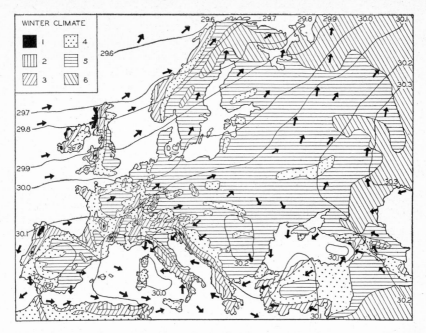

Winter climatic conditions. Isobars for each tenth of inch of pressure. Arrows fly with the wind. Precipitation shown by general patterns: 1 = over 40 in.; 2 = 30-40 in.; 3 = 20-30 in.; 4 = 10-20 in.; 5 = 5-10 in.; 6 = under 5 in. (Adapted from Philips's *Comparative Wall Atlas*)

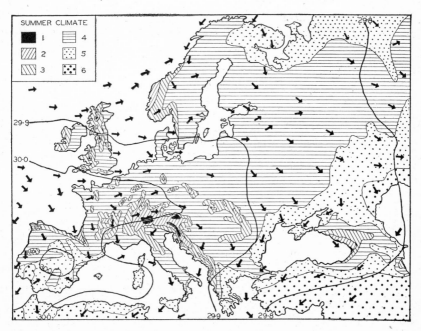

Summer climatic conditions. Isobars for each tenth of inch of pressure. Arrows fly with the wind. Precipitation shown by ruling, dots, shading: 1 = over 40 in.; 2 = 30-40 in.; 3 = 20-30 in.; 4 = 10-20 in.; 5 = 5-10 in.; 6 = under 5 in. (Adapted from Philips's *Comparative Wall Atlas*)

Pyrenees, Alps, and Caucasus the winter pressure map of Europe shows a gradual increase of pressure from the sea to the Caspian and Urals. In the latitude of Scotland this amounts to six tenths of an inch. Isobars are nearly parallel with the coast—northeast to southwest. Winds, however, cannot enter the great high of central Asia, so trending more toward the north in Russia, they blow nearly parallel with the isobars over much of this northern part of Europe. The average winds (prevailing westerlies) are tremendously disturbed by the migrating lows and highs, which slip across the countries from west to east. South of the mountains no such constancy of prevailing winds exists over broad areas because of the local distribution of pressure described in the last paragraph.

In summer the pressure difference across all Europe scarcely exceeds two tenths of an inch. The highest pressures are in the southwest, controlled by the Azores high and the subtropical high belt, while the lowest are along the eastern side, influenced by the great, warm, summer low of central Asia. Since in summer the winds can blow across these isobars as they could not in the winter, the winds are then strongly toward the east entirely across the continent, thus bringing climate even more transitional than in winter. They are not strong unless augmented by local highs and lows. In average conditions one can go from Iceland to the Caspian Sea without finding a one-tenth-inch difference in pressure. In winter on the same journey one would find eight tenths of an inch of difference. The northeast trades dominate the entire Mediterranean region in summer.

Precipitation. Since precipitation, or the moisture for it, must come largely from the sea, its distribution is closely related to the relative positions of land and sea and to the wind directions. Since precipitation occurs when the vaporized moisture of the air is cooled to condensation, relief is profoundly influential in its distribution. Warm, moist air drawn up mountainsides or lifted in a low-pressure area is generally cooled sufficiently to cause precipitation of its moisture.

Winter rainfall is less than 10 inches over much more than half of the continent. The eastern half of Spain falls in this low-precipitation area. A line from Salonika to northwest Germany will have almost all the winter rainfall of over 10 inches on the west side and that of less than 10 inches on the east—the dry continental interior. Norway, Caucasus, and a few higher places on the east side have more than 10 inches, while the Paris Basin, Rhône and Po troughs, east England, and a few other scattered low areas southwest of the line have less than 10 inches.

In summer the rainfall area of over 10 inches is greatly expanded. Less of Spain and Sicily, Greece and Asia Minor than in winter, have over 10 inches, but all France, Britain, Germany, Sweden, Poland, and vast areas of Russia have 10 to 20 inches. Only the far north and the lands round the Caspian and Black seas fall below 10 inches. Highlands, mountains, and ocean coasts receive 20 to 30 inches, 30 to 40 inches, and in scattered

patches over 40 inches. The Atlantic coast countries, from Galicia in northwest Spain to northern Norway, have ample rainfall every month; likewise
the Yugoslavic-Adriatic coast, the western Caucasus, and the interior mountains. The Mediterranean has sufficient winter rains; the central plains have
sufficient summer rains. Rainfall adequate for agriculture may mean less
inches far north than in lands of lower altitudes, because in these cooler
lands, frozen so many months, evaporation is slight.

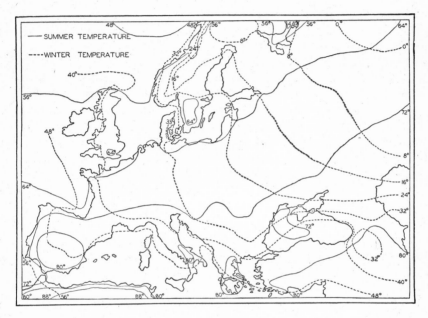

Summer and winter temperatures. Isotherms drawn every 8° F. Note intersections of winter lines
with those for summer numbered 64° and 72°. (Adapted from Philips's *Comparative Wall Atlas*)

Temperature. Temperature distributions show as clearly as rainfall the
transitional character of the continent. Summer isotherms nearly parallel
the Atlantic and Arctic coasts. The 56° F. line crosses Scotland approximately west to east and lies on Norway to latitude 69°, then turns east, and
after a south curve round the White Sea runs east to Asia. The 64° F. line
is found in the Bay of Biscay and extends across France, the Low Countries,
north Germany, the Baltic states, and south of Leningrad to the mid-Urals.
Isotherm 72° F. is found in Portugal, France, the Alps, Hungary, Rumania,
Ukraine, and to the southern end of the Urals. The 80° F. line closes around
a large area in Spain, a small one in south Italy, and another in south
Greece. The same line also follows closely the south Mediterranean coast
to Cairo, then cuts across Asia Minor and the Caspian Sea. These lines
show the strong influence of the sea entirely across Europe and the power
of the westerlies to deliver cooling marine influences.

Winter isotherms run crosswise of the summer lines.[1] The winter lines portray over most of Europe the strong influence of the cold outblowing winds of Siberia, and in the south the warming influence of insolation and the "warming pans" [2] of the Mediterranean. Together, the summer and winter isotherms record the slight ranges of temperature on the Atlantic side and in the Mediterranean countries, and the steadily increasing range across transitional Europe toward the great Asiatic continental interior where is recorded the greatest range of temperature on earth. Follow the 72° F. summer line from near Gibraltar, where it crosses the winter line of 56° F. (range 16°), to the southern Urals, where it crosses the 0° F. line (range 72°). These are not extreme ranges but the range between the means of the warmest and of the coldest months.

Relations of climate to relief. Whereas in warmer lands like Mexico relief is a very important control of climate, in Europe it is subordinate. Yet it is significant enough to require a paragraph. We have seen how much relief has to do with precipitation. In addition it determines, in considerable measure, the absolute humidity, the proportion of snow in the total precipitation, the actual amount of snow, and the persistence of snow into warm weather. Relief modifies, in their turn, the rate and season of run-off and hence of floods.

Inasmuch as isotherms and isobars are drawn after the temperature and pressure observations are corrected to sea level, the maps show no trace of the effects of relief on these elements. Pressure, we know, decreases uniformly aloft. This is not true of temperature. Ben Nevis (4,406 feet) stands near Fort William (171 feet) in Scotland. The former has a mean annual temperature of 31.4° F., the latter 47.1° F., and the difference month by month is about the same. Biarritz (115 feet) and Pic du Midi (9,383 feet) in southwest France have respective temperatures of 56.7° F. and 28.6° F. Exposure to sunshine is likewise important. With the same precipitation the snow line is much lower on a north slope than on the south one. Crops are retarded on cold slopes. Harvests are a whole month later on the north

---

[1] The 0° F. winter line lies along the Urals, crossing there summer lines 72° F. to 48° F. The winter line of 8° F. runs from Caspian plains to White Sea. The 16° F. line follows along Norway coast and mountains from the Arctic Sea nearly to Oslo, then folds back to the head of the Baltic and sweeps southeast to Astrakhan. The 24° F. line follows a similar course, crossing the 48° F. and 56° F. summer lines in Norway, the 64° F. in Lithuania, the 72° F. in Ukraine, and the 80° F. near the east shore of the Caspian. The 32° F. winter line runs from Iceland to northern Norway, along the coast to Denmark, south to the Alps, then east to the Caspian Sea, crossing all summer lines from 48° F. to 80° F. The 40° F. winter line runs north-south through the British Isles and France, then east through Yugoslavia and the Black Sea. The 48° F. line is found crossing the summer 64° F. in the Bay of Biscay and then dodging across land and sea near the northern shore of the Mediterranean into Asia Minor.

[2] Water in each of four basins of the Mediterranean Sea becomes warm during the long, sunny summer and serves to temper the cold during the rest of the year.

side of the Sudetes than on the south. Many examples of these relief effects are given in climatological tables and in discussions of the same.

CLIMATIC REGIONS

While all the various climatic factors show transitions from place to place, with no rigid lines like shorelines or political boundaries, it is possible and profitable to divide the continent into climatic regions with more or less definite characteristics, worked out from data presented on previous pages.

The Mediterranean region. Nearly every climatologist recognizes the Mediterranean type of climate with its winter rainfall, its warm, dry sunny summers, and its slight range of temperature from cool in winter to hot in summer, except on certain coasts where water influence is strong enough to reduce the range even lower. A related characteristic is a delayed summer maximum temperature. The coldest month in different sections of the region varies from 40° to 50° F. Bright, sunny blue skies are banished only by the passage of winter cyclonic storms, bringing prolonged drizzles; but the summer cloudless skies ripen olives, grapes, and other fruits. This region belongs to the Sahara in summer and to the northwest European coast in winter. Temperatures are highest in the east, and not only lowest but most uniform toward the Atlantic. North winds often bring dust clouds, and winter siroccos from the south do likewise.

In summer only irrigated fields have beauty; many are sear and brown, with the landscape dry and parched. Rapid evaporation from one's skin makes heat bearable; but plants have developed thick skins, oily or gummy saps, hairy leaf surfaces, and even modified leaves to protect themselves from heavy loss by evaporation, and deep roots to reach the permanent supply of water. They guard themselves against breaks in their bark and consequent bleeding by the use of thorns, spikes, bristles, and knobs— modified leaves—to keep marauders away; and their gummy sap makes healing of wounds almost instantaneous. Some plants have developed large cells for water storage.

Mediterranean waters conserve summer heat to winter months; they evaporate, and also give off heat to lands. Being warmer than the lands in winter, they cause low-pressure areas, one in each basin, and contribute to the circulation of air. Winds thus drawn into the warm lows transport moisture upward to be added to the winter rainfall. "Mediterranean climate is the gift of the sea and is only found near its shores." (Kendrew.)

Temperatures have great local differences connected with exposure to sunshine, cold continental winds, and reflected sunshine from sea, and with shelter from cold and winds. Autumn is warmer than spring because of maritime retardation. In winter western sides of peninsulas are warmer than eastern because of westerly winds. Interiors are cooler in winter and warmer in summer; they are also cooler at night and warmer in daytime than are the seas. This daily variation produces salubrious land and sea breezes.

Rainfall is variable: 10 inches in southern Spain, and 183 inches on east Adriatic coasts. In general it is characterized by its rapidity of falling and by its periodicity. Clouds gather, rain falls quickly, clouds pass, letting the sun shine again. The rainfall period is mostly in the winter half of the year, but northern districts frequently experience two rainy seasons, autumn and spring, while the south has only a winter one. More rain falls around the Mediterranean in winter than over much of continental Europe. Snow is rare, but it sometimes blocks winter traffic in the Po Valley and lies in the Sierras all summer. Such slow melting is a help to irrigation around Granada.

Several special winds are recognized. The mistral, or masterful, wind pours down cold, violent gusts in the southern provinces of France when there is a low over the Gulf of Genoa and a high in the northwest. The cold, dry mass or front is thus drawn down from the Alps or Cevennes into the Rhône funnel and is spread out along the coasts. Although it is descending air which warms adiabatically, it is so cold at the start that it is often still destructive when it arrives. Men plant cypress trees around their gardens as shelter, and the humble dwellings have doors and windows only on the east and south sides. The bora of the Adriatic, named long before its genesis was known, carries in its name its northern (cold) origin. In some respects it is much like the mistral. When a calm anticyclone lies over the Dalmatian karst [3] country, valleys become full of cold, still air. If now a low comes into the Adriatic, this cold, dry air is sucked into its mechanism and brought swooping down to the coast with the sky clear and radiation unhindered. Similar cold winds come down from the Balkan Mountains when a low in the Ægeans begins to draw in air.

The sirocco is as characteristic a warm wind as the bora is a cold wind. The name is used in central and eastern Mediterranean lands; it is also known as *khamsin* in Egypt, *gibbi* in Tripoli, *leveche* in southeast Spain. If a low be centered over the Tyrrhenian Sea, it may have a sirocco in the east side, warm and muggy because it has just crossed warm sea, and a mistral on the northwest. When any low comes from the west into the Mediterranean, it draws warm, dry, dusty, or even sandy air from northern Africa or Arabia. If the air descends from mountains, it warms adiabatically. The sirocco may spend four to five days advancing with its causal cyclone from Algeria to the Levant. As a rule it is most frequent in spring, when cyclones are most frequent, and most rare in the east, where cyclones are rare. So warm and dry are these winds that they may ruin fruit or leaves, if they come when fruit is in bloom. They curl up the leaves, even

[3] Cavern and sink-hole topography made by solution work of ground water.

wither them, and depress man and beast. Although some of the Mediterranean states do not lie entirely in a Mediterranean climate, and France and Russia have small areas with somewhat similar qualities, the six states most characteristically Mediterranean in climate will be taken as our first regional group. Spain and Portugal will be followed by Italy, Albania, Greece, and Turkey. Details of climate and departures from the type must be discussed under each country.

The Northwest coast or marine climate states. Three facts characterize the climate of the Northwest states: (*a*) ample rainfall all year, (*b*) strong southwest winds, (*c*) equable temperatures remarkably warm for the latitude. Winds in Norway and Färoe Islands are strong enough to stunt tree growth and force all branches to one side, or to break them from the top and make the tree look stumpy. Air over the north Atlantic close to these lands is 40° F. warmer than the average temperature for this latitude. Thorshavn, Färoes, has 38° F. for January mean; Yakutsk, Siberia, in the same latitude has —46° F. In the Orkney Islands 39° F. is the January mean, while at Hebron, Labrador, it is —21° F. Open sea northwest and north of Europe is never frozen. Hammerfest, Norway, 71° N., and Kola Bay, Russia, 69° N., are always ice-free harbors. Temperature decreases rapidly from west to east and slowly toward north. Brest has a mean annual temperature of 43° F.; Paris, 300 miles inland, has 36° F. Paris is colder than Thorshavn, although it is 850 miles farther south. In this whole region summers are cool, autumns are warmer than springs; and coasts, in summer, cooler than interiors—all characteristics of a marine climate. Rainfall shows marked decrease inland. Bergen has 73 inches, while a hundred miles inland on Sogne fiord there are only 30 inches. Mountains catch the heaviest rainfall. Snowdon (3,560 feet) has 200 inches; low countries have only 20 to 30 inches. Altitude is generally responsible for heavy rainfall records. Near coasts this oceanic type of climate has more rain in winter than in summer, but inland a few miles the reverse is true. Cloudiness and heavy fog are well-known characteristics. Sun is not seen for days, even weeks at a time. We shall consider France, the British Isles, Belgium, Netherlands, Denmark, and Norway in this type, although eastern portions of France are well within the central European type, and small portions in the south are Mediterranean.

Central Europe. Some authors put together under this heading most of the rest of Europe except Russia. It is true that the remaining states have much in common: cold winters, warm summers, and more rain in the summer months than in the winter months; but all this is true also of Russia. East Europe or Russia is separated from Central Europe only by having its climatic characteristics in more extreme form. It grades into Central Europe types. The Lower Danube states have several items in common with the Mediterranean type and grade southward into it. The climate of the Baltic area is transitional between Russian types and the Northwest

European type. With these two regions, Lower Danube states and Baltic region, separated from the larger Central Europe, there is left a central core of states transitional between the French-Belgian type of oceanic climate and the purely continental types of Russia. These six states have an intermediate type of climate of the so-called Central Europe group with transitional climate, neither northern nor southern.

Thus, it has seemed more convenient and possibly more exact to group the Central Europe states of some authors into three climatic blocks; Sweden and Finland, with the Baltic Sea, called the Baltic Transition region; Germany, Poland, Switzerland, Austria, Hungary, and Czechoslovakia, the Central Europe (proper) region; and Rumania, Bulgaria, and Yugoslavia, the Lower Danube region. East Europe, or European Russia region, will include the remaining portion of the continent.

Baltic Transition region. Two factors enter to make this region depart from the normal for its latitude and distance from the ocean: (*a*) the strong barrier of mountains that shuts out marine influences and sharpens the boundary between this type of climate and the Northwest coast type; (*b*) the tempering value of the Baltic Sea, which is especially important when the sea is not frozen. Winds blow eastward across it in summer, carrying its coolness and moisture to the lands, but in winter they blow much more northward; hence the tempering value does not come so much from the sea alone as it does from the influence of low latitude on high. Temperatures in winter decrease northward from 30° to 8° F., in summer eastward less than 10° F. and northward the same.

Notwithstanding that here temperatures are more severe than in either region so far considered, they still are tempered and cover less range than farther east. The Gulf of Finland marks the middle north and south, and its temperatures are July, 63° F.; January, 20° F. Stockholm has January, 28° F.; July, 64° F.

Winter precipitation of 5 to 10 inches is always snow, and in the northern part of the region snow covers the ground seven months in the year. The number of rainy or snowy and cloudy days increases northward. Precipitation, everywhere in small drops or flakes, becomes finer northward, and the total annual precipitation decreases in the same direction. A winter rain shadow with precipitation of less than 5 inches east of the Kiolens extends from the Arctic coast nearly to Wener Lake and the Glommen Valley. Summer precipitation is everywhere from 10 to 20 inches, except for a strip on the Kattegat coast which has over 20 inches and a small area in the far north which has less than 10 inches. The relief is so slight that the precipitation varies only a little and is everywhere sufficient for all the agriculture the temperature and short growing season will permit. Streams freeze every winter. Parts of the Gulf of Finland are frozen every winter, and in severe winters all harbors are closed at least a few days. The upper, fresher part of Bothnia is frozen completely almost every winter, while all the Arctic ports, 250 to 300 miles farther north, are open all winter because of north Atlantic influences.

The growing season, none too long in the southern part, becomes shorter toward the north; but, as the number of days between spring and fall frosts decreases, the length of daylight of days increases, until in June plants grow almost the whole twenty-four hours for a short season.

East European region—Russia. In Kendrew's *Climates of the Continents* this whole region is included in Asia because of its essentially Asiatic climate, but a text discussing the geography of Europe cannot omit it. In every other region has been found some item to show that the climate is related to the great Asiatic interior. In this region the connection is more vital and intimate than in any other. The cold of winter is a result of the coldness of an all-winter continental high in Siberia and of the winds blowing out therefrom, which turn westerlies almost directly north in the northeastern part and give to the northeast corner of the region a mean annual temperature of 24° F. with a range between July and January means of 64° F. Isotherms of winter, therefore, are concentric round the fringe of the high, but those of summer are more nearly east and west, showing the predominance, at that season, of the influence of insolation. The fact that, in their Atlantic portions, isotherms depart from their mean east-and-west direction by lying farther south in summer and north in winter shows still some marine influence.

East European climate is noted for its monotony over large areas, a response to the uniform levelness of its topography. Monotony expresses itself in temperature, in range of temperature, in rainfall both as to amount and season, in humidity, and in winds, which are prevailingly from the west and southwest. This climate is further characterized by cold winters, steadily cold for three to five months, and long winters, but not severe because the air is relatively dry. The three great external climatic influences have quite different values from those found in other geographic regions. Here marine influence is slight, but the power of summer sunshine and of the cold, continental high are strong.

Isotherms on the map of this region, even when corrected to sea level, are very nearly like the actual temperatures, because the land is so low that the correction is trivial and uniform. Range of monthly mean temperatures increases eastward as does the mean annual temperature.[4] A range of 48° F. at Leningrad (July 64° F. to January 16° F.) is topped by 64° F. at Turinskie-Rudniki (64° F. to 0° F.) in the mid-Urals. Leningrad is influenced more by the sea and has a mean annual temperature of 40° F. while the mid-Urals are influenced more by the Asiatic cold and have a mean annual of 32° F.

A comparison of Orenburg and Leningrad temperatures brings out this

[4] The table on page 38 shows both range and mean annual temperatures for several places. See the maps also.

contrast in another way. The two towns have the same mean annual temperature, although Orenburg is 8° farther south; but Orenburg has a mean monthly range of 68° F., while Leningrad has only 48° F. In general, mean annual isotherms bend southward inland, as does this one of 40° F., and emphasize the Asiatic or land control of climate. Moscow is in the midst of the most typical part of this East European climatic area. Its January mean of 12° F. and its July mean of 66° F. give a mean annual range of 54° F., but its absolute minimum and maximum of —44° F. and 99° F. give it the unattractive absolute range of 143° F.

Place	July mean °F.	Jan. mean °F.	Range °F.	Mean annual temp. °F.
Archangel	58	8	50	33
North of Urals	56	—8	64	24
Leningrad	64	16	48	40
Turinskie-Rudniki	64	0	64	32
Russian-Polish border on Lat. 50° N.	68	26	42	47
South end of Urals on Lat. 50° N.	74	2	72	38

Many local anomalies of temperature occur in the south, where high relief introduces a new factor. The Caucasus Mountains show great differences in temperature at the same altitude on opposite sides; they also show great differences in unlike exposures and varying altitudes, differences to which plants and animals have responded. Men can have the vine and mulberry close to coniferous forests. The rigors of Alpine snows, winds, and cold with the characteristic wild life, bears, wolves, and foxes, are within a day's climb of subtropical gardens. Yaila Mountains in the Crimea produce somewhat the same effects, though to a less degree because they are not so lofty. The Crimea has the mildest, most Mediterranean-like climate in this whole region because nearly surrounded by water and warmed by the deep waters of the Black Sea. The place has not a truly Mediterranean type of climate, for the shallow seas around it freeze in winter.

Streams everywhere freeze in winter and are often used for smooth sled highways. The northern Dwina is closed 180 days, the Volga at Kazan 140 days, and the Kama, its northern tributary, twenty days longer. The Volga mouths are closed 100 days, the lower Dnieper is closed 80 days, the middle Dnieper 100 to 120 days, the Dwina in west Russia about 120.

Lakes Ladoga and Onega are closed by ice about 160 days; the White Sea head 180 days, and its mouth 200 days. The Murman coast is never obstructed with ice, but the eastern Arctic coasts are perennially closed. The Baltic is so shallow that it has little effect on East European climate. When frozen it gives as great freedom to winds as would a level land surface. The deeply indented Arctic has little effect on temperature east of the White Sea but favors wind movement. The Caspian and Black seas develop in winter small low-pressure areas which draw air toward the water from all sides.

Spring is late and is frequently interrupted by returns of cold snaps. Temperature in spring and fall changes often, quickly, and critically; in summer, changes are rarer, slower, and stimulating; in winter, cold is steady and continuous.

This East European region has over 10 inches of rainfall in summer except in the far southeast, and less than 10 inches in winter except for a small area south of Moscow. The Urals have a trifle more rainfall in winter than do the adjacent lands and produce a small rain shadow along their eastern flanks in summer, but their influence is not to be compared with that of the Caucasus in developing local heavy rains and in protecting low areas on the leeward sides. The heaviest rainfall of the region, over 100 inches, occurs in favored localities on Black Sea-Caucasus slopes, but plains bordering Black and Caspian seas have the least effective rainfalls [5] of the whole region. Portions of the Caspian plains are below sea level; and they are further unfortunate in having either the high-pressure belt, or northern trades, or winds blowing out from the Asiatic interior most of the year. Arctic ocean and polar winds are not rain-producing, a fact which explains the meager rainfall of northern areas. Through the larger portion of this continental region the heaviest rains occur in August and September, when the continental low of Asia is best developed, and when active cyclones and anticyclones of the westerlies are not hindered from traveling far eastward by the continental high whose checking influence comes a few weeks later. These rains moisten the ground for planting winter wheat.

From December to March the precipitation of the region is mostly in the form of snow—fine, dust-like flakes or grains of frost. Three feet of this snow is not uncommon in the coniferous forests, where the tree-shelter prevents its melting and blowing about. If snow falls when the ground has not yet frozen hard, it shields soil and plants from severe freezing as long as it remains. Weikof reports finding near Leningrad air temperature above snow of −39° F., in the ground beneath the snow cover, 27° F., and in bare ground, −31° F. Such snow protection is very beneficial to forests and ensures them ample moisture for the next growing season.

On the steppes in the southeast, precipitation is so low that no forests can grow; snow blows about in fierce, piercing winds; ground freezes deeply, thaws late in spring, and with no snow to melt has little moisture. Only grass can get a start.

East European skies are usually gray, six tenths to eight tenths overcast in the winter on the average, but less in the summer because air is warmer and relative humidity low.

Central Europe proper. This region is more isolated from marine influences than any region of Europe outside of Russia. It has more relief and more detail of topographic pattern, more varied rainfall, more local dif-

---

[5] By *effective rainfall* is meant the amount of precipitation in relation to the rate of evaporation.

ferences in temperature, more diversity in the length of the growing season, and greater variability of winds than any other part of the transitional zone. It is not only intermediate between the Oceanic and true Continental types of climate, but intermediate between the northern and southeastern parts of the transitional zone. Its rainfall and mean annual temperatures decrease eastward; its range of temperature and amount of clear weather increase eastward; and its summer temperatures increase southward because insolation is the chief control of temperature. It is easily the most densely populated and most industrial part of the transitional zone.

Rainfall is everywhere sufficient. In winter such mountain areas as Harz, Black Forest, Alps, and the Great Glockner have nearly 40 inches. Lesser mountains receive over 20 inches, while all low lands have less than 10 inches. In summer the precipitation is everywhere over 10 inches but only exceeds 20 on the mountains. On most of these it exceeds 30, and on Glockner it exceeds 40 inches.

Winds are prevailingly from the west, a little south of west in the winter and a little north of west in the summer, but in both summer and winter they are frequently disturbed by the passage of numerous cyclones and anticyclones. Sudden changes from warm, moist, or rainy to clear, even, crisp, and frosty weather are characteristic. This sort of change is the stimulus that is so much valued in developing human energy. Mean January temperatures decrease eastward only about 10 degrees (34° to 24° F.) across the entire width of the region. Mean July temperatures differ by only eight degrees (72° to 64° F.), decreasing northward. The range of temperature therefore is about 48° F. over all the area. All rivers are frozen for short times. The Rhine at Köln is closed twenty-one days, and those rivers farther east for longer seasons.

Lower Danube region. Of the three transitional zones this region is farthest from the Atlantic and owes but little of its character to that sea, but it is near the Ægean and Black seas and partakes somewhat of the Mediterranean type both in seasonal rainfall and in temperature. It is really intermediate between that type and the Continental type of Russia. Having water on three sides, it has a peninsular high-pressure area like Spain in winter. In fact it lies in the northern high-pressure axis of the Mediterranean region. It further partakes of this southern type in having a northerly or northeasterly wind most of the year, for it lies in the border of the trade-wind belt. In the south the region has more rainfall in winter than in summer, but in the north it partakes of the Continental type in having its maximum rainfall in the summer months. Zagreb (Agram) in northwest Yugoslavia is far enough from the Adriatic (80 miles) so that 56 per cent of its annual precipitation comes in the summer months and February is its driest month. Bucharest has 61 per cent in the summer half of the year. Much of the Lower Danube region is Mediterranean in having its maximum temperature soon after its highest sun.

Summer temperatures for the warmest month range from 72° F. in the north to 80° F. in the south. Winter temperatures range from 44° F. to 28° F. In both summer and winter the isotherms trend east and west, a characteristic again of Mediterranean climate. Because of the strong relief over much of this region, rainfall and actual temperatures are very diverse. In the Dinaric Mountains precipitation reaches the wasteful figure of 100 inches, but on the Black Sea coast it is similar in summer and winter in that in neither half of the year does rainfall exceed 10 inches. The mountains are covered with snow every winter. Rivers flood when the snow melts. Balkan winters are reported to be severe and trying for travel and commerce. The snow of winters and the moist air of summer clothe most of the mountains with forest. Bulgaria and Rumania have a good maize summer.

This chapter has been devoted to description and explanation of the types and characteristics of climates in Europe. In later regional studies more will be said of the relations of man to these items.

QUESTIONS

1. It has been said that "conservation of water is necessary because of the unequal distribution of precipitation in time and space." Examine rainfall maps of Europe and discuss them as an illustration of the idea.

2. Why do the July and January isotherms intersect regularly from the Pyrenees to the Urals? Why do the isotherms remain nearly parallel all year in Norway?

3. What do isotherms indicate as to the truth of the name "warming-pan of Europe" sometimes given to the Mediterranean?

4. What country of Europe probably has the most complete relief control of climate? Why?

5. While the Caspian, Black, and Mediterranean seas show characteristic low pressure in winter, and the Balkans and Spain show highs in winter, the continent shows no characteristic high in winter and low in summer. Why? Explain your answer.

6. Which mountain chain, Caucasus, Alps, or Pyrenees, exercises the most influence upon precipitation?

7. Examine the maps of climatic elements and discuss the validity of the division of the continent into the climatic regions treated subsequently.

BIBLIOGRAPHY

BLAIR, Thomas A., *Climatology* (New York, Prentice-Hall, Inc., 1942).

HANN, Julius, *Handbook of Climatology*, trans. by R. DeC. Ward (New York, The Macmillan Company, 1903; in German, 1932).

HUNTINGTON, Ellsworth, *Civilization and Climate* (New Haven, Yale University Press, 1924).

KENDREW, W. G., *Climates of the Continents* (Oxford, Clarendon Press, 1942).

MARKHAM, Sydney F., *Climate and the Energy of Nations* (New York, Oxford University Press, 1944).

MILHAM, W. I., *Meteorology* (New York, The Macmillan Company, 1921).

SHAW, Sir Napier, *Manual of Meteorology* (Cambridge, England, Cambridge Press, 1926-31).

CHAPTER 4

Geography of Prehistoric Men in Europe

Race on race goes chasing through
Finding always more to do
To make its conquest sure.
—ANON

INTRODUCTION

"Whence the peoples of Europe?" is a question often asked. Over all the continent men have roamed and settled; today very little really habitable land is unoccupied. Are these people that now live in every valley and corner natives of Europe? For how many generations have their ancestors lived in Europe? And how long in the specific places where *they* now live? Why so much diversity of physique, of language, of civilization, of spirit and culture? Did the previous occupants enjoy their homes as the present people do? Did they take advantage of their resources and were they buffeted by their climate as are the present inhabitants?

Bonds between man and his environment. The distribution of land and water always seems to have been significant to man. In very primitive times he made of the land both home and highway and was sharply restricted by waterways. For this reason the changes in land and water distributions, such as are mentioned in Chapter 2, were supremely important.

An uplift of continental shelf with the British Isles, establishing land connections between them and the continent, made it possible for man to go with ease from the Somme basin of today to the valley of the Thames and even on northwest to Ireland without crossing waters wider than a stream made by the union of the Thames and Rhine. Such a depression of the lands as permitted the Arctic Sea to spread inland to the Caspian Sea, made highways for Arctic seals and sturgeon; but this marine invasion, while it lasted, must have checked westward migrations of Asiatic men toward Europe. Men in Europe were then spared the Mongoloid invasions so frequent in more recent millenniums.

Slow movements of the lands up and down, as described above, not only made and broke important land connections by changing the distribution of sea and land, but they disturbed the people who desired to live or travel along the shorelines. In far northern Norway are relics of the camps of

Paleolithic fishermen and hunters along a moraine which was washed and carved by the sea after the ice melted. The campers lived, in part at least, on sea food and established their residence with reference to the shoreline. Below these remains on a younger shoreline, made by the sea after the first moraine and shoreline had been elevated, may be found Neolithic implements. Thousands of years passed between the dates of occupation of these two camps; but the lure of sea food seems to have been equally powerful for each race of people, and the people equally responsive to the influence of the sea. Thousands of miles of elevated shorelines are known around seas and headlands of northwestern Europe. Other shorelines have been lowered beneath the sea. Wherever there is evidence of human use of the beaches, there is also evidence of adjustment to their changed elevations.

Equally serious in the requirements made of men are the delta growths. The great Rhine-Scheldt-Meuse delta is essentially post-glacial. How many times through prehistory have there been adjustments and minor migrations of delta peoples upon the widening delta plains! How many more must be made as the delta grows farther and farther out into the North Sea! Nothing as spectacular has ever been undertaken as the project of the present generation, the diking and draining of the Zuider Zee; but when the millions of guilders have been spent and the work completed, extensive adjustments will necessarily be made if there comes a change of 20 feet either up or down in the relative level of the sea. The Po delta, graded with reference to the present sea level, began in post-glacial times not far from Mantua and has grown forward about 75 miles. Such a migration of the sandbars, lagoons, distributaries, and delta lakes as this delta growth involves must have unsettled many a beachcomber.

But even more common, though probably much slower, were the necessary adjustments of people affected by changes of climate. Europe has been invaded four times by a continental glacier. If its coming was not due to climatic changes, it certainly induced changes in climate as well as profound changes in the distribution of habitable land, of grasslands and running animals, of forests with their wild life, of routes of travel and migration, and of seas with their fish. Primitive men are known to have lived in southern England before the first advance of the ice. They lived in France and Germany in the first interglacial stage and encountered hippopotamuses and both Asiatic and African elephants roaming over the lands. In Germany remains of the Heidelberg man, a remote ancestor of Neandertal man, are associated with those of the Etruscan rhinoceros. How much farther north the beast may have gone is not known, because his remains could have been disturbed by the ice. To date there is wholly lacking the fascinating evidence of cave occupation found for later interglacial stages. Man's relics found among river gravels suggest his use of the alluvial lands built up by rivers and of fish, water animals, possibly waterfowl, and eggs.

It seems impossible that man could have remained in these northern localities during the second advance of the ice, for great glaciers formed in the Alps extended far beyond the borders of Switzerland west and south and those originating in Scandinavia reached Britain and northern Germany. Climate of this stage has been described as "tolerable in the river valleys of Spain, France, and southern England." Men occupied these valleys, fed on the life of the streams, and as evidence left their implements in the accumulating sands and gravels and their bones to be buried and preserved to present times. As the ice sheet melted and gave place to the second interglacial stage, man followed the retreating ice, as did the forest, the smaller plants, and the wild life.

In the third glacial stage and its succeeding interglacial stage, conditions and responses seem to have repeated themselves so that on the opening of warmer conditions we find the probable immediate ancestor of Neandertal man living as before in the open and also occupying caves in the Dordogne region of Central France. Before the return of the ice the fourth time, man had taken possession of caves. He seems to have occupied rock shelters, overhanging ledges, and the mouths of caves and finally to have moved much farther back into the better shelter of true caves. His contemporaries were the last survivors of the large mammals of Asia and Africa, the so-called second fauna, *Elephas antiquus, Rhinoceros merckii,* and *Ursus spelæus* (the cave bear).

In the fourth glacial stage (Würm of Europe, Wisconsin of America), a period of maximum refrigeration, the men were of the true Neandertal race, commonly cave men of low-browed type. The mammoths and reindeer were driven far south, the latter certainly to northern Spain. The woolly rhinoceros shared with man the lands and climate. In post-glacial time the forest and the wild life, including man, followed the ice back to the north. The great mammoth and the reindeer retreated finally from France, the former subsequently becoming extinct even in the north but the latter surviving to the present. Man not only migrated but also in considerable numbers continued to live in Spain, France, the Rhine Valley, and other favorable places of western Europe. A new type of man, the Cro-Magnon race,[1] dominated western Europe, became numerous for a savage, primitive man, and made himself quite at home.

Already it has been suggested that a strong bond exists between man and his food supply. Through these early periods of man's occupation of Europe his food was largely wild life. There is found little evidence that he domesticated animals and less that he cultivated crops. He must have lived where he could obtain berries, nuts, seeds, fish, and meat of wild animals. His limitations are more appreciated when one recalls that there was no

---

[1] In some instances the term *race* may be used rather specifically, but in many cases it is used by writers more loosely because definite boundaries between races cannot be located. Race is a biologic term like family and tribe, and is sometimes applied to a people or nation believed to belong mostly to one stock.

commerce in such items and that he lived in a strongly accentuated seasonal climate. Seasons must have stimulated him to seek methods of storing foods and of protecting himself in winter. Seasonal migration was a much later acquisition of Europeans and must have been related to food supply as it now is in grazing transhumance. In like manner the progress of glacial cycles may have driven races of men to aperiodic migrations to and from many places where the climate and plant and animal life were influenced by invading ice.

Shortly after the retreat of the last ice sheet, simple exchanges of goods and treasures over considerable distances arose and established extremely profitable bonds between man and his broadening horizons. Both materials and men counted in this expansion of interest. Proximity to tool-makers or to ingenious neighbors was a valuable item in early as well as later environments. Mental horizons also expanded. As soon as a people rises to live part of the time in the realm of ideas, superior thinkers at once unconsciously acquire new responsibilities and new values in other men's environment.

Sources of information. Several sources of information regarding European prehistoric life and geography have been incidentally mentioned. Others are the human physique, ornaments, relics and burial remains, and such philological items as can be ascertained. These last gain in significance as languages evolved but are probably valueless for the ice age. Another source of information on ancient races and customs is the behavior today of races in similar stages of culture and civilization. Remote and isolated communities of men are found living today in every simple stage of evolution, Old Stone Age, New Stone Age, Copper, Bronze, and early Iron ages —cave dwellers, lake dwellers, and seashore dwellers.

Obvious difficulties are encountered in efforts to piece together a connected story of the races of Europe. The most serious one is the inescapable fact that vastly more of record has been destroyed than has been preserved for our study. There is trouble in working out the chronology of steps in the rise of the races and in determining what items in different regions are synchronous. It has become evident that stages much alike among different people were not always reached at even approximately the same time. Men made more advancement when they had progressive neighbors or lived in "a house by the side of the road Where the sons of men passed by." Then, too, the duration of time involved in the development of the race embarrasses the mind. A million years is a long time to us who have been accustomed to think in terms of the few thousands of years compassing European history.

PALEOLITHIC TIME

A composite chronology. The table on pages 48-49 sets in order the four glacial stages with their three interglacial stages but does not carry the story far beyond the retreat of the last ice sheet. The table reads upward from oldest events mentioned toward the present. The third column gives the general culture types and the subtypes recognized more or less locally. The fifth column gives by names the chief human remains or types of men that date from the glacial period.

A few comments on some of these items will lead to a better evaluation of them. Although the first spreading of the ice began about 1,000,000 years ago, the last retreat may not have been more than 40,000 years ago in northern Germany, 25,000 years in Finland, and 15,000 in Sweden. The end of the Pliocene epoch of the Tertiary era is marked by the beginning of the ice age. The ice advances were not of equal extent or of equal duration, and interglacial stages were very unequal, as is shown by the distribution and weathering of the several sheets of drift. Great lapses of time are shown by the faunal changes from stage to stage. The first fauna contains forms that became extinct before the second interglacial stage, and the second fauna contains forms that have evolved or made a long migration since the first interglacial stage. The fact that the ice generated, gained thickness enough to flow, and then flowed 600 to 1,000 miles, halted repeatedly during its retreat, long enough to build successive recessional moraines, and then melted back to the original stand; and did so at least four times, leaving long interglacial stages between, is cumulative evidence of a long duration for the ice age. The changes in the types of men suggest great time, but the progress in industry is surprisingly slow.

Types of industry in Pleistocene time. In the third column of the table, headed "Culture [2] Stages," are mentioned a few selected types of implements men have made and used. Beginning with the oldest—the bottom of the column—they may be examined to show increasing use of materials and growing responses to the environment. Foxhall [3] implements and evidences of the use of fire are found beneath the oldest glacial drift and the Red Crag formation. This layer of rocks is classed as Pliocene by some geologists and early glacial by others. No human bones have been found, but crudely chipped flints called *eoliths* have been discovered. The Foxhall jaw is a different find and was not seen in place by one fitted to pass on its occurrence. The long succession of finds reveals considerable progress in the stone industries and development of skill in the hand of man.

Eoliths ("dawn stones") or pre-Chellean implements are of flint derived from the flint or chert of limestone beds in the Downs of southern Eng-

---

[2] *Culture* as here used refers to the character of things made and not to mental or spiritual traits of men.

[3] Foxhall is a small place near Ipswich, northeast of London.

land, in the chalk of western and northern France and in limestones of
many places in Italy, Germany, Switzerland, and countries farther east.
While all the tools are crude, they are obviously chipped and shaped for
definite purposes; knives, sharp on one edge only; scrapers, both double-
edged and with notched edges; hammer stones manifesting much battering;
hatchet knives, usually adapted to the right hand; fine points for boring;
and blades for planing—all in stone. Ingenious minds have suggested many
ways in which such fragments might be formed by accident, but it seems
easier to believe that simple primitive men made them than to believe that
various conditions of "sand pressure" and "temperature changes" could
have been localized to produce them where they are found and nowhere
else.

The Paleolithic implements, much better finished than the Eolithic but
never polished, are chipped over all the surface and much more specifically pointed, edged, fitted to the hand, and devised for specific uses. They
are classified in several types as the table shows, and each type shows improvements over its predecessors. The Chellean type of tools seems to have
been developed from the simpler forms of eoliths as men became more skilful
in meeting their needs. The typical implements of Chellean patterns and
art are found southeast of Paris, but similar ones are so generally scattered
over France, south England, Italy, and Spain, as well as over north Africa
from the Atlantic to Egypt and over Asia Minor, as to convince one that
men in this crude stage of culture hunted and subsisted over all this range
of territory. The Acheulian patterns described and named from Saint
Acheul, a suburb of Amiens, in the valley of the Somme, were evolved directly from the Chellean and have been found widely scattered over much
of southern Europe. The mammalian remains found in the same deposits
indicate a warm climate and suggest the time as that of the long interglacial
interval between the second and third glacial stages.

On the advent of the Neandertal man late in this second warm interglacial interval, tools again improved. This stage is called the Mousterian
culture. The men lived in caves and carried on their own tool industry in
camps inhabited by little groups. This is interpreted to be a response to
the approach of the Riss ice sheet and the accompanying colder climate.
In the several small isolated centers of Mousterian culture, local phases
developed, such as the Combe-Capelle of Dordogne. Diversity in the industry points to more sedentary habits of the people, leading to advances
in skill and industry. Caves of France and Belgium, of the Island of Jersey,
and of Torquay in south England were centers of Mousterian culture.
Corsica and Sardinia had become islands and so far have yielded no remains of these Paleolithic stages of man, but grottoes in northern Italy
(Grimaldi, Enfants, Prince) were well occupied. Spain also was the home
of many camps and cave groups, principally in the northern part.

The Aurignacian types of implements seem to have come with an inva-

Glacial stages and their approximate duration	Animals	Culture stages
Ice Retreat 30,000 yrs.		
IV. Würm (Wisconsin)..... Advance of last ice....... 30,000 yrs.	Third Fauna (repeated) *Elephas primogenius* *Rhinoceros tichorhinus* (woolly)	Magdelenian of Dordogne Solutrian on Saône north of Lyons Cave paintings and carvings, N. Spain Aurignacian
Short interglacial stage .... 50,000 yrs.	Second Fauna (repeated) *Elephas antiquus* *Rhinoceros merckii* *Ursus spelæus*	
III. Riss (Illinois)........ 50,000 yrs.	Third Fauna *Elephas primogenius* *Rhinoceros tichorhinus* (woolly)	Mousterian in caves on Dordogne
Very long interglacial stage 300,000 yrs.	Second Fauna *Elephas antiquus* *Elephas meridionalis* *Rhinoceros merckii* *Hippopotamus*	Acheulian Chellean, S.E. of Paris
II. Mindel (Kansan)...... 50,000 yrs. Long interglacial stage..... 200,000 yrs.	First Fauna *Megaceros* (Giant deer) Musk-ox *Bison antiquum* *Equus stenonois*	Pre-Chellean
I. Günz (Pre-Kansan)..... 50,000 yrs. Interglacial stage .... 100,000 yrs. Nebraskan .... 50,000 yrs. Interglacial .... 100,000 yrs. Jerseyan .... 50,000 yrs.	Etruscan rhinoceros Saber-tooth tiger Giant beaver *Mastodon avernensis*	
Pliocene .... Oligocene		Foxhallian

Eras	Human remains	Localities
	Cro-Magnon (Reindeer man)	Many places
Stone Age [Neolithic Era]	Grimaldi remains Neandertal remains Grimaldi (Negroid) Neandertal type	Mentone caves in Italy Germany Rhodesia, South Africa
Paleolithic or Old	{ Spy man Krapina man La Chapelle aux Saints Le Moustier Neandertal	Belgium Croatia Yugoslavia } France
	Foxhall jaw bone (not seen *in situ* by scientists)	England
Stone Age	Heidelberg man Piltdown skull	Heidelberg, Germany Sussex—south of London
Dawn of		
	Pithecanthropus man	Java
Eolithic or	No human remains but implements and fire	Red Crag, Pliocene, near Ipswich—N.E. of London

sion of new tribes who, after developing these better tools, had migrated late in the third interglacial interval into western and central Europe. Although these tools may have been a product of the Mediterranean regions, they probably arose farther east. They mark a development of skill and style in the favorable climatic and general living conditions there during the waning of the third or Riss ice sheet. Other types more specialized and more closely adapted to men's needs and uses were devised; then by gradual steps during long periods of time in late Riss-Würm interglacial and Würm glacial stages, through tribal contacts and migrations the new styles spread over wide areas. In certain localities these people worked out a higher culture called Solutrian, as on the Saône [4] north of Lyons, and another, the Magdelenian, on the Dordogne. The people who made the Aurignacian and Magdelenian implements lived ordinarily in caves and developed a splendid technique in the use of pigments and graving tools on the walls of their cave homes, leaving ample record of the contemporaneous animals, their methods of hunting and killing, of their bows, arrows, and spears, and even illustrations of their painting processes. An abundance of late Paleolithic art has been found in northern Spain, some in France, and a little in Italy. It seems to have come to an end rather suddenly shortly after the withdrawal of the last ice and the amelioration of the climate, perhaps when men came to live in the open again.

Types of men and their adjustments in the ice age. While undoubtedly men lived in Europe before and during the earliest stage of the ice age, the oldest human fossil is the Piltdown skull found in Sussex, a county south of London. The skull was found in conditions and with mammal associations which assign it to the first long interglacial stage, [5] when there was a warm, temperate climate with grass in broad valleys and forest on the uplands. No later fossils of this type have yet been found, so students conclude that this species, *Eoanthropus dawsoni,* became extinct.

Remains of the Heidelberg man were first found near Heidelberg in sands of probable early second interglacial time. Osborn puts the date of this man at about 250,000 years ago or midway between the time of the Piltdown man and the men of today. While the Mauer jaw is the only human fragment of the Heidelberg race, Eolithic implements of this time, widespread over western and southern Europe, make it clear that there were many men living in those mild interglacial times. Later came the Neandertal men, whose remains suggest that they were lineal descendants of the Heidelberg men, and who are believed to have lived in Europe perhaps 100,000 years; such a record makes modern history look short, not to say unimportant. They roamed widely, and their remains are found in

[4] Solutrian culture is thought by some to have been brought from the east to northeastern France, to have developed further there, and then to have spread widely.
[5] Fluorine tests indicate that skull and jaw are both younger than the associated mammalian bones.

many places. Like the Piltdown man their line became extinct after the third interglacial stage, possibly during the Würm ice stage. These people made the Acheulian and Mousterian implements. They began to live in caves and have thus made and left us a better record than the earlier races who lived in the open and whose origin remains unknown.

The Cro-Magnon race, sometimes called reindeer men, seems to have exterminated the Neandertal race in Europe and to have spread north and west as far as France and Great Britain. Sollas says they came to Europe earlier than 13,000 B.C.; Tyler says they came 25,000 years ago. Penck estimates they deployed over Europe 24,000 to 16,000 years ago, thus having a duration of 8,000 years. Bean thinks Neandertal man has not been in Europe since 20,000 years ago. If Cro-Magnon men were in Europe before the Würm glacier, they were there more than 35,000 years ago.

To those who have followed the trails of their remains and their tools, it seems probable that they spread from a great area in the region of the Iranian Plateau, including present Persia and Afghanistan, in a more or less periodic or aperiodic wave migration. They probably emigrated from southwestern Asia because of climatic changes toward aridity, and followed afar off the retreating ice and its cool climate as warmer conditions ensued. They seem to have been a well-developed race when they came, accustomed to a cool moist climate such as the Würm and Riss stages of the ice age must have given to this plateau country. They were accustomed to the reindeer which then roamed over Europe north of the Pyrenees, Alps, and Black Sea. (See map, Obermaier, *Fossil Man in Spain,* p. 51.) They probably were familiar with tundra and steppe, both of which were common landscapes in central Europe at that time. They came to Europe apparently by three routes, though not in simultaneous streams. One route on the south side of the Mediterranean crossed on the Sicilian land bridge, another led along the north side of the Great Sea, and the third ran northward east of the Caspian across the plains, now steppes, around the northern end of that sea and across southern Russia into the Danube plains. This route had become possible because of the withdrawal of the Arctic waters which in late Pleistocene time had spread in the Obi Basin far enough to connect with the Caspian Sea.

As their implements indicate, these people were hunters, not even herdsmen. They did no farming but seem to have dug roots from the ground. Their homes became established near flint pits, along streams where fishing was easy, and where their remains were sometimes covered by alluvium. Not only did they live in the open but they took advantage of the shelter of ledges and the protection afforded by caves. To keep out bears and other marauding beasts, fires were kept in the cave entrances. Calcined hearthstones are of frequent occurrence. Flint and pyrite struck fire for them. For light they carried lamps of soft stone or chalk, hollowed out to hold oil.

Flint-working in open pits or quarries was their universal industry, and it frequently developed to commercial proportions. Their stone implements show careful workmanship characteristic of late Paleolithic specimens. Bone implements are nicely smoothed and finished; needles, awls, and pins suggest the sewing together of furs for clothing. Harpoons of deer horn and ivory indicate successful chase and more effective utilization of materials than their predecessors attained. They also had commerce in marine shells of Mediterranean species, to be used as necklaces and other ornaments. Teeth of mammals, fragments of ivory and bone, alternate with shells in some necklaces. As the use of bone and ivory increased, the use of flint waned.

The makers and users of Aurignacian tools were dolichocephalic with large brain capacity, strong forehead and chin, and only slight bony projection over the eyes—altogether a fine type of body. Some of them were 6 feet tall; others were nearly a foot shorter. They differed in no marked way from succeeding races and bore a close resemblance to existing Europeans. The appearance of a negroid type of man in the Grimaldi caves of Italy suggests that Negroes came to Europe with these tribes of Aurignacian culture, and further discoveries of skulls with negroid affinities in Spain, Brittany, and possibly in Caithness of Scotland indicate their wide range and probably a negroid strain in the Cro-Magnon blood.

As the Würm Ice Stage began, the winds spread the Old Loess over many Cro-Magnon camps, workshops, and refuse heaps and buried them for future study. The withdrawal of the ice was accompanied by the laying of the Young Loess and a repetition of the steppe condition with additional burials of late paleoliths and bone implements. During the long cold of the Würm many of the Cro-Magnon men lived in caves where they drew, engraved, and painted pictures. Line drawings suggest framework of logs over which hides and boughs could be placed to make houses. None of the early drawing suggest more clothing than a loin cloth, but in later drawings men have skins over their shoulders.

During the Würm time men labored under many difficulties. Beasts desired the same shelters and caves as man. Winters required the preservation of foods if aught but meat and nuts were to be eaten in the cold months. The race seems to have broken up into several groups or tribes which persisted into later periods though probably not as pure strains. Men of similar stature and head proportions are today found in the Landes of France near the Garonne, at Lannion in Brittany (nearly one third of the population), and along the Dordogne, where men true to type huddle in caves and under the ledges partly shut in by stone walls just as they seem to have done in the late Paleolithic times. This race gave us the Aurignacian, Solutrian, and Magdelenian culture-stages.

The stream of progress from Paleolithic to Neolithic flowed in waves. Cro-Magnon history and geography cover a wave of rapid progress. By the end of the Paleolithic era man was still only a gatherer. He gathered stones and shaped them roughly; he gathered many animals for food, cooked the flesh, used the skins and furs, and made tools of bones; he gathered fruits, nuts, and seeds for his food; but he seems not yet to have done more. In the Mesolithic time he began in a small way to produce. He had lived in a steppe climate with loessal dust blown and deposited over many of his camps. Following the gradual retreat of the ice, forests began to spread over the evacuated plains and valleys; the wild horse fled, reindeer journeyed northward as the tundra belt shifted with the ice margin. Thus forests grew up around man, and his animal associates migrated. Life in the forests was difficult, so man migrated to the seashore, to lake fringes, and to stream borders. His numbers were greatly reduced. Five new types of culture arose in Europe, located in areas scattered from Spain to the Baltic region and always on the borders of water.

NEOLITHIC PEOPLES

The Neolithic culture stage is thought by some to begin properly among the Cro-Magnons and before the Würm glaciation had passed; but inasmuch as there was no domestication of animals, no farming, and no polishing of flint tools, it seems best to save the terms *Neolithic* and *New Stone Age* for the time of these improvements.

The Neolithic stands for much larger use of the environments and for much closer adjustment to geographic conditions than previously. Progress is marked in four items. Animals were domesticated. Cattle first, then pigs, goats, and a little later sheep were bred and reared to serve men. Crops were planted and harvested; cereals and grasses were probably the first among many captures and adaptations. Pottery in much variety was made from local clays. Textiles of linen and wool came on the scenes. Woven baskets and mats of grass and twigs and of bark and reeds were used and dumped in the waste heaps. With these four advances there came a partial desertion of the caves, a great decrease in the amount of nomadism, and an equal increase in fixed habitations.

Origins of Neolithic men. Routes traced by abandoned implements and other items make it seem probable that the people bringing the new elements of Neolithic culture came from western Asia, where they had been developing for some centuries. In Susa 15,000 to 18,000 years ago, in Chaldea 7,000 to 8,000 years ago, and in Anau just east of the south end of the Caspian at least 7,000 to 10,000 years ago were cultures of the European Neolithic type. Racially these people were similar to the Cro-Magnon; culturally, they were more advanced. Urged out from these Asian centers by climatic changes, they came to Europe as a trickling stream, not in waves or hordes, for several thousand years. They followed routes similar to those of Cro-Magnon men, reached Crete about 14,000 years ago and localities farther west at successively later dates, generations later.

Their ideas and methods may not have reached Denmark, Britain, and Sweden until 7,000 to 8,000 years ago. On the northern route round the Caspian Sea, herdsmen probably advanced ahead of farmers. After the herdsmen had gone on into western Europe the farmers settled in many places in the Danubian plain and there established more or less permanent habitations. As ever, the migrant was the ambitious, venturesome, substantial person. Hardship apparently sorts people into two groups, the more and the less aggressive, and when migration is necessary the stronger group goes to the new land.

So again there came to south Europe a virile type of people bringing new methods of subsistence and defense which they shared with the residues of the Cro-Magnon peoples. Not only their physical characteristics but their elements of culture were grafted upon the previous stocks. As they took up their abodes generation after generation and century after century in new places farther west and north their adaptations and adjustments brought into being several new types of home and community. As one new type of utilization, villages were built on platforms supported on piles pushed or driven down into the mud of shallow zones of lakes, marshes, and streams. Another new type is correlated with the kitchen middens of northwestern Europe; a third with the land colonies as rural people on plains. The fourth was the island type best exemplified in the Minoans of Crete.

The Minoan developments. The earliest occupants of Crete were seafarers. Dates are uncertain and not required, though interesting; the order of events is more easily established and more valuable. Other Neolithic activities in the Ægean region included settlements in Thessaly and probably in the Peloponnesus, but the development of island people outstripped that of all others. Their new location, stimulating climate, abundance of stone, a modicum of isolation, the opportunity for commerce, and the necessity of subduing both land and sea stirred the Minoans to achievement. They built cities, roads, water and drainage systems, pavements, and libraries of clay tablets, and created many works of art, surpassing many of their neighbors. After a time less cultured people from the mainland overthrew them, borrowed freely from them, and developed the great Mycenean culture of more than 3,000 years ago which in its turn helped furnish foundations for the Greeks.

The lake dwellers. This form of special adaptation is often spoken of as that of the Swiss Lake Dwellers but it was by no means limited to Switzerland. Lakes in Germany, Austria, Hungary, and most of the Balkan states have piles, beds of waste, or something to indicate their active occupance. There are many such places in Russia, others at Ravenna and Venice in Italy, and several in the British Isles. Perhaps the relics have been most thoroughly studied in Switzerland. Lake Neuchâtel is known to have had about fifty villages along its shores. In some places the piles still stick out of the water when the lake is low. Lake Geneva had about forty villages, several of which were near the western end within the limits of the waters of the city of Geneva; Lake Constance had as many more, and Zurich, though small and hemmed in by mountains, had ten villages. Whether people built over the water for protection, for fishing, or for coolness and the thrill of the esthetic sense they do not tell us. There must have been a widespread urge to have drawn so many people into this type of residence.

Pile dwellings at Unter-Uhldingen on Lake Constance reconstructed from remnants. Road to land on right.

The village consisted of log or brush houses on a log platform supported above the water on piles pushed down into the mud. Such piles as have been pulled up show sharpening either by crude tools or by fire. Some of the houses were made of wattles and some were thatch-roofed. The refuse in the lake or marsh beneath village sites has furnished traces of 170 different species of plants, including barley, wheat, caraway and poppy-seeds, linseed; apples and pears apparently cut and dried, cherry and plum stones; seeds of wild grapes, of strawberry, raspberry, elderberry and blackberry; acorns, hazel and beech nuts; and loaves of bread (charred). Textiles preserved in the trash are of both wool and linen in scores of weave patterns and some knot patterns; also skins and furs. Baskets and mats of reeds and willows and fragments of pottery witness to the diversity of industry and to the range of resources laid under tribute. Colors used in decoration and still preserved are blue, red, yellow, and black. Boats and fishing tackle of several kinds were used. Game taken on the hills near other parts of the lake was brought to the platforms in a boat.

Prehistoric graves. These are common details of the landscape in many parts of Europe. This type is' found in the Lueneburger Heath in the northwest part of Germany. (Courtesy German Railroads Information Office)

Lake dwellers seem to have been Neolithic always in their early stages but to have entered the Bronze stage before the sites were abandoned. Commercial connections were many and reached out in several directions to other types of culture and environment and to diverse resources.

Coast peoples. Just as island people and lake dwellers illustrate methods of response to geographic conditions, so the people who dwelt along shorelines reveal another way men found of subsisting and using resources. In hundreds of places along shorelines of western Europe from the Baltic to the Bay of Biscay and on the open Atlantic, groups of families gathered in villages, probably in flimsy habitations, to work out their domestic economy. They gathered clams, periwinkles, and other edible shellfish; they made dugout boats and went to sea, capturing herring and cod; they used digging implements, fish-hooks, and harpoons of bone but not many devices

Dowth tumulus. A burial mound of the early Bronze Age, 2500 B.C., on the River Boyne, eastern central Ireland.

for land subsistence. Their village or camp refuse lies near the shores in heaps known as kitchen middens. Some attain heights of several feet, widths of many yards, and lengths of as many rods. Camp was probably moved along as the heap grew. The heaps carry the evidence of the kinds of fish and other water life used and the tools and utensils made, and suggest the restrictions on diet and range as well as the duration of residence in one place. In some kitchen middens are found remains of waterfowl. These wasteheaps represent a change in the mode of life from hunting to fishing, from the pursuit of land life on steppes and in open woods to the capture of sea life after forests became dense and exclusive.

The kitchen middens on the Baltic and those of Denmark are so placed with reference to shorelines, moraines, and lake deposits of varved or laminated clays that their chronology fits fairly well into the chronology of the varves, and ranges from 7,000 to 5,000 years ago. Tools in the middens indicate that the people were transitional between Mesolithic and Neolithic. There was much higher culture then in south Europe and the Near East than on the Atlantic borders.

Land dwellers. Typical land dwellers inhabited areas away from lakes, shorelines, and marshes. Villages of such people stood along the lands from Austria through Moravia and Galicia on the Carpathian slopes. Other villages contemporaneous with the lake dwellers were in Bavaria and France. In England near Cissbury manufacturing and mining villages were fortified. In southeastern Europe, Thessaly for example, there were others. People living on the land in this way were herdsmen and farmers in a crude, simple way. Some were partly nomadic, but in general they became villagers permanently attached to the soil. They were the founders of the great rural interests over central, western, and southern Europe.

Druid circle near Keswick, Lake District. Farms on lower slopes of Saddleback Mountain in the distance. Advanced mature topography. (Courtesy G. P. Abraham, Keswick)

Megalith builders. Several types of stone and earth structures were erected in many parts of Europe, some in the Neolithic and some in the Bronze age. They do not represent the work of any one race but rather the spread of an idea and a method of expressing it. A *megalith* is a great stone. A *dolmen* is a stone chamber made by placing two or four large stones on edge and resting a flat stone across them. Often these dolmens were burial places, in many cases covered with earth to make *tumuli.*[6] *Cromlechs* are stone circles, in some places erected in the open,[7] in others covered. *Menhirs* are standing stones, in some instances weighing twenty to thirty tons, placed on end 10 to 15 feet high in rows, ovals, and various designs. Cap-stones

[6] Dowth in Ireland is a good example.
[7] For example, the Druid Circle of Keswick, Lake District, England.

were frequently placed across the tops of two or three stones.[8] How the people of those remote times could so accurately plumb such massive stones that 3,000 to 5,000 years of frost and other agents have been unable to throw the last one down is a marvel! How they could even transport them and set them up is also a wonder! French archeologists report that about 4,500 of these stone patterns in France are still extant in spite of their use as quarries in many places. Numbers of them remain in England, Denmark, Sweden, Germany, Spain, the Ægean region, Africa, Palestine, and India.

Entrance passage into New Grange earthen burial mound. The sepulchral chamber is about 70 feet within, at the end of this passage. The tumulus is 44 feet high and 250 feet in diameter.

METALS AND MAN

The Copper and Bronze ages. One is astonished at the slow progress of civilization through the several hundred thousand years of the stone ages and its rapid progress in the metal ages. Copper in metallic form was found in several places in the Near East and began to be used in Chaldea 7,000

[8] Such stones stand in Stonehenge on the Salisbury plain of South England.

years ago, in Cyprus 4,500 years ago, and in Spain and Italy 4,000 years ago. Not until it was hardened by alloying with other metals, notably tin, was copper a very serviceable element. Its beauty must have been a large factor in its use. The knowledge of the use of bronze, an alloy of copper and tin, spread rapidly; and within a few generations after its discovery in the Near East, about 4,500 years ago, men in all parts of Europe would barter nearly anything for tin and copper, or for bronze, unless they found supplies of these metals near at home. The use of bronze reached Troy, Greece, and Sicily 4,000 to 4,400 years ago; Spain and the plains of Hungary 3,900 years ago; mid-Europe, France, and Switzerland about the same time; Britain, Germany, and Scandinavia a hundred years later. While it required 3,000 years for the use of copper to spread from Chaldea to Spain, the use of bronze covered the same journey in 1,000 years. Two reasons are at once suggested for the greater speed of the latter. Bronze is a much better tool and implement medium, and commerce as an institution had made great progress since copper was first used. In fact the fitness of bronze for tools, vessels, spears, axes, vases, and other ornaments both gave a great impetus to industry and craft and at the same time was a stimulus to commerce.

Gold from western parts of Ireland enriched the ornaments and tools of the late Neolithic people and entered into early commerce. No richer gold mines are known in Europe than these old ones in Ireland; and they were probably mostly placer gold deposits.

The Iron Age. The discovery of a process of smelting iron likewise opened to men new and bewildering possibilities for tools, building, and weapons. The use of iron arose in several places. Men remained in the Stone Age in some places, while in others they were rising through the Bronze Age and into the Iron Age. Egypt used iron over 5,000 years ago, Mesopotamia 4,500 years ago, Greece 4,000 years ago, the Hittites at least 3,500 years ago (possibly over 5,000), and the Cyprus-Phœnicians about 3,000 years ago. Here is a marvelous testimony to the difference between their means and ours of communication of news, processes, and commodities. Could Egypt today use iron for 2,000 years and not let Cyprus and Tyre know about it? Or an American chemist discover illinium and European chemists remain ignorant of the fact?

THE THREE GREAT RACES OF EUROPE

Origins. In the immigrations to Europe those who came by the southern routes to peninsular Europe and mingled their blood with that of relic peoples already on the ground became the foundations for the Mediterranean race. Those who came north of the Caspian Sea spent generations under less sunny skies, with the sun at a lower angle, and with more shelter of clouds and forest. Combined with the northern relic peoples they became the Nordics. There were a few scattered brachycephalic groups in the mountains of Central Europe in Neolithic time who shared in the lake-dweller culture and methods of life, but they were too few to make much impression on Europe. Following these Neolithic migrants came many brachycephalic men, short, dark, and roundfaced, from the steppes of Asia to the hills and mountains of Europe. They are known as the Alpine race. They absorbed or superseded the roundheads of the Alps, the Carpathians, and in general of the difficult, mountainous country of Central Europe. Later they spread over much of the Balkan highlands, Russia, and the Polish plains; thus they became respectively the southern Slavs, Russian Slavs, and western Slavs (Czechs, Slovaks, and Poles). They followed across south Russia the people who became the Nordics.

Characteristics. Mediterraneans occupy southern Europe, Spain, Portugal, southern Britain and France, most of Italy, Greece, Crete, and lands eastward to Persia; returning westward they are found south of the Mediterranean in Africa; in many places they grade into Semites and Hamites. They are characterized by a dolichocephalic head and rounded face, by a head projecting backward, hair dark to black, beard evenly distributed and rather thick and black, eyes medium to dark brown. Their skin is normally white but tans easily and is usually tawny, tan to brown in the Mediterranean sunshine. Nose is straight, small, not thick; mouth small with curved lips; stature medium, not stout.

The northern or Nordic race is fair, ruddy rather than tawny or ivory skinned, and does not easily tan. Their heads are long, and faces long from chin to brow; hair is light golden—reddish yellow; the beard is light in color and thinner than that of Mediterraneans. Eyes are generally blue or gray, rarely brown; nose is narrow, long and prominent; stature tall, rarely stout. They occupy most of the northwestern Europe, Scotland, the Low Countries, Denmark, Scandinavia, and Germany. The Nordics and Mediterraneans are similar in so many characteristics that strong probability is added to the evidence from the prehistoric relics to confirm the interpretation of a common origin.

The Alpine race has a brachycephalic head, round or short face, back of head nearly straight from the neck. Nose is often broad, and pointing out or turned up; chin less prominent than in either race above. Hair is brown to chestnut; eyes gray to brown; beard darker and ample. The skin is dry, whitish, parchment-like, resembling that of an Oriental; stature medium, tending toward a heavy, stocky build.

Genesis of some race characteristics. It has been pointed out that sunshine, hot winds, and lack of forest and clouds would tend to give the Mediterranean a darker complexion than other Europeans. His pre-European home would also give him a set in that direction. A warm climate is said to induce early sex maturity and encourage early marriage. Both results shorten the growing period and make for short stature and less muscular,

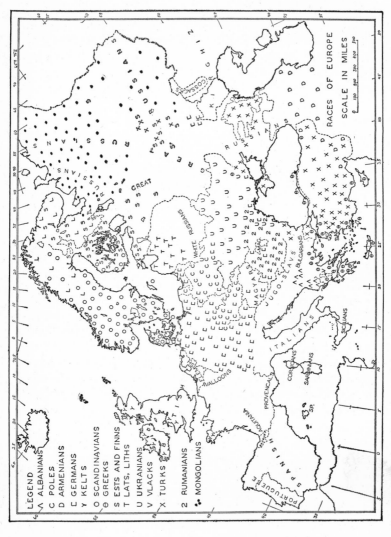

LEGEND

∧ ALBANIANS
C POLES
D ARMENIANS
E GERMANS
Y KELTS
O SCANDINAVIANS
Θ GREEKS
S ESTS AND FINNS
T LATS, LITHS
U UKRANIANS
V VLACKS
X TURKS
2 RUMANIANS
Mongolians

RACES OF EUROPE

SCALE IN MILES
0 100 200 300 400 500

Races of Europe. Open places among the symbols mean the people of the name used near are spread among those indicated by the symbol (i.e., Russians among Mongols and Tatars, Italians in Switzerland among Germans and French). Race is based more upon language than is desirable. (Adapted from *National Geographic Magazine*. Map made by National Geographic Society, 1919)

rugged physique. Smoothness of bone, frequently noted, results from just these limitations. The dry, dusty air would give advantage to a small mouth and a narrow, short, turned-down nose.

In like manner the fair complexions of Nordics are ascribed to a long period of residence in meager sunshine. The cold, slow season seems to give to most high-temperate-latitude people a late sex maturity; hence the longer growing period and the greater stature so universal among Nordics. The long face may go with this circumstance also. Big bone and frame with notable muscularity are other results. The long, thin nose ensures that frosty air will be warmed somewhat before it gets far into the system.

Comparative progress of the three races. Just as these races were differentiated physically in large part by the conditions under which they arose and developed, so their industrial and commercial life was influenced by the environmental helps and hindrances; and there seem to be also as marked differences in their spiritual development, which may be related to the stimulus of geographic conditions. The dominant factor influencing progress may have been climate then, as it seems to be today. Several other items of environment, themselves climatically determined, were significant, namely, forests and possible crops, wild life, and freedom of movement for commerce. After climate, resources that might be used or developed were important; and third, distribution of land, water, valley, plain, and mountain, as these influenced communications and contacts with neighbors, played its part.

It seems reasonably probable that ultimate progress should be greatest where the conditions of life strained but did not overstrain man's powers, where a tension would be set up between the man and his opportunities, where subsistence would require and requite labor and thought. In Paleolithic time there seems to have been but little difference in the stages of civilization reached by the people in central and those in southern Europe; but in Neolithic times the peoples pulled far apart; and in historic time they have again diverged but in quite the reverse direction. At first the Mediterraneans far outstripped the more northern races, but in the last two millenniums the northern races have far outdistanced the southern.

As conditions change, races and people change, for men must adjust to an altered environment. Most groups take advantage of the changes, profit by them whether they are in material or in culture, in resources or in human traits, customs, skills, and arts.

Along the margins of areas occupied by these three so-called races are mixtures made by intermarrying and intermingling. Portions of any one of the races more or less isolated from other parts became differentiated in many ways, until now there are several nations with their own characteristics in each of the race areas, and several nations that contain portions of two or three races.

SUMMARY AND CONCLUSIONS

This chapter has traveled over most of Europe and has swept through a thousand millenniums. It has glimpsed the types of men inhabiting Europe at occasional dates and tried to catch something of their geographic relationships, their responses in personal adjustment and in modifications of conditions, their uses of resources, their movements, and their reactions toward or upon each other, and with it all, to trace the expanding connections between man and his environment, the strengthening of bonds between people and conditions.

Step by step men have laid more and more under tribute. At first a food supply seems to have been the only necessity; then tools were needed, and chert quarries were worked. Shelters were adopted and adapted, and systems of exchange were set up. As the ages passed, routes for movement of people gained significance and several types of sites were appropriated. Diversity of occupation, of industry, and of raw materials appeared. Men began to build of stone, of brush, and of logs and needed much more material than when they just appropriated a shelter. They began to domesticate animals and plants, and to utilize further the surrounding life. They began to weave and to make baskets and pottery. They established relations with fiber as well as food plants, with clay as well as with flint. They carved bone into tools, made paints of ochers, and figurines of clay and stone; they started their arts by using these new materials. They made improvements in their tools, made boats and ropes, and began to fish in the sea or to find tracks across narrow waters. They made better clothing and to do so had to cultivate flax, weave wool, or mat hair. New devices, new processes strengthened their grip on their surroundings. They found copper, tin, zinc, gold, and later iron; and greatly improved their tools, dishes, armament, and art, also their industry and construction. They found new means of transportation, overcame space and time, worked out new routes, improved old ones, and in almost every move extended their reach or tightened their hold on things nearby.

Beyond the scope and aim of this chapter lie the historic steps that were taken. No great breaks occurred between the prehistoric and the early historic or between the early historic and medieval or between medieval and modern. No generation probably noted any great changes, but slowly out of one stage came the next, until the inventions and adjustments of our century dominate the scene. Steamboats, railroad trains, automobiles and planes, telephone, telegraph, radio, and television have entered, developing perhaps at a quickened pace, but no less surely from past achievements.

Always man has responded to his environment; always he has increased his response. Always he has gathered his food and his property from widening fields; always he has better adjusted himself to climate, to topography, to soils, to minerals, and to living organisms. And always his civilization has risen, sometimes slowly, sometimes rapidly. Can it be that one can measure the civilization of a people by the perfection of the harmonies between the people and their physical surroundings?

QUESTIONS

1. What grounds are there for saying that "Civilization can be measured by the grip man takes on his physical environment"? Cite illustrations.

2. Will all men ultimately pass out of the nomadic stage of civilization? Why?

3. In the past men who were nomadic were in the Paleolithic and Neolithic stages. Is there any reason why modern nomads should not attain the iron and steel stage, as industrial groups have done? What differences between ancient and modern nomads can you indicate?

4. Do you see any tendency for any of the three great races to displace any of the others? In case of such displacement would there be grounds for alarm?

5. Is it fair to discuss the progress of the three great races in Europe alone? Why?

6. What is the evidence for thinking some of the older types of men have persisted and mingled their blood with one or more of the three great races? How good is the evidence?

7. Why have these older types of men given place so largely to the three great races?

8. What is the basis for the belief that race in Europe may mean little more than adjustment through a long time to an influencing environment?

9. What aids to progress had Mediterranean people? Discuss several and note their relative values.

10. Which conditions favored and which ones hindered the progress of Nordics in northwest Europe?

11. Discuss geographic reasons for the great shift in the relative importance of Mediterraneans and Nordics in the last two millenniums?

12. What favorable and unfavorable circumstances had the Alpine race? What reasons can be suggested for its migration from the mountains to the northern and eastern lowlands?

13. What is meant by *race?* What has environment to do with race? Distinguish from *nation.* From *language.*

BIBLIOGRAPHY

BOAZ, Franz, *General Anthropology* (New York, D. C. Heath & Company, 1938).

BREASTED, James H., *The Conquest of Civilization* (New York, Harper and Brothers, 1926).

CHAPPLE, Eliot D., and COON, Carleton Stevens, *Principles of Anthropology* (New York, Henry Holt & Company, Inc., 1942).

CHATER, Melville, "The Danube, Highway of Races," *National Geographic Magazine,* Vol. 56 (December, 1929), pp. 643-697.

CHILDE, V. Gordon, *The Dawn of European Civilization* (New York, Alfred A. Knopf, Inc., 1927).

COON, Carleton S., *The Races of Europe* (New York, The Macmillan Company, 1939).

Coon, Carleton S., *et al., Race—Race Formation in Man* (Springfield, Illinois, 1950).

Daly, R. A., *The Changing World of the Ice Age* (New Haven, Yale University Press, 1934).

Dixon, Roland B., *Racial History of Man* (New York, Charles Scribner's Sons, 1923).

Fawcett, C. B., "The Nordic Region," *Scottish Geographical Magazine,* Vol. 48 (March, 1932), pp. 78-83.

Feibelman, James, *Theory of Human Culture* (New York, Duell, Sloan, and Pearce, 1946).

Forde, C. Daryll, *Habit, Economy and Society* (New York, Harcourt, Brace & Company, Inc., 1937), especially last chapter.

Glasgow, George, *The Minoans* (London, Jonathan Cape, 1923).

Hooton, Earnest A., "Plain Statement about Race," *Science,* Vol. 83 (May 29, 1936), pp. 511-513.

———, *Up from the Ape* (New York, The Macmillan Company, 1946).

Jefferson, M. S. W., *Man in Europe* (Ypsilanti, Michigan, Evans-Starr Printing Company, 1936).

Keith, Arthur, *New Discoveries Relating to the Antiquity of Man* (New York, W. W. Norton & Company, Inc., 1931).

Linton, Ralph, *The Science of Man in the World Crisis* (New York, Columbia University Press, 1945).

MacCurdy, George Grant, *The Coming of Man* (New York, The University Society, Inc., 1932).

Morgan, Jacques de, *Pre-Historic Man* (New York, Alfred A. Knopf, Inc., 1925).

Nelson, N. C., "The Origin and Development of Material Culture," *Sigma Xi Quarterly,* Vol. 20 (1932), pp. 102-123.

Obermaier, Hugo, *Fossil Man in Spain* (New Haven, Yale University Press, 1925).

Osborn, Henry Fairfield, *Men of the Old Stone Age* (New York, Charles Scribner's Sons, 1928).

Peake, Harold, and Fleure, H. J., *The Corridors of Time,* 8 vols. (London, Humphrey Milford, Oxford University Press, 1926-1934).

Ripley, W. Z., *Races of Europe* (New York, D. Appleton and Co., 1899).

Tyler, John M., *The New Stone Age in Northern Europe* (New York, Charles Scribner's Sons, 1921).

Usher, A. P., "The History of Population and Settlement in Eurasia," *Geographical Review,* Vol. 20 (1930), pp. 110-132.

CHAPTER 5

Changes and Conditions Induced
by State of War

"Triumphs are equal to defeats when their fruit consists in
lamentation and boundless hatred of the world."
—AUGUST VON PLATEN (1796-1835)

Introduction. A war like World War I or II produces many conditions
and changes that have to be considered in a geography course. World
War I was so far past when the first edition of this book was in preparation
that many of its effects had been mellowed and a relatively normal set-up
had arrived; but this revision is coming so closely on the heels of the second
war that many nations of Europe are still not back to prewar conditions.
They were also more disturbed than in the first cataclysm.

Inasmuch as this book draws its main divisions from climatic types in
which each country is treated by physical subdivisions, its main lines are
not seriously disturbed; but when a war machine gets into motion, its
activities and those developed in opposition make profound changes in
buildings, roads, bridges, harbors, the distribution of men and industries,
and the direction of many industrial and economic activities. It is the purpose in this chapter to trace some of the items in the geography of war
much as one would trace the geography of colonization, commerce, or
agriculture.

Friction—economic, sociologic, and ideologic—between groups of human beings seems to make wars necessary; but the wars have little lasting
effect upon the course of history. War is not ideal; it is incidental, often
promoted by myth or jealousy and not by any clear vision of true goals.

Boundaries. National boundaries have been modified in several ways.
People have been transferred from one place to another by flight or force.
Millions of French, of Russians, and other Slavs were brought as laborers
into Germany. Boundary lines themselves have been shifted until great areas
of territory long in one nation have been placed within the limits of another.
Unless the people occupying such areas are now permitted or made to move
elsewhere, they must change their nationality and allegiance. Croatia, Bessarabia, and parts of Finland illustrate the case, although both Croatia and
Bessarabia had been transferred more than once before the recent war and

67

its postwar adjustments. Likewise, the *departments* of Alsace-Lorraine have been moved again, once each way in connection with World War II. In some cases, whole republics and national units were transferred bodily to nations having entirely different forms of government and economic organization. Note Estonia, Latvia, Lithuania, and East Prussia.

People were transferred great distances within their own lands by government decree. As the hostile German armies advanced into U.S.S.R., Germanic farming and industrial communities in the mid-Volga area were transferred and settled in far eastern Siberia. A similar number of Jews, perhaps a million, were gathered from European Russia where they were accessible to the Germans and transported to a new Jewish colony, Birobijan, north of the Amur River. About 10 to 12 per cent of these were moved before the war. Such changes as these create minorities and minority problems; in some instances they redirect commerce, because active industries are involved in the transfer.

Displaced persons. Closely related to some of the boundary changes is the problem of displaced persons. As in China where 50 million citizens fled before Japanese armies from the coast provinces to the western interior, so in Poland, Czechoslovakia, Russia, and France, millions of refugees crowded the roads leading to safer places as hostile armies invaded their lands and cities. Many moved into unfamiliar parts of their own country, arriving penniless and nearly destitute, without work, frequently ill from exposure or lack of food. As time passed some of these refugees returned home. Many had lost their homes or farm equipment by fire or demolition. Great numbers could not return. Some went beyond their own national borders with no plan to return.

Health, food, clothing, housing, and labor problems follow such hordes of refugees. Unless they can be readily absorbed by their adopted communities—and millions cannot be so assimilated—they enter the catalogue of displaced persons, or D.P.'s. Those halting outside their own lands encounter linguistic, cultural, and often religious difficulties. They become a political minority. In any case they help disturb or unbalance the economy of the community into which they come.

Agricultural changes. In 1937 it was stated that in the early thirties the normal annual agricultural output of Britain would feed her people only six weeks. The First World War stimulated a small agricultural revival and a little increase in cultivated land, but not until the thirties was there real progress. Yet by 1939 Britain still produced less than one-third of her food consumption. When U-boat warfare in World War II cut importation down to almost nothing, many changes came quickly, such as increased drainage under Drainage Acts, plowing and planting of grazing lands and of much pasture before its scheduled rotation time. Intensive cultivation, use of high-grade fertilizers, and crop improvement followed. Agricultural experts circulated everywhere to advise farmers. Labor was regulated, wages fixed, everything possible was mechanized; and by 1943 tillage area was increased 50 per cent, mostly at the expense of permanent pasture and former road-sides. Crop improvement was such that 50 to 100 per cent more of wheat, barley, oats, and potatoes were produced than in 1939. Britain learned what she could do to supply her food needs; not nearly enough, but far better than she did 30 years before. This emphasis has not seriously cut down her industrial output.

Asopos railroad bridge in Greece, demolished during the war. Note the three parts of the bridge; one part near us at the right; another part tumbled into the valley; and a third part wrecked on the opposite slope. (U.S. Army photograph)

Italy's agriculture was not stimulated and improved by the war; but rather the deficiencies are more serious than before. Many countries in Europe can blame no agricultural changes on the war except the temporary destruction of fruit trees, shrubs, and acres of arable land trampled over by armies, coupled with occasional deep-seated injury to the soil itself, where severely bombed and shelled. An interesting side issue has been the appearance of little-known flowers and weeds, whose seeds have lain dormant under buildings for generations.

Buildings, roads, harbors, shipping. Both sides in World War II went all out to destroy commerce and industry. Until 1945 there was devastation with very little attempt at constructional activity. War shattered the results of generations of building, and years will still be necessary to restore to their former efficiency the means of commerce in Europe. The ports of Cherbourg, Bergen, Brest, Dunkirk, Bremen, Hamburg, Havre, Antwerp, Genoa, Marseilles, Naples, Rotterdam, and many lesser ones suffered enormous destruction. One can get some idea of what it meant to European commerce to have the ports all but useless, when he recalls that Europe's commerce with other continents was larger than that of the other five continents among themselves.

Not only were piers and docks razed, and warehouses and storage buildings demolished, but harbor machinery, cranes, trams, elevators, tugs, and fire equipment were often put out of use. Railroads, automobile and truck roads were bombed and torn up to render them useless; rolling stock was wrecked, bridges blown up, and overheads blasted to make them to fall on highways below. Hundreds of miles of the best truck and rail roads in the world were systematically demolished mile by mile. If enemy efforts were not sufficient to destroy all, retreating armies, even on their own soil, completed the work by dynamiting each bridge as they passed it. Heavy traffic and lack of repairs played their part. This wreckage was accomplished in the Low Countries, in France, Italy, Germany, U.S.S.R., and to a less extent in Poland, Austria, and Czechoslovakia.

Shipping of all belligerent coast countries was as nearly destroyed as possible. It was not enough to smash ships of war, but all merchant marine, passenger, and pleasure craft fell before the war machine. Germany and Italy were most severely crippled, but England, France, and the Netherlands were very hard hit. Norway saved many of her vessels by keeping them away at sea or in foreign ports until the U-boat and torpedo menace was subdued.

In 1941 it was admitted that commerce between North America and Europe had been almost destroyed. The purpose was to check commerce in war supplies, food, and the movement of men; but when shipping for these purposes was destroyed, it was gone for legitimate trade for as many years as it takes to build and equip an adequate merchant marine and a passenger service. As a check on rate of recovery, it is reported that in 1947 the United Kingdom built thirty-seven ships; this was more than the total built by six other European nations, Sweden, France, Netherlands, Spain, Denmark, Italy, plus the United States and the British Commonwealth other than the United Kingdom.

Public buildings for government use, for school, church and hospital purposes were often damaged but usually as accidental targets. Industrial plants and the accumulation of stocks for use in them were attacked. Many tanks of petroleum products, coal piles, ores, and partly processed materials fell under the destroyer's hand. Residences were damaged more than were factories. While much of this is individual or personal loss, the total effect is destructive to national economy.

Rehousing Britain. 1,500,000 houses were damaged in World War II. Here a man is sifting refuse to find his wife's engagement ring, April, 1945. (Courtesy British Information Services)

A view of a portion of London in the spring of 1946, a year after V-E Day. St. Paul's near the center. Note hundreds of damaged buildings all about it. (Courtesy British Information Services)

Roads, railroads, harbors, and buildings have been extensively repaired, but this repair uses material that might otherwise go into new construction.

Movement of industries. Even before the Germans reached the U.S.S.R., many of its heavy industries, particularly those for war equipment, were on the move to and beyond the Urals. Such transfer continued until Germany withdrew from Russia. These industrial plants have never returned but continue to operate with many new ones erected in the Urals, in the Kuznets Basin, and even farther east. Germans attempted as in World War I to move French industries from northeastern France into Germany, and Belgian industries into western Germany. Many plants in Poland and Czechoslovakia were moved to places more agreeable to Germany; others were manned by management and labor sympathetic with the Germans. Some of these Slavic plants have been returned. Poland acquired industries east of her new German boundary, the Oder-Neisse line. Industries flourishing in southeastern Finland and others blossoming out in Estonia and Latvia before the war are now in U.S.S.R. because of the incorporation of territory into the expanding Russian domain. Such transfer means no new site for the plant or for its material but a change of markets and other commercial relations. Mining was very much checked in the Rhine Valley and in the

Saar. In Lorraine it was all but stopped, but in the Urals both iron and coal mining advanced; the latter was doubled during World War II. Swedish production of iron ore increased, and both Sweden and U.S.S.R. propose to continue output on this higher level. Some of the German and French mines were sabotaged with water or explosions; others deteriorated with disuse. A great job for the industry is to get these mines back into production. The task is not wholly geographic and is made more difficult by political tactics and national jealousies.

Urged by the necessities of the war the Russians developed a combustible shale near Kuibyshev and Saratov on the Volga. Its production rose in 1942 to nearly 15 million tons which were used in part for the development of power and heat. Many kinds of mining and mineral extraction and reduction were stimulated to phenomenal heights during the restrictions of war; others were more or less impaired by disuse or by the forcible transfer of labor.

Redirected economic activities and service. During the war thousands of industrial plants in Europe turned from the production of consumer and producer goods, for which they were built, to the manufacture of war equipment; from civilian clothing to army uniforms and arms, from machines and autos to planes, tanks, bombs, and rockets. This direction of production can be and has been reversed now in many plants. New plants built for war industries have not yet all been transformed. In fact, not a few are deteriorating for lack of care and use. Some will be a total loss.

Perhaps the greatest difficulties hampering economic recovery stem from the collapse and failure of German production. Formerly Germany furnished to trade, coal, iron, steel, chemicals, and ceramics, and many finished articles from these fundamental materials; at present many of the raw products are not available even enough for home use; and none for export as before the war. This situation deprives both west Europe and east Europe of great quantities of raw and semi-raw materials as well as of a wealth of machines, appliances, gadgets, and consumer goods that formerly flowed from west to east. Such a drying up of eastward flow means that no raw agricultural, forest, and mining products from the east are needed in Germany.

Growing out of this economic stagnation and augmented by a nationalism in both east and west that opposes exchange of goods between east and west through Germany, or even over a north-south belt across the continent, has come almost complete cessation of the former active commerce between the rural eastern and the industrial western states.

During the war millions of prisoners were shifted from several surrounding countries into Germany to man the war industries. When Russia took over parts of Germany, some of these men were again forcibly displaced and with thousands of Germans put to work in industry in Russia. It is estimated that some 10 million persons are now so displaced and required to work in Russia for U.S.S.R. Any such postwar displacement of labor has its effect on distribution of labor and markets in all countries concerned.

Incentives and blueprints of industry are not back to prewar levels, and impending postwar changes in distributions of factories and men hinder and delay the return of prewar harmony and efficiency in production. Meanwhile, European trade is critically curtailed. So much in industry in the modern world hinges on mutual trust and reciprocal commercial exchanges that conditions and procedures of the above description prevent the usual response to geographic conditions and hinder the best national uses of environment.

Conservation ignored. In mining and quarrying, and to some extent in agriculture, the feeling that the "ends (total war) justify the means" led to vicious anti-conservation practices in extractive industries. Soil was "mined out" in many places, stock was sacrificed by slaughtering large herds of dairy cattle; carefully bred hogs and egg-poultry were used for meat. Thus herds and flocks built up through scores of years for special purposes were totally sacrificed for current needs in Denmark, the Netherlands, and to a less extent in other countries. It will take years to restore soils, mines, and stock to the useful conditions of prewar economy.

National recoveries. Nations least upset by war are first to come back. Sweden, Spain and Portugal, Switzerland, and Turkey, all neutrals, are already running on a fairly even keel. Of those disturbed, Italy, the Low Countries, and Norway are foremost in recovery. France has been slower in many ways, but her coal production has already surpassed prewar level, and her industries are being systematically rehabilitated. Czechoslovakia, not so severely damaged as Poland, is recovering with great speed; Poland, partly because of her newly acquired former German industries east of the Oder-Neisse line, has reported production nearly restored to prewar level.

Hungary is making very slow progress. She has had an inflation period similar to that following World War I and still has little assurance of stability. The failure to restore the Danube to prewar status, even though its freedom for trade is stipulated in all peace treaties of riparian nations, cripples trade among Danubian states. Austria is on relief, and German economy is a menace to all central Europe. Shortage of raw materials seems to be the greatest geographic factor, but political unrest is still an important obstacle to recovery.

The human factor. Permeating and qualifying the solution of all material problems in European recovery is the human factor. Each man with his training, personality, character, and attitude toward life is part of the environment of every other man. Social unrest and emotional instability have developed in the minds of European people during and since the recent war as after World War I, but these products of the second war are larger and more serious than those of the first; more time and probably more conscious effort will be necessary for recovery from them.

Reconstruction of quays damaged at Rotterdam, Netherlands. (Courtesy Netherlands Information Bureau)

Reconstruction at Amsterdam. A harbor crane, blown up and sunk by invaders, is being lifted to the surface to clear the dock for future use when the piers are rebuilt. (Courtesy Netherlands Information Bureau)

The defeated nations were so thoroughly and obviously conquered that the rank and file in Germany and Italy know that they were beaten. France, Poland, Czechoslovakia, U.S.S.R., England, and to a less degree other countries are conscious of the material blight of war. Millions of people in Europe are faced daily with depressing physical conditions. Add to these the mental depression provoked by the tremendous loss of life, both military and civilian, which cut into almost every family, plus the ravages of hunger, exposure, and consequent disease, and one gets a glimpse of the state of mind that pervades the masses.

Some people feel that it makes little difference now what happens. Others confess impotence to do anything that will help the situation. Some drift into crime, some into despondency; many are too disheartened to work, and others see no point in working.

The simple physical destruction is only a small part of the trouble. The millions of broken families, the tragic loss of leadership through liquidation of liberal, efficient men and women, the exile of others, the physical and intellectual starvation of students, the future leaders; and malnutrition, cold, poverty, have all been factors in the mental depression. Those who joined resistance groups underground or in alien lands lived hunted lives, and found adventure and patriotism in sabotage of the existing law and order. They were the most courageous, resourceful, and far-seeing citizens of their country, and great numbers were lost for present leadership. The current uncertain political and economic outlook offers little hope and kindles no ambition. The spiritual losses to man have been more serious than the physical. Rallying points for recovery of morale, spiritual vision, and enthusiasm have been destroyed; such physical means as schools, churches, and libraries are in many localities in ruins. These disheartened, frustrated people are those who must use the tools of recovery.

Moves toward coöperation. The tide of nationalism so rampant between the two wars has had a serious jolt. It has failed to work. The idea of a league of two or three nations has not given the security needed. Many schemes for federations, unions or broad treaties have arisen; some dare to suggest that the only security worth having is in a league of all the nations of Europe. The war has shown that nations with confidence enough in each other to establish trade treaties, coöperative leagues, economic unions, or some international coöperation fare best. Coöperation on the economic level seems the most natural starting point. Nations hesitate to yield any national sovereignty for a political union; but the need of economic and commercial federation and coöperation is obvious in the present reconstructive effort.

Geographic differences between national units emphasize the advantages of such coöperation. Varying sunshine, wind, and rainfall with their climatic influences; scarcity or abundance of mineral, forest, and foods in adjacent countries; river highways, mountain passes, and open seaports; all unalterable geographic differences, constitute reasons for leagues, unions, coöperatives, and trade agreements. Such differences have been among the first reasons for commerce; they have also provided the background for raids, invasion, theft, and usurpation; but the ensuing destruction has defeated the purpose of the aggressor. Perhaps the time is ripe for carefully considered, honest, reciprocal trade organizations as a beginning of federation.[1]

Nations should know each other, know their intellectual, educational as well as economic resources and should build to exchange values for the common good. If geography has any political lesson, it is that no people or nation can live as richly unto itself as it can by coöperation and exchange of goods. The wars, particularly the last, have called attention to these international relations; and the crop of plans for unions, leagues, and agreements from "Union Now" to "A United States of Europe" or even for a "World Federation" is one of the rewarding harvests of World War II.

---

[1] The Benelux agreement is a sample of what can be done.

BIBLIOGRAPHY

Britannica Book of the Year (Chicago, Encyclopedia Britannica), for years 1939-47.

British Information Service (New York, Rockefeller Plaza), various pamphlets available, 1940-48.

Foreign Commerce Weekly, Vols. 1943-48, U. S. Dept. Commerce (Washington, D. C., Government Printing Office).

GRAY, G. D. B., *Soviet Land* (London, A. & C. Black, Ltd., 1947).

HAAS, Ernest B., "The United States of Europe," *Political Science Quarterly,* Vol. LXIII, No. 4 (1948), pp. 528-550.

KIRK, Dudley, *Europe's Population in the Interwar Years* (New York, A League of Nations Publication, Columbia University Press, 1946).

KUBISCHER, Eugene M., *Europe on the Move* (New York, Columbia University Press, 1948).

National Planning Association, Planning Pamphlet 53, *Recovery in Europe* (Washington, 1946).

News Week, a weekly magazine. Consult numbers issued during the war and on to 1946.

SCHECHTMAN, Joseph B., *European Population Transfers* (New York, Oxford University Press, 1946).

SULLAM, Victor E., *Recent Developments in Italian Agriculture,* Foreign Agric., IX, No. 5, U. S. Dept. of Agriculture, (Washington, D. C., Government Printing Office, 1945).

Time, a weekly magazine. Consult numbers issued during the war, 1939-45.

Part II

LANDS HAVING MEDITERRANEAN CLIMATE

GENERAL SURVEY OF MEDITERRANEAN LANDS

Mediterranean lands have great similarity, for much of which their climate is responsible. However, minor departures from the typical climate occur. Portugal and northwest Spain have some characteristics of marine climate, but they have a winter rainfall, scanty over all but the higher parts, and the warmth characteristic of the latitude. Because of its size the interior of Iberia has a continental range of temperature and inblowing winds in summer, reversed in winter; unlike the large continental interiors it is never cold and does have Mediterranean winter rain. As there are less differences of climate between Spain, Portugal, Italy, Albania, Greece, and Turkey than exist between any one of them and states farther north, so are there less differences among the people of these states than exist between any of them and any people farther north.

The vegetation across all of Portugal, a narrow strip of southern France, and eastward through Asia Minor is of the Mediterranean type, a unifying factor, climatically determined, and clearly indicating the justice of treating these six countries together. France nowhere else has Mediterranean evergreen vegetation and everywhere else has summer rains. Very little of France belongs in this section, whereas very little of Spain and less of Portugal could be left out. Adriatic portions of Yugoslavia and small areas in the southeast have evergreen vegetation, but even these parts have summer rainfall and most of the country has the severity of near-continental winters and deciduous forests. The people are not Mediterranean but Slavic Alpines. The small groups of non-Mediterranean peoples, Albanians and Turks, are in as typical Mediterranean climate as any and could not be omitted.

All through their history these Mediterranean lands have struggled together. They were a commercial unit until America was discovered. They were repeatedly under the same political régime. Peoples have migrated and blended in these states until the same Mediterranean race is found nearly everywhere. Languages are all Aryan, except those of the Basques and the small groups of Albanians and Turks.

Culture, as well as civilization, advanced more or less uniformly across this group of states and steadily pulled away from the rest of Europe. No doubt the considerable physical isolation from other European peoples was a factor in this unity of progress.

CHAPTER 6

Spain

The Sun once stood still; the wheel of fortune never.
—Gomez de Quevedo

GENERAL

Position. A most obvious item in Spain's situation is its contact with two seas and proximity to two continents. The long shoreline on the Mediterranean has always given it a flavor that the purely Atlantic countries have never had; and after the lure of the Pillars of Hercules overcame its ancient portentous restraints, Spain's touch upon the Atlantic gave the people an outlook and quality that Italy and Greece never possessed. But in the main, its land boundaries have been barriers and have led to isolation from both benefits and injuries that proximal continents from time to time have offered. The Pyrenees have been a more effective barrier than have the Straits, for Spain has been in respect to both plants and animals, including man, more African than European.

For 400 years Spain was considered a part of the Roman Empire, but in spite of this contact the Spanish people were always on the outskirts of Mediterranean life and culture. Lacking the climatic stimulus that seems to have kindled intelligence and incited nervous energy in the Near East, they failed to develop a parallel master empire within their own borders. By virtue of the position of the Iberian Peninsula far west in the Mediterranean world and the obstruction offered by the Pyrenees to the north the people missed much of the influence of Reformation and Renaissance.

While a growing commerce in spices, amber, and peacock feathers was drawing out the best in the east Mediterranean lands, Spain, far off the highway, lagged behind. But when the New World was revealed to Columbus, as if with a flash of long-suppressed energy the two nations of this western peninsula, Spain and Portugal, came into their own and in a hundred years made marvelous progress in exploration, exploitation, and domination. As the nations of northwestern Europe entered the lists with their more vigorous spirits and better methods for commerce and colonization, Spain and Portugal were soon surpassed; and now for a hundred years both lands have been again somewhat off the main lines of commerce and

81

trade which have been leading into central Europe. So geographic position has shifting values.

Geology. Some of the foundations for the present geography of Spain were laid many millions of years ago. Builders have long found valuable building stones in the Archean granites of the Salamanca region and have utilized slates produced from the earlier sediments by the intrusion of these granites. On the flanks of these and other ancient rocks were laid Paleozoic sediments, including carboniferous coals which were folded into mountains at the end of the Paleozoic era during what is called the Hercynian Revolution. Here in Spain the great central massif consists of roots of the Hercynian system. This block was separated from other parts of the system by diastrophic movements which drowned intervening sections beneath the sea in early Mesozoic time. Mesozoic and Tertiary rocks were deposited around this old core; great beds of the Tertiary were laid across it until now more than half is buried beneath these younger rocks, which, distributed in nearly horizontal layers, furnish the soil for much of the uplands. In the latest of geologic revolutions, these younger rocks were folded into the Pyrenees on the north, the Sierra Nevadas on the south, and the Catalonians on the northeast athwart the Ebro Valley. At this time the coal of the southwest provinces was folded; and in several places igneous intrusions caused heated waters to segregate the mercury deposits of Almaden, the silver, lead, and zinc of more southern provinces, and the copper sulphides of Rio Tinto.

So recent are some of the mountains that they still are youthful, lofty, rugged, even snow-capped, and afford fine mountain scenery and recreation grounds for the native people and tourists. So long have great areas of the central Meseta, or table-land, been subjected to erosion that they present very old, grandly rolling, peneplain topography with scattered monadnocks or serrate ridges where harder rocks have been more durable than the rest. These peneplain areas are the great grazing lands of central Spain, the country where dry farming is practised, the home of extensive wheat fields, olive groves, and, in the southwestern part of Spain, of the cork oak. Cork is produced even more abundantly in the Guadalquivir Valley.

Soils formed from the decay of the rocks differ somewhat on the different kinds of stone but much more with reference to climatic conditions and vegetation cover. Sandy and micaceous soils on the granite areas in the west and northwest are the best for the great forests which have helped produce them; red and yellow clay soils, formed in a drier climate under grass, make the best wheat fields; and loam soils, composed by the streams and laid along their valleys or as deltas at their mouths, serve the most intensive agriculture. These areas can be irrigated in part and make possible the sugar-cane and beet lands of the coastal plains and the vegetable and flower gardens of Valencian, Alicartean, and Murcian plains.

According to the latest studies in soils these Spanish soils belong to the chestnut-colored types developed under conditions of insufficient moisture and meager, patchy forest cover. They are low in humus because the climatic conditions favor its oxidation. They vary in color from the gray earths to red tints. The former, around Madrid developed on Pleistocene deposits, are almost white to feeble gray and represent the products of the semi-arid conditions. Red soils, according to Raman, may be found in the vicinity of Salamanca, Valladolid, and on the Pyrenean slopes. These red soils characterize slightly moister conditions than the gray earths. Spanish upland soils are of mature types.

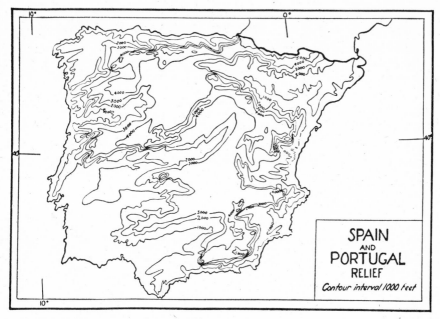

SPAIN
AND
PORTUGAL
RELIEF
Contour interval 1000 feet

Relief of the Iberian peninsula, generalized in this contour map. (Adapted from *Oxford Advanced Atlas*)

Clays and loams furnish the basis for the many brick and tile manufactories that provide the plain, red tile and many-colored brick so much used in Spanish building, and also provide the body for the ornamental *azulejos* (glazed and strongly colored tile, a gift to Spain of the Moorish occupation) and the pottery for which Seville and its vicinity are famous. Seventeen great factories produce their beautiful wares along the west side of the Guadalquivir River.

Of all mineral products bituminous coal has been mined in largest value. A good grade, in part anthracite, is worked in two regions, the Oviedo-León-Palencia region in the north, and the Ciudad Real-Cordova-Seville region in the south, the former producing over four fifths of the total. All these beds are in rocks of Pennsylvanian and Permian age. In spite of this leadership, the coal-mining industry and production are quite insignificant compared with what they might and should be for Spain's prosperity. Coal for the industries in seacoast provinces is imported by sea more cheaply than it can be shipped overland from these interior mines. Very little coal is used in metallurgical industries because large quantities of ore are shipped to other countries for reduction.

Lead ores of Cordova, Jaen, and Murcia in older rocks and mountain structures are worked and in part smelted near the mines but in part shipped (unwisely) to foreign lands to be refined. Even the lead prepared at home is shipped in pigs and bars to other lands for manufacturing. This is also true of the silver-bearing lead ores of the north slopes of the Morena Mountains of the Meseta.

The Almaden mines of western Ciudad Real have been for centuries, and can still be, large producers of mercury. Spain has little mining use for mercury at home; therefore most of the product is exported in flasks to South and North American gold-producing countries for use in the amalgamation process. Mercury production and sale are in Spain a government monopoly.

Spanish iron ore is of high grade and is in demand in both England and America. The large deposits of the Biscayan provinces, Viscaya and Santander, are extensively worked; Teruel in the east and Almeria in the southeast are small producers. The pyrite of Huelva contains copper; part of the ore of this region is reduced at home; some is shipped to America, first roasted for sulphur, then treated for its copper, and finally refined for its iron content. The sulphur is made into sulphuric acid. Each process yields a profit in America; why not in Spain? The country has an abundance of copper, cobalt, zinc, silver, sulphur, phosphates, gypsum, and soda; but there is no notable production of any of these resources. In the extraction of ores of copper, lead, and mercury Spain has often headed the list. It has been also a large relative producer of salt and silver. Exploration for oil and gas has recently been made in several northern provinces. The total mineral production of Spain is relatively very low for a land of its size and known wealth. In 1933 the mine-mouth value of all was only about $50 million, in 1939 it fell to $39 million.

No European country produces so great a variety of minerals, yet it is just to say that mineral production in Spain is in its retarded infancy. A long history of crude work, some mere investigation, much of it unscientific exploitation without careful surveys and estimates of reserves, characterizes the mining methods and procedure. Spain has been as illogical, unskilled, and irresponsible in mining as in agriculture and other activities. Because of a mental and physical antipathy to painstaking industry it has not responded to the challenge, and this lethargy has been credited both to race and to climate. One finds the people jovial in conversation, very active in sports and lighter work, in play, in the dance and light music, but lacking in the force and sustained endurance necessary to conduct mining, industry, and

agriculture in a substantial, creditable way. Little valuable scientific literature has come from Spain.

Climate. Although Spain is here discussed as having Mediterranean climate, there is much diversity. Climate of three types, marine, Mediterranean, and continental, leads to distinctive agricultural and domiciliary
responses. In much of the northwestern part (Galician Hills) there is a
marine type, damp, bleak, cold, with violent northerly gales during much
of the winter, ample rainfall all the year, and scarce warmth enough for
comfort until June and then during little more than two months. In these two
summer months, however, it can be most charming, and some travelers
say here is the best place in all Europe to spend July. Kendrew names this
Galician climate the West European coastal type. These provinces enjoy
this climate because of their proximity to the sea, their situation in the belt
of the westerlies, and their position on the windward side of the land. In
this part of Spain the houses are built more securely and snugly than in any
other; better roofs are necessary, more glass and less open porch, tighter
walls, and better facilities for heating. Clothing is generally made of wool.
Deciduous forests grow readily, and the usual evergreen vegetation of the
rest of Spain is almost wholly wanting. Corn, introduced from America,
prospers better here than elsewhere. Chestnuts and hardy fruits, especially
apples, pears, and stone fruits, flourish in the Galician-Cantabrian regions.
Many of the people live by fishing for salmon and sardines. While the land
is generally hilly, the density of population is as great as anywhere except
in the best eastern and southeastern plains. The Galician Hills and the
Cantabrian Old Mountains are two of the regions into which Spain is
divided for study.

Extending from the eastern end of the Pyrenees southwards, coastwise
and round the Cartagenian corner to Cadiz, and spreading 20 to 50
miles inland over lower lands occurs the best Spanish Mediterranean climate. The "warming pan" of the western basin of the Great Sea contributes
much heat to this strip of land. Lower-latitude sunshine is also partly responsible for the warmth. Since the land is in the lee of the interior plateau,
it is in general dry all the year but has some rain in the winter months.

Here the vegetation is Mediterranean evergreen, though rarely coniferous, with date-palms, agave, and sugar-cane along the south coast. The
general dryness has encouraged irrigation, and the mountains not far inland
have been sufficiently high to bring to their own slopes rainfall enough to
make much irrigation possible. With this supply of water have come intensive agriculture, floriculture, vegetable gardening, and, in Valencia, rice-
growing. A denser population than elsewhere is here possible and present,
and a higher type of social life and responsibility has grown out of the public
interest and closer coöperation necessary for the best development of irrigation. Houses of brick, plastered, whitewashed, and covered with red tile or
flat earth-roofs, are usually grouped in villages and towns and not scattered

on the farms. These cool houses serve the peasants well in the mild climate. The lack of rainfall and the abundant sunshine with low relative humidity combine to nurture the salt industry in several places along the east coast, on the Balearic Islands, and near Cadiz. The water is led from the sea into shallow evaporating basins; as the water vaporizes, the salt is left on the floors of the basins to be stacked, dried, and prepared for market. In this Mediterranean climate belt are two more of the Spanish geographic regions, the Catalonian Hills lying across the mouth of the Ebro Valley and the Eastern Coastal Plains.

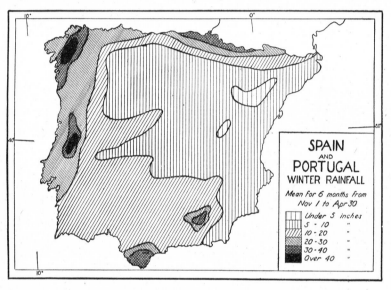

SPAIN
AND
PORTUGAL
WINTER RAINFALL
Mean for 6 months from
Nov 1 to Apr 30
Under 5 inches
5 - 10   "
10 - 20   "
20 - 30   "
30 - 40   "
Over 40   "

Winter rainfall map of the Iberian Peninsula, showing the influence of relief on precipitation in several places. (Adapted from Philips's *Comparative Wall Atlas*)

Over the Meseta, more than half of Spain, the climate is typically continental, even though the peninsula is only of medium size. The winters are dry, cold, windy, and dusty. The meager rain falls in the winter and spring in preparation for summer crops. April is the most delightful month on most of the Meseta. The usual conditions for a continental climate are augmented here by 2,000 to 3,000 feet of altitude and by abrupt slopes from the coastal lands up to the plateau surface. Inblowing winds seeking the warm, interior, low-pressure area are cooled on the border slopes, there precipitating most of their moisture, and hence they have little to give when they reach the interior. The plateau is so warm that this partly dried air is rewarmed and rises high over the interior, so high before cumulus clouds form that much possible precipitation is revaporized in falling before it reaches the ground or is wafted off the plateau before actual condensation can occur. In winter, cold descending air can bring little rain; hence it has been said, "From Zaragoza toward Lerida it is very dry, waterless, African," a phrase which also characterizes thousands of square miles of upland.

Since these uplands are an old erosion surface and generally dry, their best use is for dry farming. Many thousands of acres are green in the spring with winter wheat, which grows with the spring rains and is hurried on by the approaching dry summer to an early harvest. Such drought-resisting trees as the olive cover other thousands of acres; in many places wheat is grown between the rows of olives, and in other places grapevines. Rye and barley are subsidiary cereal crops used mostly for forage. Legumes—peas, beans, and some alfalfa—are grown partly as a rotation crop, partly to be plowed under. This latter step is taken only where a turning plow is used.

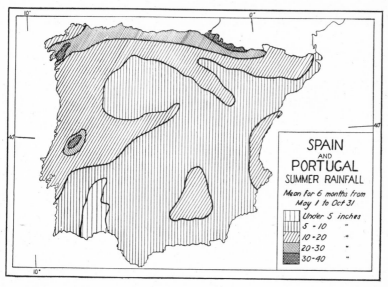

Summer rainfall is less than that of winter in most portions of the Iberian Peninsula. (Adapted from Philips's *Comparative Wall Atlas*)

Probably 80 to 90 per cent of the plateau farming is done with a simple, spreading plow. This country is adapted to, and would amply repay, tractor gang plowing of the deep, overturning sort; but its interior situation and continental climate promote conservatism in farming as well as in religion and government. Many upland houses are adobe with thatched roofs. Some are clustered in squalid villages; others are scattered among the farms. Simple dirt roads tramped by many donkey and human feet radiate from village to village and village to farm. Everybody walks to and from his work. Irrigation is not common on these uplands, for the higher mountains are not frequent enough to condense and precipitate the necessary water. The Meseta constitutes by far the largest of the regions of Spain. For study it may be divided into Eastern Dry Meseta and Western Moist Meseta. Much of the western division lies in Portugal.

It should be understood that these three climatic types have no distinct boundaries. Since the elements of climate vary gradually from place to place, and the topography knows few sharp boundaries, there is a gradual transition from one climatic type to another. The rainfall becomes less and less in the Galician marine type, while the sunshine comes more and more to dominate as one moves in toward the smoother plateaus. Similar transitions occur where the more severe interior conditions give place to the milder Mediterranean type of climate along the eastern and southern coasts. A fourth type of climate is found in very limited areas on the mountains. Here, as the altitude increases, the table-land climate gives way to mountain phases in both the Pyrenees and the Sierras and to a less extent in the mountains which rise from the plateau itself. On some of the lofty slopes forests respond to the increased rainfall of mountain climates and completely clothe the slopes, only to be superseded at greater altitudes by snow, ice, and even considerable glaciers. Three mountain regions are recognized: the Pyrenean Slopes; the Guadarrama Sierras; and the Andalusian System, consisting of Sierra Nevada young mountains as its chief ranges. See Regions on map. Other regions delimited more by topography and geologic history than by climate are the Ebro Dry Valley in the north and the Guadalquivir Plains in the south. There are left the Portuguese Lowlands to complete the Iberian Peninsula. They will be described under Portugal.

GEOGRAPHIC REGIONS

No country lends itself better to a regional approach than Spain.

The Meseta. Two thirds of Spain, indeed of the whole peninsula, is the Meseta, a plateau of ancient rocks very much eroded and half covered in two large areas, one the upper Douro basin and the other southeast of Madrid, by Tertiary and recent sediments. Its average height is about 2,500 feet. As it is the core geologically, so it is the center agriculturally. Its people practise grazing and large-scale farming. Spain is essentially a rural land and agricultural production its mainstay; 46 per cent of its surface is cultivated and over 40 per cent is grazed. Some of its mountains and steep valley walls are forest-clad. Its people are bound closely to the soil. Little of manufacturing has ever come to lift them from the soil, so there they remain where the conditions put them when they first left a purely nomadic life. The climate is not generally dry enough to eliminate cropping the soil or to force nomadic stock-raising. Nor does the climate encourage diligence, provident thrift, and commerce.

The story of the arrival of the agricultural régime began to unfold a thousand years ago. The Moors of Berber blood were a pastoral people here among a pastoral people, but they found much more opportunity for sedentary agriculture on the Meseta than they had known in north Africa, and they became the agriculturists of Spain. They introduced several new crops from the Near East—almonds, dates, figs, oranges, rice, and sugar-cane—and practised selective breeding of livestock.

Early Iberians and Visigoths were pastoral and moved their herds of sheep long distances for pasture. The Berber was, in Africa, an even more nomadic shepherd and availed himself of the conditions in Spain by organiz-ing to perpetuate his hold on the nomadic régime in addition to developing his marvelous systems of tillage and irrigation. Migration of shepherds with their flocks was due to the sharp contrasts of climate and of topography between different parts of the country, differences which made semi-annual

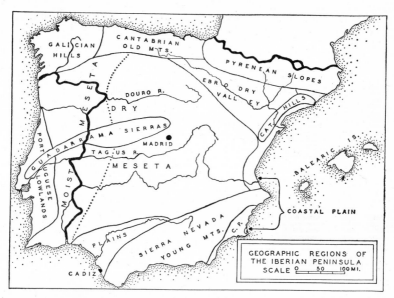

Geographic regions of Spain and Portugal. (Based on geologic, physiographic, climatic, and land utilization maps)

changes in pasture lands desirable. The direction of migration from south to north in the spring and back in the fall is seasonal, following the migra-tion of the sun's vertical ray which causes the alternating rainy and dry seasons.

Shepherds had developed local organizations for centuries, but in 1273 Alfonso the Learned assembled the shepherds of Castile and gave them the name *Mesta* with a charter conveying many rights and perpetuating many laws and privileges the local groups had enjoyed. Some of the sheep routes had their southern ends in the Guadalquivir Valley, in La Mancha (the "dry lands"), and even in Murcia. They led northward, receiving tributary routes, intercommunicating in the central part of the peninsula, and ending in León, Palencia, Segovia, and Navarra. Many sheep reached the slopes of the Pyrenees. Some flocks traveled 200 to 300 miles. As the autumn approached, the return migrations began. The sheep were raised primarily for wool, which was clipped soon after the migration began, washed, carried on carts north-ward to the northern ports, and shipped to England and Flanders.

During the next two and a half centuries this industry flourished and menaced the crude agriculture of the little white, squalid villages in spite of its contribution of meat, wool, and labor to their inhabitants. By the first quarter of the sixteenth century the records of the royal toll-gates, where the sheep were counted in order to determine the *pro rata* tax assessments, show the number of the sheep to have been as high as 3 millions; but by the middle of the century the number had begun to decline. This breaking-

Segovia, a Meseta city. Roman aqueduct spans the valley, left to center; note cathedral on hill and Segovia monument. (Courtesy Spanish American Embassy)

up of the Mesta and the migratory system of stock-raising grew out of a conflict between the shepherds and the rising towns with their agricultural interests. The village was necessary to aid in the marketing of wool and as an outlet for surplus sheep. Villages were encouraged to buy sheep both for food and for local flocks; as the village thus served the Mesta, more and more it gained relative strength, raising many of its own sheep, and the Mesta lost its market. Sovereigns thus lost their income and struggled hard to recover it; but with the increase in population the growing use of the land for cultivation was inevitable, and the decline of the Mesta was con-tinually accelerated by the growth of sedentary sheep-raising and cattle-raising. In the latter part of the eighteenth century, the encroachment of "enclosures" of the true farmers upon the sheep paths and grazing grounds of the migratory herds had become so serious that the Mesta collapsed. Enclosures for gardens, wheat fields, vineyards, and olive orchards, as well as for the non-migratory stock, obtained the right of way, and the stage of nomadic shepherdism passed in favor of true agrarian occupation of the soil. However, the land did not then revert in any general way to peasant ownership. During the past century many steps toward diversified and intensive agriculture have followed.

Meseta agriculture today produces wheat, especially in the moist northwest, barley and chick peas, olives and esparto grass in the south, and many grapes in the southern valleys. Olives and almonds are scattered over much of the upland. The grapes are gathered to the growing cities of Madrid and Toledo. Esparto is cut and dried much as is hay. Large quantities are made into paper; more is twisted into cords and ropes. The cords often are woven into baskets very convenient to fill with earth, sand, or produce to be placed on a donkey's back. Smaller cords are woven into the staple matting common on the floors of Spanish houses of all classes. This grass is grown because of its adaptation to the dry climate and because its tough stems and leaves resist the wear put upon them in a dry region better than do many other coarse fibers.

Madrid, the capital (1,141,000), has had a rapid modern growth. It is isolated, for it has neither natural highway nor resources, yet it is central in the country. It spreads most casually over the old topography of the Meseta, limited only by the stream, a small branch of the Tagus, along whose banks are the Palace, a new cathedral, the railroad station, beautiful parks, and drives. It is conservative yet animated by government, university, opera, and palace life. Its governmental functions, buildings, and connections have recently expanded greatly. Additions are frequently made to the city, and Madrid has a modern political city aspect. Its industries are very limited. In the civil war, 1936-39, there was vicious and wanton destruction of the city purely for political reasons.

Toledo (26,000) on the Tagus River is about 40 miles south of Madrid and in many respects has a more desirable site. Its only fame is due to its wonderful sword blades and its cathedral. Valladolid (116,000) near the Douro is about 100 miles northwest of Madrid and is a typical Meseta town. There are many such towns with a population of 10,000 to 30,000, a palace, church, or some other notable historic building, towns which serve as local market towns or district capitals and draw tourists to see their fine old edifices.

The Guadarrama Sierra. A rugged mountain system of old granite and metamorphic rocks rises in ridges and masses with occasional peaks 7,000 to 9,000 feet high. Slopes are too steep for cultivation, but attain altitudes sufficient to catch the rain and therefore become clothed with deciduous forests. This sierra extends between the Douro and Tagus rivers from Portugal eastward beyond Madrid and is a marked area of heavy precipitation in both summer and winter. It is small and does not have much irrigation and power value, but it is a conspicuous landmark in the mid-Meseta, and a source of good lumber.

Galician Hills. The Galician Hills include that northwestern corner of the peninsula, about 10,000 square miles, of ancient crystalline rocks (Meseta in type) drained by the Minho River. Its shoreline is much indented by submergence with the ria type of embayment. Its capes are rocky, rugged headlands. The coast towns of Vigo and La Coruña are not well connected with their hinterland. The altitude varies between sea level and 3,500 feet, and the climate is rainy, marine, temperate. This sort of climate forbids

Ceramics factory in the foothills of Galicia, Vigo. (Courtesy Spanish American Embassy)

citrus fruits and most of the typical Mediterranean vegetation but encourages most temperate-zone trees and crops. Corn is the main cultivated crop. Stock-raising furnishes employment to many people.

Anchovy and sardine fisheries are well supported off the northwest coast where the waters are coolest, making Vigo a packing and commercial town.

Pyrenean Slopes. This region contains the highest points in Spain, though not the most rugged, grand scenery. There is little cultivation because of rainfall deficiency. Sheep pastures are abundant and grazed both by great transhumance and lesser transhumance. Lumbering belongs only to the higher slopes. Little or no mineral wealth is known. Roads wind along the steep valleys and pass over to the French side, and two railroads also cross the mountains in tunnels, one east of Andorra and one west of Pic du Midi ("Southern Peak"). The lower slopes are irrigated somewhat, but the best waters are taken down to be used in the Ebro Dry Valley. An interesting picture of a small part of these Pyrenean Slopes will be found in the section on Andorra near the end of this chapter.

Cantabrian Old Mountains. The Cantabrian Mountains are a continuation of the Pyrenean structure and stratigraphy, but they were not raised so high and hence have not been eroded deeply enough to expose the old resistant rocks which make up a large part of the exposures in the Pyrenees. They have become more mature in slope, receive sufficient rain at all seasons to be forest-clad and, where cleared, to support grazing, dairying, and

Interior of a ceramics factory, Vigo, showing the section for hand decoration. (Courtesy Spanish American Embassy)

agriculture. Seed and stone fruits, wheat, corn, rye, and legumes grow excellently in this region. Apple cider is a common drink. Individual farmhouses provide homes for many industrious farmers. Minerals are known in workable quantities. Pyritiferous iron ore, the most important, is smelted at Oviedo near northern coal fields, and is shipped as ore with zinc ore to England from Bilbao and Santander. These are active modern harbor towns full of the noise and industry so rare in Spain. Bilbao (208,000) is the other leading iron-making center; it operates with imported coal.

Ebro Dry Valley. The valley of the Ebro River is partly structural. It is a broad lowland between the Pyrenees and the north edge of the Meseta; hence it is well shut away from rain and would normally be steppe. But the limiting mountains catch the rainfall and return it to the valley. Sediments of late Tertiary age have leveled up the structural valley floor and made a great plain.

The melting snows of the high Pyrenees beneficently send their waters laughing down over broad alluvial fans and great flood-plain terraces and bottoms. Irrigation and agriculture have flourished here since an early date. The very dry climate made irrigation essential; slopes and water supply were most inviting, and man responded by developing on a large scale terraced and irrigated agriculture. Wheat is the main crop, but fruits and vegetables share generously. In recent years the development of hydro-electric power to share the expense of irrigating the land has opened up

Beautiful forested young topography in Asturias. Why so well forested? What motive power on the vehicle on the bridge? (Courtesy Patronato Nacional del Turismo)

larger irrigation possibilities, and the government is doing much to extend development. Land under this type of agriculture yields five to twelve times as much in crops as does the unirrigated. Saragossa (266,000) has a commanding situation on both trans-Pyrenean railroads and on the Ebro River. It enjoys its opportunities in the midst of great *huertas* of irrigated wheat fields and fruit orchards. Cæsar Augustus, whose name has been modified into the Spanish name of the city, chose well a city site.

Catalonian Hills. This region is a long mountain barrier between the Ebro Valley and the sea. While never rugged and completely breached by the Ebro, it may properly be considered a branch of the Pyrenean chain. Geologically it is intimately connected with the Pyrenees, but topographi-

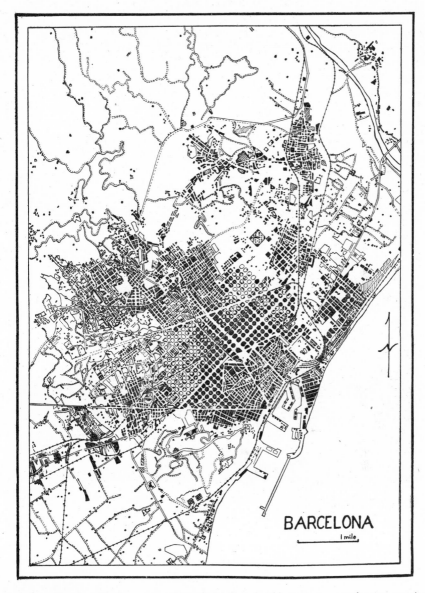

BARCELONA

1 mile

Barcelona, the city with the corners of its blocks clipped. Old city is in central part near the harbor. (Adapted from British Admiralty charts and Spanish topographic sheet)

cally it is more like the Cantabrians. The region never has a rainy season and is not well covered with vegetation. Only its lower slopes can be irrigated; hence the region makes slight contribution to the national economy. Its fields yield grapes, olives, cork, and vegetables for Barcelona. Rocky headlands extend to the sea, with small deltas and coastal plains between, and these are cultivated intensively.

Barcelona (1,109,000) is the leading industrial and commercial city of Spain and one of the greatest on the Mediterranean coasts. It is prosperous, spacious, progressive, cosmopolitan. It has been able to make a splendid harbor of its coast, though mostly artificial, on the Great Sea highway.

Docks for building ships. Beneath the great cranes lies the *Empress Bazan*, under construction. Probably in the spacious Barcelona harbor. (Courtesy Spanish American Embassy)

When founded, Barcelona sprawled on the shores with its feet in the water, a fishing town. A section was walled and fortified. Now the wall is down, the city is thoroughly modernized and has climbed up the valleys and inland over the foothills for residences and parks. While the city is 75 miles north of the mouth of the Ebro River, it is the outlet of the great valley and of much of northern Spain. Its industries also reflect its position. It has local hydro-electric power, imports coal, iron, and cotton, manufactures glass, chemicals, and flour, and preserves fruit from local resources. The city and its province are well isolated physically, historically, and even linguistically from the rest of Spain, are in close contact with active, aggressive France and Italy, and have developed a regional consciousness strongly anti-

Monastery called Pablet, near Catalona. The scantily timbered hills are characteristic of much of Spain. (Courtesy Spanish American Embassy)

"Serrated Mountain," so called because of peculiar weathering along joints and cracks in the rock. The monastery at its base, founded in 886 A.D., is about 30 miles northwest of Barcelona. (By Ewing Galloway, N.Y.)

Castilian. In 1932 the region requested and was granted an autonomous government.

Eastern Coastal Plains. Extending along the coast almost continuously from Barcelona to Almeria are fringes of coastal and delta plains. They are separated into two parts, each about 175 miles long, by the spurs of the Andalusian System.

In Valencia and Murcia the streams afford opportunity for irrigation, and man has marvelously adapted his methods to the use of these waters. Terraces are very common, and for rice culture thousands of acres are enclosed with mud and stone walls, so they can be flooded at the proper times. Rice is the only cereal produced in sufficient quantities to be profitably exported. Flowers and vegetables are grown here in wildest profusion. *Huertas,* gardens with a network of canals fed by diverting a whole river back in the foothills, are among the most attractive and interesting sights. In these states other cereals in addition to rice and wheat are grown by irrigation; oranges, grapes, and almonds, exported to England, add to the beauty of Valencian gardens; the figs, chestnuts, filberts, onions, garlic, and peppers enter into Spanish export lists but are mainly used at home. In these irrigated areas the density of population often exceeds 2,000 per square mile.

The towns of the south and east coasts use large quantities of Mediterranean sea foods, cuttlefish, sea cucumbers, clams, and fish. Catholic dietary regulations encourage fisheries and the importation of fish. Towns of these coastal plains are numerous but never large. Valencia (508,000) excels all others and engages in local industries, using the citrus fruits, olives, and cereals to prepare extracts, marmalades, salted olives, oil, and flour. It is a beautiful city in the midst of rich gardens of vegetables, fruits, and flowers and is typical of this irrigated Coastal Plains region. Murcia (210,000), Cartagena (97,000), and Alicante (74,000) are south of the mountain spurs. Murcia is near the foot of the mountains that furnish the water, commanding a large alluvial valley overflowing with luxuriant vegetation. Each large irrigation project produces a *huerta* and a town. Alicante and Cartagena are coast towns, the latter with a good harbor and commensurate commerce. Nearly all Spanish towns of 30,000 or more are along the coasts, and these plains have a generous quota.

Andalusian System. The most complex geologic structures and most inspiring scenery of Spain are in the Sierra Nevada, a portion of the Andalusian System. This region lies between the Guadalquivir Valley and the Mediterranean; it extends to the Meseta on the northeast and to the Mediterranean Sea on the east, where its structure passes beneath the water and emerges in the Balearic Islands. The reader may refer to Chapter 2 for other structural connections.

This region is lofty, 5,000 to 10,000 feet, culminating in Mulhacén, 11,500 feet, and intercepts the winds enough to have an appreciably greater winter rainfall than the plateaus and valleys near. Its streams have carved

Transplanting rice in water-covered paddies. The plants are transferred in small bunches of two to four stalks from the seed beds. (Courtesy Spanish American Embassy)

Reservoir and aqueduct for irrigation of Coastal Plain gardens and crops. Banana and tobacco plants are shown here. (Courtesy Spanish American Embassy)

deeply and grandly, and forests have tried to cover the higher slopes with deciduous trees. Some of the large valleys within the mountains are prosperous. Granada (155,000) stands in such a rural valley. While the crops and scenery around the city are interesting, the Moorish palace, Alhambra, is the greatest attraction. Sugar-cane is grown in the valley among orchards of olives and almonds and extensive vineyards. The cane is carried in a cable tram across the mountains 35 miles to Motril, where it is manufactured into sugar with other cane from several delta fields along the coast. Many modern roads penetrate these mountains, linking towns and rural valleys with the coast and great valley to the north. Málaga (259,000) on the coast is a grape market as well as another sugar town. The mountains rise behind it in solemn grandeur and send their waters down to refresh the vineyards and gardens. Málaga grapes are exported to many foreign lands. Grapes for raisins and table use are trained on espaliers (horizontal trellises of living trees), because branches are not subject to so much change of temperature as are walls and wires. The dry mellowing climate of many terraced slopes improves the quality of grapes throughout the Mediterranean coast.

The Balearic Islands have gardens and intensive agricultural activities. Progressive people with many foreign contacts surpass even the Catalonians. Poultry flourishes on the islands. Outstanding are two breeds of chickens, the Black and White Minorcas.

Guadalquivir Valley. With a master fault along the north side of this valley the depression is explained as tectonic. After the fault let the floor down, waste from the Meseta and especially from the rugged mountains to the south was washed into the valley all through late Tertiary time and a broad plain was built. Long sandbars, built by the waves across the mouth of this valley, shut a large lagoon off from the sea. Sediments have been poured into the lagoon for centuries, but it is filled only to the marsh stage. Its low altitude gives the valley warmth but prevents rain, and the bordering slopes have little run-off; therefore much of the plain is steppe or waste land. Where watered it is most productive, raising more olives than all other parts of Spain, and many excellent grapes.

Because Spain has more land climatically adapted to olive culture than has Italy, it produces 50 per cent more olives. Great numbers are packed in jars, but even larger numbers are pressed for oil. The oil industry yields 100 million to 125 million gallons per year and centers around Cordova (143,000), while the packing for table use centers at Seville. A connected series of geographic adjustments occurs in the nature of the olive, whose leathery leaves and dense, hard stems are prepared anatomically to meet the drought, and whose fruit juices are oils, hence slow to evaporate. Many Spaniards eat the olives and use the oil as a food, a diet which may account in large part for their obesity. Since some tart substance is necessary to counteract the oil, the Spaniard grows grapes among his olives and in the

By means of two kinds of boundary lines the map shows large and small administrative areas of the Iberian countries. Other cities appear on the railroad map (p. 104). (Compiled from historical maps)

Court of Lions of the Moorish Alhambra palace in Granada. The palace is rich in ornamental decoration. (Courtesy Pan American World Airways System)

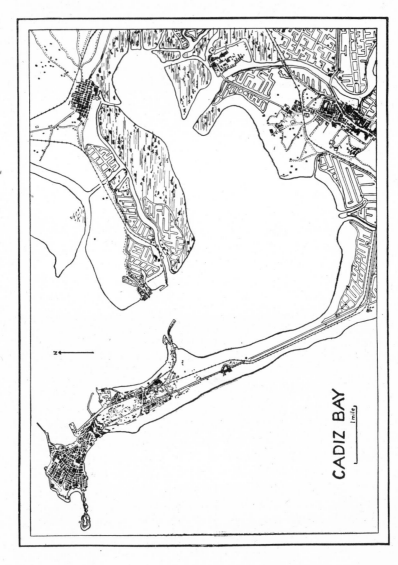

CADIZ BAY

1 mile

Cádiz and its surroundings. Located on a long sandbar that encloses the bay, Cádiz is an old town, one of the three that grew up on the bay. Many square miles around the bay are devoted to salt evaporating pits. (Adapted from British Admiralty chart and Spanish topographic sheets)

light wines finds a satisfactory drink to cut the oil of the olive; thus one industry becomes a complement of the other.

Like the oily olive, many kinds of nuts can meet the aridity of the climate. Almonds are very widespread; hazelnuts and large, delicious filberts are cultivated over many acres. Chestnuts flourish best on sandy or alluvial soils.

Seville (348,000), the master city of the valley in art, industry, and commerce, is the only city that approaches Madrid as a social and cultural center. The recent King Alfonso preferred his palace at Seville. It is a gem of Moorish construction with gardens, running water, lattices, colonnades, and porches. Stalactiform decorations, used freely, are copied from the frequent caves. Imported plants are set profusely about the palace and by virtue of water and care they grow luxuriously. The harbor receives ocean vessels and is the only river port in Spain. Rio Tinto copper ores are exported through Huelva and Seville; the latter is the leading cork market of Spain. Seville's pottery, tiles, and *azulejos* have been mentioned. Other mining is done in the valley, and Cordova handles the lead ores. The tax assessor of Moorish times counted there 260,377 houses and 10,000 mansions and palaces. When one thinks of Moslem families he can easily envisage a city of a million people, nearly ten times as many as the modern city contains. Cádiz (Gades) (76,000), on a sandspit across a bay of the coast, has a good and historic harbor, but it is not deep enough for more than coastwise vessels. It has had a continuous history, under the same name, for more than 3,000 years. Built on an island for defense among hostile people, the town did not allow its encircling waters, a natural moat, to fill up until late Roman times when protection was no longer needed.

THE COUNTRY AS A WHOLE

Communications. Because the peninsula is not large and is nearly surrounded by navigable waters, through routes across the country have been slow to develop. Lack of a master, radial, or converging system of river valleys has checked the development of a centralizing transportation pattern. Strong relief, particularly the mountain ranges, has made road-building difficult and expensive. The abrupt rim of the Meseta and the 2,000-3,000 foot difference in altitude between coastal plains and ports and the great interior upland have also imposed considerable difficulty on cross-country road construction. The Romans built a few roads during their residence of 400 years, fragments of which can still be seen in the Douro and Ebro valleys, but actually internal communications in the modern sense date from the beginnings of railroad construction.

No navigable waterways serve the country, except the Guadalquivir, from the sea to Seville. Only small craft travel on any other river. Canal travel has never been introduced, mainly because there is so little water in the interior. France, a smaller country, has over 25,000 miles of railways, whereas Spain has about 8,500. France has 4,500 miles of navigable rivers and 3,000 miles of canals, with which Spain has nothing to compare.

Since 1927 many good automobile roads have been built, about 60,000 miles in recent years, and automobile transportation and trucking have developed as a result. Some of the newest roads are among the best in Europe. Cement rock and limestone for crushed rock roadbed are both abundant in Spain but are not yet widely used.

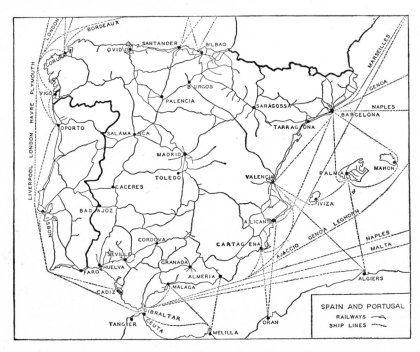

Railroad and steamship map of Iberia. (Adapted from railroad publicity)

In the days when the little harbor of Palos would float any ocean vessel, Spain had plenty of harbors and many more roadsteads or poorly protected bays which could be improved. As the size and draft of ships increased, Spain did little to meet the new conditions, and the country was soon out of the commercial game except at the river port, Seville, the northwest harbors, and two others that have been improved, Barcelona and Bilbao. Still thousands of coastwise trading craft and fishing vessels use small harbors as at Santander, Cartagena, Valencia, Cádiz, Málaga, Alicante, and Huelva. Several of these harbors have small shipyards. Spain's foreign commerce is very small, for two fundamental reasons: it has but little to sell and no large buying capacity on the one hand, and not much harbor facility on the other. Its 1,000 ships of 1 million tons' burden carry 3,000,000 tons, about one third of its foreign commerce.

In such a topographic setting as Spain presents, airways would seem to offer relatively exceptional opportunities. They are developing slowly. The Iberia company, with a radial airline pattern central on the capital, schedules flights between Madrid and peripheral points, such as coastal cities, Balearic Islands, Canaries, Spanish Morocco, and Lisbon in Portugal. Like Spanish railroads, most airports and equipment are still backward and inefficient.

Alicante, as seen from Santa Barbara Hill above the city. The quiet harbor is well protected by two artificial breakwaters. Exports are linen, cotton, wool, and other agricultural products. (By Ewing Galloway, N.Y.)

Industries. Industry, commerce, and agriculture measure a nation's economic status. For centuries Spanish industry has been essentially the preparation of agricultural products for food and the partial preparation of some minerals. The people have not been spurred by the seasons to enter enthusiastically into industry; hence their manufacturing has lagged far behind that of many of their northern neighbors. Local gristmills, sawmills, tanneries, brick-kilns (over 2,000 plants), rock-crushers, and lime-kilns to make lime for whitewashing the houses, constructed to work up local raw materials and to prepare them for local markets, are common over all the country. Many windmills and small mule-power plants grind flour, meal, and stock feed. Electric power plants, many of them hydro-electric, have recently been erected. These came in response to a call for more and better illumination, for local power in small industries, and also through a conservation move to save the wood so long used as power fuel.

Cordova is the center for an active leather industry inherited from the Moors. Wine is made in some vineyard areas in part for export. Besides the coal-iron industry near Oviedo and Irun, the hydro-electric industrial center described under Barcelona merits attention.

A wine cellar. Probably not underground, but cool, dry, spacious, and simple. (Courtesy Patronato Nacional del Turismo)

Economic conditions. In general, Spain has for a hundred years been classed as a backward nation; but there has been through all this time a political, social, and economic ebullition which, in 1931, culminated politically in the new republic, and socially in educational, agrarian, and religious reforms.

The civil war in 1936-39 delayed Spanish development, and recovery is far from complete. Much property was damaged and life destroyed. Agriculture, industry, transportation, and foreign trade suffered. How much this strife was prompted by the geographic proximity of Spain to North Africa, whence part of the trouble came, cannot yet be estimated.

Spain was vastly better off from an economic standpoint under the rule of the Moors than it has been since, but a modern Arab invasion and rule would be of less advantage. After the expulsion of the Moors there followed a long political and social decline and a dependence not on internal worth as formerly but on external acquisitions. The people seemed to feel that the stream of silver and gold flowing from the New World would be perennial and would solve all their problems, compensating for the losses sustained in the going of the Moors. This economic and political depression extended from 1500 to about 1814.

Many of the factors that fostered the low economic condition of old are still operating to retard progress—much infertile and poorly watered land, great obstacles to transportation and communication, the glamour of the past, miserable agricultural methods, and a none too stimulating climate.

In the interim between World War I and Franco's civil war much agricultural machinery was imported. The tractor and turning plow arrived. Irrigation was extended and many projects were initiated involving hydroelectric works. Spain has 2 million horsepower possible, only one fourth developed.

Spain is predominantly agricultural and stock-breeding, a response to her climate in defiance of her mineral wealth. The industrial revolution matured very slowly because of poor communication with the countries in which it flourished. At present 4.5 million workers are on the land, and only 2 million are in industry. Of the 125 million acres about 52 million are cultivated, 58.8 million are in pasture and hay crops, and 15 million are totally unproductive. Either the land under cork, mulberry, and nut trees is classed as cultivated or the trees are scattered over pasture land.

Areas with reasonable rainfall have the smallest land holdings. (See rainfall map.) Communities here work out their own agrarian problems, for they are far from Madrid. Areas of less but moderate rainfall, as in Guadalquivir Valley, have somewhat larger farms; very dry areas have large estates for grazing; in the southeast rainless plains, where irrigation is absolutely essential, holdings are large because no small unit can promote needed irrigation. Here most farmers are renters or hired laborers, and much of the land produces three to five crops per annum.

Diverse remedies for backward agriculture and poverty will need to be applied in the several areas after the whole problem has been thoroughly studied. As agriculture is improved, labor can be liberated for industry. Agricultural production, low for several years, shows some improvement in recent years. The latest figures for grains (1945) were wheat, 1,687,180 tons; rye, 526,930 tons; barley, 797,510 tons; corn, 719,800 tons; oats, 283,150 tons. Agriculture was stimulated in 1946 by government action (a) making the equivalent of $100 million available for loans to farmers, (b) approving a new agrarian law in the hope of breaking up more of the large estates and opening idle lands for the benefit of the small farmers.

Trade. Foreign trade, which 200 years ago was largely export of wool, has been for many years too strongly importation; but the larger production of olive oil, cork, and early vegetables and the beginnings of the rise of domestic manufactures, together with the decrease in the import of silk, rice, and cotton have helped to turn the balance.

Tariff barriers, formerly erected to "protect" infant industries and production, have been lowered, and trade agreements have been vigorously pushed, not so strongly with nations most valuable for trade as with nations more or less sympathetic, such as Italy and Argentina.

Social geography. Spanish people are gregarious. As a rule they do not live in isolated farmhouses but in rural villages from which they go out to their rural occupations. Scanty water supply has been very important in bringing families to dwell together. Another factor is the "commons," public pasture and water for cattle and sheep, an institution inherited from nomadic days. The fear of marauders has played its part. The water supply could be increased by drilling deep wells on the farms, for the structure and rocks are often well adapted to the use of drilled wells. If wells could be drilled on the individual farms, the old-time attachment to the "commons" would be broken down, and the great waste of time going and coming one to three miles on foot or donkey between town and farm would be eliminated. Farms are usually so small that two or three families could live sociably around a common well.

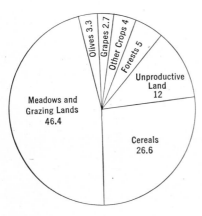

Spanish land utilization. About one fourth of the surface is in wheat and other cereals, about 12 per cent is unproductive land. (Compiled from yearbooks)

Coöperatives and communal organizations exist in many forms, most frequently in agriculture; rarely in grazing, irrigated and pasture lands, and in fishing. Such a system grows in isolated areas where rather close interdependence among families persists.

Out of some 27 million people, less than 30 per cent are in cities of 30,000 and upward; 70 per cent are in small towns and rural villages; very few live on farms. In the United States, 40 per cent of the people are in cities of 25,000 and upward, and more than half the remainder are on farms. Spain's population trend has been markedly cityward in the last 15 to 20 years. Twice as many cities now have 30,000 and over as in 1932. Eight cities have over 200,000; twelve others have over 100,000 and twenty more have between 30,000 and 100,000; Greater Barcelona has 2,301,000.

Most of the forty larger towns and cities are within 50 miles of the coast; and all the districts having a population of 125 per square mile or more, except Madrid, are less than 30 miles from the sea, facts which emphasize the influence of the sea on population density. The areas of sparse population come down to the coast only where mountains extend to the shore or in the marshland of inhospitable deltas as at Huelva and Palos at the mouth of Odiel River. Compare the population density and relief maps to ascertain the influence of relief. Which is more potent, relief or water?

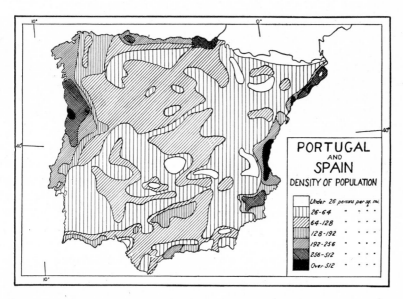

Population of the Iberian Peninsula. Coast regions seem most favored. Much of the upland has a sparse population. (Adapted from *Oxford Advanced Atlas*)

The rural village home is usually built of pressed brick or stone, whitewashed, covered with thatch of straw, corn fodder, grass, or brush, with red tile roof or occasionally in the dry south with little or no roof. Houses have often but one story, because it is easier and simpler to build thus, and are frequently arranged in long rows with common walls between them, a narrow cobblestone street in front of them, and little gardens behind. Often a better house is built around a court or flower garden with the rooms of the house side by side along the surrounding wall. House rooms share space with cart and tool room, granary, poultry house, sheep and horse stables, and other rural accessories. If this series of quarters does not completely enclose the garden, a wall fills the gap.

As in all warm countries the siesta, or afternoon rest, is a custom which brings the people together for gossip and games. It will persist as long as the sunshine is strong and abundant and the air dry when warm. Business houses close; many kinds of employment cease for two to three hours after lunch, and the men and women do not return to work until three o'clock. Of course then they cannot stop for the night at four-thirty or five o'clock as our workers can. Work continues in many quarters until seven or eight. This habit establishes the dinner hour at nine to ten in the evening, which to a tourist is quite disconcerting. Because this program must be followed six to eight months of the twelve, it is followed the year round except in the northwest, where it has no serious hold, again for climatic reasons.

People. While one speaks of the Spanish people as a unit, one easily recognizes several race types and at least three languages, and finds diverse origins for culture, architecture, plants, wild animals, and domesticated animals. The dominant human type in Spain is Mediterranean, dark, dolichocephalic, and of medium stature. This may well be a result of position, in line with the general march of the races of Europe, and under a climate that emphasizes some of these characteristics.

In the Old Stone Age men came to the Iberian Peninsula from northern Africa in two or three waves and apparently found Spain unoccupied. Ten thousand years or more after these early tribes arrived, Neolithic stone industries came from the north, probably brought by men of the Cro-Magnon race. These were the artists who decorated the cave walls with their illustrations of the chase, their conflicts with wild life, and their agricultural practices; and at the same time revealed how dangerously the early people lived. There was a third invasion of the Old Stone Age culture and industry, this time well developed in north Africa before coming, which spread over southern Spain and up the valleys into eastern sections.

Spain later was the home of New Stone Age men who came first from earlier centers of the Mediterranean race along the northern and eastern shores of the Great Sea. These people, coming about 5,000 to 9,000 years ago, brought domesticated animals and improvements in stonework, pottery, and agriculture. They were probably the people known to the early Romans as Iberians.

The use of bronze was brought to Spain from the mountains of central Europe some 4,500 to 5,000 years ago by members of the Alpine race. Liking hills and mountains and finding much of Spain more or less occupied, these dark, round-headed, rural immigrants moved into northwest sections of Spain and became the first settlers in the present Galician and Asturian provinces.

Because of the tin in Cornwall and copper in Spain, Phœnicians came to trade as early as 1100 B.C.; and their early trade routes, among the very earliest converging on Spain, were laid out in response to influences still potent in Spanish commercial life. In the third and second centuries before our era, these Semitic people made many settlements, of which Cartagena is one. Greek colonizers and traders came to Spain in 500 to 600 B.C.

Romans, another group of the Mediterranean race, modified by many invasions from the north, whose civilization the Iberians adopted, came in numbers for the conquest of a goodly land. Trade was the chief motive, but remains of their settlements—walls of towns, aqueducts, and roads—can be seen today in many places. During the four to five hundred years that Romans occupied Spain, they gave the people another infusion of Mediterranean race which is still noticeable and a valuable addition to the Spanish stock. Roman major political divisions followed essentially the linguistic lines of today, lines that are strongly physical and along which the nation would cleave were it to break up today into east, west, and central parts.

Segovia Aqueduct, a well-preserved Roman water transfer built 40 miles northwest of Madrid by Trajan in the early years of the second century. The stones were fitted and laid without mortar. (By Ewing Galloway, N.Y.)

The Nordics came to Spain in the invasions by Vandals, Suebi, Alans, and barbaric Visigoths covering the years 406 to 419 A.D. The last ruled for nearly 300 years. This Nordic blood, now well mixed with the Mediterranean race, is still evident in the tall men of Seville and Valencia and in the fair peoples of parts of the north.

The proximity of Spain to Africa and its fine agricultural possibilities tempted the Moors, who came as herders with oasis agriculture and conquered most of the peninsula, utilizing the irrigable southeast and the Ebro Valley for crops and the Castile uplands for their sheep. They also brought the Moslem religion, strong government, and the rudiments of dry agriculture. Coming from Africa, they made their strongest impact in southern Spain. Cordova was their capital and there the Caliphs built magnificent Moorish palaces and the greatest mosque in all Islam. They never built in, or occupied so fully, the northern sections as they did the Granada and Guadalquivir areas. When their power declined, multitudes of true Moors and many men of mixed blood remained in the land. Thus the present people of Spain have their foundations in prehistoric races with infusions of Alpine, Nordic, and Semitic into the more abundant Mediterranean race. Climate and soil have helped to shift, mix, and fix these elements, until now much race unity appears throughout the country.

The Basque is probably a remnant of one, perhaps the first, of the migrations from Africa. He has, because of his isolation at the western end of the Pyrenees, retained an old agglutinating language and a notable independence, not to say arrogance. Pride in his traditions and racial exclusiveness continue to keep him separate and different from his neighbors. The Basques have thought themselves the only descendants of Adam and have claimed Basque was spoken in Eden. Their eyes turn to centuries and conditions far past. They stubbornly lead the same life as their fathers, are conservative and superstitious.

Language. Three languages other than Basque are geographically separated and preserved today. In Galicia, so separate from Spain and so close to Portugal that it almost became a part of that state, the Portuguese language is spoken. Throughout central Spain, including more than half of the peninsula, the Castilian tongue is used. It is considered the true, upperclass Spanish. The Catalan tongue is spoken on a coastal strip from France as far south as Cartagena and the Balearic Isles. It differs more from Castilian than does the Portuguese but resembles southern French-Provençal, of which it is a branch.

These three languages date in their present form from the anti-Moorish struggle which rose in three geographic centers. The mountains of Galicia served as a refuge for many Christians who rose to resist the Saracen and, because of their isolation from Castile and León and close connection geographically as well as historically with Portugal, came to use the Portuguese tongue. Castile, particularly in the north, was a refuge for many more Spanish expelled from the south. They rose under the kings of Castile, united, and devoted their strength to the expulsion of the Moslem. This common struggle fused them and merged the dialects into true Spanish. Aragon in the northeast was peopled by refugees who after fleeing into France reasserted themselves and became the third nucleus of organized opposition. Each of these units as it drove out Moors forced its language on conquered lands. Castilian thus advanced southward between the gorges and mountains that have been chosen for Portugal's boundary and the steep Meseta slopes that prevent free intercourse between Castile and its eastern neighbors; Catalan spread south over the coast provinces. Unfortunately, because of these two north-south barriers, these groups of provinces have been commercially and socially back to back for 400 to 500 years. They have had their eyes toward the sea—one east, one west, and one south. The Basque language is disappearing, on the north in favor of French, on the south of Spanish, because the Basque autonomy has long been dissolved, and his territory is on a highway which is becoming more and more important every year. The universal compulsory education now available in Spain will, as it overcomes the present 50 per cent illiteracy, tend to unify the provinces linguistically. As trade becomes more important than defense, another basis for unity of speech will gain potency.

Buildings, architecture, and art. The long, checkered history of migrations and invasions has left a heritage in Spanish buildings. Roman walls and roads still abound, but very little of immediate pre-Roman remains can be found. Nor did the Nordics leave much permanent architecture, but the Moors were elaborate and distinctive builders. Castles of both Roman and Moorish style still perch on hills and headlands.

The broad overhanging roofs, in many instances with gentle slopes, are especially adapted to the bright sunshine, heat, and meager rain. Business houses and some factories, as well as residences, are thus protected. In parks artificial shelters are constructed of earth or rock for coolness and to house the soda fountains, dancing floors, and conversation seats. In the newer parts of cities streets are broad and shaded. Barcelona has hundreds of squares with the corners clipped away 20 to 30 feet to give more turning space, permit breezes to move more freely, and make the city look more spacious.

In the warmer parts of Spain, especially around Seville, Cordova, and Granada and in the mountains to the south, many people live in caves or under ledges partly walled up. This custom affords the advantage of coolness in summer, shelter from winds and cold in winter, and cheap but permanent construction. Because of lack of timber and abundance of rock, the wooden house is rare, while stone and brick are common. A dry climate calls for large use of adobe, or even packed clay, for walls. An element of neatness, resulting in monotonous similarity, is achieved by applying whitewash to rural and village buildings, walls, and fences. This requires the ubiquitous limestone quarry and lime-kiln. Granite and slate are used in buildings, but beautiful red tiles made of the local clays are common on the better city houses. Through the central and southern part the colored *azulejos* or glazed tile furnish charming architectural variety.

The Spanish have used in art the materials they had—marble, granite, clay, iron, bronze, silver. Their jars and vases bearing characteristic patterns are large, numerous, and exquisite; metallic lusters are distinctive; their chinaware is good; their tiles for walls, floors, and roofs are often very artistic. But many substances used in other lands are wanting in art here because unavailable. The same materials have been used through all three régimes, Roman, Moor, and modern—a use showing the persistence of geographic influences.

Because Spain was long under Roman influence and far from the centers of the Reformation, it is mainly Roman Catholic in religion; and because of its unfortunate experience with Moslemism, it was for many centuries intolerant and bigoted; now there is no state religion and, theoretically, no favored cult but complete religious freedom. This tolerance has been difficult to obtain and was impeded in its progress because of the religious contacts of previous centuries. Spanish arrogance and haughtiness manifested in colonial dealings are no doubt related to the harassing and difficult experiences with invaders expelled immediately before the rapid colonial expansion.

Future. Spain is fast losing the quaint, old, and picturesque in dress, custom, and rural building. Roads, although still wholly inadequate, by opening up the country have permitted the people to know each other and to visit their own cities, and have admitted the tourist into the more remote sections. Spain is surpassed in per capita railroad mileage by all but four or five countries of Europe, so difficult has road and railroad construction been; but the autobus road has been tried out and is proving its worth. It will make great changes possible in communications. Both educational programs and the system of landholding have been studied with reform in mind and are being revamped along modern lines. When the illiterate half of the people can read and write and find an interest in public affairs, there will be twice the present enthusiasm and urge for political, social, industrial, and religious reform. Hope grows as men own their own lands, so these rural reforms are another reason for a modernizing of the Spaniard's outlook. Improvements in sanitation, industry, and transportation with a vision of things national and international must come if the country is to keep up with world progress. The 1931 change from kingdom to republic, even though the monarch and monarchy were both liberal, is the result of a century of development and education. The civil war, replacing the republic with a military dictator, is another expression of the desire for economic and political improvement, coming too rapidly for growth and hence taking the form of revolution. This haste after long delay comes as a response to a flood of modern ideas rushing in from neighboring nations by modern means of propaganda after centuries of sluggish development in partial isolation.

Two small geographic problems lie on the borders of Spain: Gibraltar and Andorra. Gibraltar seems to have come on the horizon of human activities as a Phœnician trading station and commercial outpost centuries before the Christian era. Romans ventured beyond it about 200 B.C., but traders were previously forbidden to pass it because its horizon was fraught with mystery. Gibraltar is a great limestone rock mass, two-and-one-half

miles long and three fourths of a mile wide, rising about 1,400 feet above
the straits it guards. It possesses considerable sandy foreshore on the west
side and much less on the east. The rock once was an island; but through
sand deposition to the north aided by uplift, it has been tied to the mainland by a sandy plain about as large as the rock and by a dune area of
equal size, both on the Spanish side of the boundary line. In the plain are
a Spanish town, La Linea, and several ruins, witnesses to the ancient importance attached to the place. Between La Linea and the great rock is
a "neutral ground" stretching across the sandy neck. On the rock are a
Moorish wall and castle and some other ruins.

Republic of Andorra; a gateway and hermitage on the road up from Spain. (Courtesy Alice
Langelier)

Such great significance was attached to the place as a guard to shipping that British officers in 1704 took it and hoisted the Union Jack. In
the 200 and more years since this last capture the town has expanded with
its ill-adapted English-type houses; signal stations, fortifications, and great
ammunition galleries honeycombing the rock have been constructed; watch-
towers, batteries of guns, coal-yards, and, more recently, wireless towers
and commercial and tourist piers have been built. Its climate is attractive,
and the rich historic associations and commanding views have led to active
efforts to make it a tourist point.

Andorra, the last survivor of the independent states of the Pyrenean
valleys, is a republic of 5,500 people occupying 195 square miles spread
over six mountain valleys and their slopes along the boundary between
Spain and France. It is best reached from the Spanish side up the Segre
Valley from Lerida to Urgel, then up the Valira into Andorra; but it has
a poor road leading down toward France by the Ariège River. Its close
Spanish affiliation is shown in its coinage, the Spanish peseta. Undisturbed

sovereignty dates from 1278, a time when little political units were the established type of organization. Its isolation and physiographic unity have helped to keep it neutral and independent even during the recent civil war.

The agriculture of Andorra corresponds to the three levels and types of its strongly glaciated topography. Excellent grass covers the high granitic plateaus or alps where ample rainfall is conserved in surface soil because of impermeability of the rock. Here are pastured the transhumant sheep in summer. Below the alps are broad, moraine-covered valley floors with great alluvial fans, and here are pastured the cattle, and the mares with their mule colts. Most of the permanent residences are schist houses grouped on fans or moraine terraces at this mid-level. Since many small areas in the glacially filled valleys are low and yet too wet for cultivation, they are used only for cattle pasture. An effective system of irrigation serves many parts of the mid-zone in the raising of forage crops; and the necessary coöperation in construction and management has encouraged a mutually dependent, helpful, friendly spirit among the people. Meager rural industries for local markets are all that is possible in industrial life.

A local elective council rules under joint suzerainty of the Spanish Catholic bishop of Urgel and the French Republic through the Prefect of Ariège. Because of its geologic and topographic conditions, Andorra has no mining or manufacturing but raises sheep for market and a little tobacco for sale or barter. While its form of government has changed, it still is a fair sample of the type of isolated states fostered by the topography and meager communications of a thousand years ago.

Spanish possessions. Spain has had an unenviable record as administrator of colonial lands. After the voyages of Columbus great areas were taken possession of in the name of Spain or her rulers, and these possessions contributed treasure in almost fabulous amounts to the homeland. Two lines of influence were set in motion. Money was so abundant that prices became very high at home; and the people developed sluggish domestic and racial habits together with an egotistical business and national outlook that has set them back generations in the progress of races. Colonies were so arrogantly administered and developed in such a spirit of exploitation that they ceased to have permanent value, declared their independence, or were taken by other countries in war until Spain was almost stripped.

In the adjustments of north African boundaries, some territory has fallen to Spain; and several islands have long been under its rule. The Canary Islands, 2,800 square miles in area with a population of almost a half-million, lying in the Atlantic Ocean near the African coast in latitude 27° to 30° north, are two provinces of Spain. They are largely volcanic and coral trade-wind islands, miserably watered in many parts and subtropical in climate, luxuriant producers of flowers, early vegetables, particularly tomatoes, and subtropical fruits such as bananas, oranges, and dates. The vine does well, and wines are exported. Sugar-cane, coffee, tobacco, and cereals are the other crops. Because they differ more climatically from Great Britain than from Spain, the islands ship more produce to Great Britain than to their mother country. Their chief values to Spain are as scenic and tourist centers, because of their wondrous beauty and grandeur and of their use as sanatoria for pulmonary patients.

Ceuta, considered a part of the province of Cádiz, is only a fortified post in Africa opposite Gibraltar and comprises about 5 square miles with a population of some 35,000. It is an economic drain on the country instead of a help. There are two Spanish islands, Annobon and Fernando Po, in the Gulf of Guinea which are of little value. The first furnishes water and fruit to passing vessels, the second exports much cacao. In the same vicinity Spain has Rio Muni, a territory with 100 miles of coast, extending rectangularly into Africa a little more than 100 miles, comprising 10,000 square miles of equatorial territory. It is a land of possibilities in the production of equatorial fruits, fibers, and forest timber but at present makes little contribution to the economic life of Spain. Rio de Oro is a 125,000-square-mile strip of west African coast lands extending from the Canaries on southward below latitude 22°. Its name suggests "Golden River," but golden sands are more characteristic. Lying on a west coast in the belt of northern trades it is true desert land, and essentially of no value to its owners. Ifni on the southern Morocco coast is equally worthless.

Along the Mediterranean Spain controls a zone of Morocco over 200 miles long and 25 to 50 miles wide, which is worth more to the homeland than all the other possessions combined. While its rainfall is insufficient, the heavier rains in the hills and mountains of the interior make much irrigation possible. Soils in mountains made by decay of a variety of rocks are rich, fertile, and well disposed for use. The climate is mild. The chief exports are poultry and eggs, sent not to Spain but to England. Others are skins, hides, and wool from the herds of sheep and goats, for which the lands are excellent, and beans, barley, linseed, wheat, and almonds, some of which go to Spain. Fruits, grapes, and dates, are abundant regular crops. Imports are tea, textiles, and machinery, for the people are pastoral and agricultural. This country has every geographic characteristic to make it an important wheat land when the home administration can give it a stable government and much needed good roads.

In general, Spanish colonial possessions are now not worth much because they are in unproductive places or duplicate the products of the homeland.

QUESTIONS

1. In general Spain has the highest average altitude of any country in Europe, but it has few typical mountaineers. Why?

2. What elements combine to make Spain a wheat country? an olive country? a cork country?

3. It is said Spain could support two to three times as many people as it possesses. How could it best be done?

4. Why has Spain's mineral wealth not led it to become a leading industrial nation? Why is it unwise to export minerals for reduction and then buy them back?

5. Why the French proverb: "Africa begins at the Pyrenees"?

6. Why does Britain and not Spain hold Gibraltar? Look for geographic reasons. What has the strength of Spain to do with it?

BIBLIOGRAPHY

ADAMS, H. C., "European Outpost: the Azores," *National Geographic Magazine,* Vol. 67 (January, 1935), pp. 35-66.

ADAMS, Nicholson B., *Heritage of Spain* (New York, Henry Holt & Company, Inc., 1943).

ALTAMIRA, Rafael, *A History of Spanish Civilization,* trans. by P. Volkov (London, Constable & Company, Ltd., 1930).

BORKENAU, Franz, *The Spanish Cockpit* (London, Faber & Faber, Ltd., 1937).

BRENNAN, G., *Face of Spain* (London, Turnstile Press, 1950).

———, *Spanish Labyrinth* (New York, The Macmillan Company, 1943).

Cambridge Economic History of Europe, Vol. 1, *Agrarian Life of Middle Ages* (Cambridge, England, Cambridge University Press, 1941).

CARRIER, E. H., *Water and Grass* (London, Christophers, 1932).

COON, Carleton S., *The Races of Europe* (New York, The Macmillan Company, 1939).

CUNNINGHAM, Charles H., *Spain, Resources, Industries, etc.* (Washington, D. C., Government Printing Office, 1924).

DIXON, Pierson, *Iberians and Their Relations with the Aegean World* (London, Oxford University Press, 1940).

DOBBY, E. H. G., "Agrarian Problems in Spain," *Geographical Review,* Vol. 26 (April, 1936), pp. 177-189.

Europa, Encyclopedia of Europe (London, Europa Publications, Ltd.), annual.

FAIRHURST, H., "Types of Settlement in Spain," *Scottish Geographical Magazine,* Vol. 51 (May, 1935), pp. 283-305.

FERNSWORTH, L. A., "Andorra, Mountain Museum of Feudal Europe," *National Geographic Magazine,* Vol. 64 (October, 1933), pp. 493-512.

FINCH, Vernor C., and TREWARTHA, Glenn T., *Elements of Geography,* 3rd ed. (New York, McGraw-Hill Book Company, Inc., 1949).

FITZGERALD, Walter, *The New Europe* (New York, Harper and Brothers, 1946).

FORD, Richard, "Seville, More Spanish Than Spain," *National Geographic Magazine,* Vol. 55 (March, 1929), pp. 273-310.

FREEMAN, Edward A., *Historical Geography of Europe* (London, Longmans, Green & Company, 1920).

GALLOP, Rodney, *A Book of the Basques* (New York, The Macmillan Company, 1920).

GEORGE, H. B., *Relations of Geography and History* (Oxford, Clarendon Press, 1924).

GILBERT, E. W., "The Human Geography of Mallorca," *Scottish Geographical Magazine,* Vol. 50 (May, 1934), pp. 129-146.

GLINKA, Konstantine D., *The Great Soil Groups of the World,* trans. by C. F. Marbut (Ann Arbor, Edwards Brothers, 1927).

HAYES, Carlton J. H., *Wartime Mission to Spain* (New York, The Macmillan Company, 1945).

HUGHES, Emmet John, *Report from Spain* (New York, Henry Holt & Company, Inc., 1947).

KENDREW, W. G., *Climates of the Continents,* 3rd ed. (Oxford, Clarendon Press, 1942).

LONG, Georgia, *All About Spain,* New Europe Guide Series (New York, Duell, Sloan, and Pearce, 1950).

LYDE, L. W., *Peninsular Europe* (New York, Longmans, Green & Company, 1931).

McBRIDE, H. A., "On the Bypaths of Spain," *National Geographic Magazine,* Vol. 55 (March, 1929), pp. 311-372.

———, "Pursuing Spanish Bypaths Northwest of Madrid," *National Geographic Magazine,* Vol. 59 (January, 1931), pp. 121-130.

McCABE, Joseph, *Splendor of Moorish Spain* (London, C. A. Watts and Co., 1935).

MADARIAGA, Salvador de, *Spain* (New York, Creative Age Press, 1943).

MUIRHEAD, Findlay, *The Blue Guides: Northern Spain* (1930); *Southern Spain and Portugal* (1929); (New York, The Macmillan Company).

NEWBIGIN, Marion I., *The Mediterranean Lands* (New York, Alfred A. Knopf, Inc., 1924).

NEWMAN, Bernard, *The New Europe* (New York, The Macmillan Company, 1943).

OBERMAIER, Hugo, *Fossil Man in Spain* (New Haven, Yale University Press, 1925).

PEATTIE, Roderick, "Andorra, a Study in Mountain Geography," *Geographical Review,* Vol. 19 (April, 1929), pp. 218-233.

RIPLEY, W. Z., *Races of Europe* (New York, D. Appleton and Co., 1899).

SANCHEZ-CANTON, F. J., *Spain* (Graficas reunidas, 1928), in Spanish.

SCHEVILL, Ferdinand, *A History of Europe,* 5th ed. (New York, Harcourt, Brace & Company, Inc., 1947).

SEMPLE, E. C., "Irrigation and Reclamation in the Ancient Mediterranean Region," *Annals of the Association of American Geographers,* Vol. 19 (September, 1929), pp. 111-144.

SORRE, Max, "Spain," in Vidal de La Blache and Gallois, *Géographie Universelle* (Paris, Lib. Armand Colin, 1934).

TREND, John B., *Civilization of Spain* (New York, Oxford University Press, 1944).

UNSTEAD, J. F., "Geographic Regions Illustrated by Reference to the Iberian Peninsula," *Scottish Geographic Magazine,* Vol. 42 (1926), pp. 159-170.

VILLAR, Emile E. H., *Soils of Spain and Portugal* (London, Thomas Murby & Company, 1937), in Spanish and English.

WHITBECK, R. H., and FINCH, V. C., *Economic Geography* (New York, McGraw-Hill Book Company, Inc., 1924).

WHITTLESEY, C., "Trans-Pyrenean Spain, the Vall d'Aran," *Scottish Geographic Magazine,* Vol. 49 (July, 1933), pp. 217-228.

CHAPTER 7

Portugal

A mountain spur on either side
Shoots out, with the gray-mossed cork-tree hoary.
—WM. GIBSON

Spain and Portugal occupy parts of the same peninsula and are bound together by strong ties of race and soil, yet because of differences in outlook, resources, and interests they have grown far apart. Spain has looked mainly toward the Mediterranean, Portugal toward the Atlantic, Africa, and the "Isles of Bliss" and later toward the Americas. Thus, until America was made known by Columbus, Spain's conquests and alliances were Mediterranean and Continental, while Portugal's were African. For similar reasons of outlook and position Portugal missed much of the influence of the Moors which deeply colored Spain. Both went to the New World together, but Portugal, because of her open sea route around Africa, far excelled Spain in her reach to the Orient. Present colonial interests and values are strongly colored by this difference in outlook and related differences in interests as well as by the attitude taken by the two nations toward new lands and peoples.

Spain was rich in minerals and thereby had attracted the attention of Phœnicians and Romans before the Christian era. The minerals of Portugal were neglected for comparatively successful agriculture, and their delivery was hindered by poor land transportation and lack of power development. From this disparity resulted vast differences in commercial relations as well as in political and social contacts. Portugal has relatively more forest and more cultivated land than Spain, but less pasture and waste land. Portugal's forest resources always yielded lumber for ships, masts, and hulls, whereas Spain often had to buy. Because Portugal's position made communications with Equatorial Africa easier for the people than did Spain's location, Portugal had much more of African slavery and vastly more infusion of Negro blood in the people than had Spain.

Geology and resources. The upland rock topography of Portugal is old like that of Spain, but lower slopes are often younger and steeper. Structurally the two countries are intimately related, sharing in the great Meseta core of ancient rocks and in the uplifts and erosional history as well. Large granite intrusions into earlier sediments, now largely schists and slates, are responsible for the mountains in Traz-os-Montes north of the Douro. In the central part between the Tejo (Tagus) and Douro rivers are the Serra da Estrela or Mountains of Beira, mostly folded structures in younger rocks with granite intrusions. In the south is the Alemtejo or Transtagano (across or beyond the Tagus) consisting mostly of crystalline limestone shot with a valuable porphyry and presenting old stream-made topography. Among the northern mountains are two remarkable plains, Chaves and Valenca. Along the coast of the middle section extends a large coastal plain, increasing in width to 25 or 30 miles at Coimbra. South of the Tagus is a large, low plain, consisting essentially of two levels of deltas built by the Tagus River

Incised meanders of the Douro River. Roads on contours or on spurs. Note the stone fences in the foreground. (Courtesy Consulate General of Portugal)

and two lesser streams. One delta plain was elevated above sea level, and after a period of erosion and slight submergence the newer one has been built at present sea level. A fault seems to have assisted in taking the Tagus out southwest as at present, instead of south, as it once flowed. Lisbon Bay, opposite the city and upstream, is evidence of the submergence, and the great delta built by the Tagus at the present sea level into the head of this bay is evidence that the submergence is not recent. Small streams washing sediments into the bay and filling in among the seven hills of the city have formed plains over which Lisbon has spread—a complicated history to complete the setting for a wonderful city and harbor.

In the province of Algarve is a mountainous land area between the sea and the Guadiana River, bordered on the south by an irregular coastal plain and sandbars and terminated on the west by the bold, rocky headland of Cape St. Vincent, the "land's end" of Portugal. This old mountain area is a part of the Moist Meseta mentioned in the chapter on Spain.

Among mineral resources, copper in eastern Alemtejo leads, and iron at Moncorvo in Traz-os-Montes comes second; but neither takes any considerable place outside of serving Portugal's needs. Coal, far insufficient for Portugal, is found near the coast at Cape Mondego and inland near Leira. Other minerals known are pyrite, lead, and titanium. In the Serra da Estrela are the largest known wolfram ore deposits in Europe, with which is associated some tin ore. Salt from the sea obtained by evaporation of lagoon waters, a process favored by the warm summer sun and dry winds, is a large resource at Aveiro, Figueira da Foz, Lisbon, Setúbal, and Faro. This recovery of salt is very useful for the fishing and fish-curing industries.

Granite in abundance for buildings in scores of towns is found and worked in many quarries in the valley of the Douro. Slate of excellent quality and generous quantities from the same valley near the east side of Portugal is associated with a remarkable schist that splits readily in two directions nearly at right angles. This schist is split into long posts, beams and bars 2 to 4 inches square and 4 to 10 feet long, or into boards and staves. The posts and beams are extensively used to make grapevine trellises of a very durable sort. Mineral waters springing from fault zones or igneous contacts, by which in some places they have been heated, constitute a rich possession. Near Oporto are the hot sulphur springs of Vizela, which were known to the Romans. North of Lisbon are similar springs, Caldas da Rainha, the most frequented in Portugal, and east of Oporto some 50 miles is Vidago, the Portuguese Vichy.

Because of the heavy rainfall from the Atlantic, forests abound over the mountains in the north of Portugal. Here are the usual temperate-zone deciduous trees, including oak and chestnut. The former furnishes 4 per cent of the lumber; the latter furnishes nuts, but very little timber. Toward the south in Alemtejo are great areas of cork, and in Algarve, under almost subtropical climate, olives, citrus fruits, and figs predominate—a wholly Mediterranean forest type. The maritime pine covers about half the forest land and is the most valuable tree for resin, for wood, and for its improvement of the soil.

Soils in general are good. Alluvial soils, deposited along streams, and the delta and coastal plain types are very fertile except where too sandy. Residual soils on the limestones and granites are productive, but those developed on the northern slates and schists are far from satisfactory because usually there is little plant food in such rocks.

Climate. Portugal's climate is very much under marine influence. The north is generally cool and rainy even in summer owing to a monsoonal indraught of air. Toward autumn, as the vertical rays of the sun swing southward, the belt of prevailing westerlies migrates southward, carrying the rainy season with it, so that almost all Portugal has abundant winter rain, a truly Mediterranean characteristic. With the advent of spring the rain belt leaves southern Portugal and the dry season comes in. African warm winds, the "sirocco," are often felt as far north as Lisbon, and dust adds to the discomfort. Because of these climatic variations, the northern and southern parts of the country differ in their forests, fruits, flowering plants, crops, and in the general industry and push of the people. Mountains are lofty enough in the north and central sections to have mild mountain climates.

Harvesting grapes on the slopes of the Douro Valley. (Courtesy Casa de Portugal, N.Y.)

The Meseta in Portugal. Nearly three fourths of this little country belongs to the Moist Meseta as described in Spain (see the regional map, p. 89). The uplands are old erosion surfaces deeply carved and trenched by the Douro and Tagus rivers and a few of their major tributaries. Grazing and wheat culture occupy most of the population; the raising of olives, legumes, and almonds is next in importance. No cities adorn the uplands, but miserable, squalid, whitewashed rural villages are scattered over the country. Villages consist of groups of farmers, who raise the crops mentioned and keep poultry for home use. No mining is carried on in the plateau portions. The Guadarrama Sierras extend across the plateau almost to the coast, separating Portugal into its north and south parts.

In the great river valleys that cut across the Meseta are the vineyards of Portugal. In value the vine, grown through all the country, produces the principal crop but occupies only 5 per cent of the land. Extensive vineyards on terraces up the mature slopes of the Douro Valley, where the sunshine is favorable, yield the delectable port wines sold in England and central Europe. These choice, light wines are made in the villages among the vineyards, barreled, and sent in small, open boats on the exciting journey down the rapid Douro to the port (Oporto), which town has given its name to the whole country as well as to the wines. Red and white wines are made in the Tagus Valley under the higher temperature conditions prevailing there and sent from the capital to less critical markets in Brazil and the colonies. Grapes raised in the dryer climate toward the south are sold more and more for table use and for raisins.

Hundreds of boats transporting barrels of wine down the Douro River to ripening cellars. Note oars, rudders, binding poles, and type of boat. (Courtesy Consulate General of Portugal)

The cork tree, a true Mediterranean evergreen but not a conifer, is characteristic of the dryer southern and central provinces. It is planted in orchards like the olive, which when viewed from a short distance it very much resembles. So well is Portugal suited to the growing of cork, which is the second most valuable export product of the country, that it supplies one half of the world's output. Pine, oak, chestnut, and cork forests cover 19 per cent of the land. The olive is grown the whole length of the country, and both oil and bottled fruit enter in a large way into the export trade. Other tree products are the apple, cherry, and pear in the north and the fig, orange, almond, and lemon in the south, each a response to the special type of climate present. A land of flowers, Portugal produces many bees and uses quantities of honey. Of cereals, winter wheat is most important, growing most abundantly in the south, where the dry summers ripen the grain better than in the north.

The Portuguese Lowlands. One of the lowlands of Portugal begins at Oporto and widens southward along the coast until cut off by the spur of the Guadarrama Sierras. The other begins south of this spur, includes the Tagus and its great delta plains, and extends two thirds of the way to the south shore. These lowlands are mostly coastal and delta plains. Rice is cultivated in the easily irrigated lands of the lower Tagus, but like wheat its crop does not nearly meet the needs of the people. Barley, rye, oats, flax, potatoes, and maize fit into the crop rotation scheme and the cooler, wetter climate of the north. Commercial fertilizers are coming into use so generally that they are advertised in railroad stations. Legumes, especially beans and alfalfa, are used in crop rotation, following wheat, rye, oats, or barley. Cattle are fed in the north where the grains are grown, but swine and sheep, being able to subsist in more trying conditions of dust and drought, are more common in the south. In spite of much better rainfall, Portugal's tillage methods are as antiquated as those of Spain, and 40 per cent of the surface is not cultivated.

Irrigation is not practised as much as in Spain, for the more abundant rainfall makes it less essential; but if needed, water is pumped for irrigating by windmills and by cattle. The well-sweep is common and is seen near many houses, both farmhouses and others.

Fisheries are important on most of the coasts and in some of the rivers. Sardines and tunny abound, but many others, as well as shellfish, go into the daily food of the people. The length of seacoast in relation to area, the abundance of fish in neighboring waters, and the Catholic proscriptions against other meats encourage the development of fishing. Next to agriculture, it is the largest industry and in value furnishes about one fifth of the exports.

There are but two cities in Portugal, both in the Lowlands, Lisbon (a contraction of Olisipo, the ancient Lusitanian capital) located on the Tejo (Tagus), and Oporto (the Portus Cale of the Romans) situated at the mouth of the Douro. Both are on good waterways, but Oporto has no delta at present. The capital, Lisbon (770,000), overlooked by palace-crowned heights, vies in beauty with the other cities of seven hills, Istanbul and Rome. Always a harbor and commercial center, it has been besieged by enemies and decimated by pestilence brought over the seas. Earthquake and fire have destroyed its magnificence, but it has risen, scourged but improved, each time cleaner, more substantially built, and more closely adjusted to its setting than before. Old and new ascensors lift the people vertically from one street level to another, so steep and high are some of the ascents. Varied markets lay before the customer the products of sea, garden, farm, and forest. Oporto (262,000), the second city, with its many-colored houses, spreads on glorious terraces up the north bluffs of the slightly drowned [1] river, its main trade artery. A fine avenue leads from

Road near Lisbon, with a fine viaduct over the river in the very mature valley. Note limestone outcrop on the left. (Courtesy Casa de Portugal, N.Y.)

the heart of the city out to the coast and the spacious new artificial harbor under construction. Both cities are commercial: they could not fail to be.

In the southern provinces three decadent Roman fortress towns guard

[1] A river is said to be "drowned" when it has been depressed with the land sufficiently to permit the sea to set back into it.

three roads converging on the capital emporium. Elvas, at present the most important, is opposite Badajoz in Spain and possesses the best preserved Roman temple in the land; Beja stands in the hills north of a most unhealthful land that is used as pastures for fine bulls for the arena; and Evora, once famous for the gold mines near and for long the place of an annual pleasure and business fair, rests in the midst of olive orchards and vineyards reaching as far as the eye can see. Coimbra (27,000), the seat of one of the Portuguese universities, serves as trade center for a section of the rural plain of central Portugal, but its university has nothing to do with the surrounding agriculture and industry.

Historical geography. The early stages of Portuguese history were similar to those of Spain. Down through the stone ages and until the coming of Phœnician traders there was no essential political or racial divergence. Thus the Mediterranean race came to occupy the western as well as the other parts of Iberia. Probably Phœnicians were the first sailors to pass through the gate between the Great Sea and the Atlantic. In the early part of the Christian Era Romans were in both countries alike. Their walls and towers are found here and there. By 525 A.D. the Visigoths had established their empire over all the peninsula except the kingdom of the Suevi, which spread beyond Galicia into northern Portugal. This mountainous corner, with its more distinctly oceanic climate, temperate-zone vegetation, and ria type of coast, had unity enough to continue to the death of Charlemagne as a separate state, as did also the kingdom of Asturias, while the Moor ruled the rest of Iberia. The dividing line was the Douro River, a more effective barrier then than it could be with modern means of travel.

From this time on, a distinction seems to have shown clearly between the people of northern and southern west-coast states. The southern part was African, with Arab, Berber, and Negro blood infused into the earlier Mediterranean stock; the north was Galician, with Roman, Suevi, and Visigoth infusions. By the time of the Crusades, the kingdom of Portugal had arisen with the Tagus for its southern boundary, the Minho River as at present for its northern, and for its eastern line essentially the western edge of the Meseta. When the Moors were expelled and the most recently liberated Andalusian states were united with the Castile and León to make Castile, the states of Alemtejo and Algarve became a part of Portugal and have remained since 1513 A.D. with essentially the same boundaries as now. There had arisen many sharp differences between the west-facing coast folk and the east-facing plateau and Mediterranean people. The boundary between Portugal and Spain was determined largely by the inland reach of these two outlooks. One might guess that the line would come along the main divide, putting the long west slope drained by the four great west-flowing streams into Portugal; and Valencia, Catalonia, and the Ebro Valley including Navarra into Spain. But the eastern influence seems to have been strong enough to overcome this natural cleavage; therefore the boundary stretched parallel with, and about 100 miles from, the Atlantic coast, many miles west of the divide. Its specific location indicates the old river influence in that it lies along narrow sections of the Minho, Douro, Tagus, and Guadiana rivers for some 20 to 50 miles each. In no place does the boundary follow a distinct crest or ridge; but when it crosses interstream areas it traverses mountainous regions, crosses divides, and in the main lies along places difficult of access and with sparse population. Thus, if a boundary must be established between two countries in the peninsula, this one is in as satisfactory a place as could be found. The river valleys are not impassable gorges nor the mountains rugged and youthful. One flourishing railroad follows the Minho, and another the Douro up to and beyond the border into Spain, while others cross the national boundary in the highlands midway between the Douro and Tagus and the Tagus and the Guadiana rivers. Connection has now become more important than separation. There has been no important change in the boundary line in 700 years. Geographically it meant much more when first laid out than it does today.

With Portugal's outlook toward the Atlantic, her development of fishing was natural. With this outlook and the fishing, plus a poor, narrow hinterland, navigation, exploration, and commerce were natural steps. Yet the Portuguese were not the pioneers in Atlantic exploration. The streams of Greek, Roman, and later Venetian and Genoese flowed past into the Atlantic for trade with Britain, the continent, and Africa.

During the fifteenth century Henry the Navigator of Portugal sent many expeditions, which started from Sagres ("Holy"), a village at Cape St. Vincent. Vasco da Gama opened the route around southern Africa to India and started a train of events that revolutionized the history of Europe. He speaks of meeting an Arab merchant fleet loaded with "gold, silver, cloves, pepper, ginger, pearls, and rubies." These are articles that entered into west European trade with the Orient. All are goods whose values were great for their bulk and which could thus bear the costs of long journeys. So Portugal began to build up a trade with the East. By virtue of an Atlantic outlook, colonies were planted in Brazil and on the east and west African coasts south of the equator. The rise of Portugal in exploration and colonial expansion was meteoric and her decline almost as rapid, but the remnants left were of more value to the homeland than those left by many another piece of similar work. Brazil, though now independent, remains a valued outlet for much Portuguese export of wines and fish in exchange for cotton, rubber, and cacao. The African states of Mozambique and Angola furnish large quantities of raw materials—oil, seeds, waxes, gums, coffee, tobacco, ivory, coconuts—which go, some through Portugal, some directly, to the industrial countries, Britain, France, and Germany. The tariff unfortunately is now supposed to be set up so as to send all this trade through Portugal. It remains to be seen just how valuable to the mother country these lands can become; but without doubt they are fraught with great possibilities.

One should compare Portuguese colonies with those of the Netherlands, Belgium, or Britain.

Communication. Roads are poor because of the "lack of need" as seen by the average citizen. The country is largely hilly to mountainous and as yet has only agriculture to use or to pay for roads. Railroads are deficient; there are only a little over 2,000 miles of track in an area as large as Indiana, which has 7,100 miles. Many towns have no railroad, and not a few lack even a wagon road. The wagon roads, being centuries old the same as the towns, were usually built with reference to them; railroads, on the contrary, approach the towns but often do not enter them or even pass with-

Sacavem, the airport on the bay at the mouth of the River Tagus. (Courtesy Casa de Portugal, N.Y.)

in a mile. This is due to the conservatism of the people, who in the past would not grant rights of ways to the railroad company. Many towns that refused admission when railroads were built are now asking for railroad service. Centralized development of hydro-electric and carbo-electric power has brought into use long transmission lines reaching across the hills. Potentially there are available nearly 2 million horsepower on the streams, but only 5 per cent of this total energy has been developed; much of it is used for commercial purposes.

Constant travel on the sea from town to town has placed most towns on the coast and dampened the enthusiasm for easy means of travel on land.

Connections by steamship with the colonies and with the United Kingdom are good. As a result wheat from Argentina can be sold in northern Portugal in competition with that from Alemtejo. In 1939 Portugal's merchant marine had 54 vessels of 197,000 gross tons and 263,000 dead weight tons. In 1947 the corresponding figures were 72, 292,000, and 413,000; a reasonable growth in eight years. Internal waterways are scarcely known except that small boats of a few tons' burden use the rivers across the country.

Economic situation. Judging from these facts of resource and production, Portugal cannot have a wholly satisfactory economic status. Manufactures are closely limited to the processing of the products of agriculture. The making of corks, for example, is one of the most important manufacturing industries. Flour-milling, the pressing of olive oil, olive-bottling, wine-making, and fish-packing follow. Manufacture of tobacco and weaving of the plainer textiles are important industries in the north, but much of the cotton is purchased from Brazil. Many people are occupied in the quarries and clay-pits getting out and preparing granite, marble, limestone, and slate for building and paving; clays for brick, pottery, roof and floor tile; and *azulejos* for decorative purposes. Essentially all salt for home use is recovered from the sea and is used in packing fish, again mostly for home consumption. Only a few people are engaged in mining, first because there is not much mineral wealth to be gotten and secondly because the people are not generally interested in such production.

The forests cover about one fifth of the lands, and some are valuable. Rough lumber from the maritime pine is exported to Spain in large quantities for mine props. A good forestry system is in effective operation. Sawmills and furniture factories, some using water power, are utilizing the forests in central Portugal. Ever since the great expansion of Portuguese interests in her exploratory days, the capital has been the center of the social as well as the political order. It is relatively rich, and the rest of the country is poor. Wealth has been poured into the city for palaces and public buildings, whereas little effort has been made to enlighten or enrich the country town and village. Every one hopes to make a pilgrimage to Lisbon; and thousands would rather live in Lisbon in abject poverty with little work than to live in a rural village out of touch with the city, even if rural subsistence were much more remunerative.

Portugal has more trade with England than with Spain; this fact confirms the statement that water freight is cheap and possibly also substantiates the feeling that there is no cordial relation between the two Iberian countries. A third reason for such trade lies in the differences in latitude, in climate, and consequently in corresponding crops. Sub-tropical fruits, cork, wines, sardines, and some ores are the main items of export to England. On a similar geographic basis, Portugal buys her oil and gasoline and cotton and woolen textiles from Great Britain; fish from Labrador; maize, wheat, codfish, and agricultural machinery from the United States;

Interior of the Cathedral of St. Francis. (Courtesy Casa de Portugal)

railroad materials from iron-producing Belgium; and many raw materials from the colonies. Madeira hand-embroideries to the value of $10 million annually are exported to the United States. It seems quite ungeographic that this country should have to buy any foodstuffs which could be produced easily at home or in the colonies.

People. As shown in the section devoted to the historical geography of the country, Portugal has been through many of the early steps followed by Spain, and her people come from the same Mediterranean stock but with a larger negroid infusion. The Portuguese, spreading over a somewhat homogeneous land, have developed a notable unity as to head shape, com-

An old palace on a hill. Note the styles of architecture. (Courtesy Casa de Portugal, N.Y.)

plexion, stature, and language, and become a long-headed, short, brunette group. Except for the Corsicans, they are the most dolichocephalic people (index 75 to 77), in all Europe south of the Baltic. Geographically they have long been isolated from other races. Their early connections gave them a Romance language in the great Aryan family of tongues, but this same aloofness has made it different from that of their neighbors. In much the same way the national religion is Catholic, but in recent decade the people have been tolerant of freedom of worship. While there has been agitation and even strife over religious matters, there has never been an actual religious problem here as in Spain and France.

The Renaissance reached Portugal indirectly through Spain and was colored thereby. It came more directly from Italy at a later date. The Reformation really never arrived. The Inquisition came from Spain in 1536, lasting for a period of 20 years. At the far end of European lands and facing the frontier of the Atlantic, the intellectual stimulus and literary culture reaching Portugal has come mostly from Italy and such neighbors as bordered the Atlantic. There was little real literature until the end of the twelfth century, and up to the eighteenth century nearly all writers wrote in Spanish. The seven periods in Portuguese letters are named and measured by literary currents from abroad [2] and show clearly that geographic proximities and commercial relations are significant in literature as well as in warfare and diplomacy.

Portuguese architecture, reflecting local building materials, is adapted to stone construction and in the south responds to a warm, dry climate. The cathedrals, public buildings, residences, and business houses of the cities are mostly of granite and porphyry. Limestones and marbles are used locally and in the cities near their occurrence. Sandstone, very abundant, lends itself, when quarried, to the sculptor's chisel, and nature's chemistry hardens it later. Wood is little used even in rural building, and the choice of hard woods for altars and choir seats in cathedrals is evidence of the scarcity and value of the meager oak forests.

QUESTIONS

1. What differences in the colonial possessions of Portugal and Spain may be responses to differences in outlook of the two countries?

2. Why did the boundary between Portugal and Spain mean more geographically when first laid out than now?

3. What foodstuffs do the people, in defiance of geographic ideals, buy from the United States that they might well raise themselves?

4. What geographic reasons could you advance for a uniting of Portugal and Spain into one nation?

5. Why might there be geographic reasons urged against such union?

6. Discuss advantages, disadvantages, and consequences accruing if the countries had remained united from their temporary union in the sixteenth century.

7. Compare the relative historical importance of Portugal and Italy in world geography, political, economic, and colonial.

8. Which nation in the Iberian Peninsula now has the best opportunity to become a more important nation? Note many geographic factors.

9. Lisbon is called the wharf to Europe. May it become the air gate also? Why?

[2] Provinçal Period, 13th and 14th centuries; Castilian Poets, 15th century; Italian or Classical Periods, 16th century; Spanish Period, 17th century; French Period, 18th century; English and French Periods, late 18th century (a Romantic spirit); English, German, and French or Modern Period, 19th century.

BIBLIOGRAPHY

BIROT, Pierre, *Le Portugal* (Paris, Lib. Armand Colin, n.d.).

COLEMAN, Elizabeth, *Portugal, Wharf of Europe* (New York, Charles Scribner's Sons, 1944).

COON, Carleton S., *The Races of Europe* (New York, The Macmillan Company, 1939).

FREEMAN, Edward A., *Historical Geography of Europe* (New York, Longmans, Green & Company, 1920).

GADALA, Louis Papy, *Le Portugal* (Grenoble, B. Arthaud, 1935), in French.

GEORGE, H. B., *Relations of Geography and History* (Oxford, Clarendon Press, 1924).

KENDREW, W. G., *Climate of the Continents* (Oxford, Clarendon Press, 1942).

LAUTENSACH, Hermann, *(Portugal) Die Portugiesischen Landschaften, Petermanns Mitt., Ergänzungsheft.*, No. 230 (Berlin, 1937).

LIVERMORE, H. V., *History of Portugal* (Cambridge, England, Cambridge University Press, 1947).

LYDE, L. W., *Peninsular Europe* (New York, Longmans, Green & Company, 1931).

MILL, Hugh Robert, *International Geography* (New York, D. Appleton and Co., 1920).

MUIRHEAD, Findlay, *The Blue Guides: Southern Spain and Portugal* (New York, The Macmillan Company, 1929).

NEWBIGIN, Marion I., *The Mediterranean Lands* (New York, Alfred A. Knopf, Inc., 1924).

————, *Southern Europe*, 2nd ed. (London, Methuen & Co., Ltd., 1943).

NEWMAN, Bernard, *The New Europe* (New York, The Macmillan Company, 1943).

RIPLEY, W. Z., *Races of Europe* (New York, D. Appleton and Co., 1899).

SCHEVILL, Ferdinand, *A History of Europe,* 5th ed. (New York, Harcourt, Brace & Company, Inc., 1947).

SHACKLETON, Margaret R., *Europe, A Regional Geography* (London, Longmans, Green & Company, 1942).

SORRE, Max, "Portugal," in Vidal de La Blache and Gallois, *Géographie Universelle* (Paris, Lib. Armand Colin, 1934).

YOUNG, George, *Portugal, Old and Young* (Oxford, Clarendon Press, 1917).

CHAPTER 8

Italy

By position, Italy lived in classical antiquity, in early Christianity, in the Renaissance, and now binds them all three in its art and architecture.

Position. To be in the central part of the Mediterranean Sea as a peninsula of a peninsular continent is to have a long series of advantages of position. Along these Mediterranean shores a score of empires rose and fell; essentially all were continental, yet all flowed out to the sea with their own contributions to civilization and culture, and each ebbed back with its treasure from the common pool to its own valley or hill center. Besides being the seat of more than one of the early states, Italy contained stations or trading centers established by several of these empires. So, as centuries have grown into millenniums, in trade, in language, in politics, in religion, in law, and in exploration Italy has contributed to the progress of the Mediterranean race. Hence it may be described as presenting an epitome of the failures and successes of our common humanity.

To turn back in time to an age when shorelines were far different from those of today, and even islands and peninsulas were not the same, one finds an important center of late Paleolithic industry and dispersal in Italy and a corner of France. The remains of the typical Aurignacian cave dwellers who occupied this territory are burials, tools, and utensils found in the grottos Des Enfants, Cavillon, Barma Grande, Baousso da Torre, Grimaldi near Mentone, and farther south in caves near Lucca and Otranto. Eolithic and early Paleolithic men had no doubt been in Italy during the early stages of the ice age, but these were the first people to have somewhat fixed homes in Italy—the first settlers—and there probably has been no break in blood connection from these Aurignacian immigrants down to the present Mediterranean race. Many additions, however, have been made by later migrations.

In Italy, as in Spain, the earliest members of the Mediterranean race wandered in from Africa, continued to develop through countless centuries, and received new blood and successive waves of culture and methods from both north and south. Some 3,000 or 4,000 years ago, the peoples began to have names and their countries to be known by names, some of which

135

still survive. Ligurians of 2,500 years ago are probably represented among the Italians of today by the tall, dark, dolichocephalic people about Lucca. The Umbrians were a brachycephalic prehistoric people in northern Italy, who have probably come down to us not greatly disturbed by immigrations,

Map of the geographic regions of Italy, made for purposes of description. (Constructed from relief, climatic, and land utilization data)

because they occupied the hills and mountains of the east-west Apennines then as now. The Etruscan of Etruria (Tuscany) is a migrant probably from the north, who overspread the Umbrian. He came so early that he in no wise need disturb the historian, but he followed long after the indigenous broad-headed inhabitants of Umbria had become fixed. The Etruscan no doubt gave more to Italy in art and industry than any other early race, and through Italy to Europe. An indigenous pottery art peculiar to the materials and the climate of Italy grew up. The Etruscans built strongly walled cities, roads, and bridges. Rich discoveries in tombs from Bologna to Rome show their jewelry, costumes, war equipment, statuary, and architecture. They were pre-Roman, by centuries at least, but when Roman history emerged from obscurity, seven to eight centuries before Christ, the Romans had borrowed and were continuing to borrow heavily from the Etruscans in architecture, in mythology, and even in the use of luxuries. Through these centuries of change in northern Italy, southern Italy received little immigration because it had been isolated by distance and rough land. Owing to recent (Quaternary) changes of level of land and sea, conditions which had been favorable for migrations from Africa in Paleolithic time became unfavorable before historic time.

The Greeks built towns and opened up commerce on all the shores of southern Italy and Sicily. Their aggression resulted in the development of very close relations between the people of the two peninsulas, at times relations of contempt and war, at other times of friendship and valuable intercourse. The Phœnicians had settlements in Italy and carried on trade with the native population. Ostrogoths and Franks, conscious of rich values in Italy, flowed in from the north. Lombards came in troops and took up their abode in the rich Po plains. A check on the effects of these invasions may be had by comparing northern Italy with Sardinia. Because of its insularity, Sardinia never suffered these inroads of northern hordes who traveled by land, but it did have Greeks and Arabs and later Spaniards, all Mediterranean people who navigated the great common highways. To-day Sardinians are backward, conservative, and individualistic.

Italian resources are in general bulky or heavy—marble, clays, sands, iron—and all this early commerce and plundering never really touched them, any more than did the Romans of those centuries.

In the push-and-pull among the tribal states that grew up in Italy, the Romans were easily the dominant tribe. They were centrally located near the coast and on the Tiber River that served their trading interests. Spreading over the Great Sea as well as over the peninsula of which they at first occupied only the center, they took advantage of the seaway with their galleys and founded colonies and built empires to the ends of the sea, and even leagues beyond. Their commerce extended to their farthest colonies. They came to rule all the other tribes, and they gave one language, Latin, and one legal code to the whole peninsula in accord with its physical unity. Dying, this virile ancient language gave birth to a whole family of languages: modern Italian, Spanish, Portuguese, French, Rumanian, and some dialects; in these younger tongues many traces of the old language are still discernible.

Topography. Physical unity is natural to the peninsularity of Italy, but physiographically there are fourteen well marked units which have played an important rôle in the history and boundary disputes of states for 3,000 years. The Po plains comprise (1) the Venetian delta and coast lands, (2) the middle Po section, which might be named the Milan or Lombardian, and (3) the Piedmont or upper portion. Alpine slopes (4) encircle the Po plains from the sea on the French-Italian border north and east to the Yugoslav border. The Apennine folds comprise three parts, (5) northern (Ligurian and Etruscan), (6) central (Roman and Gran Sasso) and (7) southern, extending through Basilicata and Calabria. In the curve of the northern and central Apennines is (8) the Tuscan Maremma (Florence

Mount Cristallo, in the Alps, showing the summit rising above the timber line.

to Rome), and south of Gran Sasso is (9) the Campania or the Neapolitan plains and volcanoes. (10) The Apulian lowlands lie between the table of Gargano Mountain and the Apennines and follow the coast to the end of the "heel." (11) Istrian Karst. Three large islands (12) Corsica, (13) Sardinia, and (14) Sicily, make up the other three physical units. Politically Corsica has not been a part of Italy since 1768, but has belonged to France.

The Alpine slopes constitute the largest of the fourteen Italian regions. They rise in ridges, peaks, and spurs from the plains to the summits of the Alps. In places the Italian border follows the mountain crest and divide, swinging far west and north round the sources of the Dora Riparia, Dora Baltea, Ticino, Adige, Piave, and Tagliamento. In other places the boundary turns far in toward Italy, occasionally almost reaching the plain, as near Como. Several small changes in the western boundary have been made by post-War II treaties at Italy's expense. The young glaciated topography of the Alpine slopes has never supported states of its own but has been incorporated in those whose heads were in the plains. In several of the valleys north of the Po lie beautiful glacial lakes—Maggiore, Lugano, Como, Iseo, and Garda—some of which are held in by moraines. Glaciers feed some of the Alpine streams, and in earlier times, by profoundly scouring and carving all the valleys, they did much to make the valleys useful as highways through the Alps for ancient invaders, armies, or commercial missions. Thus glacial erosion encouraged Roman and modern road-building, and

Road circling Lake Garda. Such galleries are made for roads and railroads on the Riviera also.
(Courtesy of Italian Tourist Information Office)

added to the beauty of the Alpine valleys and to their interest as scenic features. But the passes are generally too high for railroads, and in consequence tunnels bored through the mountains conduct them beneath the highest, snowiest passes.

Associated with Apennine and Dinaric folding during the later stages of Alpine mountain making, the area now occupied by the Po plains and the Adriatic Sea was warped down sufficiently to admit oceanic waters. Streams from the mountains, in many instances glacier fed, have ever since been pouring their burdens into this long, curved arm of the sea. From the Piedmont to the present Venetian shoreline, what was once the sea has been filled. From the shoreline toward Gargano, a distance of nearly 200 miles, it has been partly filled, so that sea depths are generally less than 600 feet; only in the southern portion is there really deep water.

In the Piedmont portion of the plains the hills of later Tertiary rocks have been eroded to old forms throughout much of the region between

Towns, streams, and lakes of Italy. Free Territory of Trieste is shown. (Compiled from several atlas maps)

Turin, Alessandria, and the Ligurian Apennines. Quaternary and recent gravels, sands, and clays have been laid among the hills and Alpine spurs. This region was the first to be filled to sea level, and its plains are today the highest above tide. At least a thousand square miles of plains stand over

600 feet above the level of the Adriatic. In the great Lombardy or middle section the land is much smoother than in the Piedmont and descends gently seaward, as well as from each side toward the Po. Because Alpine streams in this section are longer than the Apennine tributaries, with higher sources and more rainfall, they have contributed much more alluvium and therewith have forced the Po River to flow near the Apennines. These northside streams further attest the alluvial origin of the plain by all bending strongly down valley miles before they reach the Po. So keen is this habit in the Adige in the Venetian plain that at present it does not reach the Po at all but enters the sea by its own mouth. The newest part of the Po plain is so recent as to be low, in places marshy, with changing distributaries wandering over its surface in their search for the sea. In historic times sandbars, separating lagoons from the sea, have been built for many miles along the marine margin of the plain, while the rivers have built the land forward many miles into the Adriatic. The Piedmont has always been a desirable area; armies of many a famous general have marched over Lombardy, but the Venetian plain, neither land nor water, has had a charm and attraction all its own. Two fifths of Italy's people live in these Po plains.

The Istrian Karst, a post-War I addition to the domains of Italy, is today divided into two parts. A strip 5 to 10 miles wide along the coast from 15 miles north of Trieste to 30 miles south is the Free Territory of Trieste under United Nations control. The other much larger part, often called Venezia Giulia (Venetia Julia) with reference to the Julian Alps along its eastern border, has been assigned to Yugoslavia. By this adjustment the great Italian naval base of Pola was wrested from Italy by treaty and given to Yugoslavia. It will be treated in another chapter.

The Northern Apennines, like all the Apennine range, are mountains of relatively recent origin and consist of simple, typical, folded Cretaceous and Tertiary rocks. From the Ligurian Alps west of Genoa to Carrara, a distance of 100 miles, they lie close along the coast and spread inland 15 to 50 miles; beyond Carrara the mountains extend east by southeast obliquely across the peninsula. Erosion by active but seasonal streams has developed the topography to maturity and left relief of 5,000 to 6,000 feet. No streams cross the range, but between Bologna and Florence older forms and summits lower than elsewhere make cross travel and commerce easier.

The simple folded structure continues south and southeastward through the provinces of Abruzzi and Molise in mountains called the Roman Apennines, and in the Gran Sasso the loftiest peaks of the whole system rise to altitudes up to 9,583 feet. The Arno and Tiber rivers rise near the angle between the northern and central Apennines; the Arno sweeps round a great horseshoe curve, then westward past Florence and Pisa to the sea, while the Tiber parallels the mountains southward 40 to 50 miles and works its way among the Sabine Hills, between extinct volcanoes with their crater lakes, through Rome, and into the Tyrrhenian Sea. A small stream, Pescara, in Abruzzi rises west of Gran Sasso and traverses the whole range to enter the Adriatic near Chieti. Its valley has been a significant highway for 2,500 years. The southern Apennines are less lofty, have a more confused structure, and possess numerous narrow valleys, which in olden times sheltered bandits and made military movements difficult, and in modern times have

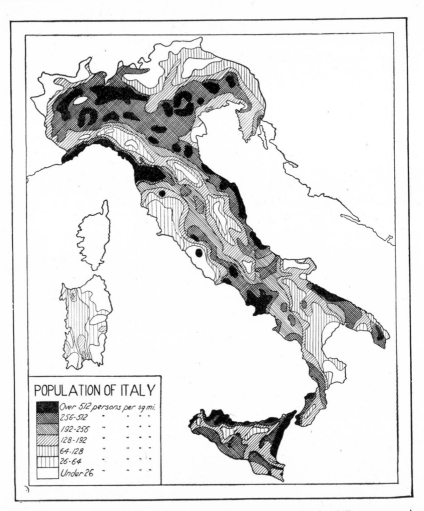

POPULATION OF ITALY

Over 512 persons per sq mi.
256-512   "   "   "   "
192-256   "   "   "   "
128-192   "   "   "   "
64-128   "   "   "   "
26-64   "   "   "   "
Under 26   "   "   "   "

Population map, suggesting several factors that influence density. "Under 26" may go as low as one per square mile. (Adapted from *Oxford Advanced Atlas*)

taxed the skill of the railroad engineer. This system of mountains bears toward the western side of Italy in Basilicata and terminates in La Sila (the forests) of Calabria. A spur extends thence to Reggio in the "toe" of Italy. In late Tertiary times straits caused by a little submergence broke southern Italy into six islands, and sediments of those times were laid in the waters.

The moderate uplift that brought the sediments out of the sea and bound the islands into one land was probably related to the greater movements and faulting that lowered the triangular Tyrrhenian block below the sea and left Sardinia, Corsica, and Sicily three larger islands. In turn, these depressed parts are now receiving recent sediments in their inter-island straits. Volcanic activity south from Tuscany seems to have been concentrated along the northeast fault zone, and near the intersection with the east-west fault zone stands the mighty Etna. Earthquakes are still frequent and must be reckoned with in much of these areas.

The Tuscan Maremma between the concavity of the central and northern Apennines on the east and the sea on the west, has been a notable physical-political unit most of the time for 3,000 years. Its surface is quite uneven, hilly but not lofty. It is not a ridge country because it has no long, parallel, geologic folds. It is not a plain because its strata have been much disturbed recently enough for the present topography to be still in advanced maturity. But it does have many hills, valleys, little plains, swampy areas—a perfect jumble of topographic detail. Its subsurface structure and kinds of rock are as varied and patchy as need be to produce such a variety of land forms. Such old topography signifies great erosion; but the waste carried out has not been deposited in the sea at present sea level, else there would be large deltas and coastal plains. Recent submergence has depressed the eroded material mostly below sea level and perhaps helped to make the streams sluggish and the land poorly drained.

Beginning at Mt. Amiata, the highest peak of Tuscany, and running southward, eruptions have been common. Four great volcanic cones of ash and lava, 8 to 12 miles across, were built up so recently that their craters contain lakes, yet so remotely that no activity is historic. One of the crater lakes was partly drained a hundred years ago because the people believed it "exhaled disease," a belief verified by modern science which found it bred *Anopheles,* the malaria-carrying mosquito. This is Lago di Nemi in the Alban Hills south of Rome, in which after more draining archeologists recently found pleasure boats of Caligula.

The Campania and the Phlegrean Fields round about the Bay of Naples include old foothills in front of the southern Apennines, plains among the hills, and a girdle of volcanoes from Ischia, past Naples, around to Vesuvius, and out again to sea. Capri at the south end of the circuit is not volcanic but consists mostly of limestone. North of this girdle are more volcanic hills; but south are delta plains along the Gulf of Salerno, making the good invasion grounds used in the fall of 1943.

The Apulian lowlands consist largely of essentially undisturbed marine sediments, uplifted and carved extensively by streams to old age, then partially submerged and covered with more sands and clays, and reëlevated so as to expose a rather extensive coastal plain which attains a width of 20 to 35 miles. Typical cuestas in the plain stretch 150 miles from Otranto to and beyond Gargano Mountain. Of all Italy this plain at the mouth of the Adriatic Sea comes closest to the Balkan Peninsula.

The topography of Sicily is rugged in the northern part and volcanic in the eastern central. It spreads southward in diminishing hills with many small plains. Most of the slopes are gentle, old enough to be cultivable, and suited to fruits, vegetables, and flowers in great profusion. Surface forms are closely related to geologic history. The northern side is a bit of the ancient land area, most of which foundered to make the Tyrrhenian Sea possible. Its shore has not undergone much developmental change since that great event. Following the faulting which broke the old block loose and let it down, lavas began to flow in several places. The latest volcanic construction along this line of weakness is the great Mt. Etna, whose symmetrical cone rises directly from the sea to almost 11,000 feet. The southern part of the island consists of late Tertiary rocks, still not well cemented but carved to advanced maturity and ready for human use.

Sardinia is another remnant of the old land and bears much better witness to its relationship than does Sicily. More than half is of rugged mountains carved from very ancient granites, schists, and gneisses. It once was three islands: the main mass, a small remnant 15 by 45 miles on the southwest, and a much smaller remnant of later rocks on the northwest. Both these last two are now welded to the main island by recent sediments, which make the most available plains and workable lands and carry the densest population on the island.

Minerals and rocks. Italy's mineral wealth is as closely knit to its mountain folding, metamorphism, and vulcanism as its topography is to its mountain structure. Carrara, long a stimulating name to sculptors, Massa, and the vicinity furnish white and colored marble in great quantities and variety. Verona is likewise in the midst of large deposits of white and red marble which are extensively used locally in buildings and monuments and in pavements, walks, floors, and porches, everywhere lending a rich, mellow, reddish color to the scene. It is not only the cheapest local building material available, but is found in such quantity that a considerable amount is exported. These marbles were made by the mashing of rocks in the orogenic work. Serpentines and granites add rich variety to wall and floor in the buildings of the Riviera, and excellent slate roofs them. Black basalts, lavas from Etna, appear in buildings, pavements, walls and curbs in many Sicilian towns. Pompeii had pavements of Vesuvian basalt. Other places have marble and crystalline limestone in variety and abundance. Probably no country is better supplied with choice building material. Quarry products amount to $60 million a year.

There is very little coal and that little is 90 per cent lignite located near Arezzo and Pisa on opposite borders of Tuscany, perhaps the worst situation possible if it is to serve the industries of the country. This lack has checked industrial growth and encouraged deforestation, but in recent years it is stimulating a survey and development of water power, a large importation of British coal, and importation of some half-made iron from Germany. Peat deposits of the Po plains are almost exhausted. Iron ore in excellent quality but limited quantity is found at Elba, a remnant of the Tyrrhenian block. One wonders if Italy would have been better off with no Tyrrhenian Sea. Lombardy has a small amount of low-grade ore, but Bergamo has a better grade and Milan has charcoal with which to smelt it.

Sardinia, consisting of crystalline rocks and great areas of granite intrusions, is the Italian mineral treasure-house. Iron, lead, zinc, gold, silver, and copper ores are well known, but only crude ancient methods of extraction are used. Because of the volcanic nature of the island, sulphur, borax, mer-

Traveling cranes, trams, and cables at Carrara marble quarries. (Courtesy Italian Tourist Information Office)

cury, and pumice are important products. Sicily has put arsenic-free sulphur on the market for many years as a government monopoly. This does not come from volcanic rocks but from sedimentary beds that contained gypsum and anhydrite from which natural processes have separated the sulphur and segregated it in crystalline seams and masses. Borax comes from Tuscany, mercury from Idria and Mt. Amiata, pumice from Lipari. Sands for glass, clays for brick and tile, and both volcanic ash and argillaceous limestone for cement abound. Thus Venice for ages has had excellent glass works; scores of places make brick and tile as did the Romans; and cement has been associated with Italy from early Roman days.

Large quantities of salt are extracted from the Adriatic and from Ionian waters on the east shores of Sicily and on the southern shores of the "boot." The dry, warm climate and long, rainless summer season make Mediterranean waters more salty than those of the Atlantic Ocean and greatly aid the evaporation process, which is carried on in prepared basins constructed between high and low tide levels.

With such a dearth of both variety and quantity in almost every item of mineral wealth except stone, Italy could not be expected to have shared fully in the Industrial Revolution; nor is it perhaps surprising that with these lacks and yet with the abundance and variety of highly superior statuary marble the Roman and the Italian, each for his time, should have developed a fine art in sculpture. Similarly the skill of Etruscan potters evokes no surprise when abundant clay resources are considered.

Sulphur works at Lercara on the Island of Sicily. (Courtesy Italian Tourist Information Office)

Soils. Residual soils are the rule throughout Italy, carrying an inheritance from the parent rocks, both granite and limestone. Over the Apennines are great stretches of similarly mature soils. Where derived from the Cretaceous limestones of central Italy they are good rich clay loams, whereas those from the younger Tertiary rocks in both northern and southern Apennines are more sandy and in the main not so strong. But it must be remembered that even the Etruscans had some sedentary agriculture and that these soils have been cropped ten times as long as have any soils in America. The soils of Tuscany are of many kinds and in small patches, some fertile, some very infertile. On the Apulian lowlands again are broad areas of uniform soils.

Back of Bari on the Puglie upland and on the limestone cuestas are the better calcareous soils, but on the lower lands sandy soils predominate. Around the active volcanoes soils derived from ash and even from lava are usually of very high grade. Vesuvius often sprinkles a layer of ash over the land that the Campanian farmer in great haste plows under to quicken its decomposition. Thus it enriches his soil for vineyards, flowers, and fruits. A layer of ash less than two or three inches thick is considered a great blessing, but if more comes at once than can be plowed under, the soil has to lie fallow a short time until enough weathering occurs to liberate some plant food. Except where glaciated, in the deltas, and on recent volcanic ejecta, soils are usually mature and resemble chernozems; but in places far south they display laterite characteristics.

The transported soils are largely in the north; but many deltas and alluvial plains as along the Arno, Tiber, Liri, and Volturno provide small areas of constantly renewed, excellent, composite soils, whose value is often attested by their density of population and intensity of agriculture. The Po Valley and lower Alpine slopes are the great area of transported soils. The rivers have always been active in bringing their soil riches down to the plains, and glaciers still greatly assist as they grind fresh rock that has lost little by weathering. Glaciers, much more extensive in the recent ice age than now, have left immense terminal moraines and large areas of ground moraine from Turin, Milan, and Verona back into the foothills—deposits which are making the finest long-lived soils of northern Italy. Where the Pontine marshes south of Rome and many rich swamp areas in Tuscany and Venetia have been drained, patches of new humic soils are available for intensive cultivation. Sicilian and Sardinian soils are in the main residual, mature, and very good. Both islands are extremely agricultural, and the distribution of the people and agriculture is a close response to the character and utility of the soils.

Climate. The January isotherm of 40° F. comes into the Po plains from France and cuts across the Adriatic into Yugoslavia near Split (Spalato). South of this line the January mean temperature ranges from 40° to 50° F. except in the islands, where it exceeds 50° F. July mean temperatures are all above 70° F. except where lowered by altitude; in Sicily and Apennine interiors they rise above 80° F. Italy is warm and sunny. Its rainfall is treacherous. Lying in the zone of transition where trade winds prevail in summer, the westerlies in winter, and the intermediate high-pressure belt with descending air in spring and autumn, it is a land of winter rainfall. The rainy season approaches from the north in early winter as the westerlies migrate southward and in early spring it retreats northward, so that southern Italy has very little rain and scatters that little over a short season. Central parts have a longer season with more rains. In the northern part the rainfall is fairly sufficient except in the Venetian country, which because of its lack of altitude has meager rain even in winter and less than 20 inches in summer. The northern Apennines and much of the Alpine slopes have over 40 inches, well distributed through the year because of the altitude and because the influence of the westerlies never wholly leaves these northern parts.

This very simple fundamental interpretation of Italian climate is inadequate because there are many local departures and sharp contrasts, in each case related to local relief, distribution of large topographic forms, or distribution of land and water. Palms grow in Venice, and frosts are rare; whereas three degrees farther south in the provinces of Abruzzi and Molise snows frequently cover the ground for weeks, and paths must be shoveled from house to house so that friends can communicate with each other. Most of southern Italy is bright and sunny, and the blue skies of Sicily are famous, but even Sicily can have beastly raw, cold, blustery days. Then, too, one who is accustomed to a type of weather can give a fairer description of it than one who is not. So strong is the influence of the weather and climate on a man that an Englishman used to the gloomy British winter weather overdoes his descriptions of Sicilian blues, and no doubt a Sicilian would say things of London or west Scotland weather that would sound quite inappropriate to a native.

The lack of rain in the lower Po Valley, even with a summer maximum, has called for devices of many kinds to meet the shortage, and not only man but most of the vegetation in southern Italy has made adaptations to the trying conditions. The so-called evergreen or Mediterranean type of vegetation is not coniferous, but thick-leaved, dark green, deep-rooted, with thick bark and leaf skin, oily seeds and fruits, and waxy, gummy, or at least thick, juices. When such a tree is wounded, its sap does not run as does that of a tapped maple in New England; the thick juice oozes out, dries down, and heals the wound quickly and permanently. Plants such as the olive, oleander, almond, fig, live-oak, and scores of kinds of shrubs, with their thick, stiff, prim foliage of dark green, make up the vegetation ensemble. Where the rainfall is greater, deciduous trees constitute good forests of chestnut, oak, ash, walnut, and elm; in the Alps conifers replace a considerable portion of the deciduous trees because of the cooler, rainier mountain climate. Only one sixth of the country is wooded, whereas more than one third is mountainous. Italy imports half the wood used and even so uses very little. A strong, wise forestry program is needed, but so far almost nothing has been done to this end. This situation is particularly unfortunate in a country with so little mineral fuel and hence so necessarily agricultural. Soil conservation and perennial water power demand extensive reforestation and the development of a first-class forestry policy.

Animal life. Wild life probably varies as much as does the natural vegetation, and that because of relief and climatic varieties. There was little for man to domesticate in these lands. Wild goats and sheep and the wild boar were common, also many waterfowl, but most of the animals that have become common and valuable were brought from Asia and Africa with the people of the spreading civilizations. Of really wild life now extant, the mountain goats, ibex, chamois, deer, and bear in the Alps stand at one end of the series, and lizards, three kinds of poisonous snakes, snails, and multitudes of small birds and butterflies in the warm southern districts stand at the other. Foxes and wolves, the latter of mythologic fame, abound in the mountains of central parts and at times prove quite destructive. So many small birds are eaten, as well as the partridge and waterfowl types, that in many northern and central districts they are scarce. Wild life seems to have little geographic significance.

Sea animals, while varied, are not as important as might be expected from the length of the shoreline. A narrow sea front, shallow for fishing and a great variety of fish, with few of any one kind, limit the fishing industry. The dolphin in the Adriatic, brilliant flying fish in the western Mediterranean, tunny, sardines, anchovies, crustaceans, and cuttlefish are taken on all coasts, and trout in many brooks on land. An Italian eats but nine pounds of fish annually; an Englishman eats seven times as much; and this difference appears in spite of certain Catholic religious requirements. Italy imports tons of fish from Portugal and Britain.

Contrary to early views, the curse of Italy, malaria, is related to its wild life. Marshes breed mosquitoes and mosquitoes carry the malaria-generating organism to the human victim whom they bite. Malaria, therefore, is closely related to undrained warm lands. That setting establishes it in the plains from Turin to Venice and Trieste, from Pisa to Rome, from Marche on the mid-Adriatic to the Gulf of Taranto, and in many small patches elsewhere. Sicily suffers with it nearly everywhere, and scarcely a spot in Sardinia is free from the malady. As late as 1900, 80 per cent of the people in the south were subject to malaria and 20,000 died of it per annum; but as the control measures have proceeded and the people have really taken advantage of the available opportunities to rid themselves of the disease, the death-rate has fallen sharply. In southern Italy, which temperature and the backwardness of the people conspire to make the worst malaria district, the rate declined from 1,280 per million people in 1891 to about 100 in a million in 1925; and the draining of marshes has given the people many thousands of acres of the best new agricultural lands in excellent climatic conditions, a gift much needed by the growing population.

Agriculture. By latitude, climate, topography, and absence of mineral resources Italy is disposed more favorably to agriculture than to any other mode of life. Over half the people still depend directly upon the use of the soil for subsistence. This is true in both north and south, but the style and value of agriculture could hardly vary more than it does. Part of the difference between the careful, intensive, irrigated, fairly well-equipped cultivation of the north and the shiftless, primitive, dry-farming methods of the south is due to the qualities of the people, but one wonders how many of these characteristics could really be traced back to the climatic and other physical conditions under which each people for many generations has lived and labored.

Cultivated lands may be divided into five zones or types, based on the trees and tree crops which respond to climatic and altitude conditions. Such a classification does not describe or interpret all the agriculture, but it well sets forth some features. (*a*) In Sicily all the lower lands produce citrus fruits, called *agrumi* by the Italians, and these characterize the first zone. This zone reaches higher levels in the island than on the mainland and skirts the southern and western coasts of Sardinia. The Riviera from the French boundary past Genoa and southward to Spezia, and the shores of the "boot" from the "spur" at Gargano Mountain round the "heel" and "toe" to the Bay of Naples always show lemons and oranges growing among their shiny dark-green leaves. (*b*) Olives with their ashy or tawny green hairy leaves and dark-green fruit flourish over the interior valleys of Sicily and up the hills and mountains a few hundred feet, in Sardinian valleys and lowlands from the northwest round the west and south shores farther inland than the oranges go, on the peninsula along the coasts with and above the citrus fruits, near the lakes of the Alpine foothills, and in many places in Verona, Venice, Vicenza, and into the foothills north of the head of the Adriatic. They thrive in dry calcareous soils or in clay soils on slopes. Drainage is imperative, but they do well with dry-farming methods. The olive will stand the mild winter frosts whose occurrence limits the orange in all this Alpine border. (*c*) Vineyards not sensitive to frost in winter find suitable climate and sunny exposures on the Alpine spurs and out over the northern and southern Po plains, throughout the Apennines at suitable altitudes higher in the south and on sheltered sunny slopes, in Sardinia on many-terraced mountain slopes but not on the higher ones, and in Sicily up mountain slopes in multitudes of terraces and up southern Etna 3,000 feet. The hills of Tuscany and of the Piedmont east of Turin produce the most celebrated vintages because of excellent soils and sunshine combined with intelligent care of both growing and manufacturing. As much as 600 million to 800 million gallons of wine are produced in a year. (*d*) Chestnut zones are higher than olives and grapes on Alpine, Apennine, and Sardinian slopes, but these trees are not allowed on the best agricultural plains. They delight in a sandy soil and are given a chance on slopes that, for steepness, should not be cultivated but devoted to forest. Sold by picturesque street venders in every city, Italian chestnuts furnish a very widely used and important element of diet. (*e*) The wooded or forest zones begin with the chestnuts and spread on up the mountainsides, where the climate is more severe and joins topography in handicapping agriculture. In the loftiest mountains, as Etna and the higher Alps, the timber line is surmounted by glistening snow covers.

The most essential element for successful growth of the citrus fruits is a very long growing season. They are not ripe before November and may be harvested all winter and the next year to July or August. The new crop comes into bloom in early spring, but not all at once, so for months in spring and summer one may find the ripe fruit of last year on the same tree with bloom and small green fruit of this year. Irrigation aids the growth and extends the area in many localities. Terracing at enormous expense over steep or rocky slopes both prevents the soil from drying out and washing and adds abundantly to the charm of the landscape. Rarely are the citrus fruits grown alone on the ground; wheat, vegetables, and frequently the vine grow between the rows.

Taking home the grape harvest. These grapes are for wine and not for the fancy market.

The olive zone has even more variety of vegetation, for grapes are often set among the trees, and figs, wheat, and vegetables abound. Olives can all be picked at one time and thus do not interfere greatly with other crops. No other country produces better olive oil or has so large an acreage planted to the trees.

In the vineyard zone man's ingenuity has been tested and developed. North of Trieste grapes are supported on nearly level trellises 5 to 6 feet high so as to cover the ground; a few miles west are grapes, wheat, and mulberry trees all on the same ground, with the trees, close cropped to keep them producing all summer tender, fresh leaves for silkworm food, serving as stakes for the vines. Two or three horizontal wires are fastened along the row of trees, and the vines are tied to the wires. Many patterns of training vines on mulberry trees have been devised. In the Padua region vines are actually trained twelve to twenty feet above the ground between the trees. The tree gives a warmer and more even temperature for the vine than either dead wood or iron posts. In the plains north of Florence olives are planted in rows about 40 feet apart, an irrigation ditch bisects the space between the rows, and two rows of grapes fringe the ditch; then a strip of wheat occupies the space between grapes and olives. Willows, extensively grown in places to provide straight, light poles for grapes, are topped low; and shoots that come up are thinned just enough to keep the stump busy and make it produce quickly the kind of poles desired. Irrigating ditches hasten the growth of willows lining their banks. Trellises are often constructed on a row of posts seven to eight feet high by mounting one oblique arm on each side so as to make a Y, and stringing wires along the arms. In this way the grapes hang down on each side, but the trellis does not cover and shade the ground, a condition favoring double crops.

It is very common to find the vine standing in a vine-pit, the counterpart of the German *Weinberg,* which catches all possible rain water and prevents the vine from drying out. The land between the rows of pits is planted in winter to peas, root crops, cauliflower, cabbage, and Brussels sprouts, and in summer cleared so grapes can have all the moisture. In many fields the land is leveled for winter crops and in summer trenched both ways, heaping the earth between the vines. This involves much work to meet the rather unfavorable climatic conditions, but it conserves moisture. Wine grapes are grown to too great an extent, while there are not sufficient table and raisin grapes for domestic use; but a change in kind grown would disturb foreign trade.

Wheat for straw and the Leghorn hat industry is grown in the north, where thick planting and the moist climate ensure a long stalk. Hard wheat for macaroni is grown in the drier southern states, and also abundantly in the northern plains; yet because the people are great consumers of wheat in both bread and macaroni, much hard wheat is imported from U.S.A. and U.S.S.R.[1] All wheat grown is of winter wheat varieties. Rice is grown in the easily flooded portions of the upper Po plain. Maize is the second cereal. Since it needs much water and good drainage, it competes for soil with neither wheat nor rice, but is cultivated extensively in the rich, well-watered portions of the northern plains and among the hills nearly everywhere in the country. It is used much as food for the poorer peasants as well as for livestock. Hay and other forage crops occupy about one third of the agricultural land, and of this third 75 per cent is pasture, a fact suggesting the short winter and the extent of the grazing industry. Grazing is favored by the hilly topography and general aridity, which in many places render the land unfit for tillage. While forage crops occupy many areas permanently, both on steeper hills and on poorly drained alluvial plains, an

---

[1] Fifteen forms or varieties of macaroni were seen at the same time on the shelves of a store in southern Italy.

increasing amount is produced as a rotation crop. Potatoes are raised everywhere, but particularly in Abruzzi and Molise, where favorable sandy soils and summer rains combine with the cooler temperatures of higher slopes and valleys. Irrigation, combined with the warmth and long growing season, makes possible four or five crops in favored localities. Among these irrigated crops, sugar beets are important in the northern plains near Venice; and hemp is a leading crop for ropes, cords, and coarse fabrics in the lower Po and Neapolitan plains.

Transplanting rice in western Lombardy. (Courtesy National Organization for the Tourist Industry)

The growing of livestock is not a large item in Italy because its large population limits pasture land. Since domestic animals for food are scarce, the Italian is not a meat-eater. Oxen are much used on the farms for hauling. Dairy cattle are most numerous in the Lombardy plains and up the Alpine slopes where the more abundant rain furthers the growth of grass. A slow intensification of dairying might be carried on in many places by making a better use of forage crops and grazing lands. Milk, butter, cheese, and meat from the dairy would be welcome for food, and on the farm the fertilizer would supply a real need. Swine occupy the corn (maize) belt and increase with the density of population—the latter primarily because they are so satisfactory in cleaning up waste. In most of the country except the Po plains sheep and goats are more numerous than any other livestock because pastures are too scanty for the larger animals and because they are particularly efficient as dairy animals where the growing of cattle is difficult. Herds of goats are still driven through the streets of many southern villages every morning and milked there as customers wait.

Agriculture varies greatly in different parts of the country. In the north, where methods resemble those of northwest Europe, it is intensive, using modern tools and a systematic rotation of crops and making careful adjustment to the details of soil, slope, climate, and markets; but in the south, except where good irrigation is possible, crude, careless methods of cultivation prevail and harvests are correspondingly light and uncertain.

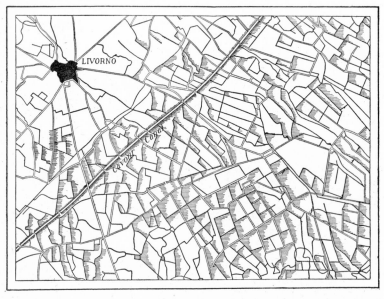

Cavour Canal and details of irrigation ditches. (Adapted from Italian government topographic maps)

Irrigation has long been practised in Italy. Reclamation is equally old. Etruscans devised ways to improve the wet as well as the dry lands a thousand years before Christ, and later they taught the Romans. The coupling of irrigation and drainage with other uses of water was also an early activity. Etruscans canalized the lower Po partly for drainage purposes and partly to improve navigation. Drainage to check malaria was practised shortly after the Hannibal campaigns (204 B.C.). A hundred years ago Count Cavour, the great statesman of Italy, built the Cavour canal primarily to take advantage of the warm rain and snow waters of the Po for irrigation by tapping that river just below Turin and leading the water northeast across the drainage as far as the Ticino River. It is distributed through large branches to smaller canals until it comes in contact with the land in thousands of small ditches. Naviglio Grande, Canal Villoresi, and Naviglio della Martesana in Lombardy take the cold glacial Ticino waters. These canals are also used for navigation and fishing. Farther east large canals gather waters that overflow the Adige and Po and take them to the sea in more direct lines. These canals are primarily for drainage, but they serve for irrigation and for commerce as well. Areas two to five miles across in the low plains about Venice have no roads but instead a network of canals, which here not only drain but serve for highways to bring in the workmen for intensive farming and gardening and to take out the produce. An area of three or four square miles without a house frequently occurs where each day hundreds of men go to work and return home by boat. The most highly developed irrigation systems of the world are found in Lombardy and Piedmont. These have been very helpful not only to the agricultural industries (rice production largely) but in eliciting good community spirit and respect for law and regulations. In many places of central and southern Italy water is pumped by donkey, wind, or electric motor to supplement the meager rainfall and runoff.

Industry. Large agricultural values and small mineral resources determine the prevailing type of industry, which may be designated as preparation of agricultural products for use. Such industries are the milling and polishing of rice, the grinding of wheat and corn, the manufacture of macaroni in a score of varieties, the preparing of straw and the braiding of hats, the manufacture of butter, cheese, chocolate, and wine, the preparing and bottling of olives, the expressing and clarifying of olive oil, and the making of extracts of lemon, orange, and lime. In the south, rope, cord, and coarse cloth are made from imported jute and northern hemp, a product of the plains south of the Po; and near Venice beet sugar is manufactured. At Naples, where bright light makes the bleaching of skins easy, hides are tanned to make leather for upholstering and shoes, and gloves are made of lambskins. The reeling and weaving of silk from silkworms grown on mulberry leaves [2] and the embroidery of shawls and throws are northern industries. Poplar wood treated with soda and sulphuric acid in the rayon factories produces four times as much fiber as the whole silk industry. Rayon is a mill product only, whereas silk growing is a rural home industry. Linoleum is made from cork and flaxseed (linseed) oil. Products of Piedmont and Tuscany flocks are used in local woolen industries. Tanning extracts are derived from chestnut and oak bark and sumac leaves.

Products of quarries, clay-pits, and shale banks are prepared for building purposes in cut stone, slate, brick, tiles, and cement. Salt, olive oil, and fish combine in the packing of tunny, sardines, and anchovies. Salt, however, has not stimulated chemical industries as in some lands. Scarcity of coal checks chemical manufacturing, but with abundant salt and sulphur more

[2] A ton of leaves and an ounce of eggs produce worms enough to make eight pounds of raw silk.

will surely be done in this line. Some steel is made from local coal and iron ore whose reserves are estimated at 150 million tons,[3] some from imported ore; much from imported scrap iron; but more steel is imported than is made. Even so, Italy has not as yet the interest and technique to manufacture the thousand and one articles that great industrial nations make of iron and steel. Neither do the textile manufacturers make such fine clothes of wool and cotton as come from the Atlantic side of Europe. The lack of the resources through the centuries has established historic reasons for these and many other differences between Italian and central European textile industry. A large supply of cheap labor with little industrial development results in much hand work.

Fiat automobile works at Turin in the Piedmont. (Courtesy National Organization for the Tourist Industry)

The shortage of coal and the presence of snow-, glacier- and rain-fed streams have called for the development of water power especially in Alpine valleys. Some three to four million horsepower, continuous low-water-stage power, is available. Rapid hydro-electric development has been the history during inter-war years. The 5 billion kilowatt-hours of hydro-electric cur-

[3] A strong factor in the stalling of the Mediterranean area in world progress and especially in European industrialization is a meager supply of coal and iron. Power and heavy industry may not be hers, but the strategy of a capital highway is hers. Not only nations bordering this sea are concerned, but Britain, Russia, France, the Balkans as they develop, and the Americas. Such commerce and traffic will bring more prosperity to Italy than a "closed sea" and its blockade.

rent generated, while calculated to be 80 per cent of the water power in use, is further estimated at one third to one quarter of the possible amount. Much of the electric current is consumed for lighting and domestic power. The fixing of nitrogen for fertilizer is another important electric industry. About 20 per cent of the railroad traffic is carried by electrified roads, and over 150 steel furnaces, many of them small, are electric. The hydro-electric development has now come to such a stage that scores of power lines reach out from the power-producing valleys to the cities and connect with each other so as to distribute the service and share the load among the many centers. Current generated in the Alps can be used now in Florence and even in Rome. Just as the north is much more intensely agricultural than the south, so is it likewise much more industrial.

Historical geography. Nearly all phases of geography and of geographic relationships are historic. This section is concerned with matters of national domains, political geography and alliances. The peninsula of Italy has rarely contained a single political unit. Usually from two to twenty nations have occupied it, but since 1870 national and peninsular lines have coincided well.

Political history has been so kaleidoscopic, and at times the shiftings have been so frequent, that one might suspect almost every physical feature of having been used at some time for a political boundary. In the beginning each occupied valley was a tribal center. Some of these valleys are quite small, but the Po, the largest, contained several tribal entities. Boundaries in these early days were of necessity largely physical lines; a comparison of such lines with the map of physical regions described on earlier pages shows remarkable coincidences. The same Alpine lines have been used almost as constantly as the shorelines. Venice has expanded and contracted repeatedly along the Adriatic both on the east and west sides, but has never reached far inland on the east side, and has not often held sway over more than the lower third of the Po plain. In fact, Venice has found it very difficult to hold any lands south of the Po. The Duchy of Beneventum, the two Sicilies, and the kingdom of Naples have drawn their northern boundary across the peninsula where the change comes in the structure of the Apennines. Tuscany, or Siena, has always been a unit except in cases where, as under Ostrogoth rule, the whole peninsula had one government. The Papal states have centered around Rome and have not encroached upon Tuscany or Naples, but have spread eastward to the Adriatic, because there was no unit area beyond the Apennines to prevent. This fact emphasizes also the feebleness of the central Apennines as a barrier. Piedmont and other names have been applied to about the same unit at various times. Lombardy and Milan (or Lombardy or Milan) and Parma have likewise been unit areas in the middle Po, almost never pinched out by Venice or Piedmont. Genova has been a very persistent state along the southern slopes of the Ligurian mountains.

It was the most natural thing, as larger federations of smaller states became the rule, that all the peninsula should pass under one government and so remain. The only relic of the tiny nations which occupied, in centuries past, the small physical units is little San Marino in the eastern

Names of Italian states and provinces. (Adapted from historical maps and Oxford Advanced Atlas)

foothills of the Etruscan Apennines. It is 1,000 years old and occupies about 32 square miles, spread over three precipitous hills each decked with a castle and fortifications. Except during a few widely scattered years it has been an independent republic through all its long history. The State of

Vatican City occupies about one sixth of a square mile west of the Tiber in Rome. It is an ecclesiastical state possessing world power and lying within a political state. In a sense it is a relic state, for the popes through many centuries have held temporal authority over portions of central Italy under the name of Papal States. During the reorganization of the kingdom of Italy consummated in 1870, this territory was incorporated in the new state, and the sovereignty of the pope as a political ruler became limited to the Palaces, St. Peter's, the Museum at Rome, and the villa of Castel Gandolfo a few miles away. There seems to be no geographic justification of such a state, but it is richly historic.

As the older states with their early languages—Celtic in the Po Valley with Germanic infusions, the peculiar Etruscan in Tuscany, the Greek in many centers in the south, and the Latin language of Rome—were being coördinated into one great Roman Empire, the Latin language spread over all, adopting much from the tongues it replaced. Out of this Latin grew the Italian of the Renaissance and later the modern Italian. This unity of language favored the rapid welding of the various states and interests into one. Yet there are blocks of foreign language in modern Italy. A Franco-Provençal tongue is spoken in several valleys to which it spread across the Alps. Lying south of Austria, Italy has six or eight towns whose people speak German. Slavic dialects brought by refugees to the Adriatic shores occur in the hills and valleys of the east. Southern Italy has many Albanian colonies which refuse to be absorbed or to abandon their own language. Greek is used by 30,000 people in southern villages, but Catalan (Spanish) has reached no farther than the western shores of Sardinia. Land and water barriers to entrance into Italy seem to have been crossed with about equal difficulty. Not more than 200,000 Italians altogether speak a foreign tongue, and their distribution is essentially peripheral near the sources of the languages.

At the end of the first seventy years of the nineteenth century modern Italy arose with great stress and tribulations by the fusion into one state of all the kingdoms and powers of the peninsula and the islands of Sicily and Sardinia. Its resources were sufficient and varied enough for those days; but it soon became apparent that in all Italy there were few natural resources upon which to build a modern state and that it had little in the way of colonies. Beginning late in the colonial game, Italy's rulers have striven for years to obtain portions of rather unsatisfactory territory in Africa. None was suitable to solve its population problems or to ease its economic difficulties.

Before World War II Mussolini and his advisers thought to build an Italian Empire around the Mediterranean Sea. There is strong geographic ground for a unifying authority over this area, but it cannot today, and could not even then, be set up by a small nation without some consideration of world interests in the sea highway.

At the close of World War II the colonial possessions of Italy were all swept away. The strategic Dodecanese Islands in the Ægean Sea were ceded to Greece. Ethiopia was returned to independence and to its ruler, Haile Selassie. On June 1, 1949, Cyrenaica was given an independent native régime, and in December, 1951, Libya became an independent kingdom. Italian Somaliland is pending in the U.N. General Assembly, and Eritrea is still a protectorate of the United Nations, under British occupation.

Monuments and old buildings. Italy has been the home of republics and empires, kingdoms and cities, for so long and has had so high a civilization that it is strewn with ruins and ancient buildings. Castles once held by feudal lords, princes, and kings still adorn hundreds of hills and crags. Monasteries on hills or in protected places on valley walls witness to the long religious history of the land. Roman roads, many of them over 2,000 years old, can be traced far and near over the country. They were of stone laid on the ground and must have been very rough to traverse, especially in springless carts and chariots. Rome, the administrative center, is the hub of the system, obviously planned not for commercial but primarily for military purposes. The roads bound the people together as nothing else could have done. They can be traced along the coast to Naples, then a few miles inland and on to Regium, and along the coast northward to the French border; branches from this north line run into the Po Valley, always seeking out lower, better places to cross the mountains. Lines connect many important points in the valley, and three to four roads climb up the major valleys and over the Alpine passes to west and north. Several lines cross the Apennines and join in a big military highway to Brindisi. The Via Appia connects Taranto through Beneventum with Rome. All this road construction shows topography as significant then as now in directing traffic. There must have been commerce on some of these roads and perhaps pleasure-seekers too, for one leads directly by the Lake of Nemi while others reach to hot springs and baths.

Ruins of aqueducts, like the one south of Rome, leading to several of the cities, show how the city, by tapping mountain streams, reached out for a better water supply than could be had in local wells. Linked with these aqueducts are city reservoirs for storing the water. Thus larger areas were brought into the environment of the Roman city, and the city was made to depend upon a greater field of resources.

Economic status. That Italy is rural and agricultural all will agree, but that it can well be anything else is a point upon which men may easily differ.

Reports state that 42 per cent of Italy's national domain is arable land; 50 per cent is in permanent grass, forest, nut, and fruit production, and only 8 per cent wholly nonproductive. Italy has a density of population of about 384 per square mile, 419 for all productive land. This is more than any other Mediterranean land possesses and more than twice as much as

France has; but the Netherlands and Belgium have over 700 per square mile. Italy's agriculture is backward. Far too much of the farming is still done by ox and cow power. The food consumption of these animals taxes the food supply heavily. Italy's land is productive and her subsistence is higher than in many nations, but not as high as it could be with more mechanization and improved, modernized farm usages. But when all is said and done, the land cannot feed the people well. Many must eat imported food paid for by products of industry.

Under improved agricultural conditions more men could engage in other work, establish a better system of forestry, do more quarrying, manufacture more wood and stone products, intensify manufacture of iron, steel, bronze, glass, and cotton for the trade, and thus put higher values on the goods before they go to market. Facilities for the manufacture of farm products are sufficient to prepare much more for foreign or home consumption. Manufactures must continue essentially in two lines, as at present: (*a*) refining the rural products; and (*b*) making very valuable small articles in which labor and skill and not raw materials constitute the value.

Good roads do much for internal commerce, but harbors are neither frequent nor good enough to render the water highway very significant for either domestic or foreign trade. Foreign trade during the war except for war purposes was reduced to almost nothing but is rapidly returning to pre-war levels. Imports are about $1 billion a year, exports about three fourths as much. Italy imports 25 to 35 per cent of its wheat for home consumption, mostly hard wheat for macaroni, but exports rice. Olive oil is exported sparingly, but citrus fruits in very large quantities. Gloves of leather, hats of straw, and embroidered shawls of silk are a large part of the exports, and machinery, cotton, and jute are imported for manufacturing. Any land with ruins and ancient history will have a tourist income; any land with such exquisite scenery, any land so glowing with warmth and sunshine in winter and so full of ancient art in painting, sculpture, and building is bound to be a tourist land. The Riviera, for beauty and interest scarcely surpassed anywhere, must be visited to be appreciated. It is a money-maker for Italy, as is Taormina for Sicily.

Cities. All through its history Italy has been much more a land of cities than many other sections of Europe. This is partly because of the need of massing for protection, partly to take advantage of some commercial situation. Three cities all very admirably situated, one as capital, one in the midst of the Neapolitan plain, one central in the Po plain, have together over 3,621,000 people. Three others, one in the western Po plain, Turin (698,000),[4] and two on the coast, Genoa and Palermo, have about a half-million people each. Fifteen additional cities have over 100,000 each, and 39 more have over 50,000 people. Sixty towns and cities contain over one fourth of the population.

[4] Populations used are Italian estimates in 1948.

Rome's title, the Eternal City, refers to its Christian history and its gigantic material structures. A pagan spirit lurking in its ancient ruins makes a great appeal to the majority of tourists and students. Rome *was* in many respects because of geographic advantages. The river was navigable eighteen miles to the city, which may be the reason for the specific location; and the river served the city nobly. In siege it had to be taken to reduce the city. A central location among these plains and rolling hills greatly aided growth. The seven old hills of volcanic ash and clays, increased to ten as the city

Via dell Impero, the road that leads to the ruins of the Colosseum in Rome. (Courtesy National Organization for the Tourist Industry)

grew, gave many advantages of drainage, guaranteed safety from Tiber floods, furnished outlook and inspiration, and supplied raw materials for brick, cement, and stone, as well as a substratum easily excavated. Rome set itself with these advantages to command other helps and to conquer disadvantages by building roads, aqueducts, and fortifications, by creating gardens, vineyards, orchards, flocks, and herds over the surrounding good agricultural land. And so the centuries passed. A new Rome was built over the old; but the dry climate has not been nearly as effective in destroying the old city as climate often is; consequently much of the present interest is in these ancient structures built by pagan hands, hands of people with less vision than men have today, but with more skill and patience.

Rome is today the capital of the kingdom because historically it must be. No other city could qualify. It is the head of the Roman Church for much the same reason. It is the center of art and architecture in Italy, the center of political life for twenty-five centuries, and hence the starting point for scientific archeologic exploration. The old walls are partly removed, and new, broad streets have taken their places. Bus and car lines take passengers up and down the hills, through the classic valleys, past the palaces, Forum, Colosseum, mausoleums, arches, and temples of old, and among the busy stores, hotels, offices, schools, parks, and factories of today. Although it contains 1,480,000 people, one cannot make out a case for Rome industrially or commercially today; although the city is a source of income to the country through its history, ruins, scenery, and museums.

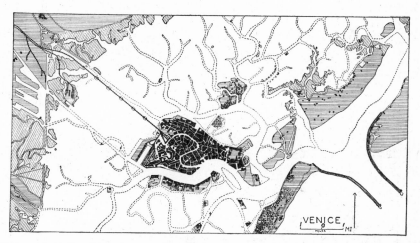

Venice and vicinity. Lido with pier; neighboring villages; tidal channels of lagoon (dash lines), docks, canals, buildings. (Adapted from Italian government map)

Venice, the Island City (259,000), has also been a center for the making and recording of history and has probably twice as many palaces as Rome. Its site at the head of the Adriatic is most remarkable, a seaport nearest the center of Europe and not approachable for conquest either by sea or by land alone but always necessarily by both. A fleet can never get near it but must unload to small boats that go to the city.

The physiography of the Venice situation is a part of that of the whole Po Valley. Present shoreline forms have been developing for many thousands of years. Gravel and boulders during the glacial period were rolled down into this head of the Adriatic Sea, making a very secure foundation, over which sands and muds were laid until the water was shallow. Waves and a west-moving current drifted sand along the shore and built a lido or bar offshore enclosing a lagoon of brackish water 6 or 7 miles wide with a feeble tide of 1 to 2 feet. Ever since the bar was built above the water the lagoon has been filling. Tides have spread in it through breaks in the bar and up the broad tidal channels and have ebbed out again. Fishing villages appeared, often on piles or on mud islands held in place by wattled osiers, the simplest kind of a *fondamenta*, bund, or quay, such as now runs along so many of the canals. There seem to have been a number of such settlements in these lagoons before Venice was founded. After the battle of Chalons in 451 A.D., groups of refugees of Aquileia and other sacked cities found asylum on the group of mud islands called Rialto and began the construction of one of the great medieval powers of Europe—Venice.

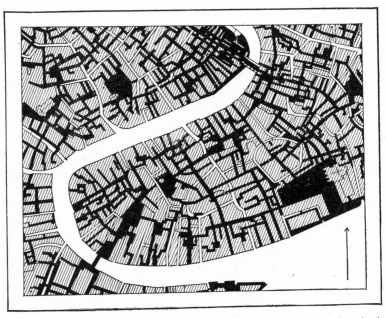

Venice detail. Canals white; paths, walks, squares, black; buildings oblique ruled. Rialto bridge near top. (Adapted from tourist advertising)

As soon as the lagoon conditions had proven the security of position which they afforded the people, trade and commerce became the principal interest of the colony. Rapidly trade expanded with the mainland, with Adriatic coast towns, with Tyre and Egypt, and then with the Orient. Wealth rolled into the city; palaces, churches, larger fleets, bridges, and warehouses were built. Genoa became jealous and pirates greedy. With opposition Venice flourished. Then came the discovery of the Cape route to the East and the blockade by the Turk across the Near East route to the Orient; these with other adversities initiated a long decline until Venice in 1866 came into the United Italy. The city is still famous for its history, its art, and its manufactures of glass, embroidery, silks, and souvenirs for the annual invasion by thousands of tourists, her chief source of revenue.

Railroad trains that run some three miles on a low bridge from the mainland, and very recently automobiles, arrive at the margin of the city. Canals are everywhere, with walks along some of them and through courts from one canal to another and bridges across canals from walk to walk, but the city is unique in having no place for wheels. In the early centuries the bridges were ramps up on one side to the middle of the canal and down on the other side. About the year 1400 restrictions on horses and mules became so heavy and so many of the bridges came to have the modern stair approaches that the horse wholly disappeared and the gondola, already well established, came into its own. The bridges over canals must be high enough to let gondolas pass under, and that means a few steps up from street to top of bridge. Children do not have little wagons or bicycles, babies travel slung in a shawl. One cannot take a walk into the country or go to the beach without a boat. Filling stations stand close to canals to serve launches. Good neighbors often have bridges across from one house to another, even at several levels. Houses upon such soft foundation cannot be tall, only three to five stories, and most of the old palaces have settled unevenly. Props are placed between some buildings to prevent them from becoming too affectionate. There are no traffic police, and pedestrians have no fear of cars or horses. All this unique condition arises because a great maritime city was founded and grew upon a marshy, tidal archipelago.

Florence (355,000), *Firenze* the flower city, has existed over 1,650 years. It occupies a commanding site on the Arno River, a little below its emergence from the Apennines and the mouth of its tributary, the Sieve. Above Florence both are good water-power streams. Below the city the Arno is navigable. The Arno Valley with its bordering hills is a rich agricultural area producing flowers, wheat, maize, vegetables, olives, grapes, and mulberry leaves for silk-worm food. Florence gained in commercial importance during medieval days as trade east and west over the passes in the Apennines grew, and north and south trade from the Po Valley to Rome and Naples increased. In modern times it has become an important railroad center. Its industrial importance has never rivaled that of Milan, for its industries have been limited to processing its rural products, such as making wheat-straw hats, wines, olive oil, and silk fabrics, porcelain from its china clays, furniture, cotton goods, and motor cars. A number of suburbs about the city share in many of these industries.

Florence early acquired other interests. It was the capital of the province of the same name, then of a group of provinces, and for six years, 1865-71, it was the capital of the new Italy set up in those days. It was the home of the wealthy banker-politicians, the Medici, and for a longer or shorter time of Savonarola, Dante, Galileo, and Michelangelo, of Botticelli, Leonardo da Vinci the painter, Brunelleschi the architect, and many others. These

A canal scene in Venice. (Publisher's Photo Service)

painters, sculptors, writers, builders, and scientists gave an artistic and scholastic tone to early Florence which has never departed. Industries and commerce gave the men of the city wealth; palaces and villas were built; churches erected and decorated by its artists. A university was founded, and the city became the intellectual center of Italy. Of its five great libraries, one serves the university; another, called the National Library, contains 650,000 volumes, 800,000 pamphlets, 21,000 portraits, 9,000 prints, 4,000 maps, 40,000 letters, 20,000 manuscripts, and 3,575 books dated before 1500 A.D. Monuments and fountains adorn the courts and squares; museums and galleries display many original works of art and archeologic discoveries, not only from Italy but from Greece, Egypt, and the Near East. For these reasons Florence is the goal of many a tourist and student. Some come to see; others to abide, enjoy, and study.

Ponte Vecchio, the famous bridge at Florence across the Arno. The bridge is almost completely lined with shops on both sides.

Milan (1,219,000) is the largest and most important city of the Po plains and the second city of all Italy. It has an age of twenty-five centuries, is centrally located in a plain of extraordinary fertility, is far enough from the larger streams to be free from the menace of floods, is at the crossing of ancient and modern highways (one across the plain east and west, the other from Rome across the Alps to the countries beyond), and is surrounded specifically by physical features—valleys and passes—that direct traffic through the city. Now submontane tunnels connect it north and south with the best route to commercial Genoa and the cities of northwest Europe. Milan seems to have been destined to be commercial first and then industrial. Because of its position on these geographic highways it has been subdued by military and political disaster, but has always risen again. Local clays have made it a center of the ceramic industries and a seller of porcelains. The great adjacent rice fields make it a continuous exporter of rice. Silks and woolen goods have made the city famous for a thousand years. A type of the plains cities at the mouths of Alpine valleys and in touch with Alpine power, Milan is the most industrial place in all the Po Valley.

Genoa (*Genova,* 660,000), at the head of the Gulf of Genoa and Ligurian Sea, across the low Ligurian Alps from Milan and the Lombardy section of the rich Po Valley, has the best harbor on a long, unfriendly coast. It boasts of depth, shelter, and many improvements that make it safe, but it has not area enough for the vessels that want to use it.

Genoa began as a Greek trading center about 400-500 B.C., was captured and destroyed by Carthaginians 209 B.C., rebuilt by Romans later, and has had a continuous commercial history ever since. Besides the harbor advantages named, the hills nearby have supplied good ship-building lumber, and the low Bocchetta Pass through the mountains behind the city opens a comparatively easy route to the Po plains. Passes over the Alps were known in early days and used for trade routes with Germanic centers. In Greek times Genoa competed with Marseilles; later its competition was with Venice, which it outstripped when its illustrious son, Columbus, discovered America and turned eyes and trade to the Atlantic. Before the Atlantic came into the picture, Genoa had colonies, fortifications, and trading centers in the Near East.

When railroads came, commerce was quickened between Genoa and inland Italian industrial centers; when the great Alpine tunnels were built, trade with Switzerland and the Low Countries was extended and strengthened. A railroad follows the coast both west and southeast. Thus Genoa is a focal center. African, Eastern, Spanish, and American goods come in and are scattered inland, in amount about 6 million tons per year, mostly bulky, coal, lumber, grain, and raw cotton; while manufactured goods from Milan, Turin, and from cities deeper in the continent, in amount about one fourth as great, come to Genoa to go to sea. Coal goes to Milan to promote her auto and silk industries, and to Turin to power her machine shops; cotton goes even to Switzerland.

Thousands of craftsmen in and round Genoa fashion into marketable ornaments the coral taken in the Mediterranean.

The city has been called "The Superb" and "The Proud" with special reference to the splendid display of palaces, villas, gardens of its wealthy merchants, and its churches and other public buildings, rising up over the hills in and behind the lower city.

Naples (925,000) is the home of an easy-going, aristocratic, in some parts dirty and uncouth, yet busy and industrious people, filling a significant place in the world. Naples stands on the seashore and is commercial. Spreading up the hillside in a great crescent overlooking the blue bay within sight of Vesuvius, it has a unique scenic setting. Its great museum of relics from the partly excavated ruins of the adjacent cities of Herculaneum and Pompeii makes Naples a center of historic interest also. The bay is nearly surrounded by volcanic vents and activity, and its quay has a marvelous aquarium and school for study of the rich marine life. Thus the city offers scientific interest and opportunity as well. It has hydro-electric power generated by mountain streams and used to make foods, machines, arms, and armor plate; consequently Naples is industrial. For 700 years it was under foreign rule (German, French, Spanish, Austrian, and Spanish Bourbon dynasties), and it has the second best port in Italy. Naples is a thoroughly cosmopolitan city.

Messina (182,000) at the northeast corner of Sicily has attracted as much attention on account of earthquakes as because of its citrus fruit exports. A deep, commodious harbor, one of the finest in Europe, has had as much to do in promoting Sicilian agriculture as have the fertile soils of the island. A great sandy hook encloses the immediate harbor. Grand hills, topographically well advanced, rise west of the city, and several small streams lead down mature valleys. The hills both east and west protect the whole strait of Messina from wind storms. The city has grown up these slopes much farther in the valleys than on the inter-stream areas, because it expands along valley highways to neighboring villages. Orchards cover the lower slopes, and fruits monopolize the business of Messina. Manufacture of fruit extracts occupies hundreds of people. Fishing in adjacent waters is an important occupation and furnishes a wide range of sea foods for the populace.

Brindisi (32,000) is a city and port far out on the "heel" of Italy. Its importance attaches to the fact that this port is the meeting place of the land and water parts of the route from the Atlantic nations to the East. It is a place for transfer of goods from land to water or the reverse. In a way it competes with Venice and even with Marseilles, for the journey can be made to Paris or the Low Countries more quickly by making the change at Brindisi, and with less risk of loss on the storm-tossed seas. The harbor is fairly good, and through it pass large quantities of freight, mail and express, and not a few passengers. It has little to fear from stream deposits and will remain good as improvements are made upon it.

Trieste (261,000), the only city on the little Free Territory of Trieste, by virtue of position has been much before the public in recent years. It has a deep, commodious harbor, rail communications with easy grades to Laibach (*Ljubljana*) where the route divides and goes to Vienna over Semmering Pass and to Belgrade down the Save Valley. Easy rail connection with Venice and the Po Valley add to its importance. The city is in the midst of rich plains and has most of the advantages of Venice with far superior harbor facilities, but less historical significance and wealth. Trieste is really of more commercial value to cities in Germany, Austria, and

The harbor in the Bay of Naples. Vesuvius shows in the upper right corner. (By Ewing Galloway, N.Y.)

Hungary which are short on maritime outlets south than it is to either Italy or Yugoslavia.

If a free city, Trieste can serve Italy and Yugoslavia easily as well as interior cities north and east over the Pear Tree Pass in the Julian Alps. Yugoslavia has Fiume and Susak behind Trieste on another bay. Italy has Venice as much at the head of the Adriatic as is Trieste. On historic grounds Italy has interest in Fiume as well as in Trieste.

Building, architecture, art. Fortunately, and for several reasons, Italian building has been very much in stone. From the rude, conical stone houses in southeast rural Italy where common loose stone is a burden on the land, to St. Peter's in Rome; from the Roman roads and walled cities built centuries before Christ to the latest university or museum buildings, the people of Italy have built their structures of stone. It is abundant, widely distributed, easily obtained, and much more durable than wood, which for at least 2,000 years has been scarce in Italy. Materials used in Rome range from tuff in red and black to marble in many colors, serpentine, alabaster, granite, and basalt. Tuff, consisting of volcanic ejecta cemented into more or less resistant rock, coarse or fine, and in many colors, finds its place in much foundation and rough work. Lava, the congealed or frozen rock that once flowed, makes excellent paving blocks.

Pozzolana, or volcanic ash, for 2,000 years has been made into very strong Roman cement. Bricks, both sun-dried and kiln-dried, have been made from residual and alluvial clays. Marble, both local and foreign, began to be used near Rome centuries before Christ and travertine at least 100 years before our era. These are used freely around Rome, and, while all are found locally, marble in particular has been imported in prodigious variety and quantities.

The abundance of so many kinds of stone found in all parts of the country, coupled with the scarcity of wood and metals, has led the people to build much more in stone than have the Finns, Swiss, and many others, whose building materials are largely wood. Cement, run in wooden molds, is quite common and very durable. Facings of handsome rock over brick or cement are frequently used and plaster or stucco is spread over the walls of cheaper materials and occasionally over marble. The common building material, however, is marble supplemented with granite. It need not have taken builders long to discover the relative permanence of buildings of the dense crystalline rocks and the inability of the elements in Italian climate to destroy them. Nor did they fail to understand the ease with which marble could be intricately fashioned. Marine corals are freely used for cameos, beads, and ornaments. Art in stone—sculpture—is highly developed, and Michelangelo has been accompanied and followed by a large group of sculptors both famous and obscure. Thus lack of wood, abundance of stone, ease of working, beauty, and permanence all seem to have been factors conducive to the extensive use the Romans made of marble through their whole history and generally over their whole land. Italy is able to export a large variety and considerable amount of marble.

Social status, education, and religion. While material civilization came early and has gone far in Italy, the spiritual culture of modern Italy has been considerably retarded. Large portions of the population are 50 to 70 per cent illiterate. These are in the backward southern third. The middle portion usually has 25 to 50 per cent who cannot read and write. The Po Valley is mostly 75 to 90 per cent literate. Contact with other nations, a more stimulating climate, and a different blood, as described above, all may have been factors in the high degree of literacy there. It cannot be signifi-

Square of St. Mark's, Venice. The Doge's palace is in the distance. (Courtesy National Organization for the Tourist Industry)

cantly a matter of religion, for the same religion, Roman Catholic, prevails everywhere. Emigration to the United States has been primarily from southern Italy with a high illiteracy.

Italy's life has been spent in the middle Mediterranean atmosphere. Twice from Rome Italy has ruled the known world, once by Roman law, once by the Roman Catholic religion. Today Italy is the residual legatee of Romanism. Custodian of the arts in medieval days, it kindled Europe with the ancient learning and beauty during the Renaissance. The Reformation scarcely reached the Italians, and had influence diminishing toward the south with the increasing distance from its German origin. For centuries

Italy's position in commerce and trade was that of the middleman between Europe and the East. Beggared of this source of wealth by the opening of the sea route round Africa, then stimulated anew by the Suez Canal and the transalpine railroad tunnels, and stripped of its isolation by the evolution of the steamship, today Italy faces a new opportunity in the airplane and radio routes over its borders. No country, let alone one situated as is Italy, can, in modern times, be outside of international affairs.

QUESTIONS

1. Discuss factors tending to make north Italy much more intensely agricultural and more industrial than the southern part. Climate, race, resources, density of population, sources of power?

2. How can Italy prosper without colonies? Why has she needed them? Discuss relative advantages of colonies and free trade with other lands.

3. How much better would it have been for the early people of Italy if the little plains had been among the mountains instead of along the coasts?

4. "All the world is heir of the Mediterranean, all the world is her debtor." Discuss.

5. Would Italy have been better off had the land that foundered to make the Tyrrhenian Sea remained above sea level as a part of modern Italy?

6. Why does Italy, and why can Italy, have two-story agriculture?

7. Why is Italy less self-sufficient today than over seventy years ago, when modern Italy was organized?

8. Why is Milan larger than Turin? Genoa than Venice? Naples than Palermo?

BIBLIOGRAPHY

ALMAGIA, Roberto, "The Repopulation of the Roman Campagna," *Geographical Review,* Vol. 19 (April, 1929), pp. 218-233.

BLANCHARD, W. O., "Malaria as a Factor in Italy," *Transactions Illinois State Academy of Science,* Vol. 21 (1928), pp. 344-351.

———, and VISHER, S. S., *Economic Georgraphy of Europe* (New York, McGraw-Hill Book Company, Inc., 1931).

BROOKS, L., *Regional Geography of the World* (London, University of London Press, 1927).

BUCHAN, John, *Italy: Nations of Today Series* (Boston, Houghton Mifflin Company, 1923).

CAETANI, Gelasio, "Redemption of the Pontine Marshes," *National Geographic Magazine,* Vol. 66 (July, 1934), pp. 201-217.

CANDEE, H. C., "Life's Pattern on the Italian Riviera," *National Geographic Magazine,* Vol. 67 (January, 1935), pp. 67-100.

CHATER, Melville, "Hunting Castles in Italy," *National Geographic Magazine,* Vol. 68, (September, 1935), pp. 329-366.

CIPPICO, A., *Italy, the Central Problem of the Mediterranean* (New Haven, Yale University Press, 1926).

COON, Carleton S., *The Races of Europe* (New York, The Macmillan Company, 1939).

COPP, Philip M., *Italy's Food in War and Peace,* Foreign Commerce Weekly, XII, No. 9, 1943, U. S. Dept. of Commerce (Washington, D.C., Government Printing Office).

DIETRICH, B. F. A., "The Italian Harbors on the Adriatic Sea," *Economic Geography*, Vol. 7 (April, 1931), pp. 202-209.

DOMINIAN, Leon, *Frontiers of Language and Nationality in Europe* (New York, Henry Holt & Company, Inc., 1917).

FITZGERALD, Walter, *The New Europe* (New York, Harper and Brothers, 1946).

FODOR, Eugene, ed., *Italy in 1951* (London, David McKay Company, 1951).

FROST, R. S., "Reclamation of the Pontine Marshes," *Geographical Review*, Vol. 24 (October, 1934), pp. 584-595.

GRAVES, C., *Italy Revisited* (Toronto, Ryerson Press, 1950).

LEPRETTE, Jacques, *Le Statut International de Trieste* (Paris, Pedone, 1949).

LEVI, Doro, "Sardinia, Isle of Antitheses," *Geographical Review*, Vol. 33 (1943), pp. 630-654.

LOBECK, A. K., "Physiographic Diagram of Europe" (New York, Geographical Press, Columbia University).

LYDE, L. W., *Peninsular Europe* (New York, Longmans, Green & Company, 1931).

MORE, Jasper, *The Land of Italy* (New York, Batsford, 1949).

NEWBIGIN, Marion I., *Mediterranean Lands* (London, Christophers, 1924).

Office of War Information, *Italy's Economy, The Situation Now*, Foreign Commerce Weekly, XVII, No. 8, U. S. Dept. of Commerce (Washington, D. C., Government Printing Office, 1944).

PEARCY, G. E., and FIFIELD, Russell H., *et al., World Political Geography* (New York, Thomas Y. Crowell Company, 1948).

RANDALL-MCIVER, David, *Greek Cities in Italy and Sicily* (Oxford, Clarendon Press, 1931).

————, *Italy before Romans* (Oxford, Clarendon Press, 1928).

RAVA, Carla, *All About Italy,* New Europe Guide Series (New York, Duell, Sloan, and Pearce, 1950).

RIPLEY, W. Z., *Races of Europe* (New York, D. Appleton and Co., 1899).

SEMPLE, Ellen C., *Geography of the Mediterranean Region* (New York, Henry Holt & Company, Inc., 1931).

SFORZA, Carlo, *Real Italians* (New York, Columbia University Press, 1942).

SION, J., "Italy," in Vidal de La Blache and Gallois, *Géographie Universelle* (Paris, Lib. Armand Colin, 1934).

STURZO, *Italy and the Coming World* trans. by B. B. Carter (New York, The Roy Publishers, 1945).

SULLAM, Victor E., *Fundamentals of Italian Agriculture,* Foreign Agriculture, VII, No. 12, U. S. Dept. of Agriculture (Washington, D. C., Government Printing Office, 1943), p. 278.

————, *Recent Developments in Italian Agriculture,* Foreign Agriculture, IX, No. 5, U. S. Dept. of Agriculture (Washington, D. C., Government Printing Office, 1945).

TOSCHI, Umberto, "The Vatican City State from the Standpoint of Political Geography," *Geographical Review*, Vol. 21 (October, 1931), pp. 529-538.

UNGER, Leonard, "Economy of Free Territory of Trieste," *Geographical Review*, Vol. 37 (1947), pp. 583-608.

WELLES, Sumner, ed., *An Intelligent American's Guide to Peace, "Italy"* (New York, The Dryden Press, 1945).

WILSTACH, Paul, "The Stone Beehive Homes of the Italian Heel," *National Geographic Magazine*, Vol. 57 (February, 1930), pp. 229-260.

CHAPTER 9

Albania

Round about unto Illyricum.
—PAUL

Albania is one of the young states of Europe, although its people are of two old groups with an ancient language. North of the Shkumbi River are the Ghegs, descended from Illyrian tribes, and south the Tosks from Pelasgian tribes, two dialect groups who occupied the land before the Aryan tongues spread through the Mediterranean area. About two thirds are Moslems; about 200,000 are Orthodox Christians; and 100,000 Roman Catholics.

This state lies along the Adriatic Sea near the mouth, just where the heel of Italy, if it should move eastward 45 miles, would touch the Balkan peninsula. Extending north and south 195 miles with a width of 45 to 80 miles, it has an area of 10,630 square miles or a trifle more than Vermont. Recent estimates give a population of 1,175,000 to compare with 375,786 in Vermont. One wonders how the land of mountainous Albania can support an average of 100 persons per square mile. It is also difficult to see how so small a unit with a backward people can soon assume much significance, save as a pawn between more powerful, unscrupulous nations.

Geology. Albania is as mountainous as Vermont, but its mountains are young and rugged in form, and the mountains of Vermont are old and subdued. In Albania almost all the rocks are Mesozoic and Tertiary sandstones, shales, and limestones; in Vermont almost all the rocks except glacial drift and alluvium are of Paleozoic age. The grain or structure of Albania is in the main north-northwest by south-southeast. Tertiary rocks, moderately folded and not very resistant, extend from Scutari to Greece and occupy about one third of the country. Basic igneous rocks, in great areas well serpentinized, monopolize the region east of the Tertiary belt, whereas later rocks and lower topography make up the western portion.

The Dalmatian coastlands in general have been deeply but only youthfully dissected and then in relatively recent times submerged sufficiently to permit the sea to enter valleys and make long, narrow bays with peninsulas and islands extending chiefly along the structure. The depression north of Albania was so recent that almost no deposition has occurred since; but it

175

was earlier in Albania, where most of the bays have been filled and islands knit to the mainland with recent deposits. There is here a physical difference, a physical basis for Albanian independence. Nearly a score of small islands in the Scutari region protrude through large areas of fans and deltas built by recent streams and graded to present sea level. Delta and filled-bay deposits continue along the coast and back into the country up the Ishm River to Tirana. The rivers Arzen and Mati and many lesser streams have built a compound delta between former islands.

The old Greek and Roman town Dyrrhachium (now Durazzo) was built on an island separated from the mainland by two miles of open sea. The island is now tied to the mainland by sandbars and marshy delta deposits. South of the Bay of Durazzo in Roman times lay three long islands continuous with the structure that makes the Durazzo Island. These reached to the Semen River, which, with the Shkumbi, has brought out waste and completely filled the straits between these islands and the mainland so that Kavaia, once on a shore near the hills, is now on the edge of a plain. Further, these streams now flow between the former islands, having built deltas beyond them in the borders of the Adriatic. Once the Vijose and smaller Shushice entered the head of a long bay separately, but recently they have filled the bay, united, and built a delta eight to ten miles into the sea. Sandbars extend from this delta southward and tie small islands together and to the mainland, but Valona Bay as yet has scarcely begun to fill.

The result of all this recent, extensive, and active deposition of waste, brought down from the rugged lofty interior, is a series of large, marshy, mosquito-infested, muddy or sandy plains, at present of small value but capable of magnificent agricultural development in the hands of a people like the Dutch of the Netherlands. In contrast with these low plains are several other plains among the highlands, for example, the plain of Elbasan, which seems to be alluvial and may have been built in a lake by the Shkumbi and Devoll rivers. Its surface stands now 150 to 350 feet above the sea. The plain of Koritza is another filled basin, in part still occupied by a small relic lake and marsh but in part well drained by the Devoll and its branches.

In the geologic events of Albania there has been little mineralization, and therefore the people have few metallic resources. Copper ores are known in several places, and mines in the mountains of the north were exporting copper a few years ago at the rate of 40,000 tons per annum. These mines produced also sulphur and nickel. Sulphur ores, apparently sulphides, are opened in two places and known in one or two others. Nickel, chromium, iron, arsenic, and gold are known sparingly; none are considered to be present in workable quantities. Asphalt stringers and small bodies have been opened in several places in the southwest, and a small production (5,000 tons a year) has resulted. Gypsum is found in sandy clays of late Tertiary age near Valona. No localities are worked. Lignitic Tertiary coal is known in several outcrops near Koritza and is worked in a few small mines. Oil and gas have been sought in many places, since seepages and the asphalt stringers suggest their presence. A pipe-line from Petrolia nearly 50 miles inland delivers enough oil to ships at Valona to rank Albania sixth among European producers. Practically all knowledge of mineral values in Albania is in the exploratory stage.

Climate. The varied topography and great meridian length of Albania are reflected in much diversity of climate. Southern coastal lowlands and terraced slopes have typical Mediterranean conditions and crops—summer drought, accentuated by high summer temperatures with scrub oak, drought-resisting evergreens, olives, grapes, melons, and wheat. Forty inches of rainfall in the central and northern lowlands, much more evenly distributed through the year, bespeaks a more varied agriculture in which maize for local consumption is the most important crop. Up the slopes both bush and tree fruits abound. Everyone has plums and cherries, many have grapes and apples. In the low, warm, fertile, irrigable valley of Elbasan, oranges, lemons, and pomegranates ripen. The higher slopes invite winter snows, more rainfall, and an approach to mountain climate, with mixed forests, temperate grasslands, and vegetables, especially over recent glacial forms. The lower lands are suitable for cultivation of corn, wheat, barley, flax, rice, tobacco, and, in the south, cotton. Eagles and other mountain birds, wolves, bear, wild boar, and several kinds of deer make hunting possible and worth while. Furs are gathered in the mountains and with sheepskins add much to the picturesqueness of men's attire. On rainy days the latter are worn with the wool inside.

Natural regions. Six physical regions may be recognized.

1. A rough, youthful, mountainous country extends from the northern frontier southward to the Osum River and reaches east to the Yugoslav boundary. It occupies nearly half the area of Albania. In the north, forests of oak, walnut, chestnut, elm, plane, pine and fir dominate the upper slopes with sheep raising over lower slopes and primitive agriculture in the valleys of the Drin and its branches. Because of isolation a tribal régime still persists. In the middle section, where two rivers assist in moving the cut, lumbering is more extensively practised. The copper mines are in this section, and both sulphide ores for sulphur and serpentine rocks for ornamental stone are worked. The southern part of this mountain belt is drained by the Shkumbi and Devoll rivers; the former has cut deeply into the serpentine rock; the latter has exposed good limestone and sandstone which are but little used because building material is obtained more readily from the forests. Although these mountains are easily accessible along the river valleys, they are largely pastoral. Valleys and lower slopes contain many villages and single houses located near springs and streams and sheltering farmers engaged in fixed agriculture.

2. In the southeast are several intermontane basins. Lake Ochrida occupies one, and parts of its floor are water-free, displaying good agricultural

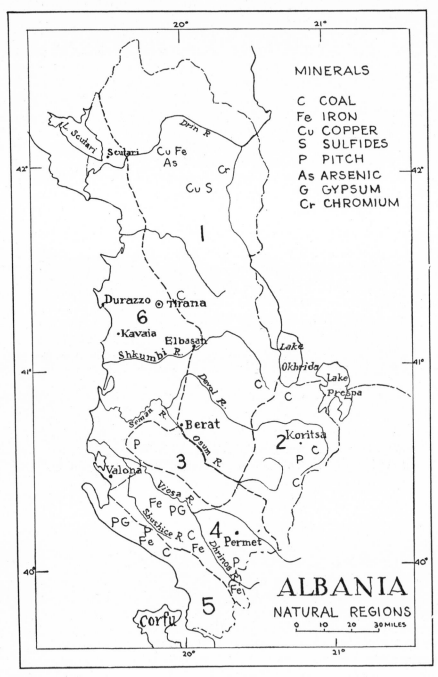

MINERALS

C COAL
Fe IRON
Cu COPPER
S SULFIDES
P PITCH
As ARSENIC
G GYPSUM
Cr CHROMIUM

ALBANIA
NATURAL REGIONS

0 10 20 30 MILES

Mineral resources and geographic regions of Albania. Mineral occurrences are shown by initials, regional boundaries by dash lines. Arabic numbers correspond with descriptions in text. (Compiled from Nowack's and Almagia's maps and other sources)

lands. Koritza is nearly central in a basin of about 60 square miles whose level floor is choice, cultivable land. Two small appendages to this basin are equally good. Farther south is Kolonia, floored with red gravelly deposits. So valuable are the soils and so attractive the location of these basins surrounded by mountains and possessing easy commercial outlets to adjacent Greece that they have a population density of about 200 to a square mile, with only a fraction as many people in the surrounding mountains. A colony of Vlachs occupies some of the mountains.

3. Between the Osum and Viosa rivers stretches a hilly, clayey strip of moderate fertility. Rural population is collected into compacted villages, whose inhabitants go out to work their little farms in the morning and return at night. A population density of about 50 to 60 per square mile corresponds to the moderate resources and opportunity.

Berat, situated in young mountains. Tomori in the distance is the loftiest peak in Albania and is cloud-capped. It is a fabled residence of the gods.

4. The basin of the Viosa and Dhrinos rivers constitutes the southern interior mountains. Its connection and open communications toward Valona attract a rural population of 135 per square mile, most of whom engage in the Mediterranean type of land culture.

5. Along the south frontier a limestone karst belt of hills and valleys with forbidding shoreline terminates northwest in a rocky headland, and trends southeast along the coast to Greece. A good harbor at Santa Quaranta serves this region and two or three times as large a portion of Greece. Villages tucked into sheltering valleys or well up the slopes of this rough country house many people. Near the coast there are lowlands, swampy, malarial, or lacking in rainfall. Valona and its harbor lie north of the west end of the area; beyond the western headland, the island of Sareno, fortified

by Italy some years ago, is now a part of Albania and defends the Valona port. Sheep and the usual Mediterranean crops, fruits, and vegetables make up the subsistence basis for the area.

6. Along the Albanian coast from Scutari to Valona is a belt, varying in width, of delta and coastal plains, hills and marshes. In the north, it has the Drin and Lake Scutari with the harbor city, Scutari, on its shores. So valuable an area is this northern section that its ownership has been hotly contested with Yugoslavia. Logically and racially it is Albanian.

The people do much sea and lake fishing; they are actively interested in their neighbors and possess a highway, not much developed, up the Drin and over the divide to the Vardar Valley and Skoplje, a valley and city with a railroad. These connections are of inestimable value in broadening the contacts and interests of Scutarians.

Permet, a town of central Albania in an open valley of older mountains.

The coast lowlands continue southward and broaden to accommodate Tirana, the capital, and Elbasan in a higher basin. On the coast is the chief Albanian seaport, Durazzo, which has an airport reached by several lines. South of Tirana is Kavaia, a thriving pottery and educational center. More than 200 people per square mile, kindled by opportunity for agricultural and industrial progress, reside in this region, a section well able to support so many inhabitants. Via Egnatia, still in use though rough, led up through this region in Roman times, followed the Shkumbi, rounded Ochrida and on to Salonika, and like the similar modern route helped to form an open-minded, more highly civilized people in the midst of the country.

Continuing the plains southward from the Shkumbi to Valona are filled bays and deltas with a more distinctly Mediterranean climate and therefore large agricultural possibilities; but, because of the variable régime of the rivers whose floods often spread loads of waste over great areas, the agricultural and economic environment is far below that which a strong engineering program could make of it. Also malaria must yet be conquered in these ill-drained lands. Sedentary population is scarce, but mountain sheep-grazers winter here, and a few large estates still persist.

History. Albanians pride themselves on a long descent. Their pre-Aryan language and their clan and feud customs suggest that their pride may be well founded; but because they occupy a land so near other great peoples, the latter have been scattered among them. Greeks, Romans, Normans, Slavs, Turks, and Italians in turn have made contributions to their race, language, social organization, and religion without assimilating them. Al-

Valona, on the southern coast of Albania. This town is the Avalona of Italian literature. It is hemmed in by mountains on the land side.

though Moslem influence spread a feeble government over all the country and gave religion to more than half the people, it permitted Norman feudalism to develop and clannish feuds to flourish. Mohammedan rule forced isolation upon the people and gave them little but stagnation for 500 years. In spite of many unusual opportunities to learn the arts and sciences in pottery, sculpture, and road-building, the Albanians themselves have stoutly resisted outside influences and remain racially intact. This keen resistance is illustrated by colonies of Albanians which, established under Turkish pressure in Egypt, Greece, and Italy hundreds of years ago, still persist almost pure. Herein lies a group of reasons for the present existence of an independent Albanian nation.

National entity is also favored by position. Jealousies of Yugoslav, Greek, and Italian make excellent reasons for a weak but independent buffer state. All three peoples have desired this area. Venice of old often had its coast. Yugoslavia wants to absorb it, and thus have access to the sea. Through Albania and its ports, Scutari, Durazzo, and Valona, run the best routes into western Balkan country. Uskub and Monastir each has a road out through Albania. A Slav outlet through Albania would prevent Italy from holding the whole Adriatic Sea. The troubles in Albania stirred up by both neighbors may be a measure of their relative interest in the little country. Greeks see Albania lying across one of their frontiers and covet a road west to the Adriatic. The present boundaries are usually drawn along divides, and from physiographic, ethnic, and language considerations they are about as satisfactorily placed as possible. Albanians would draw them 10 to 50 miles outside the present line to include all of their own people; but a very little expansion north of the lakes would take in more Yugoslavs than Albanians, as expansion south would incorporate more Greeks than Albanians. The only reasonable enlargement is to the northeast so as to include 500 to 600 square miles round Dyakova.

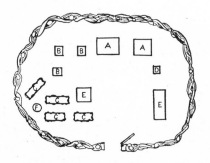

Albanian farmyard. The fence consists of posts driven into the ground, with brush woven among them. A, main houses; B, sleeping rooms of married men; C, barns for maize storage; D, dairy and milk house; E, cattle shelters; F, out-house. (From M. E. Durham, *High Albania* [Edward Arnold, London, 1909].)

Central Albania, where Turkish influence was able to overcome physical barriers and reach the people, is Moslem in creed. In this open and liberal section the Orthodox Church was corrupt and feeble and yielded easily. In the country northward, more open to Italy, the creed is Roman Catholic; but southward an inhospitable coast and valley open to Jannina and the Pindus Grecian country determined the dominance of the Orthodox Eastern Church. Religious freedom is, in practice as well as in law, universal.

Agriculture and industry. Albanians are agricultural, pastoral, patriotic. They hunt game for their own food but not for market; they fish a little but not half as much as their waters make worth while. Agriculture has been very crude, but new iron plows in large numbers have been imported recently and in some tracts have greatly changed local custom. Wheat from Albania meets most of the cereal needs of Dalmatians toward the north and though not a large crop is thus one of the national exports. Goats are far the commonest of livestock; sheep, poultry, and cattle follow. Fences, usually of the most convenient brush, are built only to prevent sheep from wandering.

Most Albanians are self-contained and willing to live on what they themselves can wrest from nature and, except for their pastoral migrations, abide practically in one place. Road-building is difficult and expensive. Beset with these obstacles and favored with little desire and use for roads, the people have been slow to construct highways. A road leads from Durazzo to Tirana, and roads radiate from the capital. One leads to Scutari, one past Kavaia to Elbasan and Koritza. Three radiate from Koritza, one of which leads through Greece to Salonika, a route followed by the Romans 2,000 years ago to connect the east and west empires. No railroads exist in the country except for some narrow-gauge lines left from World War I. Roads radiate from Tirana for political and commercial reasons, but also because topography invites them.

Industry is very restricted and rarely gets beyond the preparing of local products for local use as food, clothing, or building materials. There are no cities, and outside of the Durazzo-Tirana plains, Koritza and Elbasan in their own plains, and Scutari and Valona on their own harbors there is little else than villages, but of them more than 2,500 have been counted. The towns named are well located with reference to geographic advantage, and most of the villages are adjusted to slope, to water, and to convenience in working the soil.

Economic status. Albanian exports seem as difficult to increase as those of any nation, but imports showed a steady gain until World War II, and are now again increasing. The country imports cotton and cotton goods, corn and farm machinery; and exports cheese, wool, hides, cattle, petroleum, lumber, and copper ore. The U.S.S.R. is now believed to be giving economic aid to Albania, probably to annoy Tito and to court Greece. In 1946 the Constituent Assembly proclaimed the country a Republic which still continues five years after. The Assembly is communist-controlled.

The people hope to make theirs a tourist land. Truly there is quite enough in people, costumes and scenery to attract sight-seeing travelers, but unfortunately there are few roads from coast to mountains. Romans, centuries ago, erected baths at the hot mud springs of Elbasan, and a modern ambition of Albanians is to restore these to their former prestige. If the number of tourists should soon become what the scenery deserves, there would be trouble for the natives in providing food, shelter, and transportation for them.

QUESTIONS

1. What alliances would be most beneficial for Albania? on political grounds? on economic grounds? What do you think would be easy pitfalls for Albania?

2. Summarize reasons for independence.

3. Summarize elements of unity.

4. What are some of the most needed improvements? Discuss steps and means of getting them.

5. What lines are open for future development?

6. How could progress be best attained? What place has language as a means of expressing one's nationalism? Discuss.

BIBLIOGRAPHY

ALMAGIA, Roberto, "Modern Albania, a Review,' *Geographical Review,* Vol. 22 (July, 1932), pp. 464-473.

BLANCHARD, W. O., and VISHER, S. S., *Economic Geography of Europe* (New York, McGraw-Hill Book Company, Inc., 1931).

BOWMAN, Isaiah, *The New World* (Yonkers-on-Hudson, New York, World Book Company, 1921).

CHATER, Melville, "Europe's Newest Kingdom," *National Geographic Magazine,* Vol. 59 (1931), pp. 131-190.

CHEKREZI, C. A., *Albania, Past and Present* (New York, The Macmillan Company, 1919).

COON, Carleton S., *The Races of Europe* (New York, The Macmillan Company, 1939).

COURTADE, Pierre, *L'Albanie* (Paris, Éditions Sociales, 1950).

DAKO, Christo A., *Albania, the Master Key to the Near East* (Boston, E. L. Grimes Company, 1919).

DOMINIAN, Leon, *Frontiers of Language and Nationality in Europe* (New York, Henry Holt & Company, Inc., 1921).

DURHAM, M. E., *High Albania* (London, Edward Arnold & Co., 1909).

Europa, Encyclopedia of Europe (London, Europa Publications, Ltd.), annual.

FITZGERALD, Walter, *The New Europe* (New York, Harper and Brothers, 1946).

HALL, H. Duncan, "Zones of the International Frontier," *Geographical Review,* Vol. 38 (1948), pp. 615-625.

HUBBARD, George D., "Albania in 1931," *Bulletin Geographic Society of Philadelphia,* Vol. 30 (1932), pp. 17-35.

International Year Book of Agricultural Statistics (Rome, Printing Office, International Institute of Agriculture, 1947), annual.

MCCORMICK, Thomas C. T., ed., *Problems of a Post-War World* (New York, McGraw-Hill Book Company, Inc., 1945).

NEWMAN, Bernard, *The New Europe* (New York, The Macmillan Company, 1943).

NOWACK, Ernest A., "Contributions to the Geography of Albania," *Geographical Review,* Vol. 11 (1921), pp. 503-540.

ROUCEK, Joseph S., "Economic Conditions in Albania," *Economic Geography,* Vol. 23 (1933), pp. 256-265.

SCHEVILL, Ferdinand, *History of the Balkan Peninsula,* 5th ed. (New York, Harcourt, Brace & Company, Inc., 1947).

STICKNEY, E. P., *Southern Albania and Northern Epirus in European International Affairs* (Palo Alto, California, Stanford University, 1926).

SWIRE, John, *Albania, the Rise of the Kingdom* (London, Williams & Norgate, Ltd., 1929).

WOODS, H. C., "Albania and the Albanians," *Geographical Review,* Vol. 5 (1918), pp. 359-373.

CHAPTER 10

Greece

The isles of Greece! the isles of Greece!
Where burning Sappho loved and sung,
Where grew the arts of war and peace,
Where Delos rose, and Phoebus sprung!
—BYRON

A land of peninsulas and islands. Two main systems of mountain structure are responsible for the Balkan Peninsula from Uskub and Scutari southeastward to the tips of the Peloponnesus, Crete, and the Cyclades Islands. The eastern system, including the great and classic Olympus and Cyclades, consists largely of ancient crystalline rocks and extends eastward into Asia Minor. The western system exposes mostly younger rocks in Albania, western Greece, the Peloponnesus, and Crete. Khalkidyke, the fingered peninsula southeast of Salonika, is of ancient rock similar to that in Olympus, and its structures seem to continue in some of the islands of the Ægean Sea. These folded mountain structures were carved by streams, reduced to advanced maturity, and then warped down so completely that none of the deposits made by the carving streams are above the sea. In fact, in the Ægean portion only mountain tops show above the water, while in the peninsular part the sea enters between long, ragged arms or fingers of land, once mountain ridges, to produce bays, gulfs, and islands. The Ægean differs from the Tyrrhenian Sea, made by the dropping of a fault block wholly beneath the sea, for its area was warped down so as to make peninsulas on the margins and islands from mountain tops in the sea. Subsequent moderate erosion has furnished material for aggrading many tiny plains and building little deltas at bay heads. These processes have thus given a type of country admirably adapted to the development of the numerous small, independent city states of old, whose best means of communication was by sea. No other place in Europe is half as inviting for this type of civilization. The topography would make cultural unity difficult even today were it not for the modern efficient means of communication.

Position, boundaries. Greece today includes most of the land, except certain Asiatic shorelines, that has ever been truly Grecian. It has water boundaries everywhere except on the north and northeast, where Albania,

Yugoslavia, Bulgaria, and European Turkey rest along its frontiers. Occupying the eastern peninsula of Europe, it has been in close contact with the ancient Near East peoples and has thereby had many opportunities for commercial, social, religious, and military experiences little known by western Europe. "As iron sharpeneth iron," so nation has stimulated na-

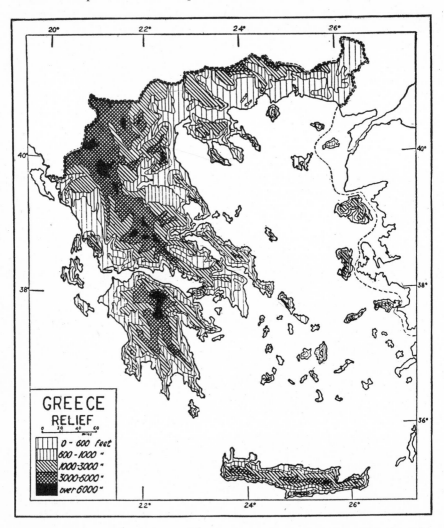

Relief detail of Greece is here shown by different rulings. The course of national boundaries among the islands is shown by a dash line on the right. (Adapted from *Oxford Advanced Atlas*)

tion in this east Mediterranean country, until no other place on earth has produced such a rare series and combination of cultures as this.

During World War II Greece, because of her location, was run over by both forces desiring the command of the eastern Mediterranean, and the subsequent civil war was a logical result. Long in contact with the west and hemmed in on the north by the Balkan mountains, she is sympathetic with democracy. Her city-state history no doubt contributed to this tendency.

Moreover, Greece is on the commercial route for southern Russia through the Black Sea and Dardanelles to the Mediterranean. As the U.S.S.R. has risen to world position and its water travel has gained in importance, the Soviet Union has manifested a growing interest in Greece, the gatekeeper. But Greece is also on the British-French highway from west to east, a route of vital interest to both nations and of more than passing concern to all western Europe and the United States. Here is a setting for a buffer state and light on an alignment different from that of other Balkan states.

The nine physical regions. With modern means of travel and communication a surprising homogeneity quickly appears in Greece, for each tiny place is a repetition of many others. But for historic, descriptive, and utilization purposes it is best to divide the present national domain of over 49,000 square miles into nine units, each with more or less definite characteristics.

1. Epirus, coinciding in large part with the ancient state of the same name, is a mountainous, embayed area of mainland and the Ionian Islands. The mild marine climate of the latter produces grapes, wine, citrus fruits, and vegetables; their position promotes a seafaring, commercial life. The population is three to six times as dense as that of the mainland. Old Epirus is pasture and forest, but with some space for wheat and olives. Goats and sheep are herded over its hills and mountains all summer and fed local hay in the valleys in winter. Seasonal migration of flocks is for short distances only, but helps to cement and unify the people.

The island of Corfu belongs with Epirus. Northern Epirus has recently been claimed by Albania because of its many Albanian inhabitants, but probably it will remain as before with Greece.

2. The Pindus-Parnassus mountain belt lies east of Epirus and is the most rugged, sparsely populated portion of Greece. It contains the main tribes of the Vlachs, who because of the character of the country are nomad shepherds or carriers. Because of isolation a patriarchal régime still persists. The best oak-chestnut-conifer forests of Greece, covering large areas of the Pindus range, are so isolated as to make lumber harvesting difficult.

3. The Peloponnesus, though wholly mountainous, is nowhere so lofty as parts of the Pindus. Its northern shores, like the Ionian Islands, produce in great abundance the sturdy little grapevine which yields the small dried "currant" of commerce. The western half is more than twice as populous as the eastern because it has much more of plains and lowlands. It produces figs, grapes for wine, and citrus fruits in its warm, marine climate. The eastern part, being rough, stony, and thin-soiled, is a wool and goat-

skin country. Communication and penetration of ideas are so difficult in many patches that well-adjusted patriarchal social patterns still persist. The second forest area of Greece crowns the central mountains of the Peloponnesus.

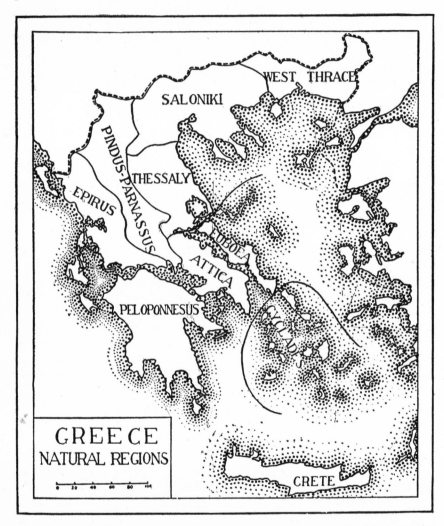

Physical or geographic regions of Greece. Boundary lines are generalized; scale is in miles. (Constructed from geologic, physiographic, and historic maps)

4. The Cyclades, so named because they are disposed more or less concentrically around the sacred island of Delos, and the Sporades ("Scattered"), both northern and southern, comprise about 300 islands, most of which belong to Greece. Since World War II the return of the Dodecanese Islands with a dominant Greek population to Greece has increased her

responsibility and perhaps her security, but added only about 1,000 square miles to her area. Syra, near Delos, and others were the sites of famous early city states and civilizations. Their location in the warm seas enables their numerous industrious people to raise figs, and their ancient crystalline rocks supply fine marble and quantities of emery.

5. Crete is a long, old, hill island which half closes the Ægean on the south. Its position midway between Greece and the Orient made it a mediary between their cultures and fostered on the island 5,000 years ago the glorious, surprising Minoan culture. Minoan ruins long lost to human knowledge now constitute its chief modern interest. From a productive standpoint it is too dry for a goat pasture.

6. Attica and Eubœa are grouped in one section, though the former is the most densely peopled and the latter nearly the least inhabited part of Greece. Attica has many small plains, cut off from each other by sea or mountain, on which numbers of city states developed, among them Athens. It has more places of historic interest and more monuments of ancient architecture than any other equal area. The cotton-growing lands stretch over its rolling northern portion. Laurium, for lead, zinc, and silver, and Pentelicus, for splendid marble, have contributed no small item to the greatness of its cities. Eubœa is still connected with Attica over a narrow channel by a little bridge, first constructed thousands of years ago.

7. Thessaly, a plain with bordering mountains, is effectively separated from the Thessalonica Basin by the famous Olympus. Radiating from its central plain many small plains are pocketed among the mountain spurs, a very stimulating area for city states. For centuries this unit, full of busy towns and intelligent people, has made little contribution to the nation's activities, but recently the sugar-beet industry has taken root in its fertile soils. Wheat and maize and barley with cotton make a diversified agriculture.

8. Thessalonica Basin, with its city built by the "victor over Thessaly," has a population density of 175 per square mile, which is nearly twice the average for the country. A part of ancient Macedonia, it contains the largest plains in Greece. These were built as deltas by large rivers, and indicate that this part has not been recently submerged. These Mediterranean shore lands have been long occupied. For centuries they have been actively cultivated, but not intensively until the modern period.

9. West Thrace is the last and perhaps the least unified section. Its unity lies in its continued exposure to the northern Ægean and its uniform protection on the north by the Rhodope Mountains. A series of coastal and delta plains of great agricultural possibilities, it has become the center of the Turkish tobacco culture which exports much leaf to Egypt and Turkey. Grapes also grow well on these plains. The section is separated from Turkey by the Maritza and crossed by the Mesta and Struma rivers which come out from the Rhodopes.

Climate and natural vegetation. Although Greece is in latitude 40° N., its climate under marine influence partakes of one characteristic of the tropics. This is its vertical zoning: tropical from sea level to 500 feet, with figs, oranges, pomegranates, melons, olives, other evergreens, and palms; warm temperate for the next 3,000 feet, with oaks, chestnut, barley, wheat, and corn; cool temperate for 2,000 feet more, with pine, beech, and grazing lands, but with very little planting and plowing. Above 5,500 feet, one finds stunted Alpine trees, shrubs, and flowers, with much snow in severe winters. Northern winds sweep in and make the more continental

A finished section of the Koila-Skafidhi flood-control ditch, made with the aid of U.N. for a Greek village. (Courtesy Unations)

and higher parts very disagreeable for two or three months, while the lower southern parts have almost Sicilian winter. It never snows in Athens. Summer trade winds from African and Asian deserts are dry and often uncomfortably warm. The northern limit of citrus fruits on the mainland is 5° farther south than in France because of less mountain protection.

Rainfall is markedly seasonal in response to the annual migration of wind and rain belts. Greece has less than 1 inch of July precipitation, but in January the rainfall exceeds 4 inches along the Adriatic side, and only in west Thrace is there less than 2 inches. This explains the winter growth of barley, wheat, and many vegetables, and the summer ripening of grapes and citrus fruits. In general the climate is strictly Mediterranean and the vegetation a response thereto. Great local variations in precipitation in the rainy season are related to the sharp differences in relief.

Historical geography. It is not the design here to write a history of Greece but rather to suggest the geography of Grecian history. Strabo had discovered and written over 1,900 years ago that "the sea presses in upon

The ancient battlefield of Sparta, showing stony pasture in the foreground, timber (probably fruit trees), a village, and beyond the plains the mountain slopes. (Underwood and Underwood, N.Y.)

the country with a thousand arms" and ascribed much of the spirit of the people to this fact. No wonder the people were seafarers and traders. But the land too, reaching up in jagged mountain chains and rugged forest-clad summits, produced mountaineers and herdsmen who worshiped Pan.

Grote interpreted history to show that the story of the Greeks began in 776 B.C., but the interpretation of modern excavations has placed that beginning 3,000 years earlier. In the Ægean copper age, the Cyclades furnished many items for the Ægean trade. Useful minerals in these islands —obsidian of Melos for weapons and tools, marble of Paros and Naxos for buildings and ornaments, emery for polishing and grinding, copper for household utensils and ornaments from Naxos, and potter's clay of Seriphos for the making of vases and other vessels—furnished the basis of much of the early trade. So limited were the island agricultural resources that many villages had to trade for food. Prevailing winds, clear skies, little fog, daily land and sea breezes, and proximity of islands all encouraged navigation. So we find a maritime people evolving in the Ægean 3,000 or more years before Christ. Finding defense easier in the small unity of an island, they there initiated permanent residences and built their first cities. As bronze came into use, Cretan civilization rose on the Neolithic foundations of 10,000 years ago. So well placed was Crete between Egypt, lands east, and lands north that by about 2500 B.C. its people were able to build up a rich civilization and a notable city, Knossos, with waterworks, a sewage disposal system, paved roads, and a well-appointed and protected harbor. Knossos, such a town as modern rural Greece, Turkey, Egypt, or Palestine would not know how to use, flourished and was a joy to its citizens. It traded with Egypt and imitated Eastern art. This thousand years of development through the Bronze Age was followed by a decline, and the Mycenæan culture and civilization in towns of the Peloponnesus arose to flourish on trade over the same wonderful Mediterranean highways in the centuries between 1600 and 1200 B.C. Thus in these glorious heroic ages, the influence of the sea inviting men out for trade and the push of the mountains repelling men from easy achievement on the lands were just as potent as now. And the Greek and Greece were then in the making with the same spirit as now. Always the Greek has been a tradesman or a mountaineer, a lover of the soil or the sea, yet reaching the richest culture and civilization where he made large use of the water and touched elbows with other evolving people.

At some time between the Homeric Greece and the real historic Greece, Dorian conquerors and colonists came from the north into the Peloponnesus. They were certainly on a lower level of civilization than the inhabitants they overran, and the old civilization comes to an abrupt end at about the time ascribed to the Dorian invasion, 1100 B.C. This overturn has left its mark even to the present in the status of the peninsular people. They never rose to the heights of the Greeks in other places who were not thus displaced.

A maritime people, the Greeks were also a race who colonized to relieve the population pressure at home. Their ships crossed the Ægean and eastern Mediterranean in every direction; before 1500 B.C. there were colonies for trade in the peninsula of Troy, a most admirable place for a commercial center, on many islands, at many places along the eastern end of the Mediterranean, and in Egypt. The Greek never seems to have conquered inland, but that slow creeping of traders and colonists along coasts has led the Greek around the eastern Mediterranean, through the Bosporus, and along the shores of the Black Sea. During the centuries to 1000 B.C. there was also a large development of the race on the land that is now Greece. Along the coast to the Hellespont, at scores of places on the west coast of Asia Minor, in Italy, Sicily, and even in Spain, colonies were established.

No other nation probably ever colonized as systematically for trade, and few ever colonized as much without penetrating the inland districts. True Greeks rarely get beyond the odor of salt water. Since trade was the great purpose, it is fair to say that colonization by Greeks was very successful, keeping a steady stream of foods, slaves, and ideas coming to Greece, and sending Greek manufactures, art, and ideas to colonial lands and far beyond.

While the scope of Grecian trade was broadened, it was a great handicap to the Greeks to be so scattered. So far flung were the settlements, mainly along coasts, that when the Slavs came, spreading from the northeast, the Greeks could not resist successfully; not only were the boundaries of Greece contracted, but many Slavs came and dwelt among Greeks in truly Grecian territory. Then came the Turk, ruling and mingling with his subjects, until Greek blood was diluted, partly by Turk, more by Slav. Out of this wide scattering and the spreading of the Turk over Greece to govern and "improve" the country came the necessity, after World War I, of the exchange of nationals. Political lines were drawn and redrawn in attempts to put the boundaries where they would be pleasing to all concerned and provocative of the least friction. But after the boundaries had been placed as well as possible, many Greeks were outside them, while many Turks and not a few Albanians, Yugoslavs, and Bulgarians were inside. The present boundaries contain about all the land that ever was wholly Grecian, except large sections of the Anatolian coast zone, left under Turkish rule. On the whole they are satisfactory to Greece, but many factors converge on the problem and raise grave questions as to the ultimate wisdom of their present location, if border nations shall have justice. One might ask why Greeks with their maritime and commercial traditions, and their distribution as carriers, colonists, and traders throughout the shorelines mentioned above, are not as much entitled to the entire Ægean as Italy is to the entire Adriatic. Then on the other side of the question, note that Greece holds the commercial outlets from the Ægean by having Crete; the Vardar-Morava highway to and from central Europe by possessing Salonika, which is likewise the eastern outlet for Albania and Yugoslavia; and the outlet for Bulgaria by occupying the north Ægean coast. Fringe settlements are very awkward for the people of the interior.

Race, language, art, and religion. Modern Greece has a mixed people, yet they are distinctly a Mediterranean race, dark in a warm, sunny climate, short because underfed in a stingy country, and with a cephalic index of 76 to 80 except where Slav influence is strong enough to make heads rounder. Aryan languages spread from central western Asia to India and to Europe. The Greek is one of the oldest of these Aryan tongues, for it had not traveled far from the center of dispersion. Linguists find so much in the present Greek speech that has come directly from the classical Greek, both in words and in construction, that they feel sure the modern Greek is essentially a lineal descendant of the ancient.

Language difficulties in these Near Eastern states have come by virtue of their proximity and are illustrated in the modern railway. The familiar railway signs about leaning out, smoking, or spitting are inscribed in three languages on most Balkan cars, but in four on the Beograd-Salonika line: German and French for foreign travelers, Greek and Yugoslav for those living along the valleys traversed. The first two languages use the Roman alphabet, but the last two use Greek and Cyrillic letters. Balkan countries are bilingual or trilingual; some have even four or five languages in their markets and public places. No wonder the Rosetta Stone was inscribed in three languages.

Greek art, particularly sculpture and architecture, has its roots deep in the materials furnished by the land. An abundance of excellent marble and a scarcity of wood, metals, and fiber plants have all suggested working in stone. Long familiarity with the medium gave a superb technique; and the wealth of permanent art treasures in building, ornament, and monument testify to the extent of Greek response. Would the Parthenon have been without Pentelicus? Residual clays of fine texture made pottery possible, and a real ceramic art developed at an early date. Over 3,700 years ago at Knossos in Crete great amphoræ for oil and wine held seven gallons each, and much larger jars contained 25 bushels each of wheat, raisins, or beans in storage. Choice vases were produced near Athens, probably made of the high-grade clays long known near Phaleros Port. Such perfection of beauty was reached, and so long were the art treasures preserved that Keats writes

> O Attic shape! Fair attitude! with brede
> Of marble men and maidens over wrought,
> With forest branches and the trodden weed;
> Thou, silent form, dost tease us out of thought
> As doth eternity:

Minor art displayed itself in gold and bronze. The scarcity of gold no doubt inspired the search for the Golden Fleece. Amber used so effectively in Crete was of Baltic origin. Modern Greek art has never come near the older works any more than has philosophy, literature, and general scholarship, and probably for similar reasons. It has been suggested that the actinic rays of the sun and the other elements of a genial climate stimulated the early Greeks to high performance in many lines, but that the same conditions by overstimulating at length caused a collapse of Greek culture and civilization from which the race has never recovered.

Over most of Greece, proximity and ease of contact led Byzantine civilization in the 7th, 8th, and 9th centuries to predominate, but because of the older foundations upon which it built it was never at its best here. The lack of continuity of civilizations here is due to position on highways and nearness to invaders as well as to a lack, for many centuries, of a firm attachment to the soil. The older people were nomadic, military, commercial, and easily displaced, whereas the people in northwest Europe, for opposite reasons, generally developed a continuity of civilization. Types of civilization are both results of, and important factors in, the conditions of life and even the mental traits and character; they assist in the interpretation of all ethnologic phenomena, for they carry elements and ideas of government, of architecture, and of religion as well as of literature and intellectual life.

The Greek Orthodox Church claims the great majority of the people, and is at its best in Greece because here it developed most directly from the early Christian Church and has adhered most closely to the Byzantine or early type of the Near East.

Distribution of population; occupations. Fifty thousand square miles and 7,778,000 people give a mean distribution of 155 persons to each square mile, but four cities, Athens (393,000), Salonika (236,000), Piræus (284,000), and Patras (61,000) contain nearly one eighth of the people. A large area in western Peloponnesus and a similar one around Salonika sustain the populations of largest density, except for Attica, where a density of 300 to 400 is easily maintained. In all three districts the land is lower and more level than elsewhere, the soil in the main is fertile, and more intensive types of agriculture predominate. An area of sparsest population is the Pindus-Parnassus mountain section with a little less than 50 persons to the square mile. Corfu, Zante, and Chios vie with Attica; and all the larger islands have a density above the average for the whole country.

The solution of health problems made large progress between the world wars. The fight on malaria in the Vardar delta was the largest single project. Here 2 million acres were drained and dedicated to agriculture for exchange returning Greek refugees. Fifteen hundred villages were built here and in the other recovered areas in the Salonika back country. Throughout the Near East there is little modern scientific sanitation, sewage disposal, and combating of disease. Great improvements have been started, however, and the world as well as the local people has hopes of better conditions. There is nothing inherent in the geography of the Near East that should make it less healthful than other places in similar latitudes. Men must take advantage of drainage possibilities, of detergents that can be manufactured as well here as anywhere, and of disinfectants, quarantines, serums, fresh air, and outdoor constructive exercise.

Agriculture: leading crops. Agriculture engages about 60 per cent of the people; commerce and trade about 17 per cent; and industry nearly 9 per cent; all other occupations (fishing, lumbering, building, professions, services, and so on) support only 14 per cent. Almost 5,800,000 men, women, and children work, and about 1,900,000 are too young or too old to work. One deduction possible is that a very large percentage of the population engages in some form of labor. Such figures illustrate what is meant by an impoverished land.

Practically the whole population, even the farmers, live in towns and villages, a response to the danger of bandits outside the town wall. Cereals, of which wheat has nearly half and maize one sixth of the acreage, occupy over 71 per cent of all cultivated lands. Legumes, extensively grown for

Thanks to U.N., a Greek village is to have acres of reclaimed agricultural land. (Courtesy Unations)

feed and as a rotation crop, occupy about 6 per cent of the farm land; crops for industry and aromatic plants—cotton, tobacco, sesame, and others—occupy over 8 per cent; forage plants, 2.5 per cent; vineyards, including the currant grape, 11.75 per cent. Small fruits and vegetables are abundant crops. Olives grow best on dry, clayey, well-drained soils.

For centuries forests have struggled for a place, but only the higher and western slopes with sufficient summer rainfall can become forest-covered. Trees were cleared off for fuel, ships, and other uses; herds of sheep and goats, war, and fires have kept the young trees from reforesting the slopes, and consequently thousands of square miles that might be under forest are pastured or bare. Some effort is being made to replant. Zon and Sparhawk estimate that some 15 per cent of the country has forest and that about two thirds of the trees are pines. It is unfortunate that a land so well suited to forests should have to import much of its lumber. At present 80 per cent of the forest land is the property of the state, and an effective forestry code and system could well be put into force.

Sponge-fishing in the warm waters among the southeast peninsulas and islands furnishes employment to a group of families and provides an item of export. Greek sponge-fishers are also found working the sponge waters of other lands.

The Drimos quarry near the Salonika-Serres road. The machines are rock crushers, operated under the supervision of U.S. Army Engineers. (U.S. Army photograph)

Minerals. In Laurium are the mines of lead, zinc, and silver which have aided the civilization of Attica for at least 3,000 years. The copper for ancient bronze came from Cyprus and Eubœa. Both are moderate producers today. Iron ores in small quantities and good quality are mined in Bœotia, Eubœa, and Melos. Greece has no coal and little lignite, no oil or gas. Emery comes from Naxos. Chromium, nickel, and aluminum are also mined. In 1944 ore production was reported as 10,000 tons for aluminum, 15,000 tons for chromium and 4,000 for lead. Volcanic ash for cement and a good grade of magnesite in several eastern states and islands furnish rough building material; marble in finest qualities and abundance occurs in many places, particularly Hymettus and Pentelicus. Other good structural stone is found in many places in the eastern divisions and islands.

The meager and uncertain rainfall offers little encouragement for the development of water power, but in northern Greece there are several high-altitude lakes which might serve as reservoirs for power and irrigation. Domestic water supply is generally a problem. For Athens water is far more important than politics, and a system adequate for the city's needs has recently been established with an artificial reservoir at Marathon. Greece is rich in mineral waters because of recent volcanic and diastrophic activities. Such springs flow in southern slopes of Rhodopian mountains, and provide people with hot and cold running water in their homes.

Industries. Manufacturing is very limited and is based on agricultural and scanty mineral resources. The finest olives are made into oil and grapes into wine; currants are dried, wheat is ground, and many dainty confections are prepared; salt is made from the sea for home consumption; cotton (partly home-grown), wool, silk, and jute are spun and woven into domestic fabrics. The manufacture of carpets and rugs once carried on by Greeks in Anatolia is now transplanted by refugee Greeks to Salonika and towns about Athens. Soap, a few chemicals, turpentine, leather, and cigarettes are made from native raw products; white lead is produced incidentally in the roasting and smelting processes at Laurium; such building materials as stone, brick, glass, cement, lime, and lumber are prepared locally, but hardware is imported. Greece is not industrial.

Commerce local and foreign. Next to agriculture, commerce and trade are leading activities in Greece, and much of the movement of goods has always been by water. Connection between islands was and is still by water, and between the city states it was likewise by sea rather than over land. So easy was the water route that there was little incentive to build roads. Further, roads between cities would cut off one element of the protection so essential to their progress and security; hence, road building has not been encouraged until the days of railroads. The same topographic difficulties that checked road construction and encouraged isolation of towns and cities for the centuries past still make road and railroad construction and maintenance both expensive and difficult. Therefore internal communications are still sadly lacking, but improvement is continuous under the new régime. Every connection established adds a new cord to the mesh that is unifying the people, and every external connection, as with Monastir and Tirana, Adrianople and Istanbul, and through the Vardar-Morava Valley with the life and industry of central Europe, not only helps to develop the Greeks but broadens their internationalism. Better sea communications and extended air service are also significant. The new Greece has no chance to be as isolated and provincial, suspicious, and belligerent as the old.

Never has there been much trade between the cities and the interior, and lack of this intercourse has left inland villagers, herders, and farmers far behind their urban neighbors in vision and spirit. Since the cities have produced diverse supplies, they have traded with each other; and since vicinal countries, as Egypt, Phœnicia, Rumania, and Russia, not to mention central Europe, reached through the great river highway, have notably different climate and resources, the varied products have furnished the finest foundation for international trade.

Today tobacco from the Salonika and West Thrace sections is the largest export, two thirds of the total, going mostly to Turkey and Egypt. Dried currants from Ionian Islands and western Peloponnesus constituting over 15 per cent of the export go to the United States, Great Britain, and Germany. Wine and tropical fruits are next in importance. Imports are about

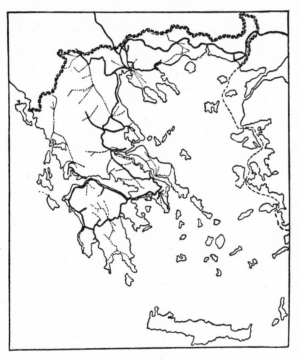

Greek railroads. Solid lines indicate main lines; dash lines are minor branches or connecting lines. Dash line in Aegean Sea marks Grecian boundary among the islands. Adopted from tourist advertising)

twice the value of exports.[1] Salt fish from Labrador comes to Patras in large quantities, despite the latter's fine marine location. In normal times Great Britain, United States, Germany, and France led the importing countries and furnished the manufactured articles, while Yugoslavia, Rumania, and Canada came next and furnished the foods. Exports amount to $75-80 million, and imports to about $140 million. Greeks in America make annual remittances to relatives or friends in Greece of about $40 mil-

[1] The largest items are wheat and other agricultural products, 25 per cent; metals and minerals, including machines, 20 per cent; textiles, nearly 20 per cent; and vehicles, 3 to 4 per cent.

lion. The balance of trade is greatly improved by such return of money to the homeland, by foreign freight carried in Grecian vessels, and by tourist trade. Greece had over 500 vessels in her merchant marine before World War II and replacement has reached 50 per cent.

Any country with as long a history of civilized peoples possessing such treasures in art and architecture as Greece may well plan for a tourist trade. Add to these records of the past the scenes of classic literature and philosophy, the scenery and climate, the quaint and interesting village life, the business, religion, and art of the present cities, and one must grant that the tourist will be well rewarded for many weeks of visiting. Then the winter resident coming from the severe cold of northern Europe finds in many parts salubrious and attractive climate. Fishing is a minor sport and capable of much expansion in the autumn and spring, especially in the northern lakes and streams; and hunting has some attractions. The forests and mountains contain pheasants, partridge, hare, deer of three or four species, wild cats, foxes, wolves, bears, and wild boars, a fine array. Mt. Olympus, a patch of wild unused scenery, is being set apart as a wild life preserve, national park, and public pleasure ground on American lines.

Cities. A land of cities and city states par excellence for ages, Greece was until a generation ago woefully lacking in anything resembling a modern city. Athens, Corinth, Larissa, Thessalonica, Patras, and Syra are names that have long been before the world. In the olden times a city must have two parts at least, *acro-polis* ("high city") and *agora* ("market" or "meeting place"). The high place was walled and secured against the enemy; the *agora* was the place where the residents met, bought and sold, conversed, taught, and played. Access to the sea was considered essential, but no city was built on the coast. Athens was four to five miles inland, and Corinth probably as far. Today the new Corinth touches the sea, and Piræus, the port of Athens, as well as Volo, the port of Larissa, are both at the water's edge. Neither port had any city life until very recently. Like Athens, the old Thessalonica was up the hills, walled and fortified, some two miles from the water, with two parallel walls running from the gate down to and across the plain until they reached the sea and boat landings. A tower by the sea still remains, but only scraps of the walls of the lane can be found.

Athens, with its port and suburbs, is growing rapidly and approaches the three-quarter million mark. Its Acropolis, holding the Parthenon and other ancient buildings, overlooks the city as well as the harbor. It was built for defense. The modern city lies north and east over old limestone topography and now extends to Old Phaleron and Piræus, both by the sea. It seems to have the most advantageous position for a city in all Greece: upon plain or low hills, but high enough to be above marsh and malaria; with plenty of room for a large modern metropolis, yet small enough to inspire and shelter early builders; near enough to the sea for commerce, yet distant enough to prevent pirates leaving their ships to pillage; with place for an excellent modern harbor; central in the old as well as the new east-facing Greece; easily connected overland with cities in the interior of Europe and easily reached by modern vessels. Long history in art and literature of the highest type make it a Mecca for scholars and tourists. It is at once the political, educational, religious, social, and economic center of the country.

Names of Greek towns, islands, mountains, and areas. (Adapted from historic and physical maps)

Both old and new Corinth are at the northwest end of the Corinthian canal, a straight artificial cut across the slender Peloponnesian neck. So great a barrier was this neck in olden times, and so fraught with storm and pirate dangers the route round, that ships were actually hauled up and over the isthmus and let down on the opposite side into the sea. The canal is too narrow and steep-sided to serve in any large way, so it calls for improvement to meet modern commercial needs. Old Corinth had a fortified height, whose walls still persist, but the wicked, commercial, cosmopolitan town was down nearer the sea and the Gulf of Corinth. It, too, had a good commercial location. Often destroyed in battle and earthquake, the old town is now being excavated, and the new stands beside the gulf. The modern town will not become nearly as important relatively as was the old city, for modern vessels and commerce can go around the peninsula easily.

The canal across the Isthmus of Corinth. A new bridge is being built under the direction of U.S. Army Engineers. (U.S. Army photograph)

The canal, an aid to east Mediterranean trade, persuades freight to pass by Corinth with no need for a stop; and the Athens-Patras railroad contributes to the same neglect. Corinth seems to have only local reason for existence.

Patras, at the outer end and narrowest throat of the Corinthian Gulf, has a fine harbor capable of improvement and large development. It is in the midst of currant-growing and has become the packing center for most of that industry. Modern machinery makes, fills, and seals the boxes, which are then loaded locally for foreign markets. Here is the southern terminal for Adriatic boats.

Larissa, an old town in Thessaly, has come forward again in recent years.

It is the center and commercial emporium of the plains of Thessaly, on the highways for rail and motor from Salonika to Athens. Its port is Volo on the Gulf of Volo, a very satisfactory harbor.

Salonika or Thessalonica is most admirably set. It has an inner and outer bay as has New York, but no Narrows. The Vardar, a considerable river, not as long as the Hudson, brings loads of sediment to the mouth instead of dropping it 150 miles inland as does the Hudson. Recent engineering works have dredged a new channel and mouth, leading the mud and water to the outer bay so as to protect the inner for navigation. After World War I with its desolation and the great fire of 1917, the city called a modern

Rehabilitation of Salonika harbor, damaged in the war, was done under the supervision of U.S. Army Engineers. (U.S. Army photograph)

engineer and rebuilt with a plan. Great boulevards were put through at intervals, streets were widened, car and bus service was inaugurated, and well-built business houses and a big mall with six public buildings were created. Altogether a modern city was established, with 236,000 people in the city and nearly as many more in suburban villages.

Salonika harbor has been internationalized, a status very helpful between the great wars. It could be of much more help to Yugoslavia and Bulgaria if there were better railroad connections. The Vardar-Morava Valley has a railroad through north to Belgrade, but branch lines westward would serve Yugoslavia. A standard-gauge, well-equipped road should be built from Salonika to Sofia through the Struma Valley to supplant the present two or three narrow-gauge, non-coördinated roads converging on the city, and thus to give Bulgaria a direct route to a harbor without going round through Yugoslavia.

New road from Salonika to Serres, built under the supervision of U.S. Army Engineers. (U.S. Army photograph)

Seres, ancient Siris or Serrai of Xerxes' times (480 B.C.), is a thriving agricultural center northeast of Salonika. Among fields of wheat and the finest tobacco in Europe, patches of marshland, thousands of acres in extent, have been redeemed. The reclaimed lands help solve the food and malaria problems. Syra on a central island of the Cyclades has become their modern commercial center because of its position and good harbor.

QUESTIONS

1. In Greece the little plains are largely among mountains. In Italy the mountains are a continuous backbone with plains along the coasts. What differences do you observe in the human response to plains in the two regions?

2. What geographic difficulties oppose the making of a strong modern state?

3. Why is Greece not industrial?

4. Why would Greece import fish?

5. What probable differences would there be in the style of homes in Greece and Illinois? Why?

6. What differences would you expect in the medium for art in Greece and Denmark? Why?

7. Why have the cities now moved to the coast when commerce has always been water-borne?
8. What stake has Greece in world peace? Consider her resources, position, neighbors, skills, etc.
9. Of what concern to Greece is the Mediterranean problem? Compare with her probable interests there two or three thousand years ago.

BIBLIOGRAPHY

CHASE, George H., ed., *Greece of Tomorrow* (New York, American Friends of Greece, 1943).
CHATAIGNEAU, Y., and SION, J., "Greece," in Vidal de La Blache and Gallois, *Géographie Universelle* (Paris, Lib. Armand Colin, 1934).
CHATER, Melville, "History's Greatest Trek," *National Geographic Magazine,* Vol. 48 (November, 1925), pp. 533-590.
CHISHOLM, Hugh I., *Hellas* (New York, J. J. Augustin, 1943).
COON, Carleton S., *The Races of Europe* (New York, The Macmillan Company, 1939).
DOMINIAN, Leon, *Frontiers of Language and Nationality in Europe* (New York, Henry Holt & Company, Inc., 1921).
FITZGERALD, Walter, *The New Europe* (New York, Harper and Brothers, 1946).
FOSTER, Edward S., *A Short History of Modern Greece, 1821-1940* (London, Methuen & Co., Ltd., 1941).
FREEMAN, Kathleen, *Greek City-States* (New York, W. W. Norton & Company, Inc., 1950).
GLASGOW, George, *The Minoans* (London, Jonathan Cape, 1923).
MCNEILL, Wm. Hardy, *The Greek Dilemma* (New York, J. B. Lippincott Company, 1947).
MEARS, E. G., *Greece Today* (London, Oxford University Press, 1929).
MILLER, Walter, *Greece and the Greeks* (New York, The Macmillan Company, 1941).
NEWBIGIN, Marion I., *Mediterranean Lands* (London, Christophers, 1928).
NEWMAN, Bernard, *The New Europe* (New York, The Macmillan Company, 1943).
RIPLEY, W. Z., *Races of Europe* (New York, D. Appleton and Co., 1899).
RISTELHUEBER, René, *Histoire des Peuples Balkaniques* (Paris, Fayard, 1950).
ROBINSON, C. E., *A History of Greece* (New York, Thomas Y. Crowell Company, 1929).
ROSTOVTSEFF, M. I., *Social and Economic History of the Hellenistic World* (Oxford, Clarendon Press, 1941).
ROUCEK, Joseph S., *Central Eastern Europe* (New York, Prentice-Hall, Inc., 1946).
———, "Economic Geography of Greece," *Economic Geography,* Vol. 11 (1935), pp. 91-104.
SEMPLE, Ellen C., *Geography of the Mediterranean Region* (New York, Henry Holt & Company, Inc., 1931).
TOYNBEE, Arthur J., ed., *Greek Civilization and Character* (Boston, The Beacon Press, 1950).

CHAPTER 11

Turkey

Where the Hellespont rolls thundering
Through the Dardanelles wide sundering
In his march their rocky gates,
Asia's coast from Europe rending.
—SCHILLER

Viewing the geography of Turkey from the European standpoint, one finds a peculiar, even unique, problem. It is a country of 282,627 square miles, only one thirty-second of which is in Europe. This European part is in no sense a nation, for its capital is at Ankara, 200 miles east of Istanbul and the corner of Europe. The situation is very different from that of England and the formerly called British Empire, for while the Commonwealth of Nations is almost 140 times as large as the British Isles, its capital, with all central interests, is in Europe. One cannot say of Turkey as he could of the Commonwealth that the parts out of Europe depend on the part in Europe, for Istanbul is simply a decadent political, social city, and the small part of the Republic within the field of our studies is an outlying corner. Yet the city has still much religious significance, for it is a focus of Mohammedanism, of the Greek Orthodox Church, and to a less extent of the Gregorian or Armenian Church. But because this tract in Europe is a part of the Turkish Republic and the European remnant of the vanishing Turkish Empire, so large and influential in Europe for 450 years, Turkey merits treatment here.

Setting. For centuries the domain of the Turks has lain athwart the most significant place on the whole earth, at the confluence of two seas, at the junction of two continents, really at the convergence of the roads of the three Old World continents. This locality must have been from earliest times a very favored, stimulating place, for within the boundaries of the Turkey of recent years are the seats of all the old empires of the Near East, Ur, Sumeria, Assyria, Babylon, the Kingdom of the Hittites, Syria, Phœnicia, Israel, Egypt, Kingdoms in Crete, Greece, and Byzantium. Over these lands and many more the Turkish Crescent and religion spread, engulfing residues of ancient peoples and medieval nations alike, appropriating treasures in history, art, religion, and architecture, subjugating nation after nation higher in the scales of civilization and philosophy than the

206

Turks, and spreading an empire from Budapest and Odessa on the north to Thebes and Aden on the south, and from Jerusalem, Caspian Sea, Persian Gulf, Tiflis, and Bagdad on the east to Cairo, Tripoli, and Algeria on the west. At the height of the expansion, Turkish territory comprised nearly 3 million square miles divided between the three continents. The permanence and endurance of Turkish rule over these domains is traceable to two factors: the wonderful strength of the geographic position and the jealousy of the nations afar.

This high value of the position was recognized in the post-World War I agreement to internationalization and demilitarization of the Dardanelles zone. The former was abolished by the 1936 Montreux Convention and at the same time Turkey was permitted to fortify the coasts of the Straits. Turkey's neutrality for most of World War II kept the Straits open. International attitudes and Turkey's acquiescence have kept them still open until the end of 1951, but final public treaties on the matter have not been made. The ability of airplanes to move independently of land and water routes, and the power of air attack, particularly of atomic warfare, modify the value of the Straits in both peace and war. An honest geographic interpretation bespeaks open straits and encouragement of easy movement of the trade of nations through their waters.

Constantinople (845,316). Some earlier geography will not be out of place. The site of Constantinople seems to have been selected for a trading center about 657 B.C. by Byzas, a Greek. There can be no criticism of this adventurer for his choice, but one wonders why such a site was left for him to choose. His wisdom was shown and amply confirmed through nearly 1,000 years, until his camp and trading center had been once destroyed, rebuilt, and had become a flourishing town. In 330 A.D. Constantine decided to use it for the Roman capital of the world power he was setting up. He saw the beauty of situation, surpassing that of modern Naples or Lisbon; he sensed the charm of the local surroundings, its seven hills comparable today with Prague and Vienna. Its strategic importance, its protection by marshland on the west, its double highways by land and also by water, its central position among three continents must have fired his imagination. Its possibilities as a world capital were much more intriguing than were those of Rome. He gave it a name to inspire and thrill, Constantinople ("City of Constantine"). Then he built to deepen all these values, and made it a city worthy of the site. His formidable works of defense were admirably located along the Golden Horn, around the point of the city peninsula, and west along the Marmara for a mile, then across the land to the Horn again. As with time the city grew, successively new and longer walls were thrown across the land from Marmara to the Golden Horn.

Roman centuries rolled on until to all the city possessed by position there were added color, tragedy, and romantic adventure, wealth, splendor, historic associations, the glamour of prestige and a mighty chain of lin-

ISTANBUL

Scale
0 ½ 1 mile

Key

Residence and Business Sections

Mosques

Military Buildings and Grounds

Sultans' Palaces

Parks, Gardens, and Cemeteries

Roads

Railroads

Tramways

Walls and Fortifications

Old Walls (now demolished)

1. Ancient Wall
2. Wall of Byzantium
3. Wall of Constantine
4. Triple Wall of 447 A.D.
5. Seraglio
6. St Sophia
7. Hippodrome
8. Sublime Porte
9. Grand Bazaar
10. Dolma-Bahtche
11. Aqueduct

BOSPORUS

SCUTARI

PERA

GALATA

GOLDEN HORN

ISTANBUL

SEA OF MARMARA

Istanbul, the only city of note on the Bosporus. It is really three or four cities; the old walled city is between the Golden Horn and the Marmara. Pera and Galata rise over the hills on the European side and Scutari on the Asiatic. (Adapted from local city maps)

gering memories, military achievements, political and religious intrigues, and a glory of commerce and intercourse commensurate with its marvelous location.

When, after many years of conquest far beyond the Straits, the Turks decided to take Constantinople, a detachment of the army quietly crossed the Bosporus some four miles above the city and the Golden Horn and occupied a small valley mouth. Across it near the water a formidable stone wall with towers and gates was built, and two or three hundred yards up the little valley another wall across the valley was erected with connecting walls along the valley sides so as to enclose a portion of the valley, Rumeli Hissar. A village of tents and shacks followed, and the Turks were established close to their goal. From this start the conquest was pushed to the

First bridge between Galata and Istanbul. Many business houses are located beside and below the bridge. The city of Galata climbs over the old hill. On the right of the bridge is Istanbul Harbor; on the left, the Golden Horn. (Courtesy General Inspection of Turkish Students)

city walls and the siege was short. In 1453 Constantinople was taken. It would not have been taken then had not its rulers become profligate, careless, and weak. This conquest gave the Turks a strategic capital continuously desired by European powers.

Turkey came with wooden-wheeled cannons, using rounded stones for balls. Its warfare was crude, cruel, but effective. When the Turkish armies returned to Asia in the early years of the twentieth century, they took back the same sort of guns and stone balls. This is one reason why Turkey returned from Europe.

The city is charmingly and strategically fitted to the topography, land and water. From ancient times almost to the present the commercial advantages of this location have loomed large. Road, water route, and even recent railroad ambitions have been motivated by the purpose of crossing Constantinople to coveted lands beyond and not of developing the city or its surroundings. There was first the trade overland between Europe and Asia Minor, Persia, India, and the Far East. Then the trade with the Caucasus arose, and with lands beyond, not to mention the Tigris-Euphrates rich agricultural lands. Products of the Balkans and the Mediterranean lands traveled east in exchange for those of the plains of southern Russia and far-off Cathay, while the rich Danube basin sent its grains and bought east Mediterranean dried fruits. Austria and Vienna wanted a trade route through the city to the East; Berlin wanted a road to Bagdad; but none of them cared to expand the city. Yet the city grew.

The cistern of 1,001 columns in Istanbul. Water for the ancient city was stored here beneath the city and among the columns. (Courtesy General Inspection of Turkish Students)

Camels and ships from many lands brought spices, fruits, seeds, woods, minerals, gems. People brought plans, ideas, philosophy, and learning. Palaces were erected along the waters and on the hills overlooking the Bosporus and were ornamented with the wealth and art of many lands. Bazaars and shops abounded, and the old bazaar of bazaars down in the heart of the ancient city probably has trinkets and utensils that have waited there a thousand years for the tempted customer to yield. No such emporium of trade as this old structure could arise in other environment. Mosques and churches, schools and monasteries, even city waterworks consisting of covered springs, many of which are out miles in the northern hills, aqueducts and tunnels to the city, and spacious cisterns beneath the streets and buildings—all contributed to its splendor and attracted and still attract the religionist, scholar, merchant, and tourist.

Many early buildings were of wood taken from the proximal hills, but frequent fires destroyed them so easily that brick and stone have now replaced many of the wooden structures. A little ancient Greek architecture and art remain in the Hippodrome and monuments; there is much of Christian art and buildings, some of which, like St. Sophia, have been Moslemized. Christian churches which had their altars so placed that the priests and worshipers faced Jerusalem were reoriented when the Turks came by putting the altar 11° to 12° round to the right of the axis of the building so as to face Mecca and then rearranging all the floor rugs to correspond. The art and the architecture from wall to mosque and palace are history. In St. Sophia, Justinian (about 535 A.D.) hoped to surpass Solomon, and when it was finished he exclaimed, "I have done it."

Spring-house northwest of Istanbul. Romans dug pits in the hillside and covered them over thus, to collect water for their city system. Another at the left. (Author's photograph)

Since Ankara has become the capital of modern Turkey, Constantinople, now called Istanbul, has declined. The seraglio where dwelt the Sultan and his family, if such a group could be called a family, is used as one museum among the many already beyond the Sublime Porte. Political significance is reduced to that of a vilayet instead of an empire; commerce is stagnant because Turkey has little territory save on the east side and little money to buy any country's products. Education and finance have both gone to the new capital. Religious leadership is still strong in the city, but it is mostly far too conservative for the modern Turk. Today, one can say with truth, Istanbul has become a living museum.

A few manufactures have been built up within the city and others just outside the Golden Gate—shoes, arms, and weapons. A revival of international trade should come as Turkey recovers, and with the commerce should come a wide range of manufactures, just as has come to other commercial centers.

In 1920 the capital functions were removed from Istanbul to Ankara because, in the words of the Mustafa Kemal Pasha, "the old city was too near Europe and too close to the borders of Turkey." The administrators felt that they would not have matters nearly so much in their own hands in the old city as in the new and that they might be subjected to interference and distractions in working out their plans. Consequently the much more central capital was established, essentially for administrative purposes, commerce, finance, and industry, but not for religion; not for splendor, pomp, and show, but for hard work in the midst of the people, by the people, and for the people. It was the first time this land had ever been ruled for the inhabitants.

The new Turk has never lamented the enormous loss of territory he experienced in the twentieth century, for he has felt that he still has quite enough responsibility and work to keep him busy. By an industrial nation the losses would have been keenly felt, because great quantities of natural resources passed from Turkey's control. Turkey, however, was not industrial or wholly rural, but extensively nomadic; and great reforms were to be carried out, great improvements made. Turkey now is the leading Moslem nation of the world, a model for others, and is respected both by its neighbors and by the nations of the world at large.

EUROPEAN TURKEY

Geology and physiography. Outside Istanbul, Turkey still has over 8,000 square miles of land in Europe. This is mainly of horizontally disposed sedimentary rocks of Tertiary and Quaternary age, though ancient crystallines show through the young rocks in three areas near the Maritza, and Devonian strata lie on both sides of the Bosporus throughout most of its length, with recent basalt on both sides near the north end. The streams have reduced the topography to advanced maturity approaching old age. No doubt this was done rather quickly, for the rocks are in the main not resistant. Then a considerable uplift prompted streams to carve young valleys below the peneplain and permitted the Maritza River, the western boundary of Turkey but not of the peneplain, to open up a valley larger than any other, while the outlet of the Black Sea carved the valley now occupied by the Bosporus. Still more recently the region has been warped and depressed so that the Marmara spreads over a part of the peneplain, as did the Ægean over other lands. While the Ægean left a few summits as islands, the slighter submergence of the Marmara produced peninsulas and drowned valley embayments, as for example the Golden Horn, Buyuk Chekmeje, Saros, and other gulfs on the south side. The general depression allowed the waters to pass through the Dardanelles and the Bosporus, establishing easily fortified ship connections between the Mediterranean and Black seas, where formerly a gorge-cutting stream had flowed. Along the south coast of the Marmara and both sides of the Bosporus many drowned stream mouths with small deltas at their heads witness to the depression of lands and testify to the recency of the movement. That it was a general depression and not a fault or fracture that caused the Bosporus is shown by the marked similarity of rocks on opposite sides, by the identical drowning and subsequent delta-building on each side, and, more convincingly, by the similarity in height and form of the peneplain on opposite sides of the channel. The Bosporus is more of a gorge than other drowned valleys around the Marmara, because carved in more resistant rocks and hence unable to reach the same stage as other valleys.

Climate and vegetation. The climate of European Turkey is characteristically wetter in winter than summer, though never especially wet, mild in winter and often uncomfortably warm in summer. The total rainfall

Drying Smyrna figs in an open field near Smyrna (Izmir). (Courtesy U.S. Dept. of Agriculture)

ranges from 20 to 40 inches per annum, fully two thirds of which falls in the winter. Frosts and occasionally snow occur, but many vegetables grow outdoors all winter. Golden glow, a flower of autumn, and forsythia, an early spring bloomer, can often both be picked in good condition in January. Raspberries are picked and served fresh for Christmas dinner. Radishes, lettuce, beets, carrots, peas, artichokes, and cabbage can be taken from the gardens every day all winter through. Palms, figs, and grapes do well; the tall, dark, commanding cypress is planted in every Turkish cemetery and grows luxuriantly. In alternate years wheat and maize are planted in many fields and are rather well cared for. This is the beginning of a much-needed crop rotation. Scrubby and young oak timber, some planted, is taking many slopes and occasional uplands, though the crops and pastures cover much of both. Less timber is found than the needs of the people and the type of topography suggest.

Rural European Turkey culminates in the north coast region of the Marmara. It does not show its drowning by embayments as does the south shore but presents a gentle slope from the water's edge inland many miles for the peneplain is little dissected here. The people look to the sea even though it is very shallow and harborless, because the higher interior is still more forbidding. For 15 miles inland the people depend on the sea for food,

Drying Sultan grapes in an open field near Smyrna (Izmir). (Courtesy U.S. Dept. of Agriculture)

for work at slack times, and for transportation. Back of the coast region the modern railroad unifies the upland people, and for 10 miles west of Istanbul it follows the coast, serving a suburban population, a few industries—leather, steel, canning, and textiles—and several recreation beaches. Farther west rural interests predominate with sugar beets, wheat, sesame, birdseed, and truck as the chief crops. The new concrete road from Silivri to the city detracts now from sea trade, but Rodosto and Eregli still depend on ship service. Many small coast towns engage in a lively fishing industry.

Resources. European Turkey has few resources other than agriculture on mature soils with meager rainfall. The rocks are mostly recent, poorly cemented as yet, and are very rarely quarried. Clays and sands, though abundant, are seldom used. Brick and cement could be made, and the latter is produced in a small way from the abundant limestones on the north shore of the Marmara; lime from the recent limestones is a possibility; but all require fuel with which the land is miserably supplied. Only one brick plant was seen in the eight-hour journey from Adrianople to Istanbul, and that near the end where the stimulus of the city may have urged its construction. Marmara Island and Marmara Sea receive their names from the quantities of beautiful marble found in the island. There is more mineral industry in Asiatic Turkey, where meerschaum, emery, clays, and many building stones

Modern tree nursery. (Courtesy U.S. Dept. of Agriculture)

abound. In lesser amounts are found chromite, zinc, manganese, copper and antimony, borax, salts, some gold and silver, a little asphalt, coal, lignite, and on the Marmara shores, petroleum.

Forests are rare in the hills of European Turkey, but there is land that should be reforested. The former president, Ataturk, had a model farm and nursery near the capital, Ankara, to furnish trees for reforestation. Active reforesting is being done in places. At present the forest areas are estimated at 25,000 to 30,000 square miles for all Turkey, or less than 3 per cent of the total area.

Among other resources should be reckoned the tourist and recreation possibilities which are spread over not only European Turkey but Anatolia as well. Such a city as Istanbul will always prove attractive. Adrianople (named for Hadrian) and the ruins of Troy and of many more ancient cities in Asiatic Turkey should be given the chance to add to the national wealth. The Bosporus is used for bathing, boating, and as a charming scenic center. On the Marmara west of Istanbul are beaches with booths and shelters, boats and bathing. More beaches occur on the south side. Princes' Islands, with their old palace and gardens, are charming places. But roads and development work of many kinds, clean and sanitary hotels and streets, literature, maps, and a tourist service, spirit, and equipment are necessary to persuade tourists to come in profitable numbers.

Turkish tobacco leaves drying on frames. (Courtesy U.S. Dept. of Agriculture)

Agriculture. Residual soils and river alluvium are the greatest resources of the republic, and they form the foundations of what must be, for centuries to come, the basic industry—agriculture. The old type of cultivation is giving place to the new. Still one finds the brush fence and thatched roof in the village all through rural Turkey. Dirt roads, muddy in winter and dry, stony, and dusty in summer, still prevail but are being replaced by crushed rock and other surfaced roads using local stone, even native asphalt in places. The old-time ox-cart carries the farmer and his plow from the village to the fields in the morning and back to safety in the evening. Often the women go too, to hoe or pull weeds in the wheat or tend the goats and sheep. Great herds of cattle graze over poorly grassed slopes, and sheep in flocks of 100 to 300 wander nibbling along all day and crowd into the brush corral at night. Its 8-foot walls lean in and make passable shelter in most weather, while the brush-and-thatch lodge hard by protects the shepherd at night.

Houses are rarely on the farms, except on lands recently redeemed for the first time, and such lands are very scarce. The same fear and conservatism that keep the farmers living in the village steer the railroads away from towns. Since formerly scores of villages and even larger groups of people objected to the railroad, its course was laid within a mile of the town but not to it; the station was built at a crossroads; and all passengers have a long walk or cart ride between train and town. Now many towns desire the railroad, and some are moving out to it. All in all, the rural population is very backward; but it is receiving new recognition and, with the rest of Turkey, is making rapid strides toward a higher level of living and a larger outlook. Most of these changes are coming as a result of taking advantage of elements of the geographic surroundings formerly neglected or used incorrectly.

People. A cosmopolitan population is inevitable in the city of Istanbul and vicinity for reasons pointed out earlier. That of European Turkey is likewise mixed, probably more than half Greek. Inhabitants on the borders of Asiatic Turkey are mixed especially with many Greeks who did not return as refugees to Greece. Armenian, and Mongoloid relatives and many citizens of European nations mingle in the life of the cosmopolitan city.

Possessed at present of a strong desire for self-expression, the Turk has made and will continue to make rapid progress toward unity, toward modern and Western ways, both in industry, trade, internal improvements, and in tolerance, toward a liberal policy in education, and toward a broader world outlook. The new modern schoolhouse in almost every village means more than many books. The Turk will be no longer illiterate but will be reading, listening over the radio, thinking for himself, and looking beyond Turkish horizons.

QUESTIONS

1. Trace the expansion of the Turk into Europe and his withdrawal from Europe. How different was he in civilization and in outlook when he left, from his condition when he came? Of what advantage to Europe or to Turkey was his coming? of what disadvantage? Discuss advantages and disadvantages, both to Europe and to Turkey, of his leaving.

2. Why is the Bosporus said to be the most significant place on the whole earth? Where is Troy with reference to the Bosporus?

3. How much does the New Turkey owe to the return of her sons from a sojourn in foreign lands? (Some families returned after having been away two or three generations.)

4. Why does glamour surround the Golden Horn?

5. Why are there palms, figs, and vegetables all winter round Istanbul? What is its latitude?

6. In what ways is modern Turkey becoming better adjusted to its environment than the former Turkey?

7. Discuss the relation of Turkey to the Atlantic Pact.

BIBLIOGRAPHY

DOMINIAN, Leon, *Frontiers of Language and Nationality in Europe* (New York, Henry Holt & Company, Inc., 1921).

EDIB, Halide, *Turkey Faces West* (New Haven, Yale University Press, 1930).

EKREM, Selma, *Turkey, Old and New* (New York, Charles Scribner's Sons, 1947).

EVERSLEY, G. J. S. L., and CHIROL, Sir V., *The Turkish Empire (1288-1922)* (London, T. F. Unwin, Ltd., 1924).

HUNTINGTON, Ellsworth, *The Character of Races* (New York, Charles Scribner's Sons, 1924).

JACKH, Ernest, *The Rising Crescent: Turkey, Yesterday, Today and Tomorrow* (New York, Farrar and Rinehart, 1944).

KEYSERLING, Hermann, *Europe* (New York, Harcourt, Brace & Company, Inc., 1928).

KOHN, Hans, "Ten Years of the Turkish Republic," *Foreign Affairs*, Vol. 12 (October, 1933), pp. 141-155.

LENGYEL, Emil, *Turkey* (New York, Random House, Inc., 1941).

McCORMICK, Thomas C. T., ed., *Problems of a Post-War World* (New York and London, McGraw-Hill Book Company, Inc., 1945).

MEARS, E. G., *Modern Turkey* (New York, The Macmillan Company, 1924).

MERRIAM, Gordon P., "The Regional Geography of Anatolia," *Economic Geography*, Vol. 2 (January, 1926), pp. 87-107.

MOMTCHILOFF, Nicolas, *Ten Years Controlled Trading in Southeast Europe* (Cambridge, England, Cambridge University Press, 1944).

PANETH, Philip, *Turkey at the Crossroads* (London, Alliance Press, 1943).

PARKER, John, and SMITH, Charles, *Modern Turkey* (London, George Routledge & Sons, Ltd., 1940).

PEARCY, G. Etzel, and FIFIELD, Russell H., *et al., World Political Geography* (New York, Thomas Y. Crowell Company, 1948).

SHOTWELL, James T., *Turkey at the Straits* (New York, The Macmillan Company, 1944).

SPENDER, J. A., *The Changing East* (New York, Frederick A. Stokes Company, 1926).

STOTZ, Carl L., "Coast Lands of the Sea of Marmara," *Journal of Geography*, Vol. 32 (1933), pp. 305-315.

———, "Life in the Communities along the Bosporus," *Journal of Geography*, Vol. 31 (1932), pp. 181-192.

STRATIL-SAUER, G., "Cereal Production in Turkey," *Economic Geography*, Vol. 9 (October, 1933), pp. 325-336.

TOBIN, Chester M., *Turkey to the East* (New York, G. P. Putnam's Sons, 1944).

TOYNBEE, Arnold J., and KIRKWOOD, Kenneth P., *Turkey* (New York, Charles Scribner's Sons, 1927).

WEBSTER, Donald E., "Turkey of Ataturk," *Political Science Quarterly* (1939).

CHAPTER 12

The Mediterranean Region

All the world is heir of the Mediterranean; all the world is her debtor.
—ELLEN CHURCHILL SEMPLE

GENERAL

Introduction. Perhaps it seems peculiar to discuss a sea region as a unit in a geography of European countries, but it is difficult to tell the geographic significance and to interpret the shifting values of the Mediterranean Sea in chapters treating national European land areas.

The influence of the Mediterranean! Picture it if you can in those days of early man—a rippling, tempting highway—in summer, gleaming with sunshine over open stretches of dancing blue water bordered with forest green and gray rocks; in winter, dark and challenging with sudden, driving tempests of wind and rain, but never blocked with ice packs or frozen waters. There it lay before the eyes of primitive man, a highway—ready for travel, no man-made barriers, no enemy weapon or treacherous ambush to meet, only the open dangers of nature whose gods and demons might be propitiated. In good weather, its horizons beckoned one to discovery of new homes; in times of stress and storm, lucky seamen could reach its islands and shores of refuge. Always its currents and winds urged the curious traveler on, caught him by surprise until he learned to master their tricks and by rudder, oar, and sail to choose his own route.

Then knowledge of its shores grew, as skill to traverse its highway increased. The far horizons lured man out till from the east he reached the Pillars of Hercules—his log floating with feeble currents of sea and air changed to a boat forced by paddle or oar, then driven by sail or steam; his voyages criss-crossed the waters; finally, the Great Sea became a known, desirable shortcut from west to east. Through the years of history, cities and empires rose and fell on its troubled shores, but the Sea remained constant, a highway for the curious and venturesome.

Commerce and war, religious raids and piracy destroyed its peace, as man increased his knowledge but failed to govern his greed and yen for power. In present years its sailors look aloft to the planes that ignore its harbors and disdain its waves. Such is the story—drawn by its possibilities, colored by its light and motion; across its waters have passed the shifting civilizations of East and West, but never has the highway become a settlement.

No doubt for centuries the Mediterranean was a barrier between people in Africa and those in Europe. The stormy sea was dangerous. But also marine horizons beckoned, even dared, men to come out; all was level unlike the forbidding mountains views. And when men learned how to ride the sea it became a friend as well as a highway. It gave the land groups who reached it equal opportunity to travel and trade. Winds pushed men to sea at night and urged them to land in the day. None could put up barriers and walls on the sea. Once men learned to sail the seas, long journeys well provisioned were much swifter and easier. The speed and range of travel were greatly increased when the engine could be applied to the boat.

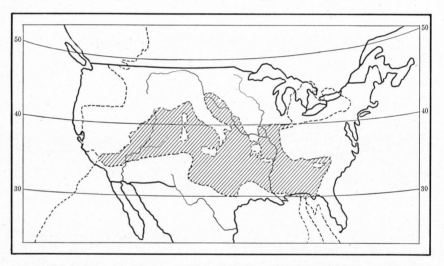

Maps of United States and Mediterranean Sea with the same scale and projection superimposed to show relative size. Cairo and New Orleans are very nearly in the same latitude, 30°N. Mediterranean is outlined in dashes.

Probably no more thorough American student of geography than Miss Ellen Semple ever wrote of this sea. In her searching and far-reaching assertion, quoted above, "All the world" is a large place and includes many people and a long time. If her estimate is half true, our inclusion of the Great Sea as a region is wholly justified.

During World War II the United States saw the importance of our mediterranean (in the midst of the lands), the Gulf of Mexico and the Caribbean Sea; and government strategists are already calling attention to the position and possible use of the Polar mediterranean, the Arctic Ocean.

Description. The European sea amid the lands—the Mediterranean—is 2,300 miles east and west measured from Gibraltar to the Syrian coast, and about 1,000 miles north and south from the Gulf of Genoa to the Gulf of

Sidra against Africa, not in a line from point to point but between the parallels passing through these gulf heads. The average width of nearly 500 miles gives it an area of over 1 million square miles; or only a little less than a third of the whole European continent.

The Mediterranean is more shut in than either the American or Arctic mediterranean, and has a more irregular embayed shoreline than either. It is as definitely constricted into basins as is the American mediterranean. Like the latter its eastern basin lies much farther south than its western basin. The middle basin in each is as deep as the others. In the Mediterranean the middle basin, Tyrrhenian Sea, is more rounded than the others. The Arctic Sea as far as known is not so divided into basins and is not so deep as the other two seas. Study a relief map of the Mediterranean and identify its eastern, central, and western basins; its depths; its great arms, Ægean and Adriatic seas; and its major gulfs, islands, and external connections.

The 35th parallel north bisects the eastern basin, and the 40th does much the same for the western basin. Thus Crete and Cyprus, islands of the eastern basin, are five degrees farther south than Sardinia and Minorca in the western basin. These parallels mark approximately the boundaries of the northern hemisphere high-pressure belt, which lies between the trades and westerlies and migrates with them a little north and south with the swing of the vertical sunshine belt. This high-pressure belt with its migrations furnishes the Mediterranean type of climate, characterized by mild temperatures, winter rains, and dry, sunny summers. A great sea like this one spread for many months under the summer sunshine never gets very cold in winter and is properly called the "Warming Pan" of southern Europe.

CHANGES IN SEA PATTERN AND SURROUNDINGS

Girdling mountains. Folded mountain structures of recent date, Tertiary, encompass the western basin almost completely from Cape Bon in Tunisia, through Spanish Morocco to Gibraltar; then, continuing in the Sierras of southeast Spain and Balearic Islands, the fold joins the Alps east of Marseilles and continues in the Apennines to the Straits of Messina, and next crosses Sicily. It then returns under the sea across the Strait of Sicily to Cape Bon.

Folded mountains of similar age and structure half encircle the eastern basin from the Po Valley through Yugoslavia to Greece. They cross Bulgaria, northwestern Black Sea below water, emerge in Crimea, and appear again in the mighty Caucasus. Taurus folds lie along the north shore of the eastern basin in Asia Minor with the beautiful Cilician gates, a stream-made valley, carved through them.

The Dinaric Alps on the east side of the Adriatic are folds that, chopped off near the coast by great faults or breaks in the rocks, determine the trend of the coast. Typical block-mountain structure, made by faulting and movements of the blocks more or less vertically, dominates the whole eastern end. The Lebanons are cut into two large blocks by the north-south Orontes-Litany rift valley. Palestine is split by the Jordan rift, which continues in the Gulf of Aqaba, Red Sea basin, and Gulf of Suez. No mountains obstruct the south shores from the Nile to Tunisia, but plateaus and sunken areas suggest the same block- or fault-mountain structure with much gentle warping. The Tyrrhenian Sea has been described in the chapter on Italy as a depressed, submerged block bounded by three faults, and the fault line in the Adriatic probably continues southeast beyond the west end of Crete giving great depth to much of the Ionian Sea.

While Sicily is a part of the recent folded mountains, Corsica and Sardinia are remnants of the block of old crystalline hard rocks mostly lost to view in making the Tyrrhenian Sea.

This Tyrrhenian Sea block is only one of several in southern Europe. The Meseta of Spain, the Auvergne Plateau of France, Bohemia, and another block north of the Carpathians extending into the Ukraine as far east as the gorge of the Dnieper are all of much older rocks than the folds named above. They have served as buttresses against which the younger rocks were pushed, aiding to make them fold into the great, sweeping, encircling mountain ranges. The Vosges Mountains in France and Belgium received the thrust of the Jura Mountains as they were pushed from the southeast making the crescentic-fold mountain area in Switzerland and France.

It would hardly be worth while to speak in such detail of these fringing structures if their growth and change were all in the past, but we must note that the movements which made them are still going on, manifested in many places by raised and lowered shorelines with their human structures. Earthquakes, accompanying the uplifts, depressions, and movements on the great faults and in the folds, have occurred repeatedly in many parts of the eastern basin; for example, at Corinth, Cyprus, the Lebanons in Palestine, and Messina. The great Lisbon earthquake in 1755 and its destructive sea wave were associated with earth movements not many miles offshore in the Atlantic and at other points in North Africa. Rome, Naples, Carthage, Tripoli, and Sinai have their records of earthquakes. The movements are a matter of human record during the last thirty or forty centuries and have left their evidences in the rocks for a million years. They have disturbed cable communications many times in recent decades.

Changes in the sea itself. Synchronous sediments laid in a sea give evidence of its former extent. The Mediterranean Sea has had very different outlines and areas at times in its history. Suess (see Bibliography) writes of the four stages in the history of this sea as deciphered by studies of its sediments. When sediments of a certain age are involved in mountain folds, it is certain that the mountains were made after the sediments were deposited.

Three times in the last 12 to 15 million years the young mountains growing in southern Europe have been disturbed by folding, thrusting, and shoving; four times the sea has spread and contracted, once before the first mountain-making, twice between periods of mountain-making, and once since the third mountain crisis. No two spreadings were alike. Austria, Switzerland, France, Germany, Rumania, and Turkey were reached in the first; several of these places were reached in the second and the Caspian Sea was invaded; in the third the Caspian was reached and it was expanded until its waters mingled with spreading Arctic waters on the Siberian Plains east of the Urals.

At the western end of the sea, Atlantic and Mediterranean were connected over Morocco in Africa and through the Guadalquivir Valley, but not until the last spread of the sea were the Straits of Gibraltar opened. In the last spread the Adriatic floor was warped down, the area of the Ægean Sea was depressed until only mountain tops remained in sight as islands, and the valley of the river that drained the Black Sea was drowned to produce the Bosporus, Sea of Marmara, and the Dardanelles. In the last spread also, depression was sufficient to establish water connection between Red and Mediterranean seas. During the last expansion of the sea the great glaciers spread from Scandinavia southward and eastward three or four times with long interglacial stages; other lesser glaciers formed in the Pyrenees, Alps, and Caucasus and flowed down the valleys toward the lowland plains. Men came into Europe before the first advance of the big Scandinavian glaciers.

Moderate uplifts not only gave elevated beaches but coastal plains such as those along eastern Italy, western Palestine (plains of Sharon and Philistia), plains of Patras along the south side of the Gulf of Corinth, and many smaller ones. Wave work has trimmed some shorelines into rugged headlands; submergence of stream-made land topography has made other headlands, subsequently accentuated by wave work. And so by diastrophic movements, wave work, stream deposition, and some wind activity the present shorelines and limits of the sea have come into place.

The processes of land and water adjustment are still going on, possibly as rapidly as at any time during the last half million years. In the chapter on Italy the instability of parts of the Italian coast in historic time was described. Earthquakes in Armenia, south of the Caucasus and in the Valley of Kura suggest subsidence here, perhaps preparing to connect the Caspian and Black seas through the trough south of the Caucasus instead of north as in previous stages.

In addition to the so-called diastrophic movements (foldings, warping, uplift, and subsidence) volcanoes have built cones and islands and belched lava into the sea. The waste from the lands carried to the sea by rivers is spread in great deltas; the pulverized rock made by waves hammering down headlands is sorted and built into beaches or transported into bays or strung out in sand bars that tie islands to the mainland or to one another. So by destructional and constructional work the shorelines are continually modified independently of diastrophism.

To have to move and adjust to the coming and melting away of the ice no doubt was a helpful stimulus to man; but all across southern Europe man had to adjust also to shifting, changing land and water distributions, and to fit his activities to the wealth of detail continually thrust upon him. Such necessities must have been the "mother of many inventions" in ideas, in forms of construction, and in methods of labor.

THE MEDITERRANEAN IN HISTORY

Movements of people. Men can walk on land, ride beasts, rig up sleds and build carts and chariots with wheels; but they can travel in none of these ways on the water. Whether a people shall be a land people, a water people, or amphibious using both land and sea, depends first upon the relations of their neighboring land and water, and secondly upon their skill and spirit of adventure. Men have used water transportation from very early times, perhaps as long as they have used fire. But the impressive fact is that people using boats and sleds, water and land transportation, were under the necessity in earliest times, as today, of a change of means of transport at the shoreline. Such a necessity, requiring the development of two kinds of transportation, has been a constant stimulus to people in the Mediterranean region. The sea was not too large to cross as was the Atlantic. Many of the arms of the sea were still less effective barriers, but all necessitated two means of transportation, if traveled.

Not enough is known of the early people in the area to state who began water travel in addition to land travel, nor to know when and whither. It is certain that the ability to travel on the water helped to make early history in the Mediterranean area.

The Minoans, a part of the Neolithic population of the Ægean Sea area, arrived by sea 5,000-6,000 years ago; they continued to use the sea and their culture grew as did that of Egypt. This Cretan culture was continually modified by influences from the Island of Melos, from the mainland people of Thessaly, and from the Egyptians—modifications disclosed by archeology showing how persistent was the use of the sea and how potent in Neolithic history was the eastern basin of the sea with its Ægean arm.   ·

From the seventeenth to the fourth century B.C. three waves of invaders came into Greece. Some believe they came by land from the north, but there seems to be plenty of evidence for the tradition that they were navigators. The Ionians came in the seventeenth century from the northeast; the Achaeans came in the early fourteenth century B.C. from the east across Ægean Sea and helped remake Mycenæan civilization in Achaia; the Dorians in the fourth century B.C. came to Peloponnesus from the east or possibly from Crete, the place to which Homer refers them, and sailed the Maliac

Sea (off the coast of Malea Cape) entering Laconia and Achaia. These movements of people were facilitated by the waters of the eastern Mediterranean.

Colonization. The Greek colonization period flourished in the eighth to sixth centuries B.C. but had been in progress for some centuries. The Greeks were moved by economic purposes, but Greek culture and civilization accompanied their commerce. Scores of towns were started or former ones possessed and Hellenized. Out the Greeks went among the islands and along shores of the Ægean Sea, through the straits connecting the Black Sea with the Ægean Sea planting the colonies from which rose the Homeric Trojan poems; they settled at many points on the Black Sea coasts; on the African coast from Egypt to Gibraltar, and at many places in Spain, France, Italy (Sicily), and the Adriatic coast of Yugoslavia (Illyricum, Corfu). This persistent colonization of areas fringing the sea gave color to the political and civilizational history of southern Europe for a thousand years.

The Phœnicians, going out from their home cities of Tyre and Sidon, also planted colonies, principally for trade, on both sides of the sea to the Straits of Gibraltar. Much of their work lasted centuries and made a very considerable contribution to the civilization and history of the area.

Egyptians contributed more to commerce than to government and civilization outside their own coasts, but they used the water for political calls upon Greeks and Romans. Armies of Assyria reached the borders of the Great Sea; and Persians in 512 B.C. had to borrow Egyptian and Phœnician ships to push their conquest of Greece. ,

During the pre-Christian history of the Mediterranean two or three memorable political moves were made partly on the water. Xerxes, the Persian king, bridged the Hellespont in 480 B.C. and went to Thrace and other parts of eastern Europe. Alexander set out for India in 334 B.C.

In the Christian era. The purposes and motives of the Crusades from 1096 A.D. to 1291 A.D. were lofty and deep, partly religious, partly to avenge Moslem insults; they accomplished less in the material way than in the spiritual, emotional and religious fields. We are more concerned with results wholly unplanned, and perhaps unthought of while the Crusades were in progress.

Nearly all of the organized Crusades moved in part as land armies from western Europe to the Levant; nearly all were supported or dominated by a naval contingent. Some forces embarked at Atlantic ports in Britain, France, or the Low Countries; some marched to ports on the Mediterranean and took ship at Marseilles, Genoa, Venice, Brindisi, or Constantinople. Some landed at Constantinople, others at intermediate points, and one at least in Egypt. Thus, all that moved by water traveled the Great Sea. Our concern is with the results in politics, government, commerce and learning; in fields that make history.

Three new governments were set up by the Crusades: the Latin Empire of Constantinople which continued 57 years; and the kingdoms of Jerusalem and Cyprus. All had collapsed nearly as soon as the Crusades were over, and the Holy Land was still in the hands of the Moslems. In spite of this political failure the people of Asia and Europe were brought closer together. Thousands had gone to the Near East and had seen it. Other thousands, from Near East lands in counter-movements had seen much of the heart of Europe as well as the Mediterranean peninsulas. Larger horizons of thought opened before men in both continents. The East was opened to travelers. Commerce was quickened. Acre in Palestine was opened as a trade emporium. After its fall Famagusta was opened on Cyprus and continued until the Turks destroyed it in 1571. Several lesser centers were opened and lasted longer. Thus 300 years of commercial history developed. European manufacturers learned new processes, dress and fabrics; farmers got new plants, mulberry, sugar-cane, lemons, and melons. Merchants of Barcelona, Marseilles, Genoa, Pisa, and Venice enlarged the scope, value, and volume of their trade. Streams of Near East commodities poured into the coast cities far beyond their capacity to use so they passed strange goods on to the European continental interior and created new tastes. The Crusades were the beginning of the discovery to Europe of Asian interior. So the commercial routes between the interiors of Asia and Europe expanded. Colonization and geographic knowledge increased.

The Moors reached Spain in 711 and later, partly by sea and partly by following the coast lands of Africa. The Turks overran southern Europe, crossing the Bosporus in 1357 to reach nearest Europe. Mediterranean waters were used extensively to reach more of southern Europe. Then followed the political, social, religious, and commercial blight of the Turkish occupation of the eastern end of the Mediterranean.

While southern Europe was under the Turk's strangling influence, Vasco da Gama sailed round Cape of Good Hope and opened a long, perilous non-Mediterranean route to the wealth of the East. The removal of the Turkish power over Mediterranean countries by the crushing naval defeat of Lepanto, 1571, reopened the way for western European countries to enter. Britain needed a route to India nearer than the Vasco da Gama way and occupied Gibraltar and Egypt to secure the route. In 1800, Britain got possession of Malta at the mid-bottleneck of the sea and has made it a commanding sea fortress. In 1869, the Suez Canal was opened to extend unbroken ship communications from England and France to British India and French Indo-China. Dutch and the East Indies were also assisted by this open highway. Over this route went the flags and influence of the established nations of western Europe through or across the sea to the awakening peoples in the Far East and southeast.

THE MEDITERRANEAN IN COMMERCE

Political dominion and power have flourished in the Mediterranean area for thousands of years; but the commercial aspect of the sea has been fully as important as the political. No doubt the commercial spirit has done as much for social and cultural evolution in the area as the political power has done for national civilization.

Trade across these waters has been carried on from prehistoric time. Laconian green porphyry was found in the palace of Knossus in Crete when recently excavated. Obsidian from Melos for arrow points and cutting tools was exported over Ægean waters in Neolithic days, and has been found in most countries of Europe that lacked flint. Cretan pottery went to Melos and Egypt and to the Greek mainland as early as 1600 B.C. Melos vases have been found in Crete. Minoans traded with Troy, Athens, Corinth, Cyprus, Philistia, Egypt, Sicily, and even with Spain and Sardinia from 2,000 to 1,000 years before Christ. As early as 700 B.C. money was coined and used in Greek transactions. Commerce is described as "strong" and "abundant" in Crete and Mycenæ before the Dorian invasion, and was checked as much by that event in the fourth century B.C. as Atlantic commerce was strangled in the world wars.

Abydos on the Dardanelles maintained a toll or tax station to profit by water commerce. This system was in operation in 680 B.C. and continued for centuries as Byzantium prospered. Commercial and industrial units organized by Mediterranean basins just as city states on land formed unions.

Phœnicians had great commerce by ship from their island cities with Egypt and towns farther west on the African coast. Quantities of Mesopotamian, Persian, and more eastern products flowed over land via the Fertile Crescent to Phœnician ports to enter their maritime commerce. For a time Crete and Melos closed the Ægean Sea to Phœnicians and monopolized the commerce with the Black Sea ports through the Straits. Streams of trade and people poured back and forth across the Ægean Sea for 1,000 years before the Aryan speech arrived or before 1300 to 1000 B.C. Then the Greeks overspread this sea, Hellenized it, and moved on into the Black Sea ports.

The Dinaric coast with few roads inland but with numerous islands, sheltered straits, and bays harbored pirates and not traders, much as the Ægean bred traders and nautical efficiency. Many pirates at later dates preyed on Mediterranean commerce from their hiding places on the Barbary Coasts of North Africa. Spain with valleys back of her ports of Cadiz, Malaga, and Gibraltar helped put the peninsula into the commercial game.

Beautifully woven colored silks, peacock's feathers, pepper and other spices were the first items of import from the Orient. Both royalty and priesthood craved these rare treasures. Skilled embroideries and metal work also came in; then wool, flax, and cloth from both with dyes to enrich them;

gold, copper, and vessels of bronze, all figured in the import lists. After Phœnicians had devised methods of blowing glass into forms and experimented with the use of colors, they carried the results in their ships up and down the coast and far west.

Medicinal herbs, drugs, and perfumes came from Egypt and the Red Sea to the borders of the Nile delta and crossed the Great Sea for the use of physicians in Greece. Varying amounts of oriental products traveling by water to Red Sea ports, then to Thebes, and down the Nile to the real Mediterranean traders poured into the thriving markets. Fragrant woods, myrrh, certain small, live, ornamental trees, ebony, ivory, incense, eye-cosmetics, rare skins, baboons, monkeys, dogs, panthers, even natives and their children as slaves. What cargoes for south European markets!

The Hebrew prophet, Ezekiel, who lived about 600 years B.C., lists many products to be seen in the markets of Tyre, a Phœnician island city. At the risk of repeating some items here is his list. "Your moorings were deep, your masts were cedars of Lebanon and your planks were cypress from Hermon; oaken oars from Bashan, larch from Cyprus and ivory for your decks; fine linen embroideries from Egypt for sails and flags, in colors of purple and blue. Great wealth of every kind; wares of silver, iron, tin, and lead; Ionians brought slaves and copper ware; Armenians sent horses and mules; Isle of Rhodes sent ivory tusks and ebony; Edom garnets, coral, agates, purple dyes, fine linen and embroidery; Palestine sent wheat, wax, honey, oil (olive) and balsam; Damascus rich merchandise; wine and wool from Syria; iron, gold, cassia, sweetcane, spices, saddle cloths, lambs, rams, goats from Arabia; Assyria sent choice fabrics and mantles embroidered in all colors." What a unique catalogue of Mediterranean articles of commerce!

Whereas Tyre is Ezekiel's picked bazaar, other foci came into play as one center waned and another rose. Such a commercial world as this must have had a cosmopolitan civilization difficult to imagine in a continental interior. Only Mesopotamia and Egypt among continental nations were near enough to catch the spirit of the Mediterranean and entertain the travelers from Phœnicia, Greece and Arabia.

As the old commercial powers waned new ones arose. Rome led the Roman world into a political unity with the Latin language, Roman law, and Roman civilization. By Justinian's time, 552 A.D., the Mediterranean was again as busy commercially as it had ever been. Saracen conquests extended to Spain and new crops were introduced from the Orient and Near East.

Venice, Pisa, and Genoa became republics and important commercial seapowers about 1200 A.D. and thereafter. They rose as the Byzantine power waned after its division. Rivalry between the cities, competition for position in Mediterranean trade and political dominion together with the spending of their trade profits in palaces, cathedrals, and commercial houses have given them history and historic monuments,

Venice rose rapidly from its little island base in the lagoon at the head of the Adriatic to be one of the greatest commercial powers of the medieval world. It conquered many cities near Italy, and at its height in the fifteenth century it held many possessions along the Dalmatian coast, in Greece, and in the Levant. It was a maritime commercial power, making intensive use of the waterways and the border cities. Like the Greeks, Venetians never penetrated the lands but sucked up the products in trade that flowed down the valleys from many interiors.

Venice had a large trade in the Red Sea trough, using one or two of the seven canals cut across the Egyptian land between the Nile and the Gulf of Suez, and it traded with the Orient by water as Tyre and Sidon had done 2,000 years before. Its civilizing influence reached as far as its ships sailed, as far as the sea permitted. The other two cities, Pisa and Genoa, worked westward in the western basin of the sea and never reached far beyond its shores.

Economic values in the sea. Fishing seems never to have played the important rôle on Mediterranean shores that it did in the North Sea and in the Irish and Norwegian seas. There are few great kitchen middens on its shores such as are found along more northern waters, an early expression of the truth that Mediterranean waters were not found as well supplied with edible fish as were the others named. Nevertheless, for many centuries fishing has played no small part in supplying food to the inhabitants. Several specialized kinds of fishing have developed. Commercial sponge fisheries have flourished for over 2,000 years in Greek and Turkish waters. Coral fishing in Italian (Sicilian) areas and in Tunisian and Algerian waters is usually very active. Tunny in both Italian and Spanish waters has long been famous. Northern shores of the sea furnish much more fishing than southern. Phœnicians derived their royal purple dyes from a species of snail of the genus *Murex* taken in eastern Mediterranean waters. In modern times only, iodine has been recovered from Black Sea kelp and could be a much more valuable industry.

As pointed out in another chapter, much life in the Black Sea has been destroyed, because it was fresh-water life, by the inflow of the excessively salty Mediterranean waters in the bottom of the Bosporus. This inflow is a strong current in a deep channel.

Mediterranean salinity [1] is higher than that of the Atlantic and water flows through the strait of Gibraltar (1,300 feet deep) outward below and inward above. No distinct surface current system is known in the Mediterranean.

The relatively high alkalinity of the Great Sea may be a factor in its life and in the solution work accomplished by the sea on the coastal rocks.

[1] 3.8 per cent in surface waters of the Levant basin and 3.65 per cent along Algerian coasts against 3.4 per cent in the ocean.

PRESENT NATIONS AROUND THE SEA

Aside from the periodic (or aperiodic) rise and fall of nations, some nations have changed the value which they attach to this sea. Spain was greatly interested for centuries in it until the New World was discovered, then she turned her attention westward. At the other end Phœnicia lost much of her interest in the Atlantic as west European peoples began to find themselves and Phœnicia's trade with the Orient grew.

In modern times, with the opening of the Atlantic, one might expect the Mediterranean to decline in importance, but the decline was relative. When the decades for real colonial expansion and the partition of Africa arrived, the sea powers were quickly in the field. Spain and Portugal grabbed stretches of African coast and groups of islands and consolidated by taking control, for commerce at least, of hinterland behind their coast settlements. Britain with large interests in the south of Asia took control of both ends of the Mediterranean. In 1805 the English and French fought a terrific sea battle at Trafalgar just outside the Gibraltar Gate. The Straits of Gibraltar needed no canal; but the French constructed the Suez Canal that easily and effectively superseded the several canals that had previously carried traffic between the Nile and the Gulf of Suez. This canal cut directly through delta sands and clays from the Great Sea to the Gulf of Suez and the Red Sea with depth and width sufficient for ocean vessels. Later the canal was mechanized so that the passage from sea to sea became as easy for modern shipping as the pre-delta passage was for ancient commerce.

Changes of level here of a few feet would make enormous differences in the canal problem; changes such as have come repeatedly in the geologic history of the sea. A lowering of the delta 20 to 40 feet would put the canal wholly out of business, but would also make it wholly unnecessary; while a 40-foot elevation of the lands containing the canal would leave it a dry ditch. It could be deepened and used, but locks up to the middle and down again, as the Panama Canal has, would be impossible because the land is desert. No rain or streams could supply the locks over the summit with water. A sea-level canal is the only possibility unless tremendous pumps are used to lift water up as much as the land had been elevated.

The French got possession of large colonies on the south side of the sea, and at a late date Italy was granted and took control of territory between Tunis and Egypt. As resources were developed on the African side, each nation tightened its hold on routes across. Italy and Britain were located at narrow bottlenecks where they could restrict other nations from passing in east and west directions. Artificial straits like the Suez Canal can be more reasonably controlled, but even here in peace time general freedom of movement has been practical with tolls. In times of war, restrictions have been applied though not universally. Military guards have been used sufficiently to enforce restricted use.

In modern times, Yugoslavia and Turkey, border nations, have no properties on the opposite side of the sea, except that Turkey is on both sides of the Bosporus. Russian power has long striven to loosen Turkey's hold on the Dardanelles and Bosporus so Russia can share in the control of the Mediterranean and the open, never frozen route to the Atlantic.

CONCERN OF MORE DISTANT NATIONS

It is much nearer from New York and Toronto to India via the Mediterranean than from Vancouver and San Francisco to India via the Pacific. True, the Pacific can be sailed without making so many crooks and turns and probably in as few days. Much of American production, particularly industrial, comes from eastern United States. Air distances and hazards for all North American shipping to India, East Africa, and Persia are less through the Mediterranean than around Cape Good Hope.

America is as much concerned with trade among South European countries, Spain to Turkey, as with trade with India. South European lands from Yugoslavia to Barcelona trade with South American nations. Thus, to all these interests the Mediterranean Sea is important. These countries want it open for trade with no serious restrictions.

Ever since Russia reached the Black Sea under Catherine II in 1795, the Russians have been interested in the Mediterranean Sea. Russia expanded to the Black Sea 150 years ago, and recently has had designs on its southern approaches. She has crowded modern Turkey for nearly 40 years. She has pulled Bulgaria and Rumania into her orbit and annoyed Greece continually since World War II. All these are expressions of her interests in the Mediterranean and a measure of the lengths she has been willing to go in order that she may dominate the route to it. Russia is deeply interested in the Mediterranean and the highway to it. South Russia has wheat, stock, fish, and metals to export and Russia needs many products of other lands that could be imported through this lane. She is not at all satisfied with her privileges in the Arctic mediterranean, and wants more on the south also. From the world's commercial lanes, the Black Sea and South Russia can be reached in no other way than through the Bosporus; and Russia is not satisfied to share it; she covets control.

Germany and Austria, not to mention lesser Danubian states, are anxious for the use of these waters. They have high commercial value to nearly all central European nations and strategic military value to Russia, Great Britain, Turkey, Greece, and perhaps others equally near.

The question might justly be raised: has any nation the right to close the sea to any of these bordering nations or even to restrict their use of it for trade so long as no purposeful damage is done to other nations. At least three nations have territory, resources, and citizens on opposite sides north and south; and at least two (four, if The Netherlands be counted with her East Indian Islands and Portugal with Timor and other smaller interests in the East) have similar interests on opposite ends of the sea. At least two thirds of Italy's maritime commerce makes heavy use of the Suez Canal. France and England use both gates and the seaway between much more than does Italy. Should, then, the Mediterranean ever be a closed sea?

It is as yet too early to appraise the postwar influence of the Mediterranean. In our own time the stubborn defense of Malta, a modern counterpart of its earlier history as a maritime fortress, the determination of all parties to control at any cost the route east and west across the Mediterranean, and its use as a modern highway with approaches to the European "heartland" speak for its continued strategic importance. What effect aviation will have on its military and commercial value is a matter of growing interest, but belongs in the realm of discussion and experience rather than in that of scientific pronouncement.

A glance at the question "Whose sea is it?" may help to clear an understanding of its problem. Considering the Black Sea as part of the sea, not to mention similar extensions of the sea in ancient days or to anticipate shiftings in its size and shape in the future, there are fourteen nations in contact today with the sea. Three of these have extensive colonies on the African side opposite their homeland. Britain has possessions in Cyprus, Malta, and nearby small islands and at Gibraltar, as well as a large interest in the internationally administered Suez Canal. The Canal Board of thirty-two has ten British members, nineteen Frenchmen, one from The Netherlands, and two from Egypt. Britain owns upwards of half the shares in the enterprise. Three more states on the Danube, Czechoslovakia, Austria, and Hungary, may well express a considerable interest in this inland sea, for their water highway flows into it.

Besides these actual contacts it has been shown above that most nations east and west, north and south, contribute to its commerce. Norwegian fish are sold on the piers of Patras for Greek food; and Corinthian grapes (currants of commerce) are shipped from Patras to America. A study of trade statistics of imports and exports of the nations the world around shows that no nation really "liveth" without the Mediterranean Sea. Then, whose sea is it? The best geographic response to the Great Sea is the full use of it by all the interested nations, and such use of it is still guaranteed in 1951.

Just as the Mediterranean and Europe are parts of the world pattern of land and sea, and the Mediterranean climate is a part of the world climatic pattern, so also are the commercial and political aspects of the sea parts of the world commercial and political patterns.

QUESTIONS

1. What evidence can be set down that the Mediterranean Sea is changing shape even today?

2. How are these changes different from past and probable future changes?

3. In other places we have considered the advance and retreat of glaciers and correlated climatic changes as a possible stimulus to civilization and culture. Compare in value and extent these glacial changes with those changes in the Mediterranean area noted above.

4. Early man's civilization and culture on the Mediterranean shores far outstripped that in other parts of Europe. Discuss from a geographic standpoint.

5. Why were so many so-called civilizations so short-lived? What other factors than sea changes can be suggested for their collapse?

6. Is the argument for international coöperation stronger in such a sea area as this than in a land area? Use particularly the geographic factors.

7. What effects may aviation have on the use of the Mediterranean?

8. May the current political split into an eastern and western Europe have any serious effects on the commerce of the Great Sea? In what ways?

BIBLIOGRAPHY

COLE, Grenville A. J., *The Growth of Europe,* Home Univ. Library (New York, Henry Holt & Company, Inc., 1914).

EAST, Gordon, "The Mediterranean Problem," *Geograpical Review,* Vol. 28 (1939), pp. 83-101.

EZEKIEL, Chapter 37, Old Testament.

GOODE, J. Paul, *School Atlas* (Chicago, Rand, McNally & Company, 1946, or later editions).

HALL, H. Duncan, "Zones of the International Frontier," *Geographical Review,* Vol. 38 (1948), pp. 615-625.

HAMMOND, C. S., *The Encyclopedia Britannica World Atlas* (New York, C. S. Hammond & Company, Inc., 1949).

LYDE, L. W., *Peninsular Europe* (New York, Longmans, Green & Company, 1931).

MYRES, John L., *Mediterranean Culture* (Cambridge, England, Cambridge University Press, 1944).

NEWBIGIN, Marion I., *The Mediterranean Lands* (New York, Alfred A. Knopf Inc., 1924).

NEWMAN, Bernard, *Mediterranean Background* (London, Robert Hale, 1949); also (New York, British Book Center, 1949).

PEARCY, G. Etzel, and FIFIELD, Russell H., *et al., World Political Geography* (New York, Thomas Y. Crowell Company, 1948).

PINE, L. G., *The Middle Sea* (London, E. Stanford, Ltd., 1950).

REITZEL, William, *The Mediterranean; Its Rôle in American Foreign Policy* (New York, Harcourt, Brace & Company, Inc., 1948).

SANFORD, E. M., *Mediterranean World in Ancient Times* (New York, The Ronald Press Co., 1950).

SEMPLE, Ellen C., *The Geography of the Mediterranean Region* (New York, Henry Holt & Company, Inc., 1931).

SIEGFRIED, Andre, trans. by Doris Hemming, *The Mediterranean* (New York, Duell, Sloan, and Pearce, 1948).

SOAMES, Jane, *The Coast of Barbary* (London, Jonathan Cape, 1938).

SUESS, Edward, *The Face of the Earth,* Vol. I and Vol. V, Atlas (Oxford, Clarendon Press, 1904-24).

WELLES, Sumner, ed., *An Intelligent American's Guide to the Peace* (New York, The Dryden Press, 1945).

WHITTLESEY, Derwent, "The Mediterranean, Mare Liberum or Mare Clausum," *Geographical Review,* Vol. 28 (1938), p. 312.

World Almanac & Book of Facts (New York, *N. Y. World Telegram,* annual).

Part III

LANDS HAVING MARINE CLIMATE

GENERAL SURVEY OF ATLANTIC MARINE LANDS

If in writing a geography of Europe one could proceed strictly according to natural or geographic regions, using climatic regions for the major divisions, with districts and sections for lesser units, it would be wise to place only the western portions of the lands in the belt of Atlantic marine climate, as does Kendrew in his *Climates of the Continents*; but one's geography, for best results, must recognize the political units. Hence, entire states are put in a climatic region if most of the state belongs in it, and other states are left out entirely even though small parts of them might be included in it.

The entire British Isles have typically marine climate. France is Mediterranean all across the south or Great Sea borders, and its eastern part is distinctly transitional toward continental, but at least three fourths of the country is profoundly influenced by the marine climate; hence France is considered under the above heading. Belgium has only a small hilly section in transitional climate and is therefore admitted to this group. Almost all of The Netherlands and Denmark likewise has a marine climate. So quickly are effective altitudes reached as one retires from the coast, that Kendrew calls much of high central Norway transitional. But since the most inhabited coastal part is typically marine and since the marine influence extends entirely across the Scandinavian Peninsula, though with waning strength, all of Norway is incorporated in this group. As already shown, Spain and Portugal are only in small part within the area of marine climate and they are therefore not included here.

The climatic unity across these six states does not bring about so much similarity in other respects as does that of the Mediterranean states because these states spread across 35° of latitude. Nevertheless, the proximity of the sea and the broken nature of the shoreline have been sufficient to make of every nation along the coast a seafaring people, a fishing population, and a commercial state with colonial interests.

CHAPTER 13

France

The further off from England the nearer is to France.—Lewis Carroll

France is an idea necessary to Civilization—Chas. Morgan

GENERAL DESCRIPTION

Situation. Perhaps the most valuable asset of France is its position on two seas, the historic Mediterranean and the progressive Atlantic. Moreover, the joint boundary with Belgium reaches the coast in such a way as to give 35 to 40 miles of exposure to the busy North Sea. These contacts have kept the people ever open to Levantine intercourse, intellectual and commercial, with all it had to offer, and at the same time have left them free to enter northern and Atlantic commerce and spirit as they rose to modern heights. Residents of the south and west sections today reflect color thus given them through many centuries. Land contacts have been less significant from a cultural, and more signal from a military and commercial point of view, yet quite important with the Teutonic people of the Low Countries and Germany as well as with people more akin in Switzerland.

Amid diversities indicated below there has been for 2,000 years a large element of unity in this country. Cæsar found all Gaul divided into three parts, but the inclusive boundaries of the three parts were not far from present French frontiers except where Italy spilled over into Mediterranean sections. Modern Belgians and proximal people of northwest France sprang from Cæsar's Belgæ; Aquitanians have their name preserved in an area larger than the one they occupied in the southwest, and the large, middle Celtic expanse has been contracted to little more than the Armorican peninsulas, a reduction which seems to have occurred because of pressure exerted by strong Alpines crowding in from their vigor-giving mountain homes on the east.

Geologic structure in geography and history. Eleven physiographic units, each with its economic entity, are distinguishable in France. They range from the ancient Central Massif to the recent coastal and delta plains, from the lofty, youthful Alps and Pyrenees to the low, old Ardennes lying astride the eastern portion of the Franco-Belgian boundary. Pre-Cambrian

237

schists, gneisses, granites, and porphyries of the Auvergne Plateau in south Central France furnish strong building stones and valuable residual clays. Little strips of Coal Measure rocks folded in with the schists carry small deposits of coal and large iron reserves. The Armorican peninsulas, Vosges, and Ardennes are the deeply eroded roots of the central European Variscan mountain systems which were uplifted in late Paleozoic time. All furnish

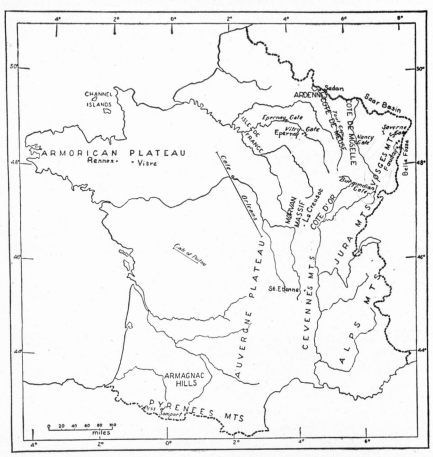

Physical features of France: mountains, passes, gates, and cuestas, and several towns. (Compiled from Goode's *School Atlas* and *Oxford Advanced Atlas*)

exceptional and abundant building stones in considerable variety: granites in Brittany, sandstones in the Vosges, and marble and slate in the Ardennes. On the flanks of the first are small coal reserves, and in the northern margins or underground prolongations of the last are very rich coal-beds which are more extensive in Belgium than in France. All these are old mountains.

Other mountains are much younger and were made by strong, slow thrusts toward these old blocks, which folded thick accumulations of sediments into the Alps on the east, the Pyrenees on the south, and, a little later, the Jura northwest of the Alps. The latter are much less complex in structure and less eroded than are the Alps but equally rich in good limestones and other building materials. Rugged and lofty topography in the path of westerly winds induces abundance of rain, copious rapid streams, and a wealth of water power in both Pyrenees and Alps. The stresses that pushed up the Alpine mountains disturbed the old Central Massif and tilted up its eastern side, giving origin to the forms called the Cevennes Mountains and initiating a series of hot springs along the zone of faulting. Therefore near the base of the Cevennes are medicinal, mineral, and thermal springs of some economic value. In the slopes of the Pyrenees are other thermal springs. No ore mineral wealth of note is found in any of these three younger mountain structures. While the great shovings that produced them were toward the Central Massif and the Vosges, they all fell short of crushing the new mountains against the old, thereby leaving all the lowlands of France in easy communication one with another.

Along the Rhône-Saône depression in the north flows the Saône; at Lyon it enters the Rhône, descending from Switzerland; and as one noble river the two proceed to the Mediterranean where their waste-depositing waters have added a large delta to the coastal plains bordering the sea. In a broad structural depression between the Jura and the Vosges the Doubs flows westward to join the Saône. A similar pass connects the Mediterranean Plains with Aquitania. The latter consists of broad plains which extend from the descending westward slopes of the Central Massif to the Bay of Biscay. The inland portion of these plains seems to be a typical, recent, uplifted coastal plain augmented by an enormous compound alluvial fan, still under construction, built by mountain streams emerging from the Central Pyrenees and enlarged by extensive shoreline deposition along what is known as the Landes. Great sandbars, heaped up by the waves, shut long, large lagoons from the sea. Waves and winds have contributed sand to the lagoons and vegetation has grown in them until they are nearly filled.

The Gate of Orléans, a low, broad, structural plain between the Central and Armorican plateaus, is traversed by the Loire. Farther southwest is the Gate of Poitou, a narrower depression where these two ancient blocks come nearest each other. No stream traverses this passway, which can be followed from Aquitania to the Paris Basin. The latter is the largest plains area in France and consists of Mesozoic, Tertiary, and Quaternary beds of rock.

As explained in the chapter dealing with Italy, the Island of Corsica is a remnant of ancient granite rock and fragments of Paleozoic folded strata left above the sea while a great block of similar structure foundered, separating this island mass from Italy, Siciliy, and Sardinia, and producing the Tyrrhenian Sea. Its values are in its forests and its abundance of building stones of superior quality.

Rivers. Besides the Rhône-Saône system already named, France has the Seine, shorter but more serviceable than either the Rhône or Loire, rising near the Saône in a score of branches that drain the gentle west slope of Côte-d'Or and flowing northwest to the English Channel at Le Havre. The Meuse and the Moselle rise farther east and empty into the Rhine. The Loire, rising on the north slopes of the Central Massif, descends northward well into the Paris Basin, then turns west, furnishing at the elbow the obvious site for Orléans, and runs directly to the coast. The great drowned

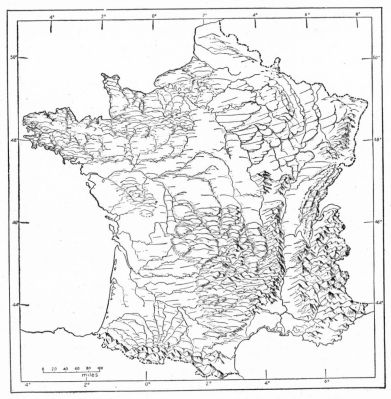

Graphic relief of France, showing relief features. (Based on International Geologic map and topographic maps by Goode and Philips)

Garonne, with its chief affluent, the Dordogne, drains the western slopes of the Auvergne and the northern slopes of the Pyrenees, reaching the sea midway between the Pyrenees and the Loire. The Adour drains the West Pyrenees and adjacent plains with their excessive rainfall. Because of perennial precipitation all streams are permanent, but all shrink in summer. Those from the snows and glaciers of the Alps and Pyrenees are the most constant in warm weather. The few lakes and the depleted forests supply only meager upstream reservoirs to regulate the flow. Because of heavy local cyclonic storms, rivers are generally subject to violent local floods and rapid movement of soil, sand, and gravel. Canalization of streams and the construction of connecting canals took place in the years before railroads came. Such hydrographic works were suggested and greatly facilitated by the extent of the plains and their low-level connections. They not only connect places in France but connect France with Belgium and Germany.

Climate. A country stretching for 3° to 4° each side of latitude 47° north and lying on the eastern borders of the Atlantic Ocean has an excellent position because under two great climatic elements, the ocean influence and the prevailing westerlies. The ocean ensures in the climate of France equability of temperature, sufficient moisture, cloudiness, and no marked rainy season. The last point is not true of the Mediterranean plains, where summer drought and winter rain are characteristics of the Mediterranean type of climate. The westerlies ensure more variations in pressure, temperature, and electrical charge than marine climates have in lower latitudes. They bring to France, among other North Atlantic lands, the "spur of the seasons" which stimulates human energy and urges excellent performance. Steady westerlies coming in from the sea or variable cyclonic winds drawn in from the south bring sufficient rain and snow, both of which increase northward and up the mountain slopes. The Cevennes have heavy fall on the west slopes, while the Rhône valley has a good excuse for dry farming, and the Alpine slopes have forest covers favored by abundance of rain and snow. The West Pyrenees, because of their position in the cyclonic westerlies, have a rainfall very abundant in winter time and ample for grazing and crops in summer. In July the 70° Fahrenheit line crosses the country from Biarritz through Orléans and on northeast to Strasbourg, while in January most of France lies between the mean monthly lines of 35° and 42° Fahrenheit. Frosts occur frequently in winter even on lowlands, and snow occasionally whitens the ground or falls to the depth of 2 to 4 inches. Temperatures are lower in the mountains, and precipitation is heavier and more largely in the form of snow. French winter is found more and more continental as one moves eastward.

PHYSIOGRAPHIC AND GEOGRAPHIC REGIONS

The physiographic units named previously are the bases for the regional treatment of France. Beginning with the oldest, their characteristics and human relations will be interpreted.

1. Central Massif. This elevated portion, often called the Auvergne Plateau, divides naturally into three sections: the upturned edge on the east called the Cevennes, a central volcanic area, and the broad plateaus to west and south, often called the *Causses.*

When the Alpine thrust pushed from the east, it forced up the eastern part of the plateau 2,000 to 3,000 feet higher than the western, thus producing a castellated scarp on the east from which the stream-furrowed land gently slopes westward. This mountainous edge has been slashed and carved by the waters of sudden, violent Mediterranean rainfall into gorges and general ruggedness exceeding any elsewhere in France. Slopes are so steep that agriculture is on narrow, rock-walled terraces. Soils are so infertile that crops are poor, except in some orchards and gardens on the alluvial valley floors. Many little valleys are so very warm that the mulberry and its eater,

Geographic regions of France as described in the text. The basis is primarily physiographic. Corsica is an island south of the Gulf of Genoa. (Adapted from Mill's *International Geography,* topographic and geologic maps)

the silkworm, flourish in great numbers. Cocoons are unwound and silk spun in many small towns and the threads are carried out to the Rhône Valley for further preparation for weaving. Sheep find splendid pasture on the heights to which they ascend from the burning, dry coastal plains in summer—a short transhumance which should endure yet many years. Skins of wild and cultivated animals of the hills are dressed in large tanneries, while wood and rags are converted into high-grade paper. Small industries flourish here in these rugged, picturesque surroundings because of small deposits of coal and iron and the perennial power furnished by abundant water and steep gradients. A sturdy, conservative, industrious, numerous, and still prolific population occupies this beautiful mountain fringe, and a row of industrial towns stands at the mouths of the valleys.

In late Tertiary time the Central Massif, cracked and warped by the Alpine mountain-building from Clermont-Ferrand south more than 60 miles, was the site of volcanic activity on a magnificent scale. Basaltic lavas and trachytes flowed freely; later ash, scoriæ, and bombs spread over thousands of square miles. Scores of conical hills locally known as *puys* dot the northern part of the area. Craters are so recent that their rims are still intact, and lava streams, still fresh, reach out across the plateau. In several places thermal waters still issue, and lava rock is quarried. Soils have been enriched by potash and phosphorus in volcanic ash, and lake beds of sediments have accumulated in waters ponded by lava flows. These are the chief values in the volcanic part of the Massif. A number of flourishing towns have grown up among these interesting volcanic relics, and recent archeologic finds suggest that primitive men may have lived here during the later but far prehistoric eruptions. Basins among the long-extinct volcanoes have fertile soils. The decay products of the lavas usually are rich in potash, lime, clay, and phosphates, and hence the residual soils of flows and basins will grow flowers, fruits, vegetables, and, in places, timber. A population, sparse because of altitude and scattered through little villages, cares for the sheep and cattle which feed over the slopes, or plants and harvests the sugar beets, wheat, and vegetables. Basins and valleys are fertile, and the slopes and hills, in spite of poor soils, are among the best stock-breeding grounds of the country. The people, dwelling in grotesque mountain villages of black basaltic rock, are strong and hard-working, such people as so unkind a country requires. They conduct great fairs at suitable seasons, both for their own purposes and for the entertainment of tourists.

To the south and west are extensive plateau areas. Rejuvenation but not faulting or vulcanism is responsible for the details of form, for the streams mostly flow or tumble through youthful gorges. Here Jurassic limestone areas dissected not only by surface streams but by solution abound in caverns, sink-holes, lost rivers and springs. Interstream areas are mesa-like table lands, often dry, barren or covered with scanty pasture. Such topography called *causses* here is called *karst* or solution topography elsewhere. Soil over limestones is fertile, but over granites is sandy and not very productive. Crops of oats, rye, and potatoes are meager in many parts; but chestnuts, particularly choice on the sandy areas, are a nutritious and plentiful food. Frequent rains and mists from the Atlantic encourage growth of grass, and pastures furnish food for many fine cattle. Famous porcelain factories have arisen at Limoges to use the residual clays from the weathering granites. Tanneries use the bark from chestnut oak and hides from the slaughtered cattle to make fine leathers. Transportation is hindered by the many gorges, which require lofty viaducts for the railroads. Roquefort cheese, from milk of sheep and goats, comes from the grazing lands of the southern chaotic limestone plateaus and is ripened in the numerous caverns. Woolen mills manufacture the homegrown wool to be sold by the people as they travel southeastward down to the Mediterranean villages in the fall. Thus the Massif finds a place in the economy of France and at the same time provides a means of livelihood for its vigorous residents. The plateau is isolated from the rest of France. It is a "center of repulsion in times of prosperity and of refuge in war."

Porcelain works, 200 years old, uses rich kaolinite near Limoges and employs thousands of workers and artists. (Courtesy French Embassy—Information Division)

2. Armorican Massif. Two rocky peninsulas stand out from northern France into the Atlantic as if to challenge the ever recurring cyclonic storms that dominate their climate or to welcome the mists and rains that clothe most of their surface with luscious grass or deciduous forests. The larger, Brittany, presents craggy granite headlands to the sea, while the smaller, Cotentin, has limestone headlands alternating with miles of sandy beaches. Structurally, the Channel Islands belong with Cotentin, although politically they belong to England. In Brittany the granite belts on north and south, leading eastward along the coasts, spread apart gently, while between these more resistant boundaries the widening belt of Paleozoic folded sediments is frequently interrupted or covered, for example, in the basin of Rennes, by tiny patches of fertile Tertiary sediments. The mature upland topography of the whole region has been elevated so that streams have been able to carve youthful valleys below it and waves have developed rugged shorelines. The former interfere much with communications, while the latter with many promontories and deep, narrow sounds favor commerce, navy yards, and arsenals, and develop a magnificent body of sailors and sardine-fishermen. Excellent upland soils, fertilized with seaweeds, and the genuine mildness of a moist climate call for flourishing agriculture. Early vegetables compete in Paris with those from the Mediterranean plains and in London with Channel Island products. Inland apple orchards are protected from the harsh winds by the bordering hills, and cider becomes the characteristic local beverage, while apples are shipped to Paris. Cattle-breeding and the growing of potatoes, rye, and buckwheat occupy the time and energy of the rural people of Normandy, Maine, and Arcoat, three inland portions of the area.

Much dredging in the lower Loire has opened the port of Nantes to vessels of 26-foot draft and by reviving the former commercial activities has produced a lively industrial center engaged in metallurgy, ship-building, and refining of food products. The largest ocean liners reach St. Nazaire at the entrance of the estuary.

Typical homes of the extensive rural population are low houses constructed in a crude manner of local stone and brick. They are usually grouped in villages so that the farmer must make a journey morning and night between his home and his farm. In the southern portion coöperative farmer organizations handle the marketing for milk and butter industries. At Quimper near the southern shore of Brittany, where weathered granite and Quaternary clays supply a high grade of varied ceramic materials, the ancient peoples made pottery, and the same conditions are still utilized to make a heavy, figured ware sold extensively in northern France.

The Armorican region was once a poor country. It lived almost wholly within itself, raised its own food, and wove its own cloth, exporting but little, because of topographic and language barriers made more effective by racial differences. New transportation, both canal and rail, to say nothing of truck and motor roads, has given means of communication, and now the Breton can broaden his geographic connections, use limestone and seaweed fertilizer wherever needed, market his products—vegetables, veal, butter, and apples—in the more densely populated Paris Basin and buy many things he could not have before. The larger adjustment has given him freedom and prosperity, and with the breaking down of his language barriers he is entering upon a new era.

3. Northeast France. In the sketch of the geology of France the Vosges and Ardennes were separated, but in this discussion the Vosges are linked with the Rhenish plains of Alsace and much territory intermediate between Ardennes and Vosges. In a more refined subdividing, five or six sections could be made of this territory, but for study here all can be grouped under the one loose geographic term. At best it is a small region and lacks topographic and utilization unity. The real unity of the region lies in the fact that none of its parts belong in any other region. The Ardennes proper are almost wholly north of the French boundary in Belgium, and the small spurs that lie in France are not separated from the Paris Basin.

The topography of the Vosges is in advanced maturity, with well-mantled, rounded hill forms, below which are much more youthful valleys,

Coal processing works in northeastern France, where coke, gas, tar and other products are made. Note the railroads and clusters of workers' homes. (Courtesy French Embassy—Information Division)

particularly on the east or Rhenish side. During the ice age, glaciers occupied many valleys, especially those on the west where larger rainfall and lower temperatures even today permit the copious snow cover to remain until May. Strong soils are the greatest resource in the Vosges. Men occupy the glaciated valleys to their heads with agriculture, lumbering, and the use of water power in local industries—grinding grain, sawing lumber, making paper and wood products, and weaving cotton and woolen cloth. The valleys are filled with little factories, whose operatives migrated two or three generations ago from the Rhine lowlands up the valleys, until the higher regions are more densely settled than the plains of Lorraine and Saône. Opportunity and pressure of German authority after 1871 were the main factors in this movement. Multitudes of quarries in the northern Vosges produce red sandstone to be used locally or sent down the valleys to Rhineland cities. Over the sandstone hills of these north Vosges lands and for many miles northward, there extends one immense spruce forest, whose products stimulate trade and wood industries even outside the hills in towns bordering the Paris Basin. No prettier country exists in the interior of France than this old mountain topography with its thickly settled population and industry; no finer culture and spirit can be found in the whole land than in this northeast hilly portion.

The Lorraine or northern portion has still older topography, lower and more level, but equally valuable for agriculture and small industry, and has in addition great iron reserves and mines with huge metal works of many kinds, which use the coal of the Saar Basin.

The Saar was German territory until after World War I, then rendered to France as reparation until a plebiscite in 1935 returned it to Germany. After World War II it went back to France to the satisfaction of most of its citizens. Its area is about 750 square miles and its density of population over 1,000 per square mile. Saarbrücken (125,000), and many towns of 20,000 to 40,000 among scores of villages everywhere, make possible this mean density. The coal, so valuable that men have frequently contended bitterly for it, has been known since Napoleon's time; its reserves are now estimated at 12 billion tons. By refined metallurgical processes in which this coal is used, the phosphorus is removed from the minette iron ores of Lorraine and is made available for fertilizers. Other related industries using local resources are glass, pottery (art wares), textiles, and machinery. Agriculture is intensive, but insufficient to meet local needs. Workmen go in trams and trains to the mines, returning only for weekends, and leave their families to work the gardens and raise pigs, cattle, poultry, and potatoes. The exchange of coking coal from the Saar Basin and minette iron ore from Lorraine makes possible a valuable steel industry in each area and thus improves French production.

Sodium and potassium salts to condition chemical and fertilizer industries, and clay and kaolin for factories, making porcelain and glass, plain and cut, are other items of resource and industry in the valleys of weathered sandstone of the Northeast region.

The Alsace plain [1] bordering the west bank of the Rhine has rich alluvial soil, warm, dry climate behind the sheltering Vosges, and magnificent transportation facilities on river and modern rail and truck roads along its level north and south thoroughfare. Five zones of soil, topography, and relief, parallel with the river and the Vosges wall, give rise to as many types of

[1] Raoul Blanchard, *Geography of France* (1917). Tr. 1919.

utilization. Next the river, water seeps through to old stream beds, and they with lowlands between are filled up by aquatic vegetation—patches of willows and poplars, reeds, rushes, and other plants of value for baskets and matting—a zone of considerable wild life, scant population, and favorite hunting opportunities. Beyond this marshy zone, but still between the Rhine and the Ill, extends a gravelly belt given over since Roman times, at least as far north as Strasbourg, to commercial activities. The Rhône (Doubs)-Rhine Canal follows this strip, but no railroad occupies it. The third zone is the alluvial plain of the quiet Ill River. Its soils are rich but too impermeable and wet from floods and seepage. Undrained, they now are fertile, marshy meadow lands, but if drained they will produce splendid crops of vegetables and cereals. Near the Vosges in the fourth zone, talus and loess soils high enough to be well drained return to the small landowner munificent harvests of cereals, tobacco, and hops. No doubt cereals were grown here by prehistoric men. The fifth zone is higher on the slopes of the Vosges and extends northward east of the sandstone ridges and plateau of Lorraine. It has an excellent east-by-southeast exposure to sunshine and protection from northwest cold and wind, thus providing a satisfactory site for the vine. Among the vineyards and at the foot of the slopes are many small, neat villages of vigorous ruralists.

The Laberne (Saverne) Pass, also called Lorraine Gate, across the northern Vosges was so significant in Roman days that Strasbourg ("Castle by the Road") as well as Metz was even then heavily walled and fortified. So much commerce moved through the Pass that Romans put in it a station for customs collection. More recently the Marne-Rhine canal and the Paris-Vienna railroad have followed the same pass.

4. Jura Mountains. A crescent of young mountains with simple folds in Mesozoic strata lies along the eastern or Swiss boundary. In spite of the broad Burgundian Gate at the north end and the narrower Rhône Valley round the south end, the most direct Paris-to-Milan railroad cuts directly through the central part of the Jura system—abundant testimony to the feebleness of the barrier imposed by the mountains. In the broader central Jura, wide valleys between the folds and considerable plateau areas at the summits offer room for much human residence and activity. Abundant precipitation fosters rich pastures and dense forests. The former are grazed by many cattle whose owners are organized into coöperative societies for dairying and the making of Gruyère cheese and butter. Long, severe winters (latitude 47° north with altitudes of 1,600 to 3,000 feet) give the village and rural people many leisure hours which are industriously occupied in making toys, clocks, watches, pipes, glass, and articles of horn, plastics, and wood—products consuming only a little material but much labor and skill. In the south the valleys are alive with silk manufacture, which is correlated with the great factories in nearby Lyon. The vine flourishes throughout the whole Jura system.

5. Alps. From the environs of Geneva and the Rhône south to the Mediterranean, spreading between the lower Rhône valley and the Italian border, are the intricate patterns of the beautiful western spurs of the Alpine mountains. A great granite and gneissic core extends the whole length, mostly in Italy, while younger folded rocks, deeply eroded, make up the ridges and valleys in France. The Durance River rises far back in

Savoy, nestled in the French Alps, is a charming and picturesque department. Between Chambery and Grenoble lies the little town of St. Pierre Entremont, alt. 2,100 ft.

the mountains, flows along lines of weaker rocks, and turns near the sea, to pour its waters into the Rhône at Avignon. Its valley separates a large crystalline mass of mountains from the main structure and permits a railroad, power development, and much industry to penetrate to the heart of the French Alps. The Isère gathers its waters in beautiful Savoy and furnishes perennial hydro-electric power for iron and steel industries centered at Grenoble. These in turn have called forth a strong technical and liberal arts university in a thriving, modern mountain city. Because of the humidity and rich pasture, the northern Alps, Savoy-Dauphine, are a land of cattle; and because of the dryness and more scanty pasture the southern Provence-Var is a land of sheep. Atlantic influence and the westerlies with their cyclonic weather predominate in the former part, whereas in the latter the Mediterranean high-pressure type of climate prevails. In the days when nations reckoned defendable barriers as the best boundaries these Alps were chosen, but their transgression from the French side was the most

Cannes, a winter resort on the southeast coast, amid diversified fruit orchards and plants for the preparation of many essences. Lérins Isles in the distance are decked with castles, palaces, and a monastery. (Courtesy French Embassy—Information Division)

tempting. As the eastern invaders came up the valleys from the Piedmont plains their armies became more and more separated until they were scattered in many places as they reached the Rhône-Saône, while the French armies, starting over in a score of valleys, descended in close conjunction in as many valleys converging on Turin.

As in Italy, so in France these Alpine slopes descending to the Great Sea provide probably the most charming portion of the country—the Riviera. Topography steep and rugged, shorelines with alternate headlands and pocket beaches, sparkling streams tumbling down ravines, the sea as blue as Sicilian skies or as limpid green as the grassy meadows, natural vegetation of rich dark evergreen, gardens, orchards, and vineyards terraced up the slopes for hundreds of feet, climate usually mild, entrancing, and inspiring—this stretch of scenery from Italy to Marseilles (Fr., Marseille) is enchanting, substantial, tempting one to revel in it the whole year around. It is a zone of memories, prehistoric and historic, from the caves of Mentone through Villefranche with its ancient commerce and Moorish castle on down to Nice and Monaco of Greek and more recent fame. That men have enjoyed these slopes and bays from Paleolithic time becomes obvious as their remains, art, and architecture are uncovered.

French Riviera: Nice, at the foot of the Maritime Alps. The Bay of Angels. (Courtesy French Embassy—Information Division)

To build a road along this coast was an ancient Roman task, but the modern automobile road fits even better into the intricacies of the pattern. It rounds every headland high above the sea and retreats up the valley to find a crossing without descending. Railroad construction calls for tunnels and galleries in abundance, because a train cannot take such short curves as an automobile.

6. Pyrenees. Another mountain section, the Pyrenees, marks the southern frontier of France in a most unfriendly and uncommercial manner. There are no front ranges; the mountains rise very steeply from the plains. Moreover the valleys up from opposite sides do not head in a low through pass as they do so frequently in the Alps; each stream is short and comes down from mountain heights in a small, steep, narrow valley to the plain. A few poor roads go over the barrier, and two railroads pass around the ends. By means of long tunnels recently built, two railroads are now operating across the range, one near the Pass of Somport, the other east of Andorra from Toulouse to Barcelona. Passage across is not so difficult but that the Basques have occupied both sides. Several tributaries of the Garonne and Adour, rising near together, diverge widely in the region of Lourdes and have built an enormous compound fan, the Armagnac Hills, far out on the plains. This latter region is an important site for irrigation, grapes, and cereals. Above this fan is the Pass of Somport dividing Western from Eastern Pyrenees.

La gorge de loup (throat of the wolf), with the railroad bridge and houses up a narrow valley in the borders of Nice. (Courtesy Rostan et Munier, Nice)

The Western Pyrenees are chiefly under the climatic influence of the Atlantic and experience the heaviest rainfall of any part of the country; therefore they have the finest grass and superior cattle. Maize, thriving in the heat and copious rains, extends far up the valleys, and the same rains make abundant power possible. Forests, too, are much finer than over the other end of the mountains. Excellent marble and some minerals are worked in these valleys, and industries based on them are developing.

The Eastern Pyrenees, partaking of the Mediterranean type of climate, are dryer—gray tones replacing the greens of the west. Houses here are built in prominent places grouped in villages, but in the Western Pyrenees they are scattered among the pastures. As hydro-electric power is developed, the mountains will include more commercial and industrial life, their isolating qualities will be overcome, and people from opposite sides will find they have much more in common than they now suppose.

7. Aquitaine. Passing now from the mountain sections, each isolated from the others, the plains are found to be each connected with others.

Aquitaine, a name surviving from Cæsar's time, is used for more than the lower lands of the drainage basin of the Garonne and its estuary, the Gironde. Aquitaine extends from the southern borders of the Armorican to the Central Massif, south to the Pyrenees, and west to the Biscayan-Atlantic shores. Its rocks are Mesozoic, Tertiary, and Quaternary sediments which still lie nearly horizontal; its soils, the result of the weathering of these loose sediments or the deposition of sand and clay in marsh, beach, or fan, are mostly local, diverse but in the main fertile and productive. Because the plain is divided into two parts, a lower, centering on Bordeaux, and an upper, centering on Toulouse, it has produced two rival cities. From an economic viewpoint, Toulouse finds its interests in the east, while Bordeaux with its wide, magnificent estuary faces west to the sea and the world. The upper basin is the finest cereal land in the south, and Toulouse is in consequence the chief milling and market center for flour. It is the only section of France that produces much maize. The lower basin is clothed with vineyards and produces on its heavy clay soils the rich, dark wines of Palus and on its limestone soils lighter wines. Bordeaux gives its name to much of the export wine of this region. The city also exports stone from up the river and lumber from the Landes, and it smelts ores from the Auvergne mines with coal from England. Connection with England dates almost from the earliest days of English history. For over 400 years after the battle of Hastings, 1066 A.D., English and French strove for possession of this Atlantic coast, and even to the present English people seem to prefer this place for vacation trips. Biarritz is quite English, as are many other places of Aquitaine.

Large portions of the seaward side, known as the Landes, consist essentially of recent plains, lifted up, built up, or shut off by sandbars from the sea. Formerly this region was low, sandy, marshy, and largely given over to pastures for sheep, whose shepherds walked about on long stilts, sat on a stilt seat which with the legs made a tripod, and knit woolen hose while the sheep grazed. Drainage projects have opened up most of these plains to cultivation, and the picturesque knitting shepherd is gone. Instead of sheep and wool these plains now furnish cork, resin, and pine lumber.

There are many caves in the limestone areas of the northern Aquitanian plateaus, and the Dordogne country seems to have been as attractive to hunting and fishing cave dwellers in the stone and bronze ages as it has been in recent centuries to viticulturists and to early fruit and truck growers who cater to the Paris market.

8. Mediterranean Plains. When the sea invaded the Aquitaine and Paris basins it also advanced into the Rhône Valley and in the embayment were laid Cretaceous and Tertiary sediments which were subsequently elevated a little above the sea as the beginnings of the Mediterranean Plains. Moderate stream erosion followed, and then a little submergence, so that the coast became embayed in many stream mouths and numbers of islands were formed. In subsequent time down to the present, waves have built sandbars enclosing lagoons, tying islands together and to the mainland; and streams have built deltas of which that of the Rhône is by far the largest. Such constructional work has filled in among the older hill-islands many square miles of new plains. Thus has arisen a low, triangular area of weak relief sheltered on two sides by Alps and Cevennes and tempered by the waters of the sea on the south.

Bauxite mine at Baux, northwest of Marseilles. This ore is refined at aluminum plants in southwestern France. (Courtesy French Embassy—Information Division)

Warmth, dryness, and easy approach over a balmy sea have helped make this little region unique in France. Its fertile soils and picturesque varied aspect, with ready fruits and vegetables, have induced its people, many of them only temporary residents, to be gay and happy. Greeks built cities on the shores; Romans constructed roads and fortifications; and the medieval inhabitants built upon their ruins. This delightful section seems to have been the most historic, the best recreational, and probably the most actively commercial part of what is now France. Today the same warm, dry climate, which has done so much to direct the interests of the people in the past, urges them to grow grapes, make wine, raise olives and press oil from them, and cultivate peaches, cherries, almonds, and acres of vegetables and flowers for local and northern markets. These plains are thickly populated with industrious, prosperous people using the natural resources of stone, sand, and clay for tiles and brick. Back in the low Cretaceous hills near Arles and Nîmes, is dug the aluminum ore bauxite, taking its name from the town of Baux. Salt extracted in great quantities from the sea water is a natural product of many lagoons. Salt, bauxite, lignite, clay, and sand stimulate manufacture of chemicals, metals, ceramic products and many related items. France does not stop in her manufacturing at the end of the first reduction processes but continues until the material is wholly ready for use, often a work of art.

9. Rhône-Saône Valley. The Rhône River, which has been so active in building the Mediterranean Plains, gathers its waste from the Cevennes and their continuation in Côte-d'Or as far as the sources of the Saône, from the Burgundian Gate and the Jura Mountains as far as to the headwaters of the Doubs, from the very heart of the Alps, the glacial sources of the Rhône, and from the high heads of the Isère and Durance. The upper Rhône flows mostly in narrow valleys whose slopes are terraced for grapes, or expands in the broad, beautiful Lake Geneva. But much more important to France than the processes and sources of the river are the highways and agricultural lands available because of the work of this drainage system. The Rhône Valley from its delta to Lyon is only in small part an alluvial plain. Midway the valley is constricted by the near approach of both Alps and Cevennes, and often the plain narrows between hard rock headlands against which the river crowds and above which rise stark, grim Roman or medieval castles built to guard the narrows or to control the movement of armies and traffic in the valley. A keen modern interest attaches to the sensitive crops—peaches, grapes, cherries, and mulberries—which nestle on every south-facing slope and to the acres of cereals and vegetables as well as to the irrigated small fruits, melons, and tomatoes toward the delta. Mulberry trees and sericulture have crept up the sheltered valleys. The industry is closely tributary to business concerns in Lyon, while agriculture and horticulture furnish products to Paris and even to London and Berlin.

The country around Lyon was once the terminus of a mighty Pleistocene glacier, whose sources tore away rocks and debris from 6,000 to 8,000 squares miles of Alps and Fore-Alps, and whose melting ends built enormous moraines near the city, making hummocky and lake-strewn hills and waste land. Malaria brought by mosquitoes from the lakes and marshes troubled the people for centuries, but now through extensive drainage the rich lake bottoms are redeemed for intensive agriculture.

The Saône has a broad, open valley, 30 by 160 miles, extending north from Lyon and communicating freely eastward with Germany through the

Burgundian Gate and northward with the Paris Basin through the "Straits of Côte-d'Or." Twice this Basin has held a lake, once in Tertiary time, and again when the Pleistocene Rhône glacier obstructed the valley at Lyon. Clay and sand, deposited in these lakes, give the rich but damp, dense soils of the valley. The warm summers bring forth on these soils an abundant vegetation, meadow grasses, cereals, and maize to feed poultry, cattle and people. Hydro-electric power contributes to the development of cotton spinning and weaving and to the manufacture of hardware, bicycles, and automobiles in the Belfort factories, while the sunshine on the terraced

Harvesting wheat in the sheaf with tractor and wagon rack. (Courtesy French Embassy—Information Division)

surrounding slopes nourishes well-cared-for vineyards from which come famous wines, the pride of the valley. Below these gardens, at intervals of a mile or so, there are white, red-tiled, picturesque villages and towns occupied by the sturdy wine-growers and wine-makers.

10. Paris Basin. The Paris Basin, the largest, most valuable natural region of France, is also the most centrally located and unifying element. A vast expanse of lowlands with nearly horizontal strata, it has stimulating, varied climate, strong, fertile soils, and extensive and well-constructed water routes and railways which connect it intimately with most of the other regions of France. The Armorican Highlands on the southwest and the Central Massif on the south border the Paris Basin, while between them the Gate of Poitou allows free communication with the Aquitaine Plains and other regions at the south. Northeastern France borders the Basin on the east, leaving a gate, between the Vosges and Côte-d'Or, which leads to the Saône-Rhône Valley, the Burgundian or Belfort Gate, and the Jura-Alpine regions. The Paris Basin has the chief commercial river, though neither the longest nor largest, and the chief city and capital. This region also touches the English Channel for many miles, communicates freely with the plains of Belgium, and reaches to the Lorraine Gate, which crosses the hills to the Rhine at Strasbourg. Because of these connections and contacts it is the most fortunate region in which to place the capital.

The geologic strata of this Basin are of Mesozoic and Tertiary age and have been warped just enough to lie like a stack of broad, very shallow saucers, near the center of which is Paris. The outcropping upturned edges of the more resistant rock layers of the Basin make cuestas which are well marked in the northeastern third of the Basin but scarcely noticeable in other parts. The structure is warped down across the English Channel but appears again in the London Basin. Its layers consist of limestones, with enormous building-stone values, and of clays and marls, with industrial significance, all producing excellent soils; the central portion for many miles round Paris is called the Garden of France. The part between the Seine and Marne is the Île de France. Six cuestas may be identified toward the northeast. If a journey be made from Paris to Metz the cuesta-ridges, very gentle on the west and steeper on the east slope, will be crossed one after the other. The first is the eastern edge of the Brie, crossed near Épernay; the second is beyond Châlons; the third is in the Argonne; the fourth, between the Argonne and Verdun, is not a continuous crest; but, like the Argonne, is a branch of the next. The fifth, Côte de Meuse, is a few miles east of the Meuse; and the sixth, Côte de Moselle, is west of the Moselle in the north but just east of it in the south. Metz guards a stream notch through this cuesta. These cuestas can be easily defended from the west side, whereas an army approaching from the east must negotiate their steeper faces. They thus delayed the march of the German armies on Paris in 1914 and in World War II.

Between the first and second cuestas is the dry Champagne with a dry limestone soil, while beyond the second is the humid Champagne extending into Argonne. The former is the home of the grape-growing industry which provides the bases for the manufacture of champagne and other wines. Caverns in the limestones, enlarged in places or connected by passages and built over to protect their entrances, furnish vast wine-cellars; and the buildings serve as press-houses in which grapes are prepared and the juice is pressed out and bottled. Millions of gallons are stored and ripened for years in a single cave cellar. Many pines have been planted successfully in this dry, poor soil. Besides the vineyards the eastern inter-ridge plains have other fruits, vegetables and flowers, and the ridge slopes have vines and wheat, but the uplands are usually clothed with deciduous forests.

Through the cuestas flow the Seine, Aube, Marne, Aisne, and lesser tributaries, and more or less parallel with them flow northward the Meuse and Moselle, deeply entrenched in the plateaus. Where the cross streams go through the ridges they have carved gates which have been of high value in military strategy and of special importance for railways. No railroad can cross the country from Paris to the eastern frontier without using several of these gates. The line up from Strasbourg passes first the Nancy gateway in the Côte de Moselle, then turning west crosses the river and climbs up a little to the Toul Gap in the Côte de Meuse. Next it swings a little north to enter the low notch through the Argonne ridge. After crossing the humid Champagne, it passes through the Vitry gateway over the dry Champagne and through the next scarp-line at the Gate of Épernay. No direct route is this for commerce; and for military purposes a train from Germany would need its German guard in at least five gateways.

The Île de France occupies most of the upper smallest "saucer," a plain surrounding the beautiful city of Paris with as attractive farming, fruit, and vegetable land as supplies any city in the world. The Seine majestically sweeps in great curves through this central Île and receives the Yonne, Marne, and Oise within a short distance. All these streams, because of their low grade and ample water supply, aid the Seine in gathering and distributing foods and merchandise, but also occasionally pour disastrous floods through central France.

North of Paris are the Picardy-Flanders lowlands, separated from each other by the Artois Hills. They are diverse areas and have been desperately contested many times by armies which have been greatly influenced by the topography and the streams, by Flanders mud, and by Picardy limestone. Flanders soils, although particularly difficult to work, are producers of luxuriant vegetation—wheat, barley, beets, hops, flax, and fields of grass and legumes. These meadows furnish food for abundant dairy herds which supply the milk for butter and cheese, meat for the dense population, hides for leather manufacture, and much valuable stable manure with which to fertilize the gardens. Industries have flourished here since the Middle Ages. The old hand methods have been all but replaced by machines for making cotton, wool, and linen cloth. In modern times abundance of labor immigrating from Belgium has stimulated this rise of machine shops to supply local markets, oil refineries, chemical works, and mills for ready-made clothing. Picardy with its limestone below the clay loam soils is admirably suited to agriculture. Such crops as sugar beets and wheat predominate. Ground water can be reached in wells at the foot of the Artois Hills, where it rises freely to the surface in artesian ("artois-ian") wells.

The channel lands of the Basin meet the sea in long, sandy beaches toward the north, but in chalk cliffs near Calais and for miles southward. Harbors there are difficult, shallow or rocky, but Dieppe does a lot of cross-channel passenger business; Calais, a roadstead, is in constant and profitable connection with Dover, England; and Dunkirk and several Belgian ports do a large freight and passenger service across the straits.

River traffic at Ste. Honorine, a village where the Oise and Seine rivers come together. (Courtesy French Embassy—Information Division)

11. Corsica. This is a rugged, mountainous, forested island south of Genoa and near Sardinia, which it resembles in position, structure, and resources. Its hills furnish a wealth and variety of building stones, such as granites, serpentine, slate, limestone and sandstone; also clays, anthracite, antimony, copper, and mineral waters. Being surrounded by the waters of the western Mediterranean, the "warming pan" of Europe, all its lowlands have a mild climate which permits its coast peoples to raise olives, lemons, and oranges, as well as early vegetables and chestnuts. This agriculture recently has been extended down the valleys to the coast, because the coasts are now safer from pirates than they were 300 to 400 years ago. Forest development is beginning. Fisheries include tunny and anchovies.

REGIONAL INTERRELATIONS

Boundaries. In 814 A.D., a date marked by the death of Charlemagne, the kingdom of the Franks included seven or eight tribes whose boundaries corresponded closely with the physiographic lines used in delimiting the above physical regions. Additions and adjustments of boundaries from time to time brought France in 1789 very nearly to the present lines. With slight changes on Belgian and Italian borders the boundaries were re-adopted in 1815, and have suffered little change since except for the vibration of Alsace-Lorraine. This section was excluded in 1871, returned in 1919, stolen by Hitler in 1940, and again returned to France in 1944. As stated under Italy a few small changes in the high Alps that were made by the final treaty of World War II favored France. Over 160 years of use attest the value of the present boundaries.

Geology and physiography combine to unite the several varied physical regions into one effective unity. Variety, so clearly seen as one surveys the regions, is linked by open commercial ways, so that any region can easily buy and sell in any other, and people can move with ease from one part to any other. From the northern border across the Paris Basin, through the Gate of Poitou and across Aquitania to the Pyrenees is a simple plains journey.

With all this freedom within the country, roads leading out of the country are not so easy. Complete change in method of travel must be made to cross any seacoast border. Around the ends of the Pyrenees and Alps the passageways are usable but narrow. Up the Rhône the road follows a gorge. Much simpler is the crossing of the Rhine into Germany or the Flanders fields into Belgium. What is within France is well united, but what is outside is not well articulated. Thus the present boundaries surround a wide diversity of all that aids and stimulates a nation, separate the people from neighboring states, and still grant remarkable internal communications.

Supplemental relations. Internal diversity of climate, exposure, resource, and outlook establishes supplemental relations. The mountain areas furnish forest products, ores, recreational playgrounds, and water power for industrial cities in the plains. Cereals in the north exchange for fruits in the south, and southern early vegetables supply the tables of the north without recourse to greenhouses. Mineral resources are varied, generally abundant, well distributed or easily moved to industrial localities. Facilities are ample for importation of such goods as no part of France can produce.

PEOPLE

So diversified a national domain, oft invaded, and even ruled at times, by different people, should possess a variety of human types.

Prehistoric people. Eoliths in Tertiary beds have been found in France, a fact which suggests a very early occupancy by extremely primitive people.

Paleolithic and Neolithic remains are common in many places, usually at such sites as show their citizens to have had some skill in choosing home locations. Many of these early peoples lived in caves in the limestones of the Dordogne Valley and the western Central Massif. Others dwelt on the lower .slopes of the Pyrenees, enjoyed the chase, and brought home the game. To the cave-dwellers must be given credit for remarkable adjustments to their habitat and resources, as well as consummate skill, art, and patience in decorating their cavern walls with drawings, paintings, and carvings. So much has now been learned of these early people that it becomes certain they contributed somewhat to the blood of the Frenchmen of today.

Mediterranean dolichocephalic heads are very common in southern France, while Nordic longheads are fully as frequent in the north, but the mass of the people are Alpine roundheads. A small relic group of Celts still occupies the rougher parts of the Armorican peninsulas, and a still smaller remnant, the Basques, occur in the Western Pyrenees. Racial lines have been largely obliterated because of the freedom of movement within the national confines.

Historic geography. Kaleidoscopic changes in size and shape of tribal lands and national boundaries in the land now embraced in France are one of the marked characteristics of its history. When men were in the habit of keeping aloof from their neighbors, except to fight them, the sea, mountains, and escarpments were the most desirable frontiers; but when buffer states were invented, the most featureless boundary was desired—witness the line between Belgium and France. The Rhine Valley and slopes have been claimed by Germans in order to establish bristling castles and fortifications on the cuestas farther west. These situations have been claimed by the French in order to set up their outposts along the eastern bluffs and bring the Rhine highway, vineyards, and ramparts all within their power. Since World War I as economic relations have loomed much larger, the navigable Rhine, with its excellent railroad sites, has been adopted as the international boundary. It is not a line but a zone, not with sparse population but a belt with many people possessing similar interests in the river and its plains. These circumstances should encourage acquaintance and call for coöpera- tion between French and Germans, the bases for permanence of boundaries and for friendly relations between the common users of the Rhine.

Language, religion, art. Aryan languages of the Latin branch prevail in France except among the Basques and some Celts; over the latter, long ago, there spread a strong Latin influence. Two French dialects have struggled with each other for hundreds of years; the one in the north has now become the foundation tongue for modern French. Dominian [2] points out that "Be- tween the langue d'oc (northern) and langue d'oil the difference was that of north and south. Southern idioms expressed feeling and harmony, hence

[2] Leon Dominian, *Frontiers of Language and Nationality in Europe* (1924), p. 11.

they were preferred by poets. The 'parlers' of the north on the other hand were endowed with the staying qualities of lucidity, order, and precision. The beauty of modern French, as well as the attraction it exerts on the cultivated minds, is due to its well-balanced blend of northern and southern elements. No other language can boast of an equally happy composition. In this respect it is a true mirror of the French mind as well as of the French nationality."

Christianity spread early into France, and when the great north-south line between the Roman and Greek Catholic, or Western and Eastern, churches was drawn, France was decidedly on the western side. Religion ever since has been essentially of the Roman Catholic type. Long in vital contact with the more progressive West, indeed a part of it, France has been quite liberal; church and state are separate, and complete religious freedom has been accorded the people.

Architecture and building materials are indeed diverse in different parts of the country. Residual, iron-bearing clays are extensively used for red, burned brick and for roof tiles. Other colors are made of less ferruginous clays. Building stone is very abundant and of fine qualities. Probably the most characteristic building is the common peasant and village type used in the northwest where the chalk limestone is used for portions of the wall, and the chert is stuck in mortar in panels for other parts. Chert in this region is dark-colored, whereas the limestone is light to white. Excellent granite is quarried in Brittany, in Auvergne, and in the Fore-Alps. Fine red sandstone in the northern Vosges gives color to thousands of houses in the hills and in Strasbourg. Slate from Ardennes and eastern Armorica is generally used for roofs in many northern cities. Quarrying of plain limestone and sandstone is a very large industry in the Paris region, which makes a stone city possible and as cheap as any permanent construction. Marble from the upper Garonne and other Pyrenean slopes and the Isère Valley is widely used for the nobler buildings. Limestone and sandstone can be had in most sections. Over $30 million worth of home-quarried building stone is used annually. With so rich a variety of high-grade building materials it is not surprising that city building is largely of the more substantial materials. In mountain and forest regions, artistic and interesting wooden structures are more conveniently and cheaply erected. French architecture is of many styles but is exceptionally artistic, graceful, and durable. A noticeable item is the frequent use of glass in roofs of porches and arcades to admit as much light as possible in the dull, cloudy weather.

Sculpture, weaving, and art-glass work have had a large development and reflect the great range of high-grade stone, fibers, and sands upon which a skilful, intelligent, artistic people have bestowed their labor. The question may well be raised whether such skill, art, harmony, and productivity in these fields would have been possible in a country less blessed with varied resources. For centuries the French have also laid many foreign lands under heavy tribute for materials.

BASIC ACTIVITIES

It is probable that the people of France are in closer touch with their resources and carry their industries to more refined stages and prepare their products in more remunerative forms than any other people in Europe. Would it then be just to say that France is most completely adjusted to its geographic conditions? Seven leading activities will be discussed as illustrations of French responses to environment.

Agriculture. Agriculture is the first occupation because of the wide variety of soils, exposures, and climate, and because of the universally good quality of the soils. Cereals and the vine are easily the most important crops. Wheat, sown in the fall and harvested in late June, almost satisfies the home market and meets the largest per capita consumption in Europe— over nine bushels. France is one of those countries whose production per acre is large as a result of excellent farm methods and of a climate with winter rains and warm, dry summers. It exceeds in this the other four leading European countries; in acreage, the proportion of cropped land is almost 30 per cent, exceeding all Europe except Italy. Acreage and production are also a response to the food needs of a numerous people with high standards of living who eat much bread, probably more than any other wheat-eating nation.

Wheat has had to compete with foreign production in Argentina, Russia, and the American Northwest by intensive cultivation and by protective tariffs. The former, much more effective than the latter, has led to crop rotation with its own competitive crops, which has improved both tilth and strength of soil. The sugar beet, tobacco, and chicory, three of the leading competitors of wheat, require much thorough cultivation which puts the soil in prime condition for the wheat crop that cannot be cultivated.

The vine requires early and continuous heat in summer and can endure winter cold, but it is unsuccessful north of a climatic line from the mouth of the Loire through Paris to Sedan. Altitudes of 2,300 feet in the northern and 3,600 feet in the southern Alps also exclude it. The competition of Algeria, a true grape land, has limited the vine in France to such places as are specially endowed by nature with supremely suitable soil and exposure, just the places which from a geographic viewpoint should alone try to produce commercial grapes. A Frenchman finds wine almost as essential as bread, which helps explain this most characteristic crop and the French peasant's large use of wine. Ease of modern transportation, thus putting wines from any part of France within the reach of any city, has greatly assisted vinegrowing as well as wheat production. The huge barrel-like wine car travels

over the French railroad by the tens of thousands. "Vineyards give employment to more than 1,500,000 growers, for the most part small landholders
who are active, and enterprising, democratically inclined, much attached to
the soil and to the cause of freedom." [3]

Gathering wine grapes grown on low trellises. Compare with American and Portuguese trellises.
(Courtesy French Embassy—Information Division)

France is one of the five largest forage-crop producers in Europe because
of the very satisfactory climate for hay, because of the place of hay in
French crop rotation, because of the modern need of meat in the diet of
the higher standards of living, because of the growing use of cheese, butter,
and milk, and because of the surrender under competition of poorer wheat
lands to forage crops. Regions specialize in certain products: Normandy,
with its very luxuriant grass, in Camembert cheese; Brittany and Poitou in

[3] R. Blanchard, *Geography of France* (1917), p. 205.

their famous butter; districts near large cities and industrial regions in milk and fat stock. Some fattening of stock, as in Flanders and Picardy, follows the sugar beet and refineries, where the pulp is fed to produce the "sugar-fattened" steers.

Extractive industries. These industries embrace such occupations as recover resources that have been prepared without man's help, namely, mining, quarrying, fishing, hunting, cutting of natural forests, working of coal, and development of water power. France is especially active in most of these occupations and well supplied with the contributing resources. Mining and quarrying have been discussed in several of the regions. Both of the French seas are good fishing grounds and together yield some $50 million worth of fish each year. Fisheries are concentrated in the English Channel and the Mediterranean Sea, but many French vessels visit the productive North Sea and Newfoundland waters.

Forests occupy about one fifth of France; conifers constitute one fifth of the forests, while hardwoods make up the balance. Topography and precipitation, temperature, and soils naturally would make a great forest land of France, but long human occupation by a large industrial population has greatly depleted the acreage. Although in recent times the supply is quite inadequate, a carefully adapted system of forestry conservation serves to keep the growth and the cut about equal. Wood is imported and is used sparingly. This situation encourages a large use of brick and stone for buildings throughout the country, even in rural villages, except in strictly forest sections. Hunting has also declined with the forests, but the bear, deer, boar, and many lesser animals still attract hunters and make possible a valued branch of recreation. Game is invariably used for food as carefully as are domestic animals.

With strong relief on two sides and reasonable all-year rainfall on much of its surface, France is unusually endowed with potential water power, to supplement her deficiencies in coal and oil. Power, therefore, has been developed until only Italy, among European countries, exceeds France in hydro-electric capacity. This great use of power supply was brought about principally by conditions during World War I when Germany controlled much French coal-mining. Under the same stimulus industries moved south where the power resources are greatest. Even the peasantry and small villagers are sensing the advantages of electricity for power and light, prominent among which is its ease of distribution and subdivision for the small industries and small plants so characteristic of French industry. Over five sixths of the 40,000 communes are electrified; less than half the 5 million kilowatts available are developed, however. The use of electricity on farms is making country life more attractive and in some localities more remunerative.

The minette ferric oxide ores of Lorraine have been mentioned. Excellent iron ores occurring in the Grenoble region of the Alps supply the hydro-electric furnaces near the city. The northern part of Auvergne Plateau feeds the steel industry of Le Creusot and St. Étienne as well as of Nancy, and two nearby industrial suburbs, Maxeville and Bouxiere. Other iron is mined near Caen in Normandy and in the Ariège Valley of the Pyrenees. Of salt, potassium, nitrates, gypsum, talc, aluminum, antimony, and pyrite for sulphur there is sufficient. France lacks in the homeland tin, arsenic, copper, nickel, chromium, cobalt, tungsten, mica, radium, uranium, petroleum, and coking coal. Gold, silver, lead, zinc, phosphates, and manganese are mined but not in sufficient amounts for home use.

French ceramics are an art at scores of famous centers for chinaware and glass. Artist M. R. Gabiroux at his wheel. (Courtesy French Embassy—Information Division)

Refined industries. More characteristic of France, however, than agriculture and extractive industries is the finishing and refining of manufactured products and the bestowal of artistic touch and style that set its products in a class by themselves. It cannot be claimed that the making of luxury articles and especially attractive finished goods is wholly a response to geographic conditions; but more than likely it is related to two geographic factors:

(1) the people occupy a beautiful country in a highly stimulating, energy-supplying climate, and (2) they dwell among nations who have become alert and sensitive to such values, and, by their own development, are financially able to purchase the choicest goods. The French sense of nice-ness, appropriateness, delicacy of design, and harmony of form and color has become highly developed. All this finds itself expressed, not only in the production of most charming and exquisite textiles, toilet articles, and dainty bits of ornament for every home, but also in the refinement of manufactures

Book making is another art. This artist is gold-tooling a book cover. (Courtesy French Embassy—Information Division)

in many lines. Iron and steel are made into engines, cars, railroads, bridges, and machines, as in any industrial land; but the engine is more graceful, the machine more artistic, and a thousand and one iron or steel trinkets, pins, and other small articles are made. A French car is not built simply to run but to please the eye and the sense of touch. Thus it is that Paris has become the city of initial designs in dress, furniture, finishings, drapes, and rugs, the center of fashion, the home of art in painting, etching, and many other lines. French shoes, heels, mirrors, perfumes, gowns, wraps, lorgnettes, and wigs are always the last word.

Internal commerce. The broad, low passes between the uplands and mountain masses, linking all the plains and permitting free intercourse between them and every hilly and mountainous area, make possible elaborate internal trade and encourage a common level of living and use of products. The people have taken advantage of the gentle grade of streams and the low divides to canalize streams and construct connecting canals until Paris can go to sea on every major stream of the country—Seine, Somme, Oise, Marne, Meuse, Moselle, Rhine, Saône, Rhône, Loire; and by turning aside from the Rhône above Arles a boat can make its way along a canal through Cette, Toulouse, and Bordeaux to the estuary of the Gironde. Such a system would not have been possible without the topographic unity mentioned. Canals were made before railroads and were given a long time in which to prove their worth and establish precedents in their favor. The economic significance of the canal system is spectacularly demonstrated, for instance, by the fact that the Marseille-Arles Canal, 50 miles in length, leads through a large tunnel four and a half miles long. Then in the last half of the nineteenth century came the railroads, following similar lines and many others as well, for they could reach far up valleys and over plateaus.

A differentiation of traffic followed. Passengers have ceased to ride on the canals and do not use the rivers as much as formerly. Likewise mail, express, and fast freight have left the boats, but canal boats are still crowded with heavy, bulky, or slow freight. The quays of Paris show clearly what things ride on canals and streams—coal, in briquettes as well as lump, stone of many kinds, gravel and sand dredged from the rivers in great quantities, brick, slate, tiles, cement, lumber, logs, boards, stove-wood, mine props, iron ore, rock for flux, wines for the cellars in the banks of the Seine in upper Paris, vegetables, hardier fruits, cereals, flour, machinery, and furniture.

France has over 4,500 miles of navigable streams, 3,000 miles of canal, and about 25,000 miles of railroads grouped into six great systems and reaching most parts of the republic. An efficient truck service has been built up on the 25,000 miles of excellent national roads and 11,400 miles of good departmental roads. There are over 400,000 miles of roads of only local interest. In many places the topography is rolling enough to facilitate elimination of railroad grade-crossings, but more than 30,000 still exist and nearly all are carefully guarded by gates or watchmen or both. While both the waterways and railroads radiate from Paris, they systematically connect with the ports and the communication systems of other nations through the various gates—Lorraine, Burgundian, and Rhône—and round the ends of the Pyrenees. Until recently one could not leave a French channel port and go directly to Switzerland, but must change at Paris.

Foreign commerce. French commercial activities are well balanced and there is little need of exchange with foreign countries. Note the difference here between England and France. Yet France has nearly 40 per cent as large a foreign trade as Great Britain. Most of the exports are of manufactures, particularly characteristic French articles, whose value is not in their material nor their bulk but in the skilled labor and the exquisite nicety both of product and wrappings. For the same reasons, namely, the lack of raw materials, the abundance of high-grade labor, plenty of power, and large, backward colonial possessions, the imports are coal, raw materials, and foods. Imports always exceed exports, but the balance is maintained by a large tourist trade, earnings of the vessels carrying goods, and the returns on French foreign investments. About 35 per cent of the foreign trade is with the colonies, the balance chiefly with the United States and immediate neighbors. Argentina is the only other distant country that has even a moderate share of the trade, sending hides, meats, corn and bird-seed.

Rehabilitation since World War II. Reconstruction in the devastated portions has been a major problem since the elections in January, 1947. Most of the mines have been restored to operation, thousands of factories have been rebuilt, a very large percentage of the damaged agricultural lands have been leveled and prepared for crops, and livestock has been bred up nearly to prewar levels. Even yet, however, many acres of land in the northwest are waste, and the forests and fruit trees are far from normal. Reconstruction has placed a very heavy tax upon the people, but definite official planning has aided the labor and the degree of recovery attained in so short a time speaks well for the resiliency of the ordinary people.

Tourists and recreation programs. Why do people go to France? The delightful French people please many tourists. The neat, attractive country homes, farms, and villages prove intriguing to others. The chateaux in many parts of France, particularly in the middle and lower Loire basin, entice many from the cities. Any land occupied through medieval time by an active people will have monuments, buildings, palaces, prisons, and walled cities. These the French have preserved, patched, and often rebuilt. France has a natural setting of river and plain, mountain and forest, seashore and headland into which these historic items have been fitted. Add to these items the history of war, love, cabal and crime, conquest, revolution, defeat, and the march of the generations over the soil for centuries, then recall that museums, galleries, churches, cathedrals, gardens, and palaces are not only adorned with furnishings, statuary, doors, windows, and ornaments made for them but with many pieces made for other places and transported hither as trophies of war or of private plundering, and you have scores of other elements of charm and interest. Modern museums and art galleries have gathered, more or less legitimately, sculpture, paintings, etchings, armor, utensils, and garments out of the past or from distant lands. Thousands of homes have pieces of antique furniture two to three times as old as any American pieces. These are some of the things men and women come to see and live among. No wonder tourists spend 200 or 300 millions of dollars a year in France and feel they have made a good bargain!

HARBORS, TOWNS, AND CITIES

Le Havre. The harbor is located on the north side of the broad estuary of the Seine where the great river, spreading over its own mud and sand flats, attains a width of 5 or 6 miles. Breakwaters of stone and docks of brick have been built; dredging has deepened many acres sufficiently to float the largest vessels and built up other acres upon which warehouses and customs offices have been erected, loading and unloading machinery installed, and pavements, railroads, and trams laid—all prepared for a large commercial and passenger service. The city of 160,000 people spreads up over the slopes of advanced mature topography, with hotels, shops, factories, and thousands of neat residences; above on the ridge nearest the sea stand the lighthouses and a battery of big guns. Over the ridge crest a steep slope of chert-filled, chalk sea-cliffs descends abruptly to the little beach at the water's edge. The harbor and city function as one of the busiest gateways for busy France. Through its portals come the products of colonial lands on three continents and the islands of the sea, the exports from a dozen countries, differently equipped than is France. Coffee from Brazil is the largest single product imported at Le Havre. From its docks ships sail to fifty nations carrying the products of the many French manufactories, or transit products from countries far inside the continent. Rapid trains hurry up the valley with freight, passengers, mail, or express to the cotton manufacturing city of Rouen or to the great capital city. Paris makes Le Havre; Le Havre is a door of Paris.

Marseilles. In the south, 25 miles east of the Rhône mouths with their loads of waste and their rapid sedimentation, is the great commercial, industrial city of 636,000 people, Marseilles. Its name has been modified from the Greek original Massilia. Two or three small, waste-laden streams come down from the hills back of the city; for many centuries they spread their burdens of sand and clay among the rocky limestone island-hills in the bay and between two Mesozoic rock ridges, one north, one south, 5 to 6 miles from the city. The delta thus constructed has filled the straits between the islands, leaving them protruding as hills above the plain. Notre Dame de la Garde, the popular seaman's cathedral, adorns one such hill; forts St. John and St. Nicholas, built long ago to guard the bay, occupy two others, and the city with its residential suburbs spreads beyond the delta over several others. Isle d'If (with Dumas's Chateau), 3 or 4 miles from the city, is one of six to eight rocky islands still beyond the reach of the sediments. The old harbor is a basin, a remnant of the bay not yet filled, capable of holding a score of Mediterranean vessels. Surrounding the bay are warehouses, fish-stalls, restaurants, and all sorts of stores and offices to handle the freight, insurance, and mariners' supplies.

The modern harbor, made necessary by the stimulus of African colonial trade, consists of a protected roadstead, three miles long, north of the city, containing modern dock machinery, warehouses, railroads and accessories. Railroads in Marseilles are modern and came so long after the building of

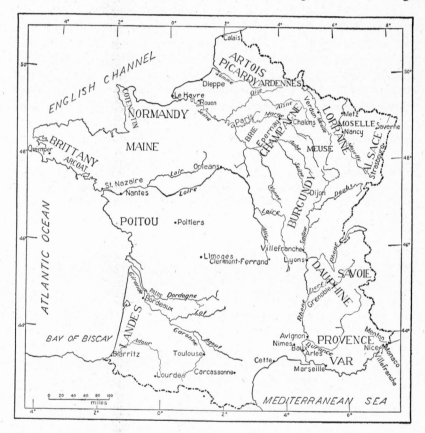

Outline map of France, with rivers, towns, sections of the country, and boundaries with adjacent countries. (Compiled from Goode's *School Atlas* and *Oxford Advanced Atlas*)

the city that they cannot enter far within its limits. The line from the east, after running most of the way along the coast from Italy, turns inland through two tunnels under portions of the south ridge and, curving frequently to avoid hills, enters the valley of one of the little streams and approaches the city. It sends a freight branch round the south side to reach the old harbor, but in so doing goes through a 2-mile tunnel beneath the city's edge. The main line, bearing round to the north, has three stations in the outskirts with a big freight service to the new harbor and a line toward

Lyon, which penetrates the north ridge in a 3-mile tunnel. Because the city is so important commercially, it has become industrial and many colonial products, especially those from Africa, are processed in its factories before they go into the French markets.

The land about Marseilles is intensively cultivated for vegetables, Mediterranean fruits, poultry, and dairy stock. Every stream that comes toward the city is used for irrigation. Three superb national highways lead out of the city, and many lesser roads serve the suburbs and vicinal villages.

Bordeaux. Bordeaux (253,700) is a river harbor and industrial city. Situated 60 miles from the sea at the head of the Gironde estuary, 12 to 13 miles above the Dordogne mouth, it enjoys all the protection, as well as suffers all the inconveniences, of being restricted to a river. The Garonne once reached the sea about 25 miles above the city when Garonne and Dordogne entered by separate mouths. The former now follows along the edge of the older topography which rises to altitudes of 300 feet. The plains extending west from the river to the sea rarely exceed half that figure and are much more nearly level.

Bordeaux is the fourth city of France, has one of the three finest harbors, and serves most of the southwest interests. It is built on the flood-plain but has begun to develop residential sections up the slopes on either side. Its harbor facilities and quays occupy both banks of the river for about five miles. Since Bordeaux is an old city, it is difficult to construct railroads which can render wholly satisfactory service. Bordeaux handles naval stores and much of the lumber business from the new pine forests of the Landes, but it is most important as a wine port, collecting and marketing about 20 per cent of the whole French vintage, to which the slopes of the Dordogne as well as those of the Garonne contribute generously.

Manufactures are in wood and in iron. Many machine-shops use iron and steel smelted elsewhere. Bricks and tiles are made from local clays on the east side. Cement blocks are molded in great numbers and variety and are extensively used in the city. The limestones in the old hills toward the east furnish material for the cement industry, while sand and gravel are dredged from the river channel to make the concrete blocks.

Lyon. At the intersection of the Rhône corridor with the east-and-west traffic, an ideal location for a city, Lyon, for a long time a Roman capital in Gaul, has come to be the third city in France with about 571,000 inhabitants. It was easily defended and is still overlooked by upwards of a score of fortresses. It still has a city wall, with bastions and towers, extending from the Rhône north of the city in a great semicircle eastward and back to the river south of the city. In early times such a junction point of valleys and streams held military and commercial significance. One of the valleys meeting here comes out of Switzerland and Germany, the other from Paris, north France, Belgium, Netherlands, and another part of Germany; the great united highway leads to the Mediterranean, whose shores are still rich with culture and commerce. Abundance of building material—granite in the hills west of town, limestones nearer the Rhône, clays and sands in the valley, together with extensive forests over the mountains on each side— give a large variety to the buildings.

Silkworms and mulberry trees find suitable climate up and down the Rhône Valley, and for many generations their culture has furnished the silk for the ribbon industry that has made Lyon famous. Cotton from America and wool from the Auvergne help to swell textile industries of this busy city. Many mills are located among the hills in the valleys that lead to the city. Coal, iron ore, and limestone close by in the western hills have made the metallurgy of steel a profitable industry, and Lyon not only reduces the ore but uses the iron in making bridges, machinery, structural steel, and boats.

Metz. Quite another type of city is found in the Moselle Valley opposite the Lorraine Gate and in the Meuse Valley on the French side of the boundary. Metz was heavily fortified by Germany, Verdun by France; both are now well within the French boundary, but in the past these two centers strove to outdo each other in preparation for defense. Both are remarkably well situated for the purpose, since both guard the east-and-west route from Paris to the mid-Rhine Valley. Each is on an entrenched north-flowing stream in the low plateaus and cuestas of the eastern part of the Paris Basin. The hills around each were capped with forts and armed with guns. For centuries Metz had a strong city wall. The valleys have canals and heavily equipped railroads. Five such roads lead into Metz, and each is in easy communication with all the others. This is different from the railroad situation in most European places of its size, where each railroad has its own station in some border of the town and no direct connection with any other road. Although Metz is a town of about 60,000 people, in days before World War I it had few interests other than military.

Paris. Within the city of Paris there are 2,800,000 people, and in the suburbs included in greater Paris there are over 2,000,000 more. There must be remarkable advantages to account for the growth of an aggregation of this size and importance and some fundamental reason for its situation. The Paris Basin needed a definite gathering point and clearing house as soon as there was any social, commercial, or political unity, and such a place should be central. This fact together with the convergence of streams would put the meeting place within 25 miles of the present city. It must be on the Seine, greatest of French waterways. Two junctions of rivers might contend for supremacy, the Seine-Marne and the Seine-Oise. It was not an approach to the sea in the very early days that helped to determine the location, but rather the relation to the interior lands through the Lorraine, Burgundian, and Rhône gates and routes into the Auvergne and Aquitania, to the Loire and Garonne rivers, and to the Carcassonne Pass; hence the upper junction had the supremacy. Add to this advantage the problem of the great meanders below the present city that must have lengthened the distance from these passes to the Oise mouth, and again the convergence of routes from the south, and the Seine-Marne confluence has still more advantage. If one comes out of the Auvergne by Loire or Allier and proceeds to a central place, the Marne mouth is best. If he ascends the Loire northeastward, he will leave it at Orléans and go most directly again to the Seine-Marne junction. These two considerations must have helped to put Orléans at the rectangular turn in the Loire, as auxiliary to Paris on the Seine.

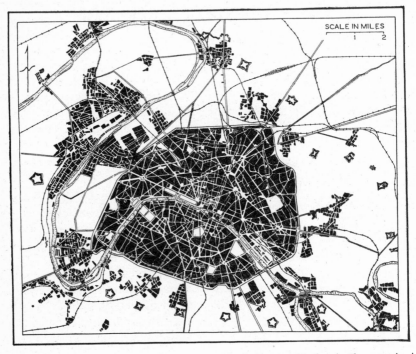

Paris, with many of its streets, bridges, suburbs, fortifications, and railroads. The great boulevard surrounding the city marks the site of the modern wall, now removed except for two or three gates or short sections. (Adapted from French government topographic maps)

The exact junction of the Seine-Marne was not a good crossing place because streams spread out over sands and shifted positions, but three or four miles downstream was a substantial island a mile in length. Chisholm wrote about 50 years ago, "The Île de la Cité unquestionably determined the precise situation of the original nucleus of Paris." [4] Cæsar notes that this island was connected with the mainland on either side by bridges, and he recognizes its commanding position as early as 53 B.C., when he designates it as the meeting-place for the Gauls on account of its central location.

[4] G. G. Chisholm, *Europe;* E. Stanford, *Compendium of Geography.*

This island, smaller then than now, held for centuries the entire city. It seems to have been a Roman official residence from the third century. Romans maintained two wooden bridges at the island, a task which was easier than to construct one over the whole river. The island was easier to defend than any place on the banks. It is recorded that, while the island was fortified, the palace, theater, temple, and baths were erected on the left (south) bank, and forest prevailed on the north. As the country became unified, the advantages of the site for a French capital were magnified con-

In an atelier of the Gobelin tapestry factory in Paris. (Courtesy French Embassy—Information Division)

currently with the development of the nation's growth. Paris increased until it reached the million mark nearly a century ago. All the advantages of early position, central on great highways, have been accentuated by canal and railroad construction. If ever "All roads led to Rome," the statement is doubly true of Paris as regards France. About fifteen national highways enter the city, and twice as many lesser roads. A circle of 6 miles radius centering on the lower end of the island crosses thirteen railroads leading into the borders of Paris. They do not cross the city but are all connected by a belt line just inside the latest wall and again by a less regular circuit

3 to 5 miles farther from the city, thus ensuring complete unity and coöperation of the several French railway systems that enter Paris.

The altitude of the city increases from 80 feet on the Seine at its lowest point to 420 feet near the north borders. It has relief enough for good drainage, yet never too much for easy movement of people and goods. Its foundation rocks are everywhere substantial but nowhere so resistant as to interfere with excavations or subways. Indeed, the growth of the city is due partly to the abundance of suitable structural rock in the Paris Basin, although more to the generous grain-bearing and other food-producing tracts in the vicinity.

The Arch of Triumph, Paris. (Courtesy T.W.A.)

The beautiful boulevards of Paris are a product and a record of its growth. In the fourteenth, sixteenth, and seventeenth centuries, after the city had grown out a mile or so beyond the limits of the island, sections of wall were built and connected as ramparts or bulwarks. Suburbs again grew outside the walls, and in the eighteenth century a new enclosing wall was erected, in some places a mile or two outside the old ones. The inner walls were demolished and "interior boulevards" opened along them, which are called the Grand Boulevards. *Boulevard* seems to be the name originally applied to the broad promenade top of the rampart or bulwark, later applied to the parked avenue occupying the site of razed walls. Still suburbs grew outside, and Paris, as if preparing for the struggle of 1870-71, built in 1860 the last city wall enclosing 8 miles of the Seine and about 30 square miles of land. At the same time outer works—twenty-five or more forts and batteries—were put in such condition that a German wrote, "Paris is the greatest fortress in the world." After this outer wall was complete, the second line was demolished and the "exterior boulevards" constructed. During the last five to ten years the latest wall has similarly been nearly destroyed to make room for boulevards, bus lines, parks, and other improvements on the circuit of the city of 1860.

The old palace of the Tuileries along the north bank of the river, so named becaused it displaced great tile factories (*tuileries*) using local clay as well as that brought in on boats, memorializes an ancient industry. Paris has a double water supply. Canal, river, and artesian water is pumped in several places in and about the city for industrial and public purposes such as washing the streets. A second system of mains carries water for domestic use, brought 50 to 100 miles in aqueducts from springs among the hills east, southeast, and west of the city.

COLONIAL POSSESSIONS

France has foreign possessions, land and people more or less under her control, amounting to twenty times as much territory and numbering one and a half times as many inhabitants as in her homeland.[5] Only Britain and Russia exceed France in area under one flag. Such holdings of lands in other types of climate, possessing other resources and crops, cannot fail to be a stimulus to the homeland even though not a great source of income. They

[5] In Africa:	Area in square miles	Population
Morocco	213,350	7,094,000
Algeria	847,552	7,235,000
Tunisia	48,313	2,606,000
French West Africa	1,844,400	15,725,000
French Equatorial Africa	1,125,745	5,940,000
Réunion	970	313,000
Madagascar	241,884	3,798,000
Somali Coast	8,492	44,000
	4,338,706	42,755,000
In America:		
French Guiana and Inini	65,000	37,000
Islands	1,166	610,000
In Asia:		
French Indo-China	286,004	23,825,000
India	196	323,000
In Oceania:	9,170	93,000
	4,692,224	67,643,000

constitute a grave responsibility and a prodigious opportunity, but today they are of greater potential than actual value. Two large units in North Africa, Algeria and Tunis, are by all reckoning the most satisfactory at the present time.

Algeria produces annually over 30 million bushels each of wheat and barley, 7 million bushels of oats, the latter for home consumption, 340 million gallons of wine, and nearly 3 million gallons of olive oil. The pastures support 6.7 million sheep, 3 million goats, and nearly 1 million cattle. The mean of imports for six years was $192 million and of exports $146 million. Algeria's budget is nearly balanced except for flood relief, which in some years is enormous. Tunis produces about two thirds as much cereals as Algeria and is a large producer of dates, grapes and wine, cork, and pine lumber. Phosphate from deposits shared by Tripoli (part of Libya Italiana) and Tunis is a large export item. In spite of these lists of products needed by France and Europe in general, the imports of both colonies are nearly 60 per cent larger than their exports. At present the balance of the budget is maintained by loans and foreign investments in the hope that when the new country is under way the tide will turn. It is probably worth while to France to maintain the colonies with this turn in mind, for where marked geographic differences occur usually reciprocal relations ultimately can be established.

Madagascar, larger than France, is chiefly agricultural and pastoral. Leading crops are rice, manioc for starch, beans, corn, coffee, vanilla, cloves, cocoa, tobacco, and sugar-cane. The forest products are scantily developed, but there are rich reserves in cabinet woods and tanning barks, in resins, gums, beeswax, and raffia. Mineral products are graphite and gold, the former being exported to the amount of 25 to 35 million pounds per annum.

In French West Africa, an area dominantly desert but nine times as large as France, the exports are nuts (especially peanuts), oils, fruits, rubber, cotton, cacao, and lumber, all needed by France. Revenues and expenditures are about equal.

French Equatorial Africa is, so far, but a land of promise. Thirty thousand square miles, only 3 or 4 per cent of the territory, is rich tropical forests but is not putting anything on the market save rubber. Metallic wealth in copper, lead, and zinc are known but still await development. All these resources are needed in France, and some day the people will no doubt broaden their economic and geographic ties and place the colony under tribute.

French Indo-China,[6] an area larger than the mother country and not half as far from the equator, may well supplement the homeland in several ways.

---

[6] French Indo-China became by agreement March 8, 1949, an independent Viet Nam Republic within the French Commonwealth.

It has 75 people per square mile, an abundance of labor for development. The people are largely of the industrious, intelligent Mongolian race, capable of work and progress. The country is nearly all agricultural but contains some good forests of tropical trees. Rice is the largest export and is almost equal in amount to that of Burma. Fish, maize, cotton yarn, and plantation rubber are among minor exports, while cotton cloth, silk, paper, oil, iron, and steel goods are among the leading imports, all items in French commerce. The colony has zinc, excellent hard coal, and many good building materials. The cleaning of rice, spinning of cotton yarn, and manufacture of cement are the only processes that could be called industrial.

French Guiana in northern South America comprises much more forest than all else combined. The forests are of rich cabinet woods but, like all else, wholly undeveloped, and the total annual trade barely exceeds $3 million.

French colonial lands are mostly sub-tropical to equatorial, supplying such things as France needs, and aside from the North African lands they are really producing only a little. They are not needed for overflow of home population. Government is good, and there are people on the land to assist in a program of increased economic expansion. When the time comes to make intensive and extensive use of tropical lands, France is in a strategic position to take a large part in such a program.

QUESTIONS

1. What regions of France are most closely related—i.e., have the strongest reciprocal or exchange relations? Discuss.

2. Is France self-sufficient? How nearly so? What country has a better physical basis for self-sufficiency?

3. What climatic items restrict certain crops to certain parts of France? How?

4. What geographic reasons can you give for the excellent and efficient railroad service in France? for the effectiveness of its canal and canalized river service?

5. Why is it feasible to produce silk and not cotton in France?

6. France is equivalent (about) to Ancient Gaul. Find Cæsar's subdivisions of Gaul. What are the geographic reasons for his subdivisions?

7. Why should there be so wide a range of race in France—Nordics, Alpines, and Mediterraneans, as well as Basques?

8. Why would it not be a wise and judicious move to unite Belgium with France and Netherlands with Germany?

9. Can the abundance of chateaux in the Loire basin be accounted for on geographic bases? How?

10. Why have Alsace and Lorraine shifted from one government to another—that is, what geographic items make them worth controversy?

11. Discuss the probable trade and industrial reactions in France to the current tensions between eastern and western Europe.

BIBLIOGRAPHY

BLACHE, Jules, ed., *Lorraine* (Paris, Berger-Levrault, 1938).

BLANCHARD, Raoul, *Geography of France,* trans. by M. Todd (Chicago, Rand, McNally & Company, 1919).

BLANCHARD, W. O., and VISHER, S. S., *Economic Geography of Europe* (New York, McGraw-Hill Book Company, Inc., 1931).

BROOKS, Leonard, *A Regional Geography of Africa and Europe* (London, University of London Press, 1927).

BUMPUS, T. F., *Cathedrals of Southern France* (London, J. Pott and Company, n.d.).

CAMERON, Elizabeth R., *French Reconstruction* (New Haven, Yale Institute of International Relations, 1948).

CHAMBERLAIN, Samuel, *France Will Live Again* (New York, Hastings House, 1940).

"Changes in the Frontier of French Language Since 1806," *Geographical Review,* Vol. 18 (1928), p. 505 (note).

CLARK, Sydney A., *All the Best in France* (New York, Dodd, Mead & Company, Inc., 1947).

COWAN, Laing G., *France and the Saar* (New York, Columbia University Press, 1950).

CLOUGH, Shepard B., *France, a History of National Economics* (New York, Charles Scribner's Sons, 1939).

CRAM, Ralph A., *Heart of Europe* (New York, Charles Scribner's Sons, 1921).

DOMINIAN, Leon, *Frontiers of Language and Nationality in Europe* (New York, Henry Holt & Company, Inc., 1924).

DUTTON, Ralph, *Land of France* (London, B. T. Batsford, Ltd., 1949).

FAIRCHILD, Johnson E., "Recent Development of Canal Systems of Europe," *Geographical Review,* Vol. 31 (1941), pp. 331-333.

FITZGERALD, Walter, *The New Europe* (New York, Harper and Brothers, 1946).

FODOR, Eugene, ed., *France in 1951* (London, David McKay Company, 1951).

FREEMAN, E. A., *Historical Geography of Europe* (New York, Longmans, Green & Company, 1920).

GEBELIN, Francois, *Les Chateaux de La Loire* (Paris, Alpina, 1948).

————, *Versailles* (Paris, Alpina, 1949).

————, *Images de Versailles,* Encyclopoedie Alpina Illustree (Paris, Alpina, 1937).

————, *Les Chateaux de La Renaissance* (Paris, Les Beaux Arts, 1937).

————, *La Sainte Chapelle and La Conciergerie* (Paris, Henri, Laurens, 1931).

————, *Le Style Renaissance in France* (Paris, Librairie Larousse, 1942).

GOLOB, Eugene O., *The Meline Tariff-French Agriculture and Economics* (New York, Columbia University Press, 1941).

HULME, Edward M., *Wandering in France* (Caldwell, Idaho, Caxton Printers, 1941).

HUNTINGTON, Ellsworth, and GREGORY, Herbert E., *Geography of Europe* (New Haven, Yale University Press, 1918).

INGWELL, P. G., "Agricultural Policy of France," *Political Science Quarterly,* Vol. 45 (June-Dec., 1930), pp. 214-230, 405-428, 527-547.

LYDE, L. W., *Peninsular Europe* (New York, Longmans, Green & Company, 1931).

McCORMICK, Thomas C. T., ed., *Problems of a Post-War World* (New York and London, McGraw-Hill Book Company, Inc., 1945).

MURRAY, Stuart, *A Traveler's Guide to France* (New York, Sheridan House, 1948).

NEWMAN, Bernard, *The New Europe* (New York, The Macmillan Company, 1943).

ORMSBY, Mrs. Hilda R., *France, a Regional and Economic Geography* (London, Methuen & Co., Ltd., 1931).

PEARCY, G. Etzel, and FIFIELD, Russell H., *et al., World Political Geography* (New York, Thomas Y. Crowell Company, 1948).

PEATTIE, Roderick, "Height Limits of Mountain Economics," *Geographical Review*, Vol. 21 (July, 1931), pp. 415-428.

PENA, Jose Luis A., *Geographia de las Grandes Potencias* (Barcelona, Bosch, 1947).

PICKLES, Dorothy M., *France Between the Republics* (London, Love & Malcolmson, Ltd., 1946).

PILLIET, Georges, *et al., Inventaire Économique de la France 1950* (Paris, Ordres de Chevalerie, 1950), French yearbook.

ROBEQUAIN, Charles, *Les Richesses de la France D'Outre-Mer* (Paris, Payot, 1949).

SCOTT, J. M., *Vineyards of France* (London, Hodder & Stoughton, Ltd., 1950).

SHACKLETON, Margaret R., *Europe, A Regional Geography* (London, Longmans, Green & Company, 1942).

SIMONDS, Frank H., *Can Europe Keep the Peace?* (New York, Harpers and Brothers, 1931).

VERMEIL, Edmond, "Religion and Politics in Alsace," *Foreign Affairs*, Vol. 10 (January, 1932), pp. 250-264.

VIDAL DE LA BLACHE, Paul M. J., *La personnalité géographique de la France* (London, Hachette, 1946).

———, and Gallois, L., "France," in *Géographie Universelle* (Paris, Lib. Armand Colin, 1944-48).

VON SCHNITZLER, Werner, "France Builds an Empire," *Living Age,* Vol. 338 (August, 1930), pp. 639-648.

WELLES, Sumner, ed., *An Intelligent American's Guide to the Peace* (New York, The Dryden Press, 1945).

WELLS, H. G., *An Outline of History* (New York, The Macmillan Company, 1921).

WRIGHT, J. K., *Geographic Basis of European History* (New York, Henry Holt & Company, Inc., 1928).

CHAPTER 14

The British Isles
Part I. Regional Problems

The English winter ending in July, to recommence in August.

INTRODUCTION

Position. No geographic interpretation of the British nation can be strong and true that does not recognize two periods of its history: 2,000 years of pre-Columbian events when Britain was at the edge of the world, and 400 years thereafter when it has been in the midst of political and commercial development. The first period is characterized by isolation in a sea on the very fringe of European history and politics; the second, by opportunity in the whirl of growing commercial, political, and economic expansion across that isolating ocean. The former period modulates into the latter through the activities of the Hanseatic League, which, until the end of the fourteenth century, built up and bound together Baltic and North sea trade in preparation for the great transatlantic expansion of later centuries. Through the developments of these more recent years men have become aware of the significance of Britain's position "in the center of the land hemisphere." "Her world-relation is perhaps best expressed historically; for her history represents a continuous series of adaptations to a progressively widening environment."

Today great social and political changes in the Isles induced by the ravages of two great wars in one generation raise the question—has she now entered a third period? Formerly the head of a world-wide empire, Great Britain has become for practical purposes of foreign policy the head of a Commonwealth of Dominions.

The British Isles comprise two large islands, Great Britain and Ireland, with about 5,000 small islands and rocks scattered in groups mostly on the north and west. Their total area is about 121,000 square miles of land with additional shallow seas among and around the islands. Great Britain contains England, Wales, and Scotland; Ireland contains the Irish Free State [1]

---

[1] Ireland (Irish Free State), under the name Eire, became completely free from England April 18, 1949. Nevertheless, most statistics are for all the British Isles.

and North Ireland. These islands and states constitute the seat of government for the British Commonwealth of Nations, parts of which are in every continent.

Geologic relations. Inasmuch as the British Isles are the emergent portions of a former large land area bordering the continent, parts of which are

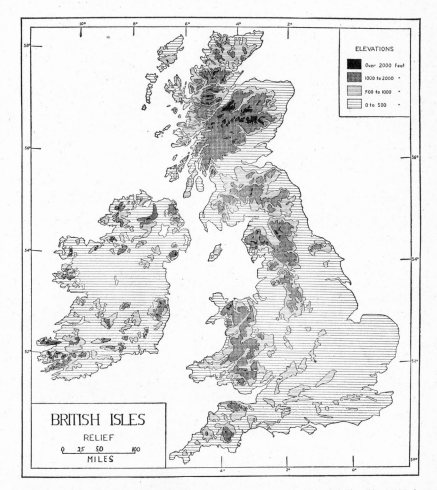

Relief of the British Isles in symbols. Showing the great expanse of surface less than 500 feet high and the old-age topography of Ireland. (Adopted from Goode's School *Atlas* and *Oxford Advanced Atlas*)

now sufficiently submerged to be covered with the North Sea, Irish Sea, St. George's Channel, and English Channel, it would be expected that many analogies could be found between the rocks and structures of the islands and those of the mainland. Such connections are now well known. The rocks in North Ireland, Scotland, and Scandinavia are of the same ancient date as similar structures trending through the three areas and beneath separating seas. Much of Wales, South Ireland, Cornwall, the Armorican Peninsula, and the Vosges Mountains of France belong to a less ancient mountain system well developed on the continent. Deep borings and geophysical surveys reveal their structures beneath more recent rocks spread among these remnants. Southeast England with its younger rocks and simpler structures, including the London Basin, Weald, and associated Downs, is a continuation of the Paris Basin.

The ancient rocks and structures in northern Scotland are remnants of an old land area that lay along the western border of the continent, when seas occupied portions east of it and accumulated the sediments eroded from the old land now constituting much of central and southern Ireland and of the Scottish Lowlands, the Pennines, Wales, and Cornwall. Subsequently these areas were uplifted and their rocks folded and crumpled into mountains. They, too, were subjected to erosion for ages and their waste was mingled with that from continental lands to make the sediments of the London and Paris basins. A later uplift with very moderate warping of the layers produced the structures of the Wolds, Downs, and intervening lowlands, plains, and vales. For many centuries the continental shelf of which these islands are parts stood so high that complete land connections existed from Ireland to France via England and from Scotland to Denmark. A river flowed southward through the lowlands now covered by the Irish Sea and St. George's Channel; and the Rhine extended far west across lands which are now the floor of the North Sea, then northward beyond Scotland, gathering many English and Scotch waters and conducting them to the edge of the continental shelf. By these rivers and a host of lesser ones the lands were reduced to maturity and, in places where the rocks were weak, to old age. Glaciers came from the northeast and overrode all Ireland and all of Great Britain but the southern strip and a small driftless area from the North York Moors to Leicester. For a short time after the ice melted, long enough for many animals and probably men to migrate from the continent, the islands were again connected with the mainland, but submergence followed and gave approximately the present distribution of land and water. Many minor developmental changes along the shorelines have produced numerous beaches, cliff headlands, deltas, and other details.

Climate. Position is the main factor in the climate of the British Isles. Moisture-laden winds from the seas lying to the southwest give a moderate range of temperature, a remarkably mild winter, and cloudy or foggy weather in spring and fall, and, with the relief, account for the heavier rainfall and greater humidity on the western slopes. This condensation aids in warming the air, as does the heat of the drift currents of the sea. Moreover, the effects are carried by the winds far across the islands so that similar winter temperatures occur in the north of Scotland and the south of England. Lyde therefore points out that the isotherms of winter are essentially sea lines, running lengthwise of the islands, while the summer isotherms are sun lines. The last is even more true of the lines of spring and autumn.

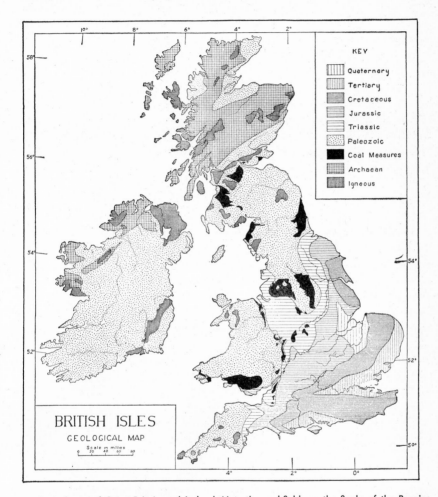

Geological map of Great Britain and Ireland. Note the coal-fields on the flanks of the Pennine chain, in the Scotch Strath, and in South Wales; also the geologic horizons responsible for the cuestas in southeastern England. (Adapted from "International Geologic Map of Europe")

Rainfall, influenced strongly by exposure and relief, is very patchy and somewhat seasonal, though all parts have ample precipitation for crops at any season. Within the Lake District the annual precipitation shows such variation as 177 inches at the Stye and 32 inches at Penrith. The Stye is 1,100 feet high in a pass where moist air forced up a narrowing valley pours out its moisture copiously. Penrith is behind the Lake District hills in a valley and not exposed well for rain. The hilly rim of Ireland has much heavier precipitation on its southwest and north flanks than have the Lowlands north of Dublin. Around the Wash a small area receives the least rainfall, under 25 inches. The charm in greenery and lake of Killarney, Wales, and Cumberland is due to the high humidity and heavy precipitation of these respective regions, and many are the responses made by men and their crops to the peculiarities of rainfall. The cyclone or low of the westerlies is a very important factor in the winter weather, as it is in the cyclonic belt of the United States. The weather is strongly influenced also by the winter Icelandic low (feeble in summer), the summer Azores high, and the summer and winter alternations of low and high pressures of central Asia. In winter, the air masses from the southwest sweep across Britain in a north to northeast direction, deflected thus by the outblowing air from the central Asian region. In summer this air flows almost directly eastward to the continental summer low.

PHYSIOGRAPHIC REGIONS

1. Scottish Highlands. From Cape Wrath and the Orkney Islands south to the Strath or Lowlands of Scotland there is a large remnant of gneisses, schists, and granite, whose surface in many parts has been cleared of soils and strewn with forbidding boulders by the continental glacier. This block is cut in two, nearly to sea level, by the Caledonian trough, canalized a hundred years ago to aid trade between Russia and towns of North Ireland and west England. Today the Russian trade is completely gone, while railroad and bus competition have captured the local freight business. The canal has locks to get the boats up the moraine loops and plugs of the valley to the summit level, 105 feet, and back down again. It parallels the grain of the rocks and marks an ancient fault line which divides the Highlands into Northern Highlands and Grampian Mountains. Both sections were eroded to advanced maturity before glaciation, but because they were stripped cruelly of the weathered rock they have now little value except as pastures. More than half of the Highlands is moor of heath and brush, while about one fourth is timber. Cattle once were common over the hills and moors; now not half enough sheep are kept to use the pasture; hunting for stag and other game has been a profitable sport and is still indulged in. Occasional herds of tawny, shaggy, long-horned Highland cattle add to the picturesqueness of the landscape. Reforestation has been started with pulpwood trees, but larch and other lumber trees might well be planted over hundreds of square miles. Water power is abundant in small units but is not developed. These valleys and hills once rang with the shouts and bagpipes of Highlander and witnessed for centuries bloody clan warfare. They still look very inviting for such a life as the Grants and MacDonalds lived among them. Toward Aberdeen there is considerable lower land, much better suited to root crops (turnips for sheep food), flowers, and cattle.

A large dairy industry might here be developed and served by the railroad. A change in breed of cattle would help.

Aberdeen is called the granite city. Around it are a score of well-equipped quarries, and in it is scarcely a house that is not built of gray granite. The University has an architectural style beautifully adapted to the abundant building stone.

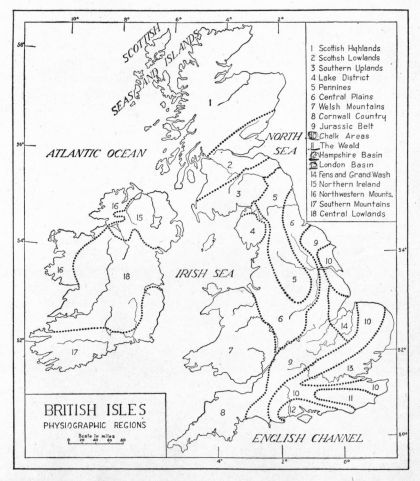

1 Scottish Highlands
2 Scottish Lowlands
3 Southern Uplands
4 Lake District
5 Pennines
6 Central Plains
7 Welsh Mountains
8 Cornwall Country
9 Jurassic Belt
10 Chalk Areas
11 The Weald
12 Hampshire Basin
13 London Basin
14 Fens and Grand Wash
15 Northern Ireland
16 Northwestern Mounts.
17 Southern Mountains
18 Central Lowlands

BRITISH ISLES
PHYSIOGRAPHIC REGIONS
Scale in miles
0 20 40 60 80

Physiographic regions of Great Britain and Ireland. (Adapted from Mill's *International Geography* and the geologic maps)

South of the canal near Fort William is the Ben Nevis mountain group, whose summit, 4,406 feet above tide, is the highest point in the British Isles. Thirty-five to forty miles farther south is the fascinating, inspiring scenery of the Trossachs immortalized by Sir Walter Scott (Ben Lomond, Loch Lomond, Loch Katrine).

The western slopes of the Highlands descend very steeply to the sea at many places because of glaciation and more recent wave work. Hundreds of islands, among them Skye and the Hebrides, break the waves into clouds of spray and produce a continuous low, weird roar, which Archibald Geikie suggests is a factor in the monotony and solemnity of the music and some of the verse from this region. It is equally true that the quiet and thrill of such scenery as that of Loch Katrine and the Caledonian Canal may be responsible for the life and sparkle of Scott's verses and the Highland music. The Scot, his customs, music, occupations, and history, could have sprung from no place more appropriately than from the Highlands of Scotland. Individualism flourishes here.

2. The Scottish Lowlands. The area reaching from North Sea to North Channel, between the southern uplands and the Highlands, is deeply invaded by the Firths of Clyde and Forth. It is bounded on both north and south by great faults and consists of a crustal block which was long ago so lowered that coal and softer rocks have been preserved in spite of great erosion. As surely as that the Highlands should be used for forests and pasture, this Lowland should be, and is, devoted to industry, farming, and mining, and supports a large population. Because depressed as just explained and because made of less resistant rocks it is lower than the Highlands, and since it is lower it has received much glacial drift eroded from the Highlands. This secures to the Lowlands a rich, deep, long-lived soil and induces productive agriculture. Easy approach of vessels from the sea far up the firths brought invaders, who surged over these plains repeatedly through many centuries. But in time the same water highways stimulated the building of commercial cities, Glasgow (1,088,000) and Edinburgh (471,000) and their satellites. Such cities call for industries to rework the imported raw materials. The wealth of coal preserved in the rocks of the depressed block now serves for power fuel in a larger way than ever did the forests on either side. For these reasons much manufacturing has grown up in the Lowlands. Since the Lowlands have always been the most populous part of Scotland, they have been the center of Scottish history. Conditions have been kindly for the making and exhibition of history, with castles, palaces, churches, and highways, and consequently tourists come in troops to see the treasures of the Lowlands and to make excursions to the Trossachs. Thus many elements have conspired to gather great numbers of people into this area, until one eighth of Scotland has about three fourths of its people.

3. Southern Uplands. The Southern Uplands consist of more resistant rocks than the Lowlands and are more maturely eroded than the Highlands. Their rounded forms under the moist air and ample precipitation are usually rich pasture and furnish range for great flocks of sheep whose celebrated wool, pelts, and early lambs constitute the chief money crop. The next largest crop is turnips, used largely to feed the sheep. Cattle for dairy and meat purposes are pastured over the hills in summer and with the sheep are, in winter, of necessity driven to lower lands and fed in shelters.

Coast-lines, estuaries, and rivers in Scotland have always been significant in directing travel and commerce and encouraging communications; but the railways are, if possible, a more excellent commentary on the influence of the physical configuration. The East Coast railway from the south closely follows the sea across the Scottish border to Edinburgh. The line from Carlisle makes its way up small valleys, over divides, and down three times before it arrives on the plains south of the capital; from Carlisle to Glasgow the railway has followed much detail of topography. Likewise the track from the north traces along the coast from Aberdeen to Strathmore, then divides, one branch edging along the sea across the Tay and Forth on great bridges to Edinburgh, the other winding along Strathmore to Perth and Sterling and on to Glasgow. Two roads go north from Perth to Inverness and Wick and from Glasgow to Fort William. Both are very circuitous as they follow lake shores, stream valleys, and shorelines. They traverse some of the finest Scottish scenery, where their trains often make slow schedules because of the crookedness of the roads and the steepness of the grades. Regions 1, 2, and 3 constitute approximately that part of the British Isles known as Scotland.

4. The Lake District. Mining and agriculture were the early interests of this section. A strip of coal measures along the coast formerly furnished ore, limestone, and coal for a very old, small iron furnace. An area of disturbed igneous (granite and volcanic ash) and sedimentary rocks, glaciated locally after the continental sheet melted away, has radial lakes, streams, and waterfalls among rugged and beautifully green mountains. The sea reaches three sides, and the Eden Valley on the east separates the district from the Pennines. Heavy, sudden rainfall on steep slopes drained by short streams makes torrents at some times and trickling threads of water at others. The Falls of Lodore are tucked back on one such stream south of Keswick and Derwentwater. Sheep pasture and meager but good agriculture occupy most of the usable land. This northwest corner of England has long been famous for its scenery and its literature. For many decades it has been given over to poetry, philosophy and history, creative intellectual pursuits, conventions, and conferences, and it is fast becoming a tourist and recreation center. No more restful, inspiring, and charming place can be found in England. Skiddaw looks down from the north, while a Druid circle near Keswick reminds one that ancient peoples also found interesting, and perhaps sacred, a little plain in the Lake District.

5. The Pennines. A chain of simple, low, folded mountains extends from the Cheviot Hills 150 miles southward, nearly in the center of the northern narrow part of England. A structure section from east to west across this fold, as from Doncaster to the Cheshire Plain, would show massive "mountain limestone" in the axis of the arch and above a thick sandstone called "millstone grit" because of its uses. These beds dip gently eastward on the east side and a little more steeply westward on the west. Above these beds on each flank, but not now remaining on the crest, are the clays, sandstones, and coal-beds of the coal measures, dipping similarly east and west. Much erosion occurred over this huge fold, and horizontal beds of newer red sandstone were laid on each side, making the basis on the west for the Cheshire Plain, and on the east for the Vale of York. These plains will be considered in the next section.

Derwentwater, in the Lake District, looking toward Borrowdale, Cumberland. Many English writers have done their best work amid this stimulating scenery. (Courtesy British Information Services)

The Pennine Chain rises to heights of 2,000 to 2,400 feet, but the highest parts are not where the fold is highest. Reference to the diagram of the cross-section shows the great limestone, the oldest beds shown, outcropping across the central part of the fold and the thick sandstones which have been eroded from the top but are preserved on the flanks, with infacing escarpments rising 100 or 200 feet above the central part. Their rugged forms present some of the finest scenery of the island. The limestone areas have karst topography, where water sinks readily into the cracks and caverns and leaves few surface streams. This causes thin soil, with little vegetation but heath and brush. Natives were asked why this land should not be forested. Two reasons were given. Some said, "Forest will not grow upon it." Others said: "It is worth much more as it is, to lease to wealthy city fellows for hunting grounds. Grouse and pheasants abound in the heather." We surmise the second reason explains the first. Sheep are pastured over these beautiful expanses of purple heath during the closed bird season, then in the fall they are driven down to better pastures and the brown heath is hunted for game. These are the Pennine Moors.

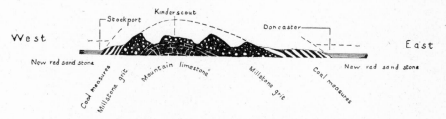

A structure section across the Pennine Mountains, showing the great upfold of rocks, the resistant ridges along the flanks, and the slightly lower heathland between.

Little of the limestone is quarried. The sandstone on the flanks of the Pennine arch is often worked, and the flags and clays among the coals lower down are much sought respectively for pavements and pottery. But the great values are in the thick, excellent coal-beds, extensively worked around the south end and on each flank. Here, fuel is obtained for the great industrial centers: Lancashire, containing Manchester (684,600), Bolton, and Oldham on the west; Yorkshire, embracing Sheffield (509,000), Leeds (493,000), and Bradford (261,700) on the east, and Midlands or Birmingham on the south. Probably more coal than yet remains in these mountains has been eroded from the tops of their folds with the removal of the massive sandstone. Buxton, now a quiet village on the limestone karst, might have been a thriving industrial city had the coal been preserved. Agriculture is confined to the little valleys, where the bountiful water power of pre-steam days called for small paper mills, using rags from the towns of the Plains, and for woolen mills, whose raw material was shorn from the moor sheep.

6. Central Plains. From the North Sea at Middlesborough a plains belt, 30 to 40 miles wide, sweeps around the southern end of the Pennines and northward to the Irish Sea and Liverpool. It consists of younger rocks than those in the Pennine folds, rocks that are still nearly horizontal but eroded in a few places, particularly round Birmingham, to permit the working of coal in older layers below. This oxbow-shaped area is blessed with excellent agricultural soils, which foster efficient, intensive agriculture in the counties of Cheshire, Lancashire, Staffordshire, and Worcester. For generations after agriculture became settled in England, these plains supported a large rural population; but when the coal was discovered and its fuel and other values became known, industrial concentration began in the region, and today several urban centers have assumed great importance. The coal-fields probably have been the most influential factor in this development.

Newcastle-on-Tyne (290,700) in the northeast part of the Central Plains is the successor to the New Castle built at a strategic point. Gateshead or narrows, in the valley and near the eastern terminal of the Roman wall across England. Romans built first, then Normans built the New Castle. At the start the town was not related to navigation; but the constriction of the

The Romans built a stone wall across north England, Northumberland and Cumberland, to keep the Picts out of the south. They made use of the great Wim sill of dark igneous rock which presents a bold front north (left) most of the distance across the island. (Courtesy British Information Services)

channel due to the bridges has increased erosion here and downstream, and probably checked it somewhat upstream, so that Newcastle is now the head of navigation. A sand constriction at the mouth of the Tyne sets off the 12 to 15 miles above as docking space, where dock equipment now makes this river section a valuable shipping place. Coal for export greatly facilitated the growth of Newcastle, giving rise to the proverbial absurdity of "carrying coals to Newcastle," and the iron industry began in the vicinity. Export stimulated import; and now iron to supplement the depleted local supplies, mine props, foodstuffs, and other raw materials arrive from Scandinavia, Finland, the Low Countries, and other parts of the continent. The export of wool through Newcastle, once very important, is now a small item because of the great development of wool manufacturing farther south. Newcastle with its coal, harbor, and food crops is well adapted to the production of iron and machinery, in which it still excels.

Similarly coal is preserved in the Leeds-Sheffield region and is mined very extensively in the eastern Pennine flanks and shipped down to these and other near-by towns on the Plains. Here is iron ore, and the combination together with abundant limestone has encouraged another large iron-steel industrial center. Machinery, high-grade steel, ship plate, and cutlery

Girls run the tractors and wheat binders (made in Australia). This is the largest wheat field (400 acres) in Britain. (Courtesy British Information Services)

are the chief iron products. The latter, the item that has made Sheffield famous, is now insignificant and employs but 2 or 3 per cent of the total iron-steel workmen. About 12 square miles in the eastern part of Sheffield are covered by the great industrial plants. Here the woolen industry finds a moist climate suitable for spinning and weaving. The market demands much wool clothing. Local wool supplies are wholly inadequate, but Flanders across the North Sea has much wool to sell for the woolen manufactures of many kinds that flourish in this vicinity. The two great industries and scores of subsidiary occupations have given rise, in the Leeds-Sheffield-Nottingham area, to several large cities and account for one of the densest populations of England.

Wolverhampton has blast furnaces and manufactures heavy goods, even though hindered by its distance from the sea. Birmingham (1,090,000) has coal close at hand but not beneath. It makes a long line of smaller miscellaneous articles, such as guns, ammunition, jewelry, scientific instruments, watches, clocks, nails, railway cars, glass, chemicals, and brass goods, all for export. Small towns also have their specialties and are as cheerless as the district name, "Black Country," suggests. Commerce and industry in this locality called for a network of local canals and for long ones to the sea at Bristol (416,500), London, Hull (319,400), and Liverpool (854,500), and in recent decades for a similar development of railroads.

A colliery and its town in the coal fields of Yorkshire. A feeder of industrial Britain. (Courtesy British Information Services)

The North Staffordshire coal-field also lies in this Central Plain on the west fringe of the Pennines. With an estimated reserve of over 4 billion tons it seems to be the richest of the British fields. It has some iron, but its claim to distinction grows from its clays, used extensively in pottery, porcelain, china, and seggars in which the china is baked. The best local clays are now exhausted, but Cornwall and Devon are producing excellent kaolins which are imported to maintain the industry.

The last of the great coal-fields of the Central Plains area is immediately north of the Mersey River. Without iron it has not called forth a great steel industry, but it has stimulated manufacturing. Cotton from America and the eastern British colonies has found its greatest opportunity here. A most excellent climate, moist, mild and constant, for working its fibers; fuel; splendid shipping facilities; and markets both at home and in India have combined to bring together throngs of workers for the greatest industrial region of England. Several little coal or iron areas in the Plains are worked and have been the basis for industries and towns, as at Leicester. Coal is shipped in great quantities from the southern fields to the London industries and from Liverpool to foreign lands.

Because they are lowlands and lie on soft rocks, these Central Plains contain a large proportion of arable lands; therefore, men raise more wheat and oats here than in many other parts of England. Potatoes, lucerne, and other rotational hay crops thrive; poultry follows all areas of denser populations, but sheep are relatively scarce.

7. Welsh Mountains. Wales is as natural a unit as any south of the Lowlands of Scotland and likewise as rugged. Our line chosen to separate the Welsh Mountains from other natural regions lies farther east than the present Welsh boundary because it limits a physiographic region, not a political one. Centuries ago the counties between the present political boundary and our regional line were called the March Shires because they were frontiers. They are mountainous, but less so than some in Wales, and because they are mountainous borderlands they were fought over through many generations.

The Welsh Mountains are a part of that ancient mountain rim of resistant rocks that so nearly surrounds the Irish Sea and St. George's Channel. Much of this unit consists of old upland topography with young forms below— gorges, waterfalls, lakes, caves in limestones, ledges, and precipitous slopes. This youth in the lower levels is due to the interference of glaciation with the drainage and to relatively recent uplift. Both elements of topography have reacted strongly on the people. The old upper slopes are grasslands, moors, bogs, and tarns and have little value except as sheep pastures and hunting grounds. The lower slopes, valley bottoms, moraine areas, old lake-beds, and terraces constitute the meager supply of arable land on which the Welsh raise their barley, wheat, oats, potatoes and turnips. Up the slopes where the grade is too steep for cultivation one finds pasture and forests. Because of so much relief and variety of slope, climate, vegetation, and form, in addition to the diversity of its rocks, Wales has a large variety of soils.

Because of the excellent pasturage, many cattle and sheep feed over the hills and mountain slopes, while wool, butter, cheese, and hides are among the leading exports. Lumber, mine props, and posts are cut in export quantities. Apples are an abundant crop in eastern shires and cider a common drink, while Herefordshire is one of Britain's notable hop-growing regions.

The shoreline is rugged and steep in many parts. Westward headlands of resistant rock hold sand, gravel, or shingle beaches festooned between them. Harbors are abundant, though but few are needed or improved. Holyhead on the northwest corner is good and has been improved as a port for transshipment of mail to and from Ireland. The mail travels by water from this port to Dublin, but from Holyhead to London by special train. With a little less of rain, mist, and fog, Welsh picturesque and varied shorelines all the way from the Mumbles near Swansea to the Dee mouth on the north would attract multitudes of tourists. On the Bristol Channel less rugged coasts and better harbors are found at Swansea, Cardiff, Barry, and Newport.

Roadway, Elsie Farm, North Wales. Stone house with roof of split shingles. (Courtesy Associated British Railways, Inc.)

The charm, quaintness, and rare beauty of Wales have not been fully appreciated. Every stream has its falls or rapids, its old mill, its ancient stone bridge, and its overlooking castle. Every mountain and hill is clothed in luscious, rank verdure, purple or brown heath and moorland, and is alive with sheep and cattle. Burial mounds, earthworks, dolmens, and crosses witness to chapters of ancient history. Valleys are adorned with picturesque villages or towns, with cottages that seem exactly to fit into their niches in garden, field, and woods. Cathedrals, churches, town halls, schools, and markets add to the interest. Resources are reflected in the buildings. Stone in rich variety is the usual material in the cities; brick from local clays found in scores of places, and wood from the forests, often used with a thatch roof in the country, are common over all the region. In the south many buildings in town are walled half with boards in pattern and half with wattles plastered white, a combination which makes a most distinctive house.

Transportation was extremely difficult in the early days. Dirt and sand were the only road materials, and in a climate so wet as that of Wales neither had any real value for roads. The Romans built a few connecting military stone roads, but the real service began when toward the end of the eighteenth century a few canals were constructed. Railroads followed in due time, and modern wagon and auto road construction is making approachable many formerly isolated places and is permitting goods to get in and out. The coracle is still used on streams and canals and is frequently seen on men's backs in portage.

In a region of such mountain structure and relief as Wales possesses one expects to find mineral resources, and the Welsh Mountains are true to form. South Wales has a large, very rich coal-field, in the western part anthracitic. For 300 years this coal has been used as heating fuel, but it was not recognized as iron-smelting fuel until the iron industry in Wales was nearly 2,000 years old. Now it supplies a large metallurgical industry and bulks very large in exports. Cardiff (236,100), a city of fine commercial situation, has become the largest coal port in the world, and Barry, a few miles southwest of Cardiff on the coast, is responding as an overflow port to ship additional export coal. The great amount of shipping needed to take the coal away makes importing very reasonable, and large quantities of ores and foodstuffs arrive at Swansea and Cardiff from many lands. Before the coal and iron of Wales were known, Cornwall produced tin and copper. Its meager supply of wood did not last long, and its ore had to be shipped to the fuel—Welsh forests. Thus Swansea metallurgy began. Then South Wales iron was found and its refinement was added. Other metals were found in Cornwall, and Wales began to produce lead and zinc. Then coal entered the industry, and the South Wales metal industries became of international note. The Cornwall production declined because of exhaustion and cheaper production elsewhere, and in consequence Wales began importing Malay and East Indian tin and other ores from many places and became even more an industrial land. The Swansea-Cardiff section now has over 140 metallurgical plants, great tin-plate works, and manufactories of many kinds, which use the metals from the furnaces.

In addition to the elaborate variety of building stone, Wales has slate in considerable variety and great abundance. The largest slate quarries in the world are worked in north Wales, and many lesser ones in other places. Limestone is burned for plaster and for a dressing for acidic, exhausted soils.

Birmingham has established a broad material geographic relationship with Wales by constructing a great reservoir for city water, back on the northern border of Brecon, whence conduits lead for 60 miles across the Severn Valley. Cardiff has water mains reaching back into the hills many miles beyond the vile stream pollution due to the mines, furnaces, and factories.

The people of Wales are so much a unit, with peculiar local characteristics, that mention of them should be made here. Paleolithic remains have been found in Gower Caves near the southwestern tip of the country, and similar crude implements have been plowed up at a number of other places. Neolithic remains are much more common, and their makers seem to have had no genetic connection with the older race but to have come in long after the former had become extinct. Neolithic man made a much larger use of the materials at hand. He domesticated cattle, planted and harvested crops, constructed dwellings on piles in some of the lakes, baked clay into crude

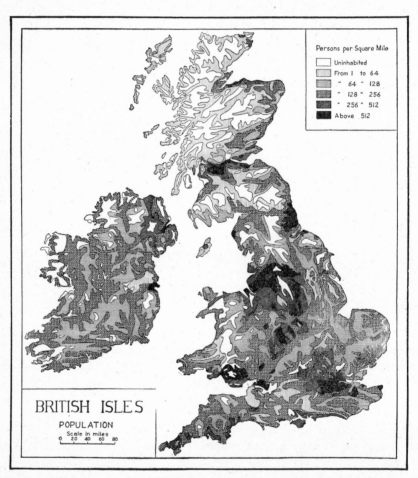

Persons per Square Mile

☐ Uninhabited
▥ From 1 to 64
▦ " 64 " 128
▦ " 128 " 256
▩ " 256 " 512
■ Above 512

BRITISH ISLES

POPULATION

Scale in miles
0   20   40   60   80

Density-of-population map of Great Britain and Ireland. Bears relations to relief, mineral resources, and transportation possibilities. (Adapted from Oxford Advanced Atlas)

earthen vessels, and set up dolmens or built long barrows for burials. These people were long-headed and short in stature; they have been called Iberians. By 1400 B.C. they became users of bronze made from the local tin and copper. About 400 B.C. they were invaded, but not exterminated, by the Celts in at least two waves—the Goidels first, later the Britons, who so completely overran Britain that they gave their name to the country. The last burned their dead, made smaller round burial barrows for the ashes, numbers of which remain, improved the arts practised by the Goidels, and mingled freely with them. Thus the three races, Iberians, Goidels, and Britons, became the foundations of the present Welsh. Their land was called by *their neighbors* "Wales" ("land of strangers"), but *they* said "Cymry" ("we are fellow-countrymen"). The Brythonic Celtic or Briton became the foundation for Welsh language, one of the Gaelic tongues.

After 350 years of amalgamation following the arrival of Britons the Cymry were invaded in 55-54 B.C. by the Romans, who remained 450 years, gave many ideas to the natives, and built a few harbors, baths, roads, and towns, but withdrew without much interbreeding and without leaving notable records. Then came Irish, Saxons, Danes, and Normans, drawing fire in many a valley or building earthworks, castles, even churches on the hills; but their conquests were short-lived and Wales became a separate constituent of the English Kingdom. The mountainous isolation of the residents of Wales prevented contacts and protected the life, habits, industries, and philosophy of the people, thus preserving until today, in many isolated valleys, ancient customs, names, and bits of language—quaint indeed, to be a part of a great, central, cosmopolitan commonwealth.

8. The Cornwall country. Cornwall, Devon, and half of Somerset, sometimes called the Southwest, are made up of old sedimentary rocks with five granite masses protruding today because of deep erosion. Herein lie the seeds of the geography of the Cornwall country. The discovery of tin and copper 3,000 years ago in this old peneplained peninsula started the metallurgy and use of bronze; and, when zinc and lead in Somerset were found, a harder, still more valuable alloy was made. Phœnicians, Greeks, and Etruscans of Italy were drawn to Cornwall. This tin magnet encouraged exploration, prompted commerce, and made possible large advances in Mediterranean culture. The supplies of tin have now become so exhausted that its mining has almost ceased. Nearly a hundred different minerals are known in the Cornwall tin mines, forty of which carry metallic values; hence, even with the tin no longer plentiful enough to support the mining industry, the many ores of copper, lead, zinc, iron, silver, bismuth, antimony, and other rarer elements make it possible to continue mining under ordinary market conditions. Most of the ores are shipped across the Channel to Swansea for reduction. Both Camborne in Cornwall and Swansea in Wales have built up strong schools of mines under the stimulus of these metal industries.

After the granite intrusions became crystallized, heated water or steam came up from below and kaolinized the feldspar in great quantities throughout the granite. The process is more nearly complete the deeper the mining goes. Today, finest white china and paper clays are removed by hydraulic processes from pits 100 to 300 feet in depth; and after washing, drying, and grading, the kaolin is shipped to parts of England for pottery and chinaware and to many other countries for filler in high-grade paper, for absorbents, and for other uses. The sand from the granite is made into cement blocks and bricks.

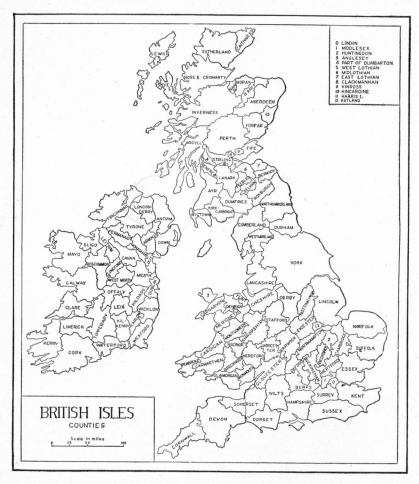

County map, showing location and size of all counties in the British Isles. Names are written in the county area unless too small, where a number refers to the legend on the map. (Adapted from *Oxford Advanced Atlas*)

But more important than the minerals of the Cornwall country are the soils and climate. Wheat does well; barley is intensively grown in several places; potatoes and early vegetables and flowers, together with cattle for meat, and dairy products, sheep, and thousands of hens for meat and eggs help to supply the food markets across the Channel and in London.

The mildness of Cornwall climate opens up the country for rest and pleasure, and the grand and beautiful shorelines inhabited by quaint fisher-folk make this whole peninsula a popular resort. Penzance, St. Ives, Plymouth, Torquay, Ilfracombe, and Falmouth are attractive, each in its own way. Historic interest centers round Plymouth with its memories of Drake and the Spanish Armada, of the Pilgrims and the *Mayflower*.

9. Jurassic Belt. A belt of lowlands 15 to 30 miles wide extends east of the Cornwall country and the Central Plains all the way from the English Channel to Whitby in Yorkshire on the North Sea. The Mendip Hills in Somerset, Cotswold Hills, Northampton Uplands, and North York Moors all are parts of this belt on its more resistant rocks, but rolling plains on softer rocks are more common than hills. While this belt is excellent farmland for diversified agriculture, it has not one town of 75,000 people, because there is no mineral wealth, fuel, power, or harbor to draw a large aggregation of people. Its hills are excellent barley and oats farms, and thousands of acres of its plains produce wheat. By quarrying stone for local use and digging clay for brick in many places, the people produce a durable but moderate-priced architecture in all the cities and towns. This quiet, dignified region gave birth in the twelfth century to the nucleus of the group of colleges which now constitutes Oxford, the most venerable seat of learning in England. No great stimulus to science and technology reached these colleges, but a profound respect for learning developed and with it classical learning, politics, and philosophy.

10. Chalk areas. The remaining portion of Britain consists entirely of rocks younger than the Jurassic and is structurally, stratigraphically, and topographically in intimate relationship to the Paris Basin. Instead of one broad, shallow basin as in France, the layers here are in two synclines with an anticline between. They are warped downward in a narrow trough known as the Hampshire Basin, involving the Isle of Wight and the adjacent mainland from Kimmeridge to points beyond Portsmouth. The chalk layers underlie the younger beds and rise to the surface in the cuestas of Purbeck, Western, and South Downs. North of this syncline is an anticline constituting the Weald to be described below. Next north is the syncline of the London Basin with the chalk layers rising in other cuestas such as White Horse Hills, Chiltern Hills, East Anglian Ridge, Lincoln and Yorkshire Wolds, all north of London; while the Hampshire Downs and North Downs, named with reference to the Weald, are similar cuestas south of London. Thus the Chalk as a region in England is a four-fingered, sprawling area. It may be thought of as heading in the central part of south England, Dorsetshire, and sending one branch east near the coast and through the south side of the Isle of Wight, a second from Wiltshire southeast to Newhaven, a third into Wiltshire and straight east to Thanet east of Canterbury, and the fourth from Wiltshire northeast between Oxford and Cambridge to the north coast of Norfolk, then to jump across the Wash and continue past Hull to Flamborough Head.

As the names Downs, Wolds, and Hills suggest, the region is hilly. It has seen several striking stream adjustments resulting in wind and water gaps

A new modern school building, with a central hall and wings for classrooms. It looks quite American. (Courtesy British Information Services)

Eton College, an efficient "public school" (in the English sense) founded in 1441, accommodating over 1,000 boys from 12-15 years old. (Courtesy British Information Services)

through which the railroads cross the area. It is eminently the region of sheep pastures, dairy herds, well-kept houses and barns for the thrifty people who farm the productive hills. It has many limestone quarries in the chalk, small acreage of farm crops, no cities or even considerable towns, no bases for their development, no convergence of highways or abundance of rich resource to call for commercial or industrial center. Its scores of towns are common local market towns to meet the needs of the farmer, grazer, or quarryman. It has for ages grown an abundance of wool which has played into England's industrial development but itself has not enjoyed the presence of mills. It is furnishing meat, dairy, and poultry products to the cities without having a city of its own. It is a region of relatively low density of population. These chalk ridge lands, standing safely above marshes and too dry for timber, were lines of march for prehistoric movements of people whose meeting-place was in the Salisbury and Avebury Plains. It was in the former that some ancient people built the Stonehenge, and in the latter long, low earthworks—subjects for fascinating antiquarian speculations. Not only have primitive people followed these ridges, but two or three invaders likewise have proceeded along their open, dry, timber-free courses. Probably Phœnician traders headed for Cornwall tin passed this way. The Romans have left enough of a trail to show that they appreciated these open highways, and Normans seem also to have used the ridges.

11. The Weald. Between the central arms of the Chalk areas is the anticline, which has been breached by erosion and from which all its chalk has been removed. A broad oval plain of clay and sand beds of older age is thus exposed. Soils are not rich, in fact in places they are poor. The forest cover, once continuous over all, has given the region its Saxon name, Weald ("woods"), but during many centuries much of the forest was cut down and a variety of farming has come in its stead. Wood and wood charcoal were used to smelt the ironstone ore, extensively distributed in one of the clay horizons. This industry is defunct because the fuel was exhausted. In portions of Kent on the Gault formation where the soils are exceptionally rich, there is the second and by far the most important hop region of England. The villages have been located quite specifically with reference to geology. Some geologic beds have none, others have scores; sands and lighter soils claim many, and the foot of the chalk slopes of the North Downs many more. One hundred twenty-five parishes lie round the chalk scarp, their long dimension across it; and in 119 of these the village is placed at the foot of the scarp, apparently that it might be near the fertile, arable land while its pastures extended up the chalk and its strip of woodland down over the clays to the south.

It was at Hastings, in the middle of the coast to which these Weald beds reach, that the Norman conquest was initiated. The harbor, in 1066 a good one, allowed William's ships to land their men, and the valleys led the conquerors inland. Modern shipping demands deeper harbors with more

Seaford Head, famous chalk cliffs, Sussex.

protection. Hastings is now only an attractive watering place with a mild sea climate, conserving great historic interests.

Other boundaries of the Weald are everywhere the chalk Down. Streams flowing northward from the Weald, whose initial courses may well have been consequent down the slope of the ancient dome, have cut through the north-dipping chalk of North Downs a series of deep gaps which now direct roads and railroads and furnish advantageous sites for local market towns. On the south, shorter streams divide the cuesta into short lengths, with towns on the coast below the gaps to serve coast fishing, scenic interests, and Weald agriculture.

12. Hampshire Basin. As the broad, uncovered anticline makes the Weald, so the southern, narrow syncline makes the Hampshire Basin. Its softer rocks were eroded into broad valleys when the land stood higher; then when the land sank, severing the islands from the continent, the Isle of Wight was separated from its mainland by the drowning of the main valleys of the basin. By these processes, too, the chalk escarpment on the south side of the syncline was partly submerged, permitting the sea to enter between Purbeck Downs and the Isle of Wight. Thus was made possible the little old harbor of Bournemouth, now the most visited seaside resort for many miles, and the great modern harbors of Portsmouth and South-ampton, the elements most significant to England in the Hampshire Basin. The town of Portsmouth (250,200) commands the harbor and lends itself admirably to defense, naval base, and dockyards, having become the most strongly fortified naval post in England. Southampton is purely commercial, with splendid passenger docks and facilities for handling freight. Its growth depends much on its spacious, deep harbor with its excellent protection behind the Isle, but perhaps equally upon its proximity to London, its direct access to Britain's interests in Africa, and its character as a steamship terminus for traffic to the countries of America and France. Seaside pleasure and health resorts, with excellent beach and climate attractions, line the coast.

13. London Basin. Like its lesser analogue on the opposite side of the Weald, this basin is also a syncline, a downward warp of a large series of relatively recent strata, including the chalk and later sands, clays, and marls, so that a broad lowland occurs between the North Downs and the Chiltern Hills. Its north boundary can be traced in the foot of the East Anglian Ridge and northward to the sea near Foulness so as to include large parts of the counties of Norfolk, Suffolk, Essex, and Middlesex and less of counties along the Thames above London. It includes the lower Thames Basin and the coastal plain from the estuary north beyond Yar-mouth. It has proved to be a most admirable place for human residence and business. While the great metropolis of London (8,700,000) owes much to geographic factors outside the basin, it also owes much to factors within. The city, its growth, and its qualities will be considered later.

The London Basin is made up of several varieties of clay, sand, and gravel, adapted to as many economic uses and all underlain by the chalk, whose artesian waters are reached everywhere by drilled wells. All the northern part was glaciated, and the heavy clays of Norfolk and Suffolk make them the first wheat and barley area in England and the latter the area of the best and most persistent beans and peas. Part of the richness of these clays is in the many fragments of limestone the glaciers plucked from the chalk scarps on the north and mingled with the till soils. Poultry and dairy

A block of modern residence flats, Regents' Park, London. (Courtesy British Information Services)

cows flourish over these northern portions and furnish part of the city's supplies. Some of the clays have supplied great brick and tile industries, and the sands and gravels have been equally valuable to the building trades. No local building stone has ever competed with the brick and tile. River sands are dredged for local use in great quantities. Abundance of gravel and sand has ensured good drainage for most parts of the metropolitan area, but has in places overdone the drainage and checked the growth of the city by limiting the supply of available well water. In places it has also limited the height of buildings.

The estuaries, of which the Thames is by far the most superior, and the

Blackwater and Harwich inlets, minor replicas, were deep enough for successful navigation in the olden days, but they were often surrounded by marshes which interfered with the approach by land. Tower Hill, upon which London Tower stands, was the bit of eminence on which in prehistoric times roads and trails from everywhere converged to avoid the marshes and yet reach the ford. Often the ford was not negotiable and traders and travelers were obliged to delay. For their benefit a village and a protecting fort were constructed. Since the crossing was favored with more substantial stream banks than most parts of the estuary, it lent itself in slow succession to ferry and bridge use; and thus drawing together roads from far and near it probably did more to unify the basin than any other one influence.

14. Fens and Grand Wash. This part of the eastern plains is unique enough to merit separate regional treatment. Long ago the cuestas forming the boundary between the Jurassic belt and the Chalk were so reduced by erosion that a slight submergence, probably that which separated the islands from the mainland, sent the waters of the North Sea back over a large tract of low, old topography, where now are the Fens and the Grand Wash. Through succeeding centuries streams bore waste into this embayment, waves eroded the shores, and currents spread the waste over the bay floor. Portions of the bay thus became a plain at sea level, a boggy area, the home of myriads of fish and waterfowl. First Romans and later, after the invasions of the Northmen, generations of monks attempted to drain portions of this area to reclaim the rich agricultural lands. So inaccessible were the Fens that they were the last stronghold of the Saxons. In the seventeenth century the English, stimulated by the success of Dutch reclamation works in the Netherlands, carried through several great engineering schemes and recovered large tracts. Men could not afford to let such fertile, well-watered, easily worked agricultural lands escape them longer. Consequently, draining and diking proceeded; and today what was muddy, reedy, mosquito-infested (ague) marsh-land has come to be most efficient, level, rich farmland. Crops and cattle utilize almost every foot of the ground. Modern roads curve round the present Wash shoreline, and other older ones followed former shorelines. Bird-hunting has given place to vegetable and cereal culture, disease and depression to health and prosperity. Wheat, market vegetables, and sugar beets are today the most important products of the area. The great Ely Cathedral towers above the fog, and the hum of small industry supplements the shouts of farmer drivers in marking the diversity of Fen occupation. Commerce, once common, and fishing, once a flourishing industry, have both been crowded out—commerce by the filling of the bay and the increased draft of commercial vessels, fishing by the limitation of the waters to occasional drainage ditches. Recovery of lands from the sea is not yet more than half accomplished. The whole Wash, like the Zuider Zee, will no doubt some day yield to man's prowess and be brought under the plow. Regions 4-14, except 7, constitute England. (See map on page 287.)

Ireland, the island long known as Great Britain's satellite, has shared the physiographic history of the other British Isles. The Wicklow Mountains are remnants of a Proto-Britain that included much of Wales, a large part of St. George's Channel, and the Irish Sea parts now warped below the water. The grain or trend of structure in the island is similar to that of Scotland, northeast to southwest, and the rocks in the Donegal Mountains, the Mountains of Mayo Muilrea, and those of Connemara are a continuation of the Scottish Highlands, both in form, structure, age, and composition. In Carboniferous time the seas and marshes seem to have covered Britain and Ireland much alike. Much of the coal of this period was subsequently warped downward in Britain and thus preserved for the present, but erosion has removed almost every fragment of it from Ireland. Likewise in middle Tertiary time, when much of northern France was receiving its later strata under the sea, most of both Ireland and Britain was exposed to stream work. This is no doubt the time when much of the Irish coal was eroded away.

15. Northern Ireland. Although this portion of the island is a political, social, and religious unit, it has much variety in form, structure, and land utilization. The northeast part is called the Antrim Plateau and consists largely of basaltic lava flows alternating with thinner early sedimentary beds, all covered by beds laid in later geologic times. The Giant's Causeway is part of one of these lava sheets. In the southeast are the Mourne Mountains, composed largely of granite, and the Uplands of County Down. In the northwest are the mountains with heath cover and the agricultural valleys of counties Londonderry and Tyrone. Cutting northeast-southwest across these sections is the rift valley, a continuation of that of Scotland. The rift has carried down a portion of the coal measures, and W. B. Wright wisely suggests the advisability of a thorough search for coal-beds across this depressed area. Lough Neagh, the largest lake of the British Isles, has resulted from glacial interference with drainage in the rift valley. All Ireland has been seriously affected by the lack of coal for industrial development, but this rift section may have enough coal for local use and a little industrial activity. The political unit Ulster or Northern Ireland, a part of the United Kingdom, includes little besides this physical region, No. 15.

Northern Ireland has good soils, ample rainfall, and topography old and low enough for excellent agricultural land. About 89 per cent of the three and one-third million acres are used for farming. In the last sixty years there has been a large shift in land utilization. Half as much land is now plowed and more than twice as much is cut for hay as formerly. Through these sixty years the amount in pasture, including grazed mountains, has remained nearly two thirds of the total acreage. This shift is in close accord with the trend for the whole British Isles, away from arable farming and toward cattle farming. The decline in products shows in wheat, oats, and root crops. Flax production, once important in these counties, has declined

more than half and has almost ceased in other parts of Ireland. The manufacture of linen and embroideries in and about Belfast (438,000) has continued, but the necessary flax and linen thread is now imported from the
Netherlands, Belgium, and Latvia (now a part of Russia), where it can be
produced more cheaply than here.

16. Northwestern mountains. As stated in the general paragraph on
Ireland, a region of ancient, crystalline, igneous and metamorphic rocks
with advanced mature to old topography lies across the peninsulas on the
northwest. County Tirconnail, the coastal part of Sligo, and the lake regions

By Killarney's lakes, in the midst of the old glaciated mountains of southwestern Ireland.
(Courtesy Independent Newspapers, Dublin)

and coasts of counties Mayo and Galway are included. Sheep are pastured
in large numbers on the verdure-clad hills. Among their attractive valleys
numbers of little fishing villages house the many fishermen and shelter the
frequent tourists, thus nurturing the two most profitable industries after
agriculture. Since Neolithic time these valleys have furnished the fisherman
with about all he gets, save the products of the sheltered seas.

17. Southern mountains. The highland rim toward the south is not connected genetically with that on the northwest. It culminates toward the east
in the charming Wicklow Mountains, rises centrally in the Knockmealdown

Mountains, and excels all else westward in the beautiful hills and lakes of Killarney. The rocks here, more resistant than in much of Ireland and shot in a small way with granite intrusions, were so high in the recent ice age that, after the continental sheet melted, local glaciers developed in their upper valleys and produced the characteristic phenomena of valley glaciers. Ponded waters made lakes around which fishermen prosper. The submergence of deep glaciated valleys produced fiords and several broad embayments which marine fishermen use for shelter. Villages of fishermen dot the shores. The moist western hilly portion of Ireland, by reason of its situation

Plowing land in County Wicklow, south of Dublin. The topography is old, much of it splendid agricultural land. (Courtesy Independent Newspapers, Dublin)

in the course of the westerlies, is counted the finest cattle and grazing land in the whole British Isles—land where the dairy cattle outnumber the human inhabitants. So thoroughly established and adjusted to the conditions has the industry become that the farmers have organized and planted coöperative creameries everywhere through the east-west parallel valleys of these highlands. The ridge and valley structure continues eastward beyond Cork and even to St. George's Channel. The Wicklow-Wexford Highlands reach along the Channel coast almost to Dublin (506,600) and in places attract many local guests and not a few foreign tourists. Sheep grazing and lumbering are, after cattle-raising, the most important occupations.

18. Central Lowland. This largest of Irish units occupies nearly one third of the whole island. It is used for general farming—the raising of barley, oats, wheat, turnips, and potatoes; but its moist climate makes it preëminently a cattle land, and near Dublin it is largely a dairy region. For farming land it is very well occupied, having nearly 200 persons per square mile.

Many parts of this area have bogs. It has been estimated that the peat is increasing in spite of its large use throughout the country and particularly in these central plains and in Antrim. The regions 16, 17, and 18 constitute the part of Ireland which became in 1949 the Irish Free State or Saorstat Eireann.

Fair day at Kinnegad in County West Meath. Somewhat like U.S. county fair. (Courtesy Independent Newspapers, Dublin)

19. Scottish seas and islands. Britain's shores are so deeply indented by bays and estuaries that the coast-line is longer in proportion to the area than in any other European country except Norway and Greece. This high ratio of shoreline is conspicuous in the Scottish seas. From Clyde to Cape Wrath the mainland is one continuous row of peninsulas between sea lochs or firths, true fiords; and off shore are the Hebrides and their many island skerries. Waters among the islands and near-islands are deep and boisterous; the lands are rocky, rough, and not very productive. Heavy rainfall and mild temperature clothe most of the soil with heaths, but the lowest slopes and narrow coast lands bear grass, oats, barley, and tiny vegetable gardens.

Dublin port on the Irish Sea. Warehouse on the right; ships on the left. (Courtesy Independent Newspapers, Dublin)

Lower O'Connell Street, Dublin. The Nelson monument marks the center of this capital city. Note the double-decked street cars and buses. (Courtesy Independent Newspapers, Dublin)

Cattle feed along the grasslands, and 200,000 sheep graze over the islands wherever grass or shrub can grow among the rocks. Herring fishing engages many men and boats in spite of the rough sea and its dangers. The Orkneys, Färoe, and Shetlands share in all these interests. All these islands are summits of highland areas carried beneath the waters in relatively recent times; the depths are stream-made valleys, now drowned by hundreds of feet of water.

20. Irish Sea. As is true of other border seas of the British Isles, the floor of the Irish Sea was stream-made and partakes of the rock structures and maturity of land forms of the islands on either side. A narrow valley-like section of the North or St. Patrick's Channel exceeds 600 feet in depth, but most of the sea and channel is less than 300 feet deep and large areas have much less depth. These shallow waters make admirable fishing-grounds. The greater depth of the North Channel suggests a deeper submergence of the western portion of the platform, more down-warping of this part than of the parts nearer the continent. The Isle of Man, from whose summit all four lands, England, Wales, Ireland, and Scotland, are visible, belongs genetically to England.

Four fifths of the oysters of all Scottish fisheries come from the slender Loch Ryan at Stranraer. Crabs, lobsters, herring, and other fish and crustaceans are common in the Irish Sea, but men have not yet responded as in the North Sea to the fishing opportunities. Large channels, arms of the sea, penetrate the land on either side, aiding both commerce and fishing, while they further temper the climate. The sea so isolated Ireland from England that the Romans never invaded the Emerald Isle; this exemption, according to an Irish Free State official, "is the reason the Irish have always been so different from the English, never having been taught law and order." As liberty is the natural privilege of an island people, so the Irish, twice removed from the continent, seem to have a double love of freedom and have found opportunity at last for expressing it in the Saorstat Eireann.

Passenger and freight boats trace lines across this sea in many directions, from Scotland, England, and Wales to the Irish ports of Dublin, Belfast and Larne, like threads drawn in a mesh to darn a great hole in a garment, for in many respects the British Isles are a single great unit.

21. North Sea. Most valuable as well as much the largest of the border seas is the North Sea, stretching almost 10°, 700 miles, from the Straits of Dover to the Shetland Islands and broadening to 10°, though scarcely half as many miles, between Denmark and Scotland. Nowhere as deep as St. Patrick's Channel but of greater significance in proportion to its greater width, the North Sea not only separates the islands from the mainland, permitting that freedom and independence of development and spirit so characteristic of England, but in later centuries has served as a trackless (or myriad-tracked) highway between British and continental ports, the ferry towns. In many respects the opposite shores are the real frontier of

Britain; and no geography of the country could be complete that omitted the British Seas. Across the North Sea came harassing Viking from fiorded Norway, restless Jute and Dane searching for more and better cattle land, Saxon and Angle to make permanent homes, and across its southern extension the conquering Normans and Bretons to rule the motley tribes of Britain. Across it too came the methods of industry developed in Flanders, the Protestant faith from the stronghold of Luther, and, twice in recent times, a call to arms from a violated neighbor. Today cables connect opposite lands; telephones and radio speak constantly across the waters; ferries and planes carry myriads of passengers, and mail-boats literally millions of written and printed messages each way.

Tides and currents of this North Sea are worth a careful study, but their relations to commerce and fishing are of chief significance here. The double tide in the Thames (two highs approaching simultaneously from different directions and likewise, twelve hours later, two lows), giving a great range to the height of the waters in this world-important harbor, not only serves as a powerful harbor-sweeper but makes possible the movement, at selected times, of any boats afloat. The migrations of fish are in part at least determined by currents. Herring, in need of oxygenated water flowing into the sea from the Atlantic, migrate in spring from Norway when the cold melt-water mingles with the sea, and they arrive on the Scottish coast in time to feed in the rich waters drifting from the north. Myriads of flatfish eggs laid in British waters, floating while hatching, drift into the Elbe embayment and there the fish are nourished by river-borne food. As they rapidly become large enough to be caught, they drift back on the bottom, months later, toward the British coasts and the ever anxious fisherman. Thus food, currents, spawning grounds, and fisherman synchronize to supply the great British market. Lobster and oyster fishing are important on English North Sea shores.

22. The English Channel. Into this long funnel, broad between Cornwall and Brittany but narrowing to the Straits of Dover, converge the ocean ways and the varied commerce from west and south, from near and far, from colony and foreign nation, all converging toward the fore-waters of Southampton, London, Le Havre, Paris, Amsterdam, Antwerp, and the Baltic ports. Just before entering this "sleeve," the commerce to Bristol, Dublin, Liverpool, and Glasgow turns off to make its way into western ports. No more admirable convergence of waterways occurs on any border, no greater commerce threads any sea on earth. The Channel too is crossed very frequently from French to British ports. In addition to its great commercial significance, it is not far behind the North Sea in fisheries, and its shorelines often afford the American traveler his first glimpse of England's famous chalk cliffs.

QUESTIONS

1. The summer isotherm of 60°F. crosses the British Isles from east to west and intersects the 40° winter isotherm (a north-south line) near Manchester. What important characteristics of Britain's agriculture depend upon this fact?

2. What reasons exist for a strong program of forestry and conservation in northern Britain?

3. Distinguish between Britain, England, and the British Isles.

4. How do the Scottish Lowlands supplement the Highlands on either side? How do the Highlands contribute to the Scottish Lowlands?

5. Why did there come a split between the people of North Ireland and those of the Irish Free State?

6. Would the English be better off if their lands extended nearly across the North Sea toward the mainland? Give reasons for your answer.

7. Should England make an effort to redeem the lands (sea-floor) of the North Sea, as the Netherlands have redeemed the South Sea or Zuider Zee? Give reasons for your answer.

BIBLIOGRAPHY

ABERCROMBIE, Patrick, *Greater London* (London, H. M. Stationery Office, 1945).

ALLAN, Nellie B., *Geographical and Industrial Studies: Europe* (Boston, Ginn and Company, 1928).

APPLETON, J. B., "The British Coal Mining Industry," *Bulletin Geographical Society of Philadelphia,* Vol. 28 (1930), pp. 123-142.

————, "Cleveland Industrial District," *Transactions Illinois State Academy of Science,* Vol. 21 (1928), pp. 358-367.

————, "Coal Industry," *Transactions Illinois State Academy of Science,* Vol. 22 (1929), pp. 511-532.

ARENSBERG, Conrad M., and KIMBALL, Solon T., *Family and Community in Ireland* (Cambridge, Harvard University Press, 1940).

BAILY, F. G., "Water Power Resources of Scotland," *Scottish Geographical Magazine,* Vol. 47 (May, 1931), pp. 129-144.

BESANT, Sir Walter, *Early London, Prehistoric, Roman, Saxon, Norman* (London, A. & C. Black, Ltd., 1908).

BLAKE, George, *The Heart of Scotland* (London, B. T. Batsford, Ltd., 1938).

BLANCHARD, W. O., and VISHER, S. S., *Economic Geography of Europe* (New York, McGraw-Hill Book Company, Inc., 1931).

British Information Service, many papers on various subjects (New York, Rockefeller Plaza, recent dates).

BROOKER, Robert W., *Great Britain and Ireland* (London, George H. Harrap & Co., Ltd., 1951).

BURKE, Thomas, *English Townsman as He Was and as He Is* (London, B. T. Batsford, Ltd., 1946).

CADELL, H. M., "Land Reclamation in the Forth Valley," *Scottish Geographical Magazine,* Vol. 45 (January and March, 1929), pp. 7-22, 81-100.

CHEYNEY, Edward P., *Industrial and Social History of England* (New York, The Macmillan Company, 1901).

CLARK, Grahame, *Prehistoric England* (London, B. T. Batsford, Ltd., 1941).

CLARK, Sydney A., *All the Best in England* (New York, Dodd, Mead, & Company, Inc., 1948).

CLAY, Henry, and BRADY, K. Russell, *Manchester at Work* (Manchester, England, 1929).

CORNISH, Vaughan, *Great Capitals, An Historical Geography* (London, Methuen & Co., Ltd., 1923).

COURT, H., and COURT, L., *The Story of British Trade and Commerce* (London, Sampson Low, Marston & Co., Ltd., 1927).

COWLING, Mary Jo, "Coal Fields and Population," *Bulletin Geographical Society of Philadelphia,* Vol. 25 (January, 1927).

CROSS, A. L., *A History of England and Greater Britain* (New York, The Macmillan Company, 1914).

CROWE, P. R., "The Scottish Coalfields," *Scottish Geographical Magazine,* Vol. 45 (November, 1929), pp. 321-337.

DARBY, H. C., *Medieval Draining of Fens* (Cambridge, England, Cambridge University Press, 1940).

DAYSH, G. H. J., and ALLEN, E., "Features of the Industrial Geography of the Tyne, Wear, and Tees," *Scottish Geographical Magazine,* Vol. 49 (January, 1933), pp. 1-18.

DEMANGEON, A., "British Isles," in Vidal de La Blache and Gallois, *Géographie Universelle* (Paris, Lib. Armand Colin, 1927).

DIBELIUS, Wilhelm, *England,* trans. by Mary A. Hamilton (London, Jonathan Cape, 1930).

DITCHFIELD, P. H., *Old Village Life* (New York, E. P. Dutton & Co., Inc., 1920).

EDEN, Anthony, "Britain in World Strategy," *Foreign Affairs,* Vol. 29 (April, 1951), pp. 341-350.

EDWARDS, George W., *London* (Philadelphia, Penn Publishing Co., 1922).

ENFIELD, R. R., *The Agricultural Crisis, 1920-23* (New York, Longmans, Green & Company, 1924).

FAWCETT, C. B., "Distribution of the Urban Population in Great Britain," *Geographical Journal,* Vol. 79 (February, 1932), pp. 100-117.

FITZGERALD, Walter, *The New Europe* (New York, Harper and Brothers, 1946).

FODOR, Eugene, ed., *England in 1951* (London, David McKay Company, 1951).

Foreign Commerce Year Book (Washington, D. C., Government Printing Office).

GEIKIE, Sir Archibald, *The Scenery of Scotland* (New York, The Macmillan Company, 1887).

GEORGE, H. B., *A Historical Geography of the British Empire* (London, Methuen & Co., Ltd., 1929).

GIBBS, Philip, *England Speaks* (New York, Literary Guild, 1935).

GRAS, Norman Scott Brien, *History of Agriculture in America and Europe* (New York, F. S. Crofts & Company, 1925).

GÜNTHER, Hans F. K., *Racial Elements of European History,* trans. by G. C. Wheeler (London, Methuen & Co., Ltd., 1927).

GWYNN, Stephen, *Ireland* (New York, Charles Scribner's Sons, 1925).

HERBERTSON, A. J., and HOWARTH, O. J. R., *The British Isles,* Vol. 1, Oxford Survey of the British Empire (Oxford, Clarendon Press, 1914).

HILDEBRAND, J. R., "Edinburgh, Athens of the North," *National Geographic Magazine,* Vol. 62 (August, 1932), pp. 219-246.

HINSLEY, F. H., *Command of the Sea* (London, Christophers, 1950).

HOWARTH, O. J. R., *Geography of the World* (Oxford, Clarendon Press, 1931).

HUGGINS, K. H., "The Scottish Highlands; A Regional Study," *Scottish Geographical Magazine,* Vol. 51 (September, 1935), pp. 296-305.

JEFFERSON, Mark S. W., "The Distribution of British Cities," *Geographical Review,* Vol. 4 (November, 1917), pp. 387-394.

JONES, Llewellyn R., *Geography of London River* (New York, Dial Press [Lincoln MacVeagh], Inc., 1932).

LABOR PARTY (Great Britain), *Reconstruction in War and Peace* (New York, League for Industrial Democracy, 1943).

LEWIN, Percy E., *Resources of the Empire* (London, William Collins Sons & Co., 1924).

LEWIS, Wilmarth S., *Three Tours through London,* in years 1748, 1776, and 1797 (New Haven, Yale University Press, 1941).

LUKE, Sir Harry C. J., *Malta: An Account and An Appreciation* (London, George G. Harrap & Co., Ltd., 1949).

MACDONALD, Sir George, *Roman Wall in Scotland* (Oxford, Clarendon Press, 1934).

MACKINDER, H. J., *Britain and British Seas* (New York, D. Appleton and Co., 1902).

MEARS, Eliot G., "Postwar Locational Changes of British Industry," *Geographical Review,* Vol. 29 (1939), pp. 233-251.

MEIKLE, Henry W., ed., *Scotland: A Description of Scotland and Scottish Life* (Edinburgh, Thomas Nelson & Sons, 1947).

MEREDITH, H. O., *Economic History of England* (New York, British Book Center, 1950).

MESSER, Malcolm, *Agricultural Atlas, England and Wales* (London, Oxford University Press, 1932).

MILL, H. R., "Flashlights on Geography—Featuring Scotland," *Scottish Geographical Magazine,* Vol. 50 (July, 1934), pp. 193-208.

MUIRHEAD, Litellus R., ed., *The Blue Guides: Ireland* (1949), *Scotland* (1949), *England* (1950). (Macmillan & Co., Ltd.)

NEWMAN, Bernard, *The New Europe* (New York, The Macmillan Company, 1943).

NOTESTEIN, Wallace, *The Scot in History* (New Haven, Yale University Press, 1946).

O'DELL, Andrew, "The Population of Scotland 1755-1931: A General Survey," *Scottish Geographical Magazine,* Vol. 48 (September, 1932), pp. 282-290.

PACKARD, Leonard O., and SINNOTT, Charles P., *Nations as Neighbors* (New York, The Macmillan Company, 1930).

PEARCY, G. Etzel, and FIFIELD, Russell H., *et al., World Political Geography* (New York, Thomas Y. Crowell Company, 1948).

POGGI, E. M., "Devon: A Study of Rural England," *Bulletin Geographical Society of Philadelphia,* Vol. 28 (July, 1930), pp. 161-173.

PROTHERO, R. Ernle, *English Farming Past and Present* (New York, Longmans, Green & Company, 1923).

PULL, J. H., *The Flint Miners of Blackpatch* (London, Williams & Norgate, Ltd., 1932).

RICKARD, T. A., *Man and Metals* (New York, McGraw-Hill Book Company, Inc., 1932).

Royal Institute of International Affairs, *British Security* (London and New York, Chatham Home Study, 1946).

RUSSEL, G. W., "Twenty-five Years of Irish Nationality," *Foreign Affairs,* Vol. 17 (January, 1929), pp. 204-220.

SMAILES, A. E., "The Development of the Northumberland and Durham Coalfield," *Scottish Geographical Magazine*, Vol. 51 (July, 1935), pp. 201-214.

SNODGRASS, C. P., "The Influence of Physical Environment on the Principal Cultivated Crops of Scotland," *Scottish Geographical Magazine*, Vol. 48 (November, 1932), pp. 329-347.

————, "Stock Farming in Scotland, and Its Relation to Environment," *Scottish Geographical Magazine*, Vol. 49 (January, 1933), pp. 24-34.

STAMP, L. Dudley, and BEAVER, Stanley H., *British Isles, A Geographic and Economic Survey* (London and New York, Longmans, Green & Company, 1933).

STAMP, Lawrence Dudley, *Agricultural Atlas, Ireland* (London, George Gill & Sons, Ltd., 1931).

————, "The Land Utilization Survey of Britain," *Geographical Journal*, Vol. 78 (July, 1931), pp. 40-53.

————, *The Land of Britain, Its Use and Misuse* (London and New York, Longmans, Green & Company, 1948).

Statistical Abstract for the United Kingdom (London, 1931, and following years).

STREET, Alicia, *Land of the English People* (Philadelphia, J. B. Lippincott Company, 1946).

TANSLEY, Arthur G., *British Isles and Their Vegetation* (Cambridge, England, Cambridge University Press, 1939).

TRAVERSIN, Guy, *L'Agriculture en Grande-Bretagne* (Paris, Institut National de la Statistique et des Études Économiques, 1949).

USSHER, Arland, *The Face and Mind of Ireland* (New York, Devin-Adair, 1950).

WALMSEY, Leo, "Between the Heather and the North Sea," *National Geographic Magazine*, Vol. 63 (February, 1933), pp. 197-232.

WARD, E. M., *English Coastal Evolution* (London, Methuen & Co., Ltd., 1922).

WARD, H. B., "Manchester Ship Canal," *Transactions Illinois State Academy of Science*, Vol. 22 (1929), pp. 555-557.

WELLES, Sumner, ed., *An Intelligent American's Guide to the Peace* (New York, The Dryden Press, 1945).

WOOD, H. J., *Agricultural Atlas, Scotland* (London, George Gill & Sons, Ltd., 1931).

WRIGHT, W. B., *Geology of Killarney and Kenmare* (Dublin, Stationery Office, 1927).

CHAPTER 15

The British Isles
Part II. National and International Problems

Whether splendidly isolated or dangerously isolated.
—SIR WILFRID LAURIER

ECONOMIC SECURITY

Unity in diversity. In spite of great diversity of resource, industry, and topography, there is much real unity throughout the British Isles. This unity reveals itself in at least three aspects. (1) All parts of the domain have the same type of boundary; no one is concerned with defending a mountain barrier, a desert border, or an arbitrary line; nor is any one set over against a foreigner. All are concerned with the care of a simple water frontier. All are near this boundary, the most distant but 70 miles away; hence all must feel a common interest in it. Half the inhabitants could walk from home to salt water in one day, and fresh marine fish can be had on nearly every table. (2) There is a similar isolation for all the citizens of these isles. No one is greatly separated from the continent, yet all are set somewhat apart from it. A feeling of unity has a much better opportunity to develop in these islands than in any country on the continent. Yet all are in close enough proximity to France and the Low Countries to sense their presence and have interests in them, without real familiarity. (3) Because of this insular marine setting, a marine type of climate, cool, moist, with no extremes in the day or year, prevails everywhere in the islands. This setting generates a common interest in building, clothing, and crops. One is climatically at home in any part of the area.

This paradox of unity in diversity is revealed even in the geological foundations of these islands. The geology is a remarkable epitome of that of the continent. Rocks of all ages occur in close proximity within the islands and give expression to many details of topographic form, yet all mellow into each other with no great departures from a common type. The resources in the rocks are similar to those of the same rocks on the continent, widely distributed, varied enough to satisfy most interests, yet interrelated. Coal is found in many places. Iron is less scattered, but distributed widely enough to necessitate no anxieties or inconveniences. Many other metals are

319

known, and good building stone and clays are available almost anywhere. Soils of nearly every type occur, and agriculture is physically possible in every county. Forests are not limited to any locality. Domestic stock is widely distributed; every farmer can have his own poultry, cow, hog, horse, or sheep.

In the last century canals were built to supplement the streams and the sea so that water communication came near every man's door; then the railroad came and if possible bound the people still more closely together. There are no barriers on the islands and no barriers to marine communications.

While the present British people send their roots back into a considerable variety of stocks, intermingling and interbreeding have melted off many angularities, and the freedom of movement plus a common language and universal education have fused them for all practical purposes into one racial unit. Politically, the people have for centuries had a common interest in their colonial possessions and responsibilities. Perhaps the separateness of the Irish is partly due to their failure to take any particular interest in Britain's colonial responsibilities. There is probably no one of the larger nations in Europe that is today nearly as unified as is the United Kingdom, a factor of inestimable value in economic security.

Situation. Both advantages and disadvantages accrue to position. Quoting Lyde, "mathematically, the British Isles are in the center of all the land on the face of the earth; climatically, they occupy one of the most temperate areas; commercially, they are on the edge of the busiest ocean; geologically, they are on the shelf of the most advanced continent." Historically, Britain was once on the far edge of commerce, culture, and religion, hence was last to enter the benefits of the Roman Empire in the first century A.D. and first to be released from it near beginning of the fifth century; now it is at the cross-roads of many lines, the transfer point from land to sea travel, the working head of a world empire, and probably, in a fine sense, the mother of modern civilization and world vision on international problems. The latter points are in some measure results of the former.

Significance of resources. One no more than begins to enumerate the great advantages of resources enjoyed by Britain before the lacks and disadvantages become apparent. In the field of building materials, there are granites, slates, sandstones, and limestones in considerable variety, but very little marble, and one response thereto is the absence of any fine art in marble as in Italy and Greece. In fuels and power, there is abundance of coal in several fine grades, with peat still forming as fast as it is used; but no oil and gas are known; the water power is meager and always in small units because of general low relief and a total absence of long or large streams. Oil shale near Edinburgh is of value but very limited in amount. Through distillation it can be made to yield oil, wax, and ammonia. In precious stones, a long intensive occupancy has to date disclosed nothing of note. In metals, iron is the most abundant; tin was once mined in relatively large quantities, but it is now nearly exhausted. Lead, zinc, and copper have been worked for years, but there are no deposits comparable with the needs of a nation high in the industrial scale. Silver is of little importance; gold, once found in Ireland on a large scale for ancient times, is now only sparingly produced from sands and gravels. Aluminum ores are almost unknown in the islands. Cement rocks, gravel, sand, and clay for the ceramic and building trades are abundant and varied. The great industrial life of the nation and a large section of the export trade rests on the enormous supplies of coal. The importation of iron ore in large quantities from Spain, Kirkenes in Norway, and Sweden tends to shift the steel industries toward the coast. Common salt, from springs in Cheshire and from the sea in the south, and other compounds for chemical industries are not frequent in native rocks but, like bones and rock for the phosphate industry, are imported extensively to be manufactured with native coal for fuel and sulphuric acid made of sulphur, derived from sulphide ores of lead, zinc, and iron.

Self-sufficiency. When still in the agricultural stage the British Isles were self-sufficient, but with the advent of modern industrial life there was a most significant change in this respect. If it were not for the extensive coal reserves which have supplied a large excess of this fuel for export after meeting the needs of the varied textile, metallurgical, and finishing industries, Britain could not possibly have risen to the high position and comfortable standards of living held before 1914.

During World War I and until the close of the Second World War Britain studied her agricultural problem from many angles. By 1930 the lowest production had been reached. Over two thirds of the nation's food had to be imported. In the latter war submarine and other destruction of shipping necessitated much greater food production. Land long in permanent pasture and some almost waste is now under the plow. Much former meadow land is cultivated; heavier cuts of hay and forage are raised by better care and fertilizer. Mechanization with tractor plows, cultivators, and combine harvesters, mostly manufactured at home, has increased 50 to 100 per cent. More efficient cultivation, more adequate fertilizer programs and better seed have increased the agricultural production until at least half the home needs are now met and there are fewer men working on the farms than for many decades. Farm machinery production was five times as great in 1947 as in 1937, and nearly three times as much was being exported as in 1937. A small two-wheeled tractor is made by tens of thousands for the small farmer.

International connections. It is in the light of the above considerations that one must approach Britain's international relations. The circumstances demand that over 50 per cent of food requirements be grown on colonial or foreign soil, that all cotton for textile industries, all rubber, much wool and flax, and a large proportion of leather, iron, and other metals must be imported in some form to supply the industrial plants; and yet it is true that more than one fourth of all the imports are manufactured articles. Britain has a large trade with other countries in the Commonwealth; 28 per cent of the imports and 44 per cent of the exports are so listed. There is a large volume of reëxport trade from the colonies and Europe to other colonies, to Ireland, Germany, France, and the United States. The volume of this business is large because, in relation to other industrial nations, Britain has a geographic position which is appropriate for such a clearing-house or market; because as an island it is altogether natural for Britain to have a large fleet and a seafaring population; and because political relations make such trade expedient. Annual exports rose by 1948 to 77 per cent of imports and now have a value of over $5 billion, which is greater than in 1938. Invisible credits to apply on the balancing of the trade sheet consist of net income from investments overseas and from shipping, commissions, banking, insurance, tourist expenditures, and other services, which, taken together, in most years, give a favorable balance. Great effort is being made to increase sales of cars, cutlery, and textiles. Some coal is exported also.

Commonwealth. Geography of the British Commonwealth of Nations would make a larger book than the geography of Europe if area and population were the measures for determining the number of pages. No such digression as an adequate description of these lands would involve could be tolerated here. Yet the geography of the British Isles cannot be adequately considered without some reference to the rest of the Commonwealth. Any good yearbook such as the *World Almanac* will give areas and populations of every unit of this great Commonwealth. Here it is necessary only to note certain elements of distribution. In Europe outside the British Isles, which so far have been regarded as including the Irish Free State, the Commonwealth-Empire comprises Gibraltar, Malta, and Cyprus, all Mediterranean fragments. Their chief national values and relations are as guards to the Suez route to India and the East, as British tourist attractions, and as coaling stations. The arrival of independence in 1947 to Union of India and to Pakistan, and in 1948 to Burma has reduced Britain's territorial interest in Asia by over 1.7 million square miles. These areas have been important traders with Britain and no doubt will continue to be.

From the Straits Settlements in British Malaya come forest products and tin ore to help supplement the waning home supplies. Borneo and Sarawak each contains 30,000 to 40,000 square miles and sends home sago, timber, rubber, petroleum, rice, gums, oils, nuts, and gold. These imports purchase machinery and tools and pay for service in directing developmental work.

In Africa Britain has about 4 million square miles of lands in all latitudes from 22° N. to 32° S. in every stage of civilization and culture. These colonies produce many kinds of raw products, equatorial, tropical, and subtemperate, including diamonds, gold, platinum, manganese, copper, ostrich plumes, sheep and wool, hides, cotton, spices, fruits, oils, and wheat. Machinery and equipment for developing new countries are purchased, as well as kerosene, cotton, cloth, salt, motor fuels, and lubricants.

Australia is a vast commonwealth, which with its scattered islands comprises a total area of over 3 million square miles. Its people are so largely of British descent that their needs are quite like those of other young English colonial nations such as Canada. Their exports are the products of agriculture and grazing, together with gold, silver, lead, copper, tin, zinc, iron, and coal. Some $20 million worth of fresh and dried fruits are annually exported. Most of these exports are very welcome in the British Isles and are used there; a few are reëxported.

In the Americas almost 4 million square miles are listed. Canada contains nearly 97 per cent of this area, and British Guiana about 2½ per cent. Canada is a great producer of furs, skins, wheat, wood and wood-pulp, gold, silver, copper, and nickel; Guiana exports forest products, rubber, and aluminum ore, but none of them in notable quantities although there are very valuable reserves of each.

The British Commonwealth of Nations comprises 12,974,410 square miles, nearly one fourth of the land surface of the earth, and 551,336,810 people. Every Colony, Protectorate, Dominion, and Trust has something the homeland needs for food or for industrial development, and each is a market for something manufactured in the homeland. With such great areas and such great and varied wealth in vegetable, animal, and mineral products, these lands make possible the superior industrial and commercial development of England. With Britain's wide range and abundance of manufactures, the development of these new countries is assured. With so large a material interest in world production there is an equally great responsibility for conservation of resources; and with these millions of people, there inheres a similar magnificent opportunity and obligation for the education and cultural improvement of the people of every land in its world-wide dominions.

A world power. No one can even summarize these resources in minerals, crops, industries, and people without perceiving that Britain is a world power. No quarter of a hemisphere, either north or south, east or west, old or new, is beyond touch of the British Isles. Navigators of the globe set their chronometers to the time of the first meridian passing through Greenwich, England. Because of her long preëminence in commerce, shipping, and banking, and despite economic and political weakness imposed upon her by World War II, her "coin of the realm," the pound sterling, is still a standard for much of the world, and the Bank of England is still one of the most important single banks. After the tremendous losses of merchant marine in the war she has recovered almost her prewar strength but not her former supremacy. Competition is strong.

Originally a fishing people by virtue of a fisherman's type of shoreline and of proximity to a wealth and variety of fish, the men became hardy seamen, then traders in foreign lands. The next step took the flag and authority to preserve order wherever the trader went. Then came arms and the assumption of political control of lands needed for trade, until a great world empire was established. Today Britain leads in responsibility for the welfare of the Commonwealth's quota of this world's goods, people, and power.

Often, during past decades, policies and programs have been inspired by selfish motives and results have been far from idealistic, but there has come out of Britain's foreign program a foreign policy which today sets a standard for all nations who would govern new lands or rule old nations. Out of the many friendly, helpful, sometimes paternal relations has come the familiar phrase, the "Mother-Country," eminently more applicable to Britain than to any other more or less imperialistic country. "Mother-Country" and "Mistress of the Seas" are reciprocal adjustments, for one cannot maintain a world control over a hundred scattered lands without having sea power and sea control; neither can a people acquire sea power to a state of mastery until they have possessed many widely scattered parcels of land. With all this a great nation cannot escape the concomitant responsibilities. World power means world responsibilities as well as world opportunities. Until near the middle of the twentieth century the British extended their geographic contacts, entered geographic relations, responded to geographic influences, laid under tribute every kind of geographic combination and every possible resource, until becoming the people most influenced by geographic factors, they used more geographic connections and were subject to more geographic conditions than any other nation.

It is in great aggregations of nations, states, colonies, and commonwealths that one sees the modern trends developing. As "no man liveth to himself," in the Biblical phrase, so in a geographic sense no nation lives to itself. It must buy and sell to get the varied elements of its own subsistence and at the same time to permit its neighbors to draw on the larger environment. For one to live within the range of his own products limits his own contacts and likewise limits his neighbor. To buy only British, meaning only products of the Commonwealth, would cramp Britain's style tremendously; but even if Britain should not object to such restrictions, they are not fair to the neighbors. And what is a working principle and growing trend within such a group as the British Commonwealth of Nations is equally workable among any neighborly group of independent nations.

Another implication follows. If elements of a great commonwealth should each produce what it can produce best, just as each type of soil on a well-managed farm produces the crop to which it is best adapted, then it follows that all nations and all parts of the earth should each make such contributions to the common good—food, raw materials, manufactures, art, or literature—as it can best produce, and let each other part do the same without placing subsidies, tariffs, taxes, or bonuses in the way. The ultimate consumer pays the subsidy, tariff, bonus, or tax, which makes the article cost more. Britain has for generations led the way in response to this noble geographic principle. Hasten the day when the British and likewise all other nations will remove tariff walls erected for protection and cease to make their consumers pay an unnecessary tax on nearly everything used.

AGRICULTURE AND NATURAL VEGETATION

Beginnings. The earliest agriculture in the British Isles was very closely related to topography and soils. Like certain elements of early migration, it followed the Downs and cuestas that converge toward the Salisbury Plains. On many slopes and uplands there remain "linches" or terraces, wholly prehistoric, which are ascribed to some form of cultivation along the drier ridge tops and upper slopes, when the lowlands were wet and choked with vegetation. These places in these most favorable southwest counties must have been first selected because of climatic and drainage advantages, because easily cleared and kept cleared, and because they were along the highways. They may be relics of methods used in agriculture of drier lands by prehistoric immigrants from eastern Mediterranean countries.

When the Romans came, they found in operation the open-field system of agriculture, in which no fences were used, but narrow strips of land were held by each farmer in order to cut across the several types of soil. At that time the tribal community of farmers existed in western England and the village community in the east, the latter perhaps in response to the proximity of continental agriculture. In both regions the open field prevailed and arable land was segregated on one side of the village, while common pasture prevailed on another side, each on land best adapted to its use. Cæsar adds that "the inland inhabitants sow no corn, (wheat, rye, barley), but live on milk and flesh and wear skins." In Saxon times the same types of agriculture prevailed but were much more widespread. By the Middle Ages rotation in a three-field system had been inaugurated, in recognition of the fact that fields became exhausted and man could make more efficient connections with his soils if he raised wheat one year, barley the next, and left his land fallow the third. Ever since Roman times farmers had used marl to "sweeten" the acid clay soils of South England.

Changes. Beans and peas came into the agricultural milieu much later than wheat and barley, while flax and hemp were still more tardy. Turnips for sheep food entered the ranks of crops still later, but all were cultivated in the open-field system in 1086 when the Domesday records were made. In the thirteenth century the old manor grew out of the village community agriculture, because some one must lead and the rest must follow or co-operate for protection.

Because of the colder, duller climate in Scotland, agriculture was much more backward there than in southern England. Crop-raising was miserably done; clover and sown grasses were introduced as late as 1720, while in 1723 the Scots were advised to plant potatoes and turnips for home use. Such backwardness was due to the inclement climate, wet, soggy, glacial soils, and remoteness from more favored, hence more progressive, rural peoples.

The Fens and marsh-lands were a temptation to early populations. Fishing prevailed at first, then the native began taking wild birds for food; but the wild life was wary, and in consequence the Fen farmer decided to corral the fish and cultivate the waterfowl. The ditching and diking that followed banished the wild life and permitted planting and cropping. For some 300 years this invasion of the Fens by crop agriculture has proceeded, ever at accelerated rate, until now some of the finest garden agriculture of Britain has expanded over former fishing and hunting grounds, putting to more and more intensive use valuable geographic settings.

Adjustments. Although the British Isles have many advantages as agricultural lands, such as mild climate, ample rainfall, and much level or gently rolling land, either of glacial or in advanced maturity in the stream cycle, they also have many disadvantages. The climate is cold and raw, foggy or cloudy so much of the time that crops requiring long growing seasons or warm sunshine are severely handicapped. A large proportion of the land is bare rock or is encumbered by poor drainage. All these unfortunate conditions increase with latitude until much of the Scottish Highlands and northwest Ireland give little encouragement to aught but grazing.

The beauty of the heath, purple in summer and brown as it ripens and dries in the fall, adds to the romance and glory of the otherwise almost worthless, rough, grazing hills and valleys of the higher and more northern parts.

Agriculture has been a fundamental industry in these islands for 2,000 years with increasing importance until the Industrial Revolution overtook it and set many manufacturing and mining industries in the front ranks. A relative, though not an actual, decline in agriculture followed.

Through the nineteenth century much was accomplished to stimulate, improve, and adjust agricultural practice. Experiment stations wrought diligently to find the best ways to prepare and till the soil, the best-adapted seeds and plants, and the most satisfactory methods of harvesting, shipping, and marketing. Every successful adjustment in all this century of testing was a closer response to some geographic factor or influence. But with the increase of food production in colonial and other new lands and the improvement of shipping in the nineteenth century Britain's agriculture declined, although the greater the progress in manufactures and mining, the greater was the market for farm products.

Present status. In the ten years 1918 to 1928 the amount of cultivated land diminished by nearly 2 million acres or about 7 per cent. This shift in utilization was brought about by laying down this amount in permanent grass and permitting a similar area of former grassland to revert to heath and rough pasture. The poorer lands with rough topography, thin or exhausted soils, or worst drainage thus were stepped down to less valuable uses.

Arable land areas were reduced for nearly every crop in these same ten years. Wheat acreage fell by many thousands of acres; but the wheat belt continues in the same counties, Norfolk, Suffolk, Essex, and Lincolnshire. This crop largely disappeared from districts over 600 feet high having over 40 inches of rainfall. Barley and oats acreage likewise suffered a marked contraction in these ten years, and only the lands best adapted for these cereals were kept in this category. The acreage of beans and peas also shrank 25 to 35 per cent through elimination of most of the wetter lands. Potatoes for human food, turnips, rutabagas, and mangolds for sheep and cattle food, all sharply declined; thus again many acres of lands poorly adapted to root culture were eliminated. Lucerne, clover, and grasses for rotation increased everywhere and came to occupy much land formerly in the crops mentioned above.

Although this shifting of acreages under the several crops is usually credited to the fall in prices for rural products, it resulted in much better adjustment of crops and of systems of agriculture to the soils, relief, altitude and rainfall than had existed for many years.

In livestock some notable changes also occurred. The general decline in agriculture and the increase in the use of motor vehicles combined to put the horse out of the race. In the decade noted above, the number of horses gradually declined about 25 per cent. Dairy cattle increased, and dairy products likewise, with the improvement in pasture and the increase in rough pasture, but sheep ran very steadily. Hogs increased 75 per cent with the increase in dairying. This large increase probably meant a more careful saving of farm waste upon which swine can feed.

Much attention has always been given to flower and vegetable gardens in these lands. Although many of the finer vegetables cannot be grown here, root and leaf crops flourish, and small fruits, such as currants, gooseberries, raspberries, and strawberries, abound in splendid perfection. The continual moist air and frequent precipitation are a great aid to such crops. The more delicate garden products are shipped from near-by islands or southern lands. Exquisite flower-gardens are luxuriant in all parts; hedges and lanes are the pride of the southern counties. Many hardy perennials and annuals do wonderfully well, and no picture of England is complete without a garden. In west Ireland and south England one is often surprised to find exotics. Such are various palms in railroad yards and other gardens, whose very physiognomy is strong witness to the struggle they maintain. Imported by seafarers in times past, they add to the variety of plant life, but they cannot become acclimated.

During World War II agriculture was diligently studied to increase home production. Roadsides were put under cultivation; lawns and many pastures were plowed and planted to food crops. Selection of seed and fertilizers added to production. The English learned much about better adjustments of crops to soils and topography. The postwar agriculture is strongly colored by experiments and practices of war years. Great Britain still imports about 80 per cent of her fruits and bread stuffs, 50 per cent of her meats, eggs, and dairy products, and over 30 per cent of her vegetables.

The forests. Forests are reduced to less than 5 per cent of the country. Such a climate as Britain possesses, in a latitude of 50° to 60°, would certainly favor a densely forested area wherever soil enough remains. One has but to read the stories of King Arthur and Robin Hood to be convinced that the geographic setting was once essentially forest. In those days men knew how to live in forest, fen, or heath as circumstances required. But with the progress of civilization trees had to give place until with the pressure of agriculture, industry, and mining nearly all forest cover has been removed. Most land is indeed worth more for other purposes than for forest. Deer-parks have increased in the north with the shift in agriculture and permanent grass acreage, but there has been no return of forest. Lands of more value for forests than for crops or grass are scarce and are usually considered more profitable for hunting than for foresting.

For these reasons ship masts were imported in American colonial days; lumber for building, furniture, mine props, and paper pulp are imported today; and there is no reason why there should be any material change in the forest or wood import situation.

MINERAL RESOURCES AND THEIR DEVELOPMENT

Early stages. Probably the first mineral resource to be used in Britain was stone for implements and memorials. All along the Downs, from eastern Kent through the South Downs of Sussex and on to Hampshire, Western and Purbeck Downs, and again in Norfolk and Suffolk, flint has been collected from the chalk and worked into implements of peace and war. These workings were developed extensively some time around 3000 to 2000 B.C. Flint, not steel, coal or gold, was the *mineral* of these early peoples. Its distribution determined the location of mines and quarries and of the chipping floors (factories) where the nodules were broken and worked into useful forms. Blackpatch in South Downs is a fine example. The chalk also was used for cups, charms, and ornaments. It seems probable that the largest aggregations of people in prehistoric days occurred in these industrial centers and near the mines. Possibly the quarrying was an important incentive to a culture higher than the savagery of nomad and hunter and to the development of fixed residences and sedentary life, for several dwelling and hearth sites are known. Clay was used for pottery by these same people, and its distribution was another factor determining the density of population and the occupations of some of the people.

Possibly stones were used for monuments in as early times as flints were used in primitive industry. The great Stonehenge of Salisbury Plains is said by astronomers to have in its alignments evidence that it was built about 1680 B.C. The Druid Circle of Keswick may be of similar antiquity. There are many other monuments, including Dowth and New Grange of Ireland, remaining in parts of the islands to show the use of megaliths and lesser stones in very ancient times. Neither the stone structures nor the great Barrows of similar prehistoric date are known on the Moors; instead they are confined to the solid plains and the chalk Downs. These items remind us that man even in his very primitive development responded to natural resources, topography, and the astronomic aspects of the heavens.

Tin and copper, both in Cornwall, were used for bronze after the flint and stone ages. The export of tin by Phœnician and Greek, then by the Romans, initiated the foreign trade of Britain. Mining settlements grew up in Cornwall very early.

The beginning of the use of iron may have been delayed in Britain until much later than 1000 B.C. though it was used earlier in the Near East. Today the smelting and manufacture of iron are the second most important phases of industrial activity.

Later stages. When the coal resources and their uses came to be recognized, Britain passed out of the agricultural stage and into the industrial. The coal reserves are enormous; production is almost half of that for all Europe. Iron reserves and production are very inadequate, but neighbors, generously supplied, trade iron ores for coal, and England thus secures what England needs. Coal is the basis of both commerce and industry, entering in a very large way into foreign exports and furnishing the bulk of the power for manufactures which constitute about three fourths of all the exports.

Many home industries have been developed on the coal-fields and nearly all the great export industries are similarly situated.

The mineral wealth justified and defrayed the expenses of these great enterprises, and the distribution of it was exceedingly favorable to both. The mines first worked were so near the river [Tyne] that, even with packhorse transport, it was possible and profitable to export coal; the height of the banks makes it equally possible and profitable to work the transport today mainly by gravitation.[1]

What has been said here of Newcastle has been almost equally true at Cardiff, whose converging valleys leading from the coal-fields to the sea have given the Cardiff center the privilege of handling over 40 per cent of all the export coal. Coal-mining is back about to prewar levels, and steel production seems to be a little greater than in 1937-38. Coal production in 1938 and 1947 were almost identical—223 million tons.

[1] L. W. Lyde, *Continent of Europe* (1926), p. 248.

The iron and steel industries illustrate the permanence of geographic control with progressive variations in the manifestations of that control. The permanence is most conspicuous in the cases of Birmingham and Sheffield. Both have historic industries of at least 1000 years standing; both had, to start with, local supplies of ore and fuel—from the forests of Arden and Sherwood; both had "local" supplies of coal, and were within easy reach of imported ore. But their non-local relations were different.[2]

Birmingham, in the very heart of England, encouraged the construction of canals and later of railways. These advantages of location and transportation are reflected in the development of manufacturing centers both of small, high-value articles and of heavy machinery and railway rolling stock. Sheffield, far at one side, had the local advantages of crucible clay, water power, and fine grinding stone, which directed the local energies into cutlery. Thus not only do the mineral resources promote their own industries, but they stimulate the growth of subsidiary plants and transportation facilities. They also amass the workers in these great mining and industrial areas and help to determine the social and economic status of several millions of people.

Coal furnishes the fuel and power for the reduction of other metals. Although Britain is not rich in many of these, there were enough to institute tin, copper, lead, zinc, and several lesser metallurgical plants. Now that there are generous supplies of coal, labor, and market, and ores of these and other metals in the colonies, the ores are imported. South Wales has perhaps the most brilliant galaxy of reduction plants scattered through many cities. Subsidiary plants for the manufacture of such products as tin-plate, copper wire, and electrical supplies are also numerous.

Upon the coal as a raw material is built a large chemical industry in dyes, salts, ammonia, gas, coke, tar and a multitude of tar products; and upon the coal as a fuel and source of power depend transportation and scores of great manufacturing industries, as well as lighting and heating of homes and business and public buildings.

The peat of Ireland and Scotland has been mentioned. Climate and topography in these sections promote the growth of peat-forming plants and favor the conservation of the vegetation in peat beds. For ages peat has served as a fuel to provide warmth and for cooking in Ireland and more sparingly in Scotland, Wales, and England. But being quick-burning and low in thermal units, it has not promoted industrial development in Ireland as does coal or even charcoal in England.

The British Isles have a wealth and variety of mineral building materials. Limestones and sandstones laid in the sea or fresh water are available in most counties. Granites and other igneous rocks are abundant in most parts of Scotland, in all corners of Ireland save the southwest, in north, northwest, and southwest England, and in many counties of Wales. Gneisses,

[2] *Ibid.*, pp. 254-255.

slates, quartzites, and schists are common in many localities—slates in North Wales, gneisses in Scotland in particular. These abundant building resources are reflected in stately, durable buildings in almost every city. Marble is found in only a few places; there is a black commercial limestone found in Ireland, north of Galway, which takes a fine polish, but no notable deposit of marble is known.

Abundant, widely distributed, and well-developed clays have given ample materials for British pottery and chinaware. A unique deposit of clay is that found in Cornwall around the borders of the granitic stocks which yielded so great a wealth of tin and associated metallic minerals. Glacial clays and local shales are used in every county to make brick and tile for building, and tile for the drain pipes so much needed in marshy areas.

Gravel and sand are found in great variety and abundance in most of the lowlands, particularly where there has been glaciation. They are also dredged continuously from many of the streams. They are extensively used on roads, alone, with tar, and as a safety coating on many asphalt roads to prevent skidding when the roads are wet, and also to make plaster, mortar, concrete and glass for the building trades.

Cement is manufactured in many places from suitable calcareous shales or mixtures of shale and limestone and used freely in buildings, roads, bridges, and walls, either in forms, as mortar, or in cement blocks. This wealth and variety of building materials, mostly so well suited to the cool, moist climate of the islands, has made possible excellent roads, bridges, pavements, and all needed buildings without resorting to the importation of wood, which has become scarce at home.

Soils. The soils of the islands are largely derived from glacial drift and are therefore in the main long-lived. Local residual soils occur principally in south England, beyond the influence of glaciation. Black earth soils are found in many places where glacial marshes and marine lagoons have become filled and have been drained for agricultural uses. Owing to the extensive and perpetual cropping many soils long ago became so depleted as to need renewing. Dressings of lime (marl) taken from glacial marl pits, have been used for hundreds of years. On some soils peat has been strewn with good results. The growth of the dairy and pork industry has increased the supply of stable manure, which is carefully conserved and used on farms and gardens. Sulphur and ammonia from the distillation of coal are combined with lime and thus prepared for use as fertilizers. Other nitrogen fertilizers must be imported or prepared with nitrogen obtained from the air. Phosphate fertilizer material is not common in England, but Canada has an abundance, and tramp steamers have for many decades brought bones from the cattle lands of Argentina to be manufactured into soluble phosphate fertilizers in England. So well have the soil and fertilizer problems been solved that there is no reason here for the breakdown of English agriculture.

Although the English people are wonderfully well supplied with coal and many building materials, they are not well furnished with many other minerals essential for an industrial nation. To these shortages the intelligence of the people has long been directed; and one element of the adjustment which they have found it necessary to make is the development of technical schools, colleges, universities, and experiment stations in engineering, mining, agriculture, and industry. The response has been adequate.

INDUSTRIES[3]

Introduction. Great Britain has had many thriving industries. Four areas have made much progress in the postwar years in development of new industries and the expansion of old ones: south Wales, Cardiff to Swansea; northeast England, Newcastle-Sunderland area; west Scotland lowland area for many miles around Glasgow; and the west Cumberland area around Whitehaven. These areas contain one seventh of Britain's population and one third of the new factories, employing 200,000 workmen. A thousand new or greatly extended factories are growing in these areas; their products are consumer goods, such as spark-plugs, roller-skates, zippers, molded plastics, buttons, combs, baby carriages, and play vehicles. In one development area in south Wales, where part of the plants are government financed and part privately, forty-five factories are making over sixty articles of consumer goods. Hydro-electric power plants in the Highlands, between high lakes and low lakes, such as Loch Lomond, are being constructed to extend current to many agricultural communities and manufacturing towns, and to carry light and power to thousands of homes that have never before emerged from the candle, oil-lamps, and hand-washer stage. Countryside and fishing, game and scenery are safeguarded by local men on the planning boards.

Textiles. The most characteristic product of British climate and soil for more than a 1,000 years has been the wool of sheep. The most characteristic fiber crop has been flax. There has been no great change in wool production in late years, but a very decided diminution of flax-growing. The latter can be grown in as fine qualities and much more cheaply in continental countries and imported; but wool seems to be grown just as profitably in the British Isles as ever. Whereas a century ago British exports included half the raw wool *produced,* imports now include half the wool *used* in the mills; and this relative change has been brought about with little change in the number of sheep or the amount of wool grown. Cotton and silk cannot be produced in the British Isles.

---

[3] Unlike outlines for treatment are used for different countries. A topical study in this country does not lend itself to a complete description of each city as is given in some countries, but it is believed that data can be found elsewhere for English towns easier than for those farther east.

Originally the manufacture of wool and flax fiber constituted two characteristic industries, because of the supply of these raw materials, the water power, the climatic demand for warm clothing, and the moist climates so admirably suited for their manufacture. Later came an abundance of power from coal and the arrival of skilled weavers from Flanders, whither much of the wool was formerly shipped. When wool-weaving really began to assume great prominence as an industry, British colonists in Canada, New Zealand, and Australia and growers in Argentina were prepared to supply the British wool market; and in consequence Britain now imports wool to

The British steel industry is the basis for many other industries. Around this steel plant are piles of ore, coal, and limestone, the raw material needs of the plant. (Courtesy British Information Services)

about the same amount that it exports woolen goods. The flax is prepared for spinning and manufacture in North Ireland, not for any particular geographic reason, but because in the early days flax was easily grown there and labor became skilled in its manufacture. Belfast is the largest linen market in the British Isles, and the greatest center for the making of laces and embroideries of flaxen threads.

The manufacture of cotton was not characteristic of Britain until the Industrial Revolution. Invention in England of the steam-engine and power-driven machines for spinning and for weaving, and in America of the cotton-gin, increased cotton manufacturing. The climate west of the Pennines is moist enough to keep the threads from snapping and splitting; this, with the abundance of coal for power, localized the industry in and around Manchester. Many wool-workers transferred to the cotton mills, and the industry became Britain's greatest. The British Indian market must have aided its growth. The drive of the British people toward industrialism swept it forward. In the last hundred years the output of British textile mills has increased 120 times for cotton, six times for linen, and three times for wool. More than 10 per cent of the people are dependent on the textile industry, and nearly 35 per cent of the exports are textiles; nearly two fifths of the world's cotton-spinning is done in this region. Such high specialization and concentration of an industry is more than a *response* to geographic conditions and is a dangerous economic circumstance.

Silk must be imported to be manufactured in Britain, and it must come from countries which themselves manufacture silk into cloth—Italy, France, Japan. The British textile worker has never taken to silk-weaving. Consequently, although the English people have used much silk, have made considerable progress in the manufacture of rayon, and have made many fabrics which were chiefly of cotton or wool but contained silk threads, they are not silk manufacturers. Jute is imported from the Bengal district of India and manufactured into cords, gunny bags, cloth, carpets, and tapestries in the Dundee area, Scotland.

FISHERIES AND SHIP-BUILDING

The intimate relation between fishing and ship-building and between both of them and Britain's commercial fleets and navy brings them into the same paragraph. From the days of kitchen middens in Neolithic time to the present, the dwellers on British shores have been fishermen. In early days the catch was largely shellfish, but more and more have true fish been taken from the waters in which they seem always to have been plentiful. (See section on North Sea.) Responding to the influence of the sea and its food resources, many settlements were on the coast. The sea invited men out to fish, and then to explore and to trade. The sea plus abundant lumber for boats and masts suggested ship-building, which, plus trading, called for sailors and a protecting navy. Many sheltered bays were good places for navy yards, and consequently Britain's men became both fishermen and sailors, merchants,[4] and explorers, and finally colonizers and students and administrators of colonial policies.

Ship-building has come to be a very important industry here. Many harbors and river mouths on the drowned shoreline furnish admirable places for such work, with protection from storms and easy access to water

---

[4] In 1939 the Commonwealth had 3,319 merchant vessels with gross tonnage of 17,771,000, and in 1948 she had 3,134 vessels with tonnage of 18,741,000 tons. In normal times there are 14,000 fishing vessels manned by 60,000 men and boys. Conditions are pretty normal now.

and to land supplies. Glasgow and its vicinity has become the chief center; the Tyne and Belfast districts rank next; but the mouths of the Tay and Firth in Scotland, the Wear, Tees, Humber, and Thames on the east of England, Bristol Channel or Severn, Mersey and Solway on the west, and the towns of Southampton, Portsmouth, Chatham, Dartmouth, Falmouth, and Devonport are all important. Portsmouth specializes in naval craft.

The Tower Bridge marks the Thames as a commercial river. The bridge is 142 feet above the water, so shipping can go beneath and people on foot can go over at any time. Wagon traffic crosses on a bascule bridge that is raised to let ships pass. London Tower, an old fortress rich in history, occupies a large area on the north side of the river. (Courtesy British Information Services)

Harbors. London harbor dates from very early English history. Until vessels became too large to use the waters about Bridge-port and the adjacent business district, every ship came into London; but for many years the shallowing waters and large size of boats have necessitated the development of docks farther down the Thames estuary. The great Tilbury docks (near the old fort of the same name), the finest in Europe, are about 35 miles below the Tower. Connections are made here with London and the interior of England by special railroads, by canal, and by road, and with many countries of Europe by ship, thus facilitating entrepôt trade with Britons overseas. Other special docks between these and the city have arisen. Victoria docks and Albert and George V docks, built in 1931—

reconstructed old royal docks—are about midway. Millwall, Surrey, and Commercial docks, the West India group, and the Uptown docks of London and St. Katherine's have been largely rebuilt to conform to modern needs and occupy sites along both sides of the Thames. Warehouses, loading cranes of many kinds, trucks, floating pneumatic elevators, and fire-fighting apparatus serve the harbors. Ship companies and cargoes are assigned to specific harbors prepared for distinct types of goods.

Regents' Canal, through the industrial area of East London, connects the River Thames and the sea with the Grand Union Canal, and floats thousands of boat loads of freight. (Courtesy British Information Services)

Edinburgh does not touch the water, but is only 4 miles distant from its port, Leith. While Glasgow is on the river which for centuries served as its harbor, several subsidiary dock towns have been built down-stream in excellent harbor localities, all uniting to serve the great city. Clyde-bank, Greenock, Dunbarton, and Port Glasgow show the extent to which the once central harbor has now been scattered and diversified.

Liverpool and Manchester, cities on the River Mersey, owe their growth primarily to commerce. The former is far enough down the river always to have access to sea-going vessels, but the latter can no longer be reached by ships on the river. Manchester's decline set in many years ago, and was so notable that its citizens became disturbed, as they recognized the enormous commercial advantage possessed by Liverpool. Not only did Liverpool expand its manufactures, but its commerce had no handicaps. Manchester was a cotton-manufacturing city with many accessory and independent industries. The cotton mills could not be transferred to Liverpool, because compared with Manchester its air was drier, its precipitation less, and its water five to ten times as hard, and the textile industry needs an abundance of soft water and high humidity. Manchester is on the sandstones encircled by higher land on the east and could meet the moisture conditions. It is also on the border of coal-fields. Its citizens saw the necessity for transshipment of cotton, wool, foods, and other overseas purchases was throttling its industry. The great Manchester Ship Canal was conceived and during the six years 1887-93 construction proceeded. Liverpool was hostile and derisive, feeling that she would lose all Manchester might gain. But not so. Shipping to Manchester began to gain, the cotton industry spread to many neighboring towns, and Manchester became the commercial center not only for her own business but also for that of all northwestern England. Liverpool, on the same highway, shared in the increases, so much so that her population grew faster than Manchester's and her commerce advanced appreciably.

The Ship Canal allows ocean vessels of 25 to 28 feet draft to come up to the Manchester docks. It has locks with a total lift of less than 60 feet. Some 3 or 4 miles below the docks there was an efficient barge aqueduct which could not be disturbed, so the Ship Canal Company constructed a large swinging bridge carrying a section of the aqueduct, which can be closed at the ends and turned to let vessels pass in the canal.

Taking advantage of the stream, the nearly level lands, and the great industrial opportunity, and avoiding the tidal fluctuations and the silting contingency at such a location as Liverpool has, this canal makes of Manchester one of the finest of British harbors. Over 150 industrial developments have been established along its course, including a steel plant at Warrington, milling companies, factories for the production of paper, chemicals, soap, leather, hardware, and dressed meats, salt-manufacturing, and petroleum storage.

Principal imports through the canal beside petroleum, are timber, lumber, grain, fruit, cotton, wool, frozen meat, tea, sugar, glucose, starch, meal, flour, leather, iron manufactures and ore, copper, nitrates, and wood-pulp; the exports are manufactured cotton and woolen goods, yarns, machinery, locomotives, implements, tools, hardware, earthenware, chemicals, coal, salt, and pitch. These lists are enough to show the great range of industry in the Manchester region and the variety of natural resources available.

One could study with equal profit, though finding less magnificence, the harbors at Dublin, Belfast, Cork, Southampton, Harwich, Hull, and Grimsby. A great commercial nation on an island must have many harbors!

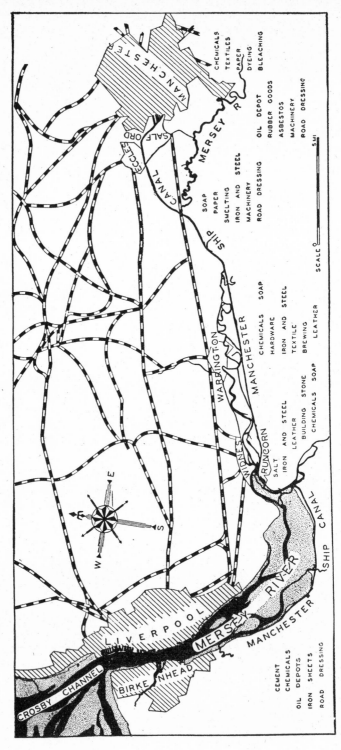

The Manchester Ship Canal. This canal opens on the Mersey River opposite the upper part of Liverpool and leads to Manchester. Railroads and towns are shown. Stippled areas in the river indicate sand-flats. Names of commercial products along the way indicate the range of goods handled and, roughly, the places where they are made. (Compiled from H. B. Ward, "Manchester Ship Canal," *Transactions Illinois State Academy of Science*, Vol. 22 (1929), pp. **555-557.**

COMMERCE AND TRADE

Internal commerce, by which foodstuffs and building materials are shipped to the cities, coal from the mines to the factories, fish to the markets, wool and ore to the mills and factories, and a wide range of manufactured goods to consumers everywhere in the islands, demands much transportation by rail and boat and a small army of workers.

Foreign commerce is probably as large as domestic. Sixty per cent of all iron ore used is imported, 50 per cent of the meat, 75 per cent of the wool, most of the tin, lead, zinc, copper, and flax, and all of the petroleum, jute and cotton. Although most of the milk is domestic, a large percentage of the butter, cheese, eggs, fruits, and vegetables and more than two thirds of the wheat and flour are imported. The annual domestic food production has been shown by statisticians to be less than one half of what is required for home consumption. Exports of coal are about 25 per cent of production, nearly equal to prewar export. About one third of the total industrial output of the Islands in all lines finds foreign markets. The annual value of all products of manufacturing industries is about $14 billion, and it is estimated that $5.7 billion or about 40 per cent of this value is added to the raw materials in manufacture. This suggests clearly the real source of export values. They go back to fuels, power, labor, and skill. Britain is not selling natural resources, except coal, in quantities sufficient to cause anxiety.

Another source of income is entrepôt trade. Britain, as shown, buys foods and raw materials, and in addition buys large quantities of many materials to be graded, standardized, sometimes stored for a season and then reëxported. London does more of this than any other center, because of position, because so long the financial and commercial center of the world, and because it is the head of a vast, widely scattered empire. Nearly every country enters the London market.

Britain holds a unique place in world commerce. It has amounted practically to world supremacy, but it has been reached by a long series of steps. On the border of Europe, the little, remote island nation was put into the midst of things by the period of discovery, exploration, and colonization following Columbus's journeys to America. For 400 years the advantages of position have been cumulative. The spirit of adventure, the enterprise, and the good judgment of its people caused the annexation to Britain in this period of a considerable number of interesting new lands and brought up colonial problems of commerce, administration, settlement, and development. Then came the Industrial Revolution and further colonial adjustments until the homeland became "the workshop and the dominions, the farm." All this, added to the nature of the home shoreline, the fishing industry, and the need of ships for commerce and for the protection of commerce and colonies, led to an unusual program of ship-building. The success of the program was assured by the home supply of building materials and of harbors for shipyards, by the ever increasing demand for ships not only for British use but for use by many other nations, and by the energy, skill, and general competency of men trained in construction and navigation. Notable advantage has accrued because of the great development of colonial and near-colonial lands. Changes in status of India, Burma, and several other colonies may modify their commercial relations with Britain.

Britain cannot live without commerce or without manufacturing. The people must buy a large percentage of their food and pay for it with labor on raw materials. They must buy many raw materials and pay for them with coal or more manufactures. Competition has become very keen as other nations have become more and more industrialized, and advantages of long standing are even now shrinking or slipping away from the British people. This whole situation raises many serious problems with which statesmen must wrestle.

The English people are now thoroughly connected with other countries by telegraph cables, steamship lines, wireless communication, postal and express service, and various forwarding agencies, by well established air service, and by many bonds of blood relationship and common interest. Along many of the ship routes they have established fueling stations, not a few of which are fortified. All these developments are expressions of the geographic situation in which they find themselves, dependent so largely on other lands for food and for materials for their factories.

THE PEOPLE

Many references have been made in previous pages to the people of the Islands, but no connected survey of their origins and the steps in their development has been given. These are closely related to the physiographic history of the islands and to the climate, resources, and connections.

Prehistoric humanity. It is necessary to glance at prehistoric mankind in order to understand modern man in Britain, because there are many lineal connections in spite of great infusions at diverse periods. The English as they issued from prehistoric shades were already separated into tribes with rudiments of institutions, which were to evolve into the peoples of today with modern organization and interrelations. They were influenced by shifting physical environments, altered by invasions, and spurred by discovered resources and opportunities encountered as they progressed. Soil fertility, land and water distribution, quality of light and rainfall, temperature and its variability, and proximity and nature of the people around have played their parts in these changes.

Archeological geography has been studied more carefully in western Europe than anywhere else on the earth, and from these studies, from philology, and from anthropology certain fundamental facts appear.

1. Widely scattered remains, though meager and of very early date, show that the first known inhabitants entered from the continent while the islands were still attached to the mainland, i.e., before the geologic changes of the ice age had effected a separation. Paleolithic man was in England in the first interglacial stage. He used chipped flint implements and occupied caves and natural shelters such as Kent's Hole at Torquay; he made implements of bone, made carvings of contemporaneous animals on bone and other materials, and thus recorded unconsciously his chronology. It is not known whether or not he survived the next advance of the ice in England, but that he did so on the continent is well attested. The record is unmistakable that he lived in western Euope during the second interglacial epoch.

2. Neolithic man appeared in England during the last withdrawal of the ice, with the accompanying amelioration of climate. Human beings were far more numerous in the British Isles then than they were during the Old Stone Age. They spread farther over the islands and used many resources which their predecessors had left untouched. Slight changes in level of land and sea were frequent during the glacial period, now separating the islands from the mainland and again restoring land connections with the continent. It is probable that people came at various times from the south and east into the region which is now the British Isles. Each migrant group brought such further adjustments to topography, plants, and animals as its members had developed in their earlier homes or had learned to make along the way.

Without any break in racial lineage, though new immigrants came from the continent, the Neolithic men became in time the men of the Bronze Age. They were of the long-headed Mediterranean type and probably represented a branch of the primitive forerunners of the modern Mediterraneans. These people and probably all others who migrated to Britain were tardy in arriving there, because of the distance from Europe and Africa, and were of course later in reaching Ireland and Scotland than Wales and west England. Their civilization during each prehistoric epoch was less advanced than that of their contemporaries on the mainland. The bronze culture in Britain is vaguely referred to the third millennium B.C., or to a period 5,000 to 4,000 years ago. Nevertheless these people showed marked progress during the Bronze Age, developing "consummate skill" in casting and hammering bronze, producing shields and spearheads that cannot be surpassed today, and carving horn, wood, and amber. They made entrenchments, underground dwellings, and long or egg-shaped burial mounds—longbarrows.

Early historic peoples. When Pytheas, a Greek, from the Greek trading colony of Massilia (Marseille) visited Britain in 330 B.C., he reported that the inhabitants practised agriculture, brewed beer, and mined tin. If civilization can be measured by the grip a people takes on its environment, these late Bronze Age folk had advanced far in civilization; but to check their actual as well as their relative progress, one should recall the heights attained by Egyptians, Greeks, and Hebrews at that same date, or the high civilization and art of Assyrians, Babylonians, Hittites, and Chaldeans even farther back in history.

Between this date, 330 B.C., and the beginnings of the Christian era, Celtic tribes migrated freely across the English Channel to spread over the drier ridges and along the coasts. There they probably mixed with the earlier tribes and well-nigh absorbed them. Celtic names for physical features are preserved in many modern place-names; Afon (Avon), Don, Ouse, Usk, Esk, Exe, and Dun (a fortified height) appear in numerous compounds. The Celts seem to have been the builders of round barrows. Cæsar reported that in 55 B.C. he found Belgæ in southeast England, and, as the Roman invasion proceeded, Celts were encountered almost everywhere. The Picts, a primitive group which retreated to the Highlands of Scotland, were either a subdivision of the Celts or a thoroughly Celticized remnant of an older race. Although the Celts had absorbed the earlier races, they themselves retreated before the later invaders to the hilly fastnesses and poorer soils of the less accessible portions of the islands. There the Celtic language still survives, and there the race is purer the farther one goes from the main highways. The Romans took advantage of topography, particularly of a great dike, in north England to build a wall to restrain the wild Pict tribes of the Highlands. They built castles and constructed fortresses at stream crossings and other strategic places for defense. They laid cobblestone roads that paid little attention to topography but climbed up hill and down again in long, straight lines from one defense to another. Obedient to the geographic ratio between distance and difficulty of invasion, the Romans never reached Ireland.

Roman occupation and rule continued through four centuries, but the Romans never were numerous and never mixed much with the previous races. When their time came to go, they left behind relatively little racial infusion, but their influence was one of the most vital in all British contacts. They gave a system of roads, a legal system, an example of good government and durable architecture, and new and great ideas of both domestic and foreign commerce, and they improved the methods of agriculture of a people centuries behind Mediterranean civilization. Even yet, however, the real English blood and language had not appeared.

The arrival of later elements. When the Roman troops were withdrawn in A.D. 407, the destiny of Britain was changed. Pictish invaders from

Scotland broke through Hadrian's Wall just where it lay behind the head-waters of the Tyne flowing east and the Irthing flowing west, in directions more or less parallel to that of the wall. The double barrier of wall and stream failed, and the native Britons of Roman England were unable to withstand the Pictish barbarian invasion. They sought aid from piratical Saxon neighbors across the southern narrows of the North Sea. The Saxons came, but they came to rule. The names of their little kingdoms are still preserved in Wessex (west Saxons) Middlesex, Sussex, and Essex. Angles who came from the north side of the Elbe gave the name "English" to the language, to the people, and to the nation that subsequently evolved. The civil organization into townships was adopted from these Germanic peoples. Angles possessed portions of England south of the Cheviot Hills, Saxons abode in a belt of land across southern England. Then Danes surged in against both Britons and the earlier Teutonic arrivals and took up their quarters in the eastern plains of York, Lincoln, and southward, while Norse-men from Norway invaded and occupied northwest Scotland, many islands, and even a corner of northeast England. Thus each invader "went up against his own house" from his homeland to the islands, and each ruled a fragment of Britain, although many were the battles which they fought with the Britons and with each other. These invasions spread a Germanic language and fair Teutonic people throughout much of England, and tall, fair, long-headed Nordics in Scotland. The Briton remnants were perpetu-ated in many places in dark, short types of people, as in the West Riding of Yorkshire, and in any territory between two advancing invasions, as well as on the western and northern fringes of the islands. Fusions of Teutonic and pre-Teutonic blood and language occurred rather freely.

But the greatest Scandinavian influences came in 1066 A.D. and subse-quent years when the Normans crossed the Channel to Hastings and adja-cent ports and pushed their way far into Saxon and Danish England. The Vikings had lived long enough in northern France, still known as Nor-mandy, to absorb much of Romance culture and civilization. With their coming English history begins. Following this, the last conquest of Eng-land, the people became more sedentary and peaceable; a belligerent group of small tribal kingdoms developed into two strong nations. It was not until 1603 that the Northern and Southern Kingdoms were united, but during these 500 years the Norman conquest spread across Wales and into Ireland. Among other accomplishments, it furnished a remarkable unifying influence to language, customs, religion, and government. At the same time the general culture advanced from that of a forest people of the chase and grazing stage to that of cultivators of the soil; forests were cleared and marshes drained. This does not mean, however, that all diversity vanished. Clans of Celts still remained intact, by virtue of geographic isolation and remoteness. Relic languages similarly persisted, to blossom out in ephemeral bursts of Irish and Welsh nationalism since World War I. And more or less pure descendants of ancient groups of people continue down to date.

One of the results of the Teutonic and Scandinavian occupation of the British Isles was the establishment of commercial relations and allied interactions between the English and the peoples of the continent. The Danês and Norwegians were commerce-minded, the British were navigators, and London became a foreign-trade center. Its commerce with Cologne and Liége recognized the importance of countries and markets up the Rhine and the Meuse, whence came the Saxons; trade with Rouen was carried on up the Seine in Normandy, the adopted land of ambitious Scandinavians. Commodities in London markets at this time included pepper and spices (brought from the East by the Rhine waterway), sacks of wool (no doubt for export), iron work from Liége, and wine and vinegar from France.

These commercial relations led to other intercourse, and the civilizing influence of Italy, France, and even the Near East became available for backward England. A copious Latin element happily came into the English language, largely through the French. English, the new language, is an interesting blend of Anglo-Saxon and Norman French. The Christian religion also made rapid progress, first through continental influences and later under its own church, until England became the leading European Protestant nation.

The above discussion has shown how these desirable islands have attracted many people, how island isolation has developed a self-reliant national individuality but one weak in ability to coöperate, how a stimulating climate has given its possessors strength and ingenuity, while a profound intermingling of several bloods, languages, and types of government and religion has produced a virile, independent people of high ideals and adventurous spirit, ready to take a responsible place in world affairs. It also shows that the present Englishman is a lineal descendent of many invaders fused into one race—Neolithic dark Mediterraneans, Celtic roundheads, fair Teutons of several branches, and fairer, taller, long-headed Scandinavians, also of several types. There seems to be no autochthonous foundation.

Present population distribution. With the growth of commerce and industrialism has come a large increase in population. Commerce brought a pacific infiltration of Jews, and industry enticed Flemings and Huguenots. Both have made real contributions to the life of the Kingdom, and many other nationalities have entered the melting pot in a small way, but there has been no great immigration since the Norman Conquest. A constant trickle of emigration, rising at times to treks and tides, has occurred through recent centuries. Many Scotsmen have emigrated to New Zealand and Australia, a multitude of English to South Africa, and the Irish, after the potato famine in 1845, to America. But in spite of it all the population has steadily increased for Great Britain and steadily fallen, after 1845, for Ireland.[5]

The areas of sparser population are closely related to topography and natural vegetation, and the latter is related to glaciation, soils, and drainage much more than to topography. Many local patches in Ireland and Wales, a few in Cornwall and north England, and large areas in Scotland are called uninhabitated, being largely moors, heaths, and bare rock ledges. The areas of denser population are industrial, and aside from London they are coincident with the coal-fields. The London district is both commercial and industrial to a high degree but must import coal for both lines of activity. The usual rural and small-town density of population ranges from 64 to 256 per square mile and covers most of Ireland and England, while the industrialized areas range from 256 to 512 and over. (See population map, p. 298.) In many places, notably in east Scotland, south Devon, Cornwall, and round all of Ireland, the shores are more attractive than the interior. More than half the people live in 60 cities with populations of over 100,000 each. Probably three fourths of the entire population is gathered into towns and cities of more than 10,000 people. This leaves only a few rural and village folk, but enough to carry on the farms as they are used in this middle twentieth-century economy.

Nearly every town of note has had water transportation, some 35 per cent on the sea, nearly as many more on rivers, and the rest on canals. Railroads came after towns were located with reference to local factors, but they grew under the stimulus of transportation. Even coast towns and cities owe much to railroad transportation. Coal and transport, or the lack of one or the other, have been the factors which have built or retarded towns during the last century.

[5] Census year	England & Wales	Scotland	Ireland	Total
1801	8,892,536	1,608,420	No census	10,500,956*
1811	10,164,256	1,805,864	No census	10,970,120*
1821	12,000,236	2,091,521	6,801,827	20,893,584
1831	13,896,797	2,364,386	7,767,401	24,028,584
1841	15,914,148	2,620,184	8,196,597	26,730,929
1851	17,927,609	2,888,742	6,574,278	27,390,629
1861	20,066,224	3,062,294	5,798,967	28,927,485
1871	22,712,266	3,160,018	5,412,377	31,484,661
1881	25,974,439	3,735,573	5,174,836	34,884,848
1891	29,002,525	4,025,647	4,704,750	37,732,922
1901	32,527,843	4,472,103	4,458,775	41,458,721
1911	36,070,492	4,476,904	4,390,219	45,221,615
1921	37,885,242	4,882,288	No census	42,767,530*
1931	39,947,031	4,842,544	4,229,124†	44,789,575*
1940	47,630,000		2,937,000	50,567,000‡
1949	39,952,337	5,169,000	2,991,000	49,617,377§

* Irish not added in.   † Irish Census of 1926.   ‡ Estimates.   § All British Isles.

CONCLUSIONS; THE FUTURE

Internal relations. Because of the extensive industrialization and the high specialization in certain localities where great numbers of people are dependent upon one line of manufactures, as steel, cotton, tin-plate, or ship-building, any break in that particular industry results in serious alterations of circumstances for many people. Because of the dependence, too, of such large proportions of the people upon coal power, a breakdown of mining through strikes or labor troubles again jeopardizes multitudes; and in similar ways great groups are dependent upon local transportation systems for fuel, market, even travel to and from work, and transport of daily food. These conditions, natural and wholly legitimate, bring up many problems for leaders in government, industry, finance, and social work to solve. Experiments in employment insurance, in charity, in the dole, in labor and employment organizations, in coöperative work, and socialized legislation are being made, and the best Christian statesmanship will be severely tried in the next generation or two.

External relations. Industrialization and the very large population in proportion to the home food supply necessitate a strong emphasis on commerce. The necessary importation of foods and raw materials and the exportation of coal and manufactured articles put Britain quite at the mercy of the world. Should there be a food shortage where Britain buys, adjustments must speedily be made. Failure in the foreign market for coal, or for any of the great manufactures, or in the foreign production of cotton, wool, iron ore, flax, wood for lumber or paper, hides for leather, phosphate or potash for fertilizers, or petroleum or gold in the colonies or foreign nations hastily cripples the home industries and brings on distress and need of readjustments.

Because of these interrelations and because each region should produce, for the world or its own citizens, what it can best produce, Britain finds it necessary to maintain friendly relations and to encourage reciprocal trade, not only with the Commonwealths and its colonial lands but with the many nations upon whom it depends. It would seem that the long-practised policy of free trade with nations everywhere is a most practical policy.

QUESTIONS

1. Compare the status of a colony-possessing country with a non-possessor in the following matters:

> Opportunity for statesmanship
> Opportunity for international studies, contacts, stimulus
> Opportunity for internal development
> Opportunity for commerce

2. What are some of the problems for Britain arising out of the increasing competition in industry and commerce? What trends do you think England will take in their solution?

3. What difference has the separation of the Irish Free State made to Britain? of India? of Burma? How would other separations affect England? Keep close to the geographic aspects of these problems.

4. What proportion of British success is attributable to position? to resources, especially tremendous reserves of mechanical power? What to the innate gifts and qualities of the people?

5. What is the significance to the British budget of the private foreign investments of British business men? (It is said the income from foreign investments is more than $1 billion a year.)

6. What are Dowth and New Grange, Ireland?

7. Why should not free trade work as well in the British family of countries as it does in the American family of states? What trends are now noticeable in trade legislation?

8. Under "Situation," near the opening of this chapter, five elements of position are mentioned. Discuss relative values of each. Have values of any changed through the centuries?

9. What difference may the trade tension between eastern and western Europe make in the economy of the British Isles?

CHAPTER 16

Belgium

The little white ewe lamb of Europe.—FATHER VINCENT MCNABB
The cockpit of the Western World.—JAMES HOWELL

THE APPROACH

Belgium and the Netherlands. The two Low Countries are very similar in size and in density of population. In the latter respect this is true because they are so similar in agricultural possibilities and attainment, and because both are similarly situated for commerce with reference to the sea and to the interior of Europe, their hinterlands. Alike, though in different ways, they have attained front rank in colonial possessions and in opening their cities for scientific, economic, and political conferences, congresses, and tribunals.

The two little countries differ in the relative rank of agriculture and industry. The Netherlands, always rural, has developed special crops, notably flowers and bulbs for export, on the loose, porous, well-watered, garden soils. Belgium has specialized in fine breeds of horses and in flax, but has also promoted manufacturing, thus using its coal, iron, and other metals, all of which the northern state lacks except for recently discovered coal close to the Belgian and German borders.

While the Netherlands is agricultural, it has a very interesting industrial development in its rural products, making annually hundreds of millions of pounds of cheese, butter, and artificial butters. Belgium manufactures steel and machinery from its iron ores, coal, and limestone, glass from its sands, and choice pottery from its clays, thus building on its mineral resources.

The two countries differ in their race and language. Belgium has a large number of Walloons of the brunette Alpine race speaking French, as well as a considerable number of Flemings of the fair Nordic race, speaking a Germanic tongue. The Netherlands on the other hand has a much more homogeneous Nordic, Dutch-speaking population. The latter country is predominantly Protestant, while Belgium is essentially Roman Catholic, a difference resulting from allegiances and connections held through many past centuries.

The Netherlands has a strong merchant marine and a large fishing industry. Belgium has neglected both, because of the unindented nature of its coast. Belgium is easily invaded from the land and is much more exposed on the lines of march between its bordering nations. The Netherlands is essentially uniform in being level delta, or coastal plains built up in recent times, whereas Belgium is higher and older, and about one third of its area is underlain by ancient mountain structures containing hard crystalline rocks and coal.

Transition territory. The Belgian plains extend into both France and the Netherlands, as also do its coal-fields; its mountains reach into France and Germany. Its marine boundary of 42 miles is the only truly natural

Blankenberge Beach, about 10 miles northeast of Ostend. The tiny shelters are for bathers. (Courtesy Belgian Government Information Center)

frontier. The line between France and Belgium crosses plains, streams, divides, complex mountain structure, and continuous bodies of coal, marble, and forests. Its details were usually determined by the position of armies at the moment armistices were signed. In the southeast the line follows in large part maximum altitude and minimum population over mountain structures but it also bends far down the Meuse, leaving Givet, a strongly fortified position, in France. Where the boundary touches the Grand Duchy of Luxembourg there is no topographic line save small streams entrenched in the Ardennes Plateau, and the German boundary is almost as unsatisfactory as it was before World War I. The Netherlands frontier has no defense or commercial value until in the east it follows the Meuse (Maas) to Maastricht and then turns east so as to include within the Netherlands Dutch Limburg and a small coal area.

A buffer state. Historically, Belgium has stood between Germany on one side and France and England on the other, and it is aptly denoted a buffer state. This name grows out of its physical transitional character, which was recognized by treaty of the leading nations of Europe in 1831,

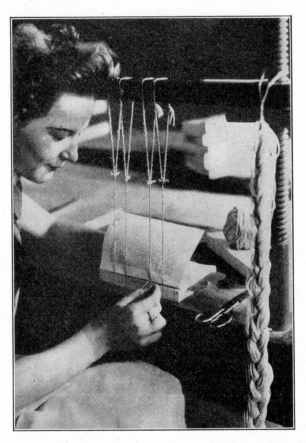

Book-binding is an artcraft in Belgium. (Courtesy Belgian Government Information Center)

when Belgium was guaranteed its integrity as an "independent and perpetually neutral state." The same transitional position and physical set-up led Germany to violate this treaty in 1914 in order to attack France, which had no strong defenses against neutral Belgium. The long military history of the Belgian plains is eloquent witness to the value of these lands. Long known as the "Military Arena of Europe," Bowman [1] styles it "the Euro-

[1] Isaiah Bowman, *The New World* (1921), p. 119.

pean Focus" and points out that although position had "brought her tragic consequences in war it had nevertheless given her prosperity in times of peace." Wallis [2] regards it as a "nodal zone, an area of convergence of conflicting interests." Belgium may serve as a buffer state between Russia and England or France but it has so little depth that its value is relatively less today than formerly.

DESCRIPTION; PHYSICAL REGIONS

Climatically a unit, Belgium is considered at this place because it is central in that group of states having a mild marine climate along the Atlantic seaboard. Geologically it is diverse, double-natured. The northwest

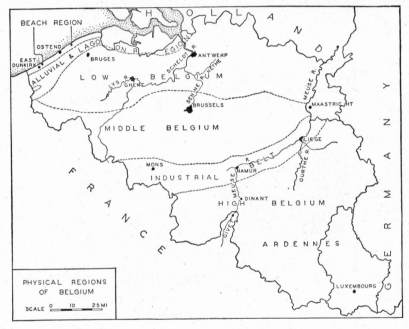

Regions of Belgium, showing important cities and towns. (Adapted from *Atlas universel de géographie* and from Belgian maps of geology and land utilization)

or plains part, the home of Flemish people, is a belted coastal plain with zones approximately parallel to the sea. The southeastern part consists of complex Paleozoic structures.

Beginning on the west, six zones are found: (1) A broad sandy beach and shallow sea, fringed by sand dunes, suggest bathing and recreation, not navigation, and declare the habit of the sea to be constructional, building new lands instead of destroying. Its performance is aided by the great rivers

[2] B. C. Wallis, *Stanford's Compendium of Geography: Europe*, I, 388.

debouching northward along the coast. (2) Back of the beach and dunes is a zone of alluvium, once lagoons behind the bars, now mostly filled and redeemed to agriculture as polders or grassland. (3) Next comes the great sand zone, or Low Belgium, occupied largely by Flanders, West and East Anvers, and Campine, rising not over 250 feet above sea level and reaching from France in a great crescent to the Meuse. Ghent and Antwerp are its leading cities. Intensive agriculture, cattle and horse raising, and several industries prosper: weaving of cotton, wool, and flax; burning of brick, tile, and pipes; ship-building at Antwerp; making of beer and soap, paper and '

"The Rocks": road and village 25 miles south of Liége in the Ardennes. The River Ourthe separates the old castle on the right bank and the new village on the left. (Courtesy Belgian Government Information Center)

rope—all except cotton weaving developed from local crops and resources. (4) Middle Belgium or the clay zone—loess zone—runs nearly east and west with Tournai and Brussels as chief towns. It was a highway for German armies in two wars. Rich soils and intensive cultivation of sugar beets, wheat, flax, tobacco, hops, and fruits lead to the manufacture of sugar, flour, and beer and the canning and preserving of vegetables and fruits. These four strips occupy the northern plains.

(5) From Mons to Liége is the coal belt with the iron and steel mills, the machine-shops, and the factories making pottery, chinaware, glass, chemicals, engines, nails, wire, and machinery and reducing lead and zinc.

Hard roads, railroads and canals furnish a superb transportation net throughout the area. The coal zone, crossing the entire country, not only concentrates industry within its limits but easily supplies fuel for industry in the zones on either side. In the eastern portion of this belt are vineyards and wine-cellars, creameries, cheese factories, and textile mills. This belt and the next, lying along the edge of the old mountain structures, have much folded and metamorphosed rock.

(6) South of the industrial belt come the quarries for slate, marble, schists, limestone, sandstone, marl, and clay and the mills for dressing the stone or preparing the marl and clay for use. This so-called High Belgium with its rock resources has mature topography with altitudes ranging from 700 to 2,000 feet. Besides the quarries there are forests with sawmills, charcoal pits, great pastures for cattle and sheep, and unsubdued wild life in some remote forest sections. Luxembourg is but a continuation of this hilly belt. Thus Belgium with its area of 11,792 square miles has in a northwest-southeast cross section a great variety of soil, topography, relief, and resource aligned in systematic order, each adapted to specific uses, and each developed by the people along the lines so clearly intended. Walloons belong essentially in the coal and rock zones, while Flemings seem best pleased in the lower lands.

PEOPLE AND THEIR HISTORY

In the spread of races, civilizations, and cultures, Belgium partook of the general European program. Within its borders have been found a number of ancient human remains of the Paleolithic, Neolithic, and Bronze ages. With these ancient men as foundation stocks the fair Nordics became fixed in Flanders (Flemish), and the dark Alpines (or Celts of some authors) spread down from the Central European mountains into Belgian Ardennes and became the Walloons.

As its people emerged from savagery and began making their impact upon, and contribution to, both south Europe and Britain, this little state found that its ultimate territory was at the meeting-place of Germanic and Mediterranean races, of barbarian and classic culture, of Teutonic and Latin tongues. Two thousand years ago it began to manifest its responses as a transitional area. Cæsar's Belgæ lived in this region, and from their name has come the present national name. In the early centuries of the Christian Era, Belgium was included in the Kingdom of the Franks under the name of Saxonia. At the beginning of the ninth century the Empire of Charlemagne found it a part of the great Roman or Western Catholic Church domain, and it became a borderland in the Holy Roman Empire. Belgium joined eagerly in the great commercial development of the Hanseatic League and furnished several of the marketplaces on coast and river, especially Antwerp on the Scheldt and Bruges, which at that time was on the coast but later was shut off by a sandbar, dunes, and the silting of a small river mouth. This favorable situation and inclusion in the Hanse contributed in no small way to the development of Flemish towns and paved the way for the great development of the woolen and flax and later the cotton industries soon to come in Flanders. The two greatest streams of European commerce, one from the Baltic and one from the Mediterranean region, converged and coalesced at Bruges, making it the leading emporium of fifteenth century commerce. In the next century, as Bruges was closed by the constructive work of sea waves, Antwerp took its place.

Little states with shifting boundaries and allegiances succeeded each other in this transitional area throughout the Reformation period. In 1536 Marie of Hungary made the first proposition to give Belgium neutrality. In the early part of the seventeenth century Spain was ruling here under the name of the Spanish Netherlands, with no particular geographic reason. Then Belgium was gathered into the Germany of that century, to be, a hundred years later, the Austrian Netherlands with again no geographic reason, except perhaps that Austria succeeded in controlling a row of territories almost continuous from Vienna through the Tyrol and the north borders of Switzerland and on to the coast north of France.

In 1795 began again the adjustments to the transitional character of this locality, which led directly to the modern state of Belgium. The French in that year obtained possession of both Low Countries, but in 1815 both had rebelled and united under the common name The Netherlands, or Low Lands: a union strongly suggested both by topography and position and the more so in that it did not include much of the southeast hilly sections.

Internal strife, however, had developed by 1830, actually urging disunion. Controversies over the use of the coast and river mouths, over polders, and over routes from the hinterland became acute. A boundary line must be drawn between two new states, Belgium and Netherlands. It must not cross established arteries of trade, either by river or by road, and it must separate the great commercial river mouths from the coast, miserable for commerce, between East Dunkirk and the west mouth of the Scheldt. The overland route came out of Prussia at Maastricht ("Maastraject" or "Meuse-crossing," first by ford, then by bridge) and continued down the Demer-Dyle and up the Senne to Brussels, or westward to Ghent and Bruges. The river routes came down the Rhine. Consequently the boundary was placed south of, but nearly parallel with, the Scheldt from the coast inland beyond Antwerp, then through the Campine-Limburg desolate areas with sparse population to the Meuse, then up the stream to Maastricht, which for military safety had been built on the west side of the river, and which the Netherlands insisted must be within its limits. So in 1830 began the independent history of these two little buffer states and though controversies continued the difficulties were ironed out. In

1839 the great powers recognized the new state of Belgium. How justly Belgium has been called the "Cockpit of Europe," and how strewn are the plains and passes with monuments of historic interest!

OCCUPATIONS

Much has been revealed of the uses the people are making of the various resources in the several physiographic regions. The working of stone is probably the oldest industry, followed by primitive ceramics and the rudiments of agriculture. All three still have most important places in Belgian economic life. Limestone and marble are worked almost entirely across the country south of the Sambre and Meuse rivers and contribute not a little to the beauty, architecture, and durability of Belgian cities. Belgium uses the sands in the Mons region to make a high-grade glass for home use and for export to the United States for automobiles.

There is coal enough for current needs, but because the coal measures are so much faulted and folded and because the mines have been worked to so great depths, coal-mining is already more expensive in Belgium than in neighboring countries. Iron, lead, and zinc, once produced in considerable quantities, are now nearly exhausted (though Luxembourg still has iron to export), and French iron ores are still abundant and extensively imported. Zinc is imported from Australia for Belgian furnaces. Shortages in mineral resources are found in oil and gas, copper, manganese, and fertilizers, all of which appear in import lists, copper from the Belgian Congo, petroleum and its products from the United States and the Netherlands East Indies.

Much of the land is better adapted to grazing than to tillage, and its meadows and pastures feed multitudes of fine horses, dairy and beef cattle; but more people are engaged in agriculture than any other occupation except manufacturing. Even the hilly part, because of rich soils and gentle slopes, is well suited to cultivation. The density of population is now over 710 per square mile. Because of the maturity of the soil and the use of much fertilizer, a high productivity is maintained, but nevertheless food must be imported in large quantities.

Forests are patchy even in the Ardennes, but they cover 15 to 18 per cent of the country south of the coal belt and 2 to 3 per cent north of it. In this hilly part many lumbering industries are carried on; natural parks are conserving wild life, and an effective system of forestry has been inaugurated.

It is in manufacturing and commerce, however, that Belgium makes its great contributions to the economic world. In normal recent years exports have averaged about $750 million and imports $850 million, the balance being made up by interest charges on foreign loans and income from tourists. About two thirds of the trade is with the four adjacent countries and the United States. Belgium imports quantities of gem stones, especially diamonds, cuts them for use, and exports them. The United States takes some $10 million worth per year and returns wheat, cotton for the high-grade mills, and automobiles to be used on the many miles of excellent roads.

Threshing colza in Flanders. This is a sort of mustard or rape which yields colza oil. (Courtesy Belgian Government Information Center)

CITIES

Antwerp (population 256,300; with suburbs, 794,280), long the leading commercial city, has profited by its location upon the Scheldt and its close connection with both rural and industrial sections. Belgium and the Netherlands have agreed to share the Scheldt for commerce, keep it closed to war vessels, and maintain coöperatively its fine navigable condition. All nations can enter it for trade, none for war. For these reasons Antwerp, at its mouth, not only leads all Belgium, but in its best years almost leads the world. Much entrepôt trade passes over its wharves, encouraged by the easy connection with Germany and Switzerland. "Antwerp" is interpreted in two ways, both of which take cognizance of its geographic significance. Legend has it that a great one lived at this turn in the stream and exacted one half of all merchandise which must pass the place. If he had any trouble in collecting this simple tariff, he cut off the right hand of the

"The Cloister" at Nivelles, built with stone from the quarries of Ardennes. (Courtesy Belgian Government Information Center)

merchant and threw it into the river; hence the place came to be called *andt werpen* ("hand-throwing"). Again, the coat of arms of the city has a castle beside the Scheldt with two upraised severed hands in protest. The other and more probable meaning alleges that it comes from the expression *aen't werp* ("at the wharf" or "on the wharf"). Antwerp is truly the gateway, the wharf of Belgium and of much hinterland—the "Head of Flanders." It has been a most heavily fortified trading center from the Middle Ages to 1874. No railroad gets into the inner or old city, but everywhere in and out of the city a network of canals leads to Antwerp hundreds of boats and barges from every town up and down the country.

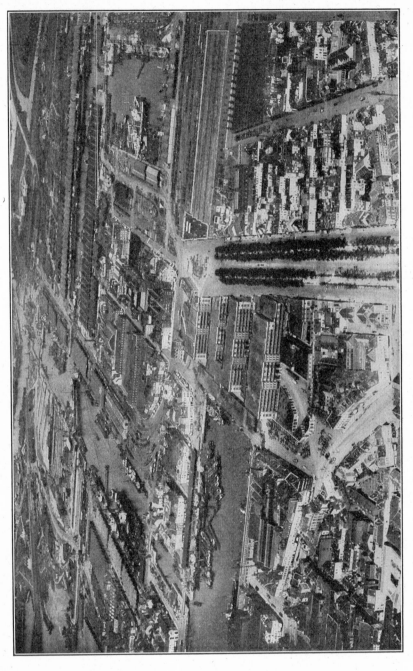

The port of Antwerp at the junction of two rivers, showing docks and piers, warehouses, factories, and railroads spread out over a broad flood-plain area. (Courtesy Belgian Government Information Center)

Miles of harbor slips have been made and assigned to some such product as grain, lumber, or salt, to specific countries as America or the Congo, or to some steamship company. Like Belgian cities in general, Antwerp is constructed of brick, molded and burned from the abundant clays of the land, or of limestone from the hills to the south. Boulevards now encircle the core of the city where once stood a massive wall, but some of the old forts outside still stand.

Brussels, the capital (911,696; 1,296,687 with suburbs) carries on many notable manufactures, favored by location with reference to foods and coal. Great quantities of imported cotton and both imported and home-grown flax are made into dainty, expensive textiles and laces. The diamond-cutting industry is returning to Belgium in nearly pre-war strength. Since it is the capital, it has also grown to be the social and intellectual center.

Ghent (442,792 with suburbs) has a ship canal connecting with the Scheldt, which serves textile industries by bringing cotton from the United States, wool from Argentina, and flax from southwest Russia, the latter to be very successfully retted in the clear, fresh, soft waters of the Lys River. Since Ghent has remarkable transportational advantages on canal and canalized rivers, a moist climate, and a long history of skilful work, it is easily the greatest center for lace-making, wool-spinning and weaving, and both hemp and cotton manufacture. Carpet manufacturers center near at Tournai, and from Oudenarde went the first workmen for the famous Gobelin tapestry works of Paris.

Convergence of the Vesdre and Ourthe valleys on the Meuse at a significant turn in the latter called for a strategic political and commercial town, so Liége (265,000; 573,176 including suburbs) was built, and, stimulated by French civilization and culture, it assumed for centuries a French cosmopolitan atmosphere like that of no other Belgian town. Later, when coal and iron were developed near, and lead, zinc, and copper at Moresnet and Verviers, metallurgical works of great significance arose. Limestone in abundance and fine coking coal are near. Waterways of excellent utility furnish transport. Therefore even yet, in spite of the exhaustion of local ores and the necessity of import of over 99 per cent of the iron ore used, Liége is a notable iron center.

BELGIAN CONGO LANDS

Belgium has, in conjunction with its temperate-zone territory of 11,792 square miles and over 8 million people, an equatorial territory in Africa of 920,600 square miles and nearly 10 million people. As a possession, the Belgian Congo has given Belgium excellent experience in administration and development. As a colony for settlement, its limitations are suggested by the fact that at the end of fifty-five years of occupation the white population scarcely exceeds 25,000, less than three fourths of whom came from

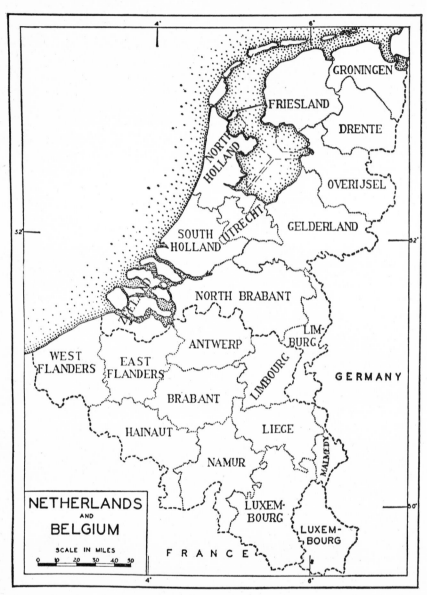

The Low Countries: administrative areas. There are twenty of these, many of whose names are familiar. (Adapted from Dutch and Belgian maps)

the mother-country. The Congo is a possible source of revenue, for its budget has come nearly to a balance. Twice in 1928-1931 the amount expended by the homeland fell just below the revenues. As a land of possibilities, it may be said to have great promise. The production and known reserves of copper put it in the front rank as a source of that metal, and the same is true as to pitchblende, a radium ore. Gold and diamonds are important exports, while cotton, ivory, rubber, palm oil, copal, coffee, cocoa, rice, and tobacco, as well as lumber, are also significant. As a country supplementary to Belgium, the Congo is most notable. So different in metal resources, it supplies much-needed materials; its agriculture produces little that competes with the homeland but instead many crops that are much needed in Belgium. No finer equatorial land is known than the Congo. Enough of it is sufficiently high to offer homes for temperate-zone people; but many insect pests and several disastrous diseases are still to be studied and conquered.

The Congo offers many problems to the Belgian scientist, manufacturer, economist, and administrator, each of whom can make in his respective field great fundamental contributions to the peoples who are holders of intertropical lands that need development. Belgium can never be truly visualized until the Congo country is put into the picture.

LUXEMBOURG

Luxembourg is a remnant of the old Grand Duchy of Luxembourg, named Lucilinburch (Lützelburg, "Little Castle") from the central town of the country. A large portion of the territory was ceded to Belgium in 1839 because its language was mostly French and its drainage and connections were down the Ourthe to the Meuse and into Belgium. The remaining part, mostly German, was made a neutral territory in 1867. Its fortress was demolished and it was too small to stand alone as a trade center, so it remained a portion of the German Customs Union. The King of Netherlands continued however to be Grand Duke of Luxembourg until 1890, when, at his death, a woman succeeded him upon the throne. Since this little state would not submit to such a ruler, it has thereafter had a separate dynasty. After World War I its allegiance to Germany was weak, and it voted to enter an economic union with France. In 1948 it became independent and formed an economic union with Belgium and Netherlands— Benelux Customs Union—a geographically well-adjusted alliance.

Luxembourg occupies a portion of the very maturely dissected Ardennes plateau, itself a peneplain across folded strata. Agriculture and grazing utilize most of the beautiful slopes. Neat hedge fences mark many property lines; tree fruits, wheat, oats, and potatoes are the chief crops. Quarrying and mining also prosper in Luxembourg; limestone is cut for building purposes and burned for agricultural lime; shales are dug for the manufacture of brick and tile. The Lorraine iron-ore belt lies across the southern portion. The ore is mined to be manufactured in Luxembourg and to be shipped to Liége in large quantities. The mature topography of the northern part is given over to agriculture.

QUESTIONS

1. Why not, in the general interest of Europe, unite Belgium and the Netherlands into one nation? Why not divide Belgium into two states on language and occupational lines?

2. Discuss the geographic reasons for the present alliance of Luxembourg with Belgium. Why should Luxembourg not become aligned with Germany?

3. What are some of the problems that the Congo offers to Belgian administrators? to manufacturers? to the medical scientist?

4. Belgium has been a "bone of contention" among the nations for centuries. Which has been more important in this contest, Belgium's position or its resources? Why?

5. What possibilities are there of the shifting in importance of some of the cities of Belgium? Discuss.

6. Explain the difference in industrial development between Belgium and the Netherlands.

7. Compare this buffer state with others of which you may know.

8. What would you say is the stake of Belgium in world peace? Why?

BIBLIOGRAPHY

Annuaire Statistique de la Belgique et du Congo Belge (Brussels).

BECKETT, Sir W. Eric, The North Atlantic Treaty, The Brussels Treaty, and The Charter of the United Nations (London, Stevens, 1950).

BOGARDUS, J. F., "The Population of the Netherlands," Economic Geography, Vol. 8 (January, 1932), pp. 43-52.

BOWMAN, Isaiah, The New World (Yonkers-on-Hudson, New York, World Book Company, 1928).

CLARK, G. N., Birth of the Dutch Republic (London, Oxford University Press, 1947).

CHATER, Melville, "Through the Back Doors of Belgium," National Geographic Magazine, Vol. 47 (May, 1925), pp. 499-540.

DEMANGEON, A., "Belgique et le Pays-Bas," in Vidal de La Blache and Gallois, Géographie Universelle (Paris, Lib. Armand Colin, 1927).

DOMINIAN, Leon, Frontiers of Language and Nationality in Europe (New York, Henry Holt & Company, Inc., 1928).

EDMUNDSEN, George, History of Holland (Cambridge, England, Cambridge University Press, 1922).

FITZGERALD, Walter, The New Europe (New York, Harper and Brothers, 1946).

GEIKIE, James, Antiquity of Man in Europe (New York, D. Van Nostrand Company, Inc., 1914).

GIBSON, Hugh, Belgium (New York, Doubleday, Doran and Company, Inc., 1939).

GORIS, Jan-Albert, Belgium, United Nations Series (Berkeley, University of California Press, 1945).

GORIS, Jan-Albert, *Growth of the Belgian Nation* (New York, Belgian Gov't. Information Center, 1946).

———, *Belgium under Occupation* (New York, Belgian Gov't. Information Center, 1947).

Handbook for the Netherlands and Overseas Territories (The Hague, Economic Section of Ministry of Foreign Affairs, annual).

HYMANS, Paul, "Belgium's Position in Europe," *Foreign Affairs*, Vol. 9 (October, 1930), pp. 54-64.

JANSMA, K., "Drainage of the Zuider Zee," *Geographical Review*, Vol. 21 (October, 1931), pp. 574-583.

KEYSERLING, H., *Europe* (New York, Harcourt, Brace and Company, Inc., 1928).

LANDHEER, Bartholomew, ed., *The Netherlands*, United Nations Series (Berkeley, University of California Press, 1943).

———, *Netherlands in a Changing World* (New York, Roy Publishers, 1947).

MACARTNEY, W. A., "The Zuider Zee Land Reclamation Scheme," *Scottish Geographical Magazine*, Vol. 49 (March, 1933), pp. 99-103.

Maps of the Kingdom of Belgium, published by the Government, Brussels.

Maps van het Koninkrijk der Nederlanden, published by the Government, Amsterdam.

MONKHOUSE, F. J., *The Belgian Kempenland* (Liverpool, University Press of Liverpool, 1949).

NASH, E. Gee, *The Hansa* (New York, Dodd, Mead & Company, Inc., 1929).

PARTSCH, Joseph, *Central Europe* (New York, D. Appleton and Co., 1903).

PEARCY, G. Etzel, and FIFIELD, Russell H., *et al., World Political Geography* (New York, Thomas Y. Crowell Company, 1948).

PIERARD, Louis, "Belgium's Language Question: French vs. Flemish," *Foreign Affairs*, Vol. 8 (July, 1930), pp. 641-651.

Publications and pictures from the Society for Making Holland Better Known Abroad, Amsterdam.

RHYS, Ernest, ed., *Literary and Historical Atlas of Europe,* (London, Everyman's Library, J. M. Dent & Sons, Ltd.; and New York, E. P. Dutton & Co., Inc., 1923).

ROBERTS, Katharine, *And the Bravest of These* (New York, Doubleday & Company, Inc., 1946).

RYCKSBARON, E. J. A., "Holland's Peaceful Conquest; Reclamation of the Zuyder Zee," *Bulletin Geographical Society of Philadelphia*, Vol. 29 (1931), pp. 247-263.

SANFORD, G. A., "A Vacation in Holland," *National Geographic Magazine*, Vol. 56 (September, 1929), pp. 363-378.

THIERRY, J. W., "The Enclosure and Partial Reclamation of the Zuider Zee," *Geographical Journal*, Vol. 77 (March, 1931), pp. 223-237.

VANDERVELDE, Emile, "Belgian Foreign Policy and the Nationalities Question," *Foreign Affairs*, Vol. 11 (July, 1933), pp. 657-670.

VAN LOON, Hendrik W., *The Rise of the Dutch Kingdom, 1795-1813* (New York, Doubleday & Company, Inc., 1915).

WELLES, Sumner, ed., *An Intelligent American's Guide to the Peace* (New York, The Dryden Press, 1945).

CHAPTER 17

The Netherlands

Where broad ocean leans against the land.
—OLIVER GOLDSMITH

INTRODUCTION

Several items concerning this country were presented in the first few paragraphs of the chapter dealing with Belgium (*q.v.*). It is a transitional area not only between Germany and Belgium, and Germany and England, but also between land and sea, for it is very near sea level, and consists essentially of unconsolidated clays and sands, delta material of the Rhine, Meuse, and Scheldt rivers. Much of the material has been reworked by the sea into beaches and bars; some has been relaid in lagoons or in lakes on the delta surface.

Surface. Almost two fifths (38 per cent) of the surface would be inundated if dike and dune were removed and the sea thus admitted. The only sections of the whole country that are not ominously near sea level are parts of Limburg, Gelderland, Overyssel, and Drente, eastern provinces where hills occur and where the extreme height of 1,057 feet is reached near Vaals in the farthest corner of Limburg, a couple of miles from Aachen (Aix-la-Chapelle), Germany. This is a portion of the Ardennes as they feather out on leaving Belgium. No other hills in the Netherlands exceed 300 feet, and the plains descend very gently from these rare and trifling heights westward and northward to some 20 feet below sea level, then rise again in the dunes and dikes along the coast. Slopes are commonly much less than one foot in a mile.

Shorelines. The coasts of Belgium and the Netherlands may be differentiated from each other as "entire" and "broken." In the latter country all the northern part from the German frontier to the Texel Gat is a series of alternating sand islands and inlets, with a continuous shallow lagoon between the islands and the mainland. This profoundly broken condition is the result of thirteenth-century storms and crustal disturbances which ruptured a rather continuous sandbar and depressed some areas below the sea. The Frisians, who occupied these sandbars, became seriously isolated by the changes of that period, hence their purity of race and speech. Behind the several islands there are extensive mud-flats, the Wadden, which are land at low tide and water at high. Between the islands the tides sweep out and in with customary regularity, dragging sediments, and building deltas both outside and inside each inlet where the current slackens once it has gone through the gate between the islands. The Dollart was formed by an inundation of the Ems in 1277. Lauwers Zee, some 20 miles west, is said

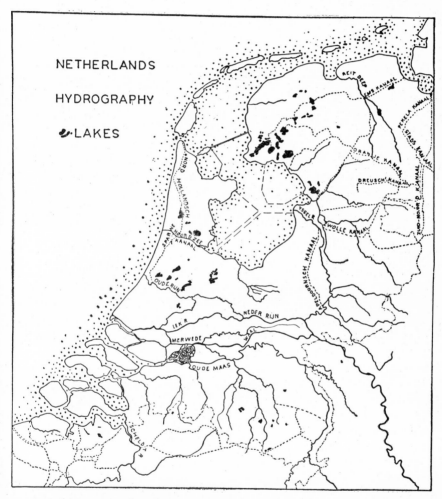

NETHERLANDS

HYDROGRAPHY

&·LAKES

Canals (dash lines) and rivers (solid lines) of Netherlands. The national boundary is shown by a dash-dot line; lakes are in black; the sea is stippled. (Adopted from Dutch government maps)

to date from the ninth century, while the Biesbosch, a maze of islands and channels along the Rhine (Woal in the Netherlands) and the Meuse near Dortrecht, dates from a submergence or settling-down of a small area in 1421. Some of these catastrophes are ascribed to neglect of the man-made embankments in times of internal political strife, but doubtless the com-

Sheep farm on Island of Texel, the most southwestern of the Frisian Islands. House and barn are combined. (Courtesy Netherlands Information Bureau)

pacting of sediments and decay of buried vegetation are largely responsible. Another factor is the floating-away of portions of the peaty soils in times of high water and strong winds over the lands.

A stretch of unbroken coast in the Netherlands lies between the Texel and the Nieuwe Waterweg, Sure or Lek, beyond which are the six or eight mouths of the combined Rhine-Scheldt-Meuse rivers. These channels are wider in some cases than before the submergence of 700 years ago, but for several centuries sediments have been narrowing and shoaling the streams by enlarging the islands and building new ones above sea level. Here, then, the coast is broken by river mouths, and northward by tidal inlets. But these are only temporary unless controlled by man. The rivers might break out sometime above Dortrecht and make for the sea by way of the Yssel River and Zuider Zee. One distributary of the Yssel does just that and now leaves the Rijn Neder at Arnhem. The others could thus reach sea level in about 22 miles, whereas now they flow from this suggested break about 75 miles to the sea. Such a change is, of course, a real danger to the inhabitants. In 1421, when the Biesbosch was made by depression of lands, 100,000 people are reported to have been drowned. On the other hand, if for a few thousands of years no more settling of the lands and no more phenomenal storms occur, and the streams continue as at present to bring out waste while man stands aside and lets the work go forward, this whole northern shoreline may be smoothed, first by sandbars, then by filling behind the bars until the Wadden Zee and the Zuider Zee are closed. At the same time the rivers may fill in at their mouths and build forward the delta many miles in finger-like projections; or they may turn north and help fill the remnants of the Zuider Zee and Yssel Zee, while waves and currents close the present mouths with sandbars.

The struggle. One says the surface of the Netherlands is threateningly near sea level, because the slight changes of level common in such regions would affect the whole economy of the country. "In no country in Europe has the character of the territory exercised so great an influence on the inhabitants as in The Netherlands; and, on the other hand, no people has so extensively modified the condition of its territory as the Dutch." [1] In Roman times the land seems to have been larger than now. The Zuider Zee or South Sea was represented then by a small, fresh lake called Flevo (later Almaro). Records show that in 1170, 1237, 1250, and 1287 the sea under the drive of great storms broke through the sandbars and man-made barriers, opening *gats* ("gates") or channels on the north; again in 1395 even more extensive breaks were made. A part of the difficulties arose because the muds of the delta sank a few feet. "Precarious position" is written across the Netherlands, because submergence may happen again and great storms may again sweep in from the Atlantic; and because the several

---

[1] *Encyclopædia Britannica* (1910), **XIII**, 588f.

interjoining distributaries of these rivers are continually silting up channels and opening new ones, building sandbars or mud-flats up to sea level or cutting away islands formerly built. And man is contending eternally with these heavy odds. He builds dikes of rock along the water's edge to keep out the sea, constructs jetties or groins at right angles to the dike to check the onslaught of the waves and to persuade the currents to drop sand between jetties and thereby strengthen the defenses. He erects dikes around areas that are a little below sea level, then cuts canals through the area at regular intervals for drainage, and on the dikes makes canals leading to the sea, into which he pumps the water from the low canals. Thus through

The village of Wieringenmeer, developed on one of the recently reclaimed polders in the Zuider Zee project. Note the drainage and commercial canals. (Courtesy Netherlands Information Bureau)

drainage canals in polders to canals on dikes, and on into the ocean, flows Holland's lowland seepage. In this way the Dutchman protects what he has, continues the work of redemption, and practises a necessary vigilance which has built and strengthened his personal character.

Haarlemmer Meer polder (the polder made from Haarlem Sea) is a fine example of this redemptive work. It is an irregular oval of about 6 by 12 miles, lying south of Haarlem and southwest of Amsterdam, and is known as the bulb farm of the Netherlands. Its canals are laid out in a rectangular pattern, more regular than in many other polders, in some of which the drainage is by radial ditches. A dike of stone and earth, with a canal and road on top, surrounds the area and separates its problem from all others. This high canal has at least four outlets to the sea. One, by the Sparne through Haarlem, Sparndam, and the Noord Zee Kanaal, one directly from the north end of the polder to the Kanaal, one that connects with the city canals of Amsterdam and there with the Kanaal, and the fourth southward toward Leiden, then seaward. Thus the products to or from this polder area can be put on boats and moved between it and any of three nearby cities. A great canal, bordered by two roads on a dike, extends the length of the polder, communicating with the border canal.

Harvesting hay on the Wieringen Sea polder. "Where once they fished, they are now farming."
Courtesy Netherlands Information Bureau)

Several cross canals and many lesser ones on the polder level give instant water communication between nearly every farm and the high canal system. Locks and gates hold the water and adjust levels where canals of different levels join. All the land below sea level, and no small part of that at sea level and immediately above, is guarded and cared for in this judicious, intimate way.

There is also a contest between the rivers and man. Dikes have been built near the streams on each side, resting on the natural levees, but far enough away to leave plenty of room for the winter and spring floods. Between the dikes (high-water level) and the summer banks (low-water level) are strips overgrown with reeds and brush which collect the sediments scattered by slack, shallow waters on these flats. It would seem that higher dikes would be necessary as the channel fills; and this would be true were the sediments not dredged and carried away. But this, too, is a part of the program. Sands and gravels are continuously dredged for building materials in plaster and concrete; while muds and silts are spread on lowlands to build them up to safety levels. Dredging also helps to maintain commercial

Sluice with locks through Wieringen dike to keep sea water out at high tide and make possible drainage of land at low tide. Vessels and barges pass through the canal, to use the harbor outside. (Courtesy Netherlands Information Bureau)

depths in the streams. This whole river composite, channels, banks, dikes, and reed strips, is above the river clays alongside. The rivers have changed their courses on the delta since man came to name features and contend for his rights, as witness the names Oude Rijn or Old Rhine, Neder Rijn or Lower Rhine, each a mere fraction of what it used to be, also the Nieuwe Maas, Oude Maas, Nieuwe Waterweg, Nieuwe Merwede, Crooken Rhine (an abandoned channel), and many others that a good detail map would show. That man has helped in these changes is witnessed by the names of his towns, Rotterdam, Amsterdam, Monnickendam, and Sparndam.

The Dutchman has waged a long battle against both sea and river. In recent centuries he is in the ascendency. To remain so he must be directed by the wisest students of shoreline and river processes and by engineers conversant with the same, as well as with the strength of materials, critical angles, grades, and other engineering data. The Dutch will continue the contest for many years to come.

A great project to redeem the floor of the Zuider Zee for agriculture was started in 1920 and was still under way when the Germans in World War II destroyed some of the dikes and permitted salt water again to flood the sea. That damage has now been repaired. The plan involves recovering about two thirds of the sea floor or 900 square miles. A dike was built from the island, Wieringen, to the west side of the entrance to the sea, then continued eastward from the island to the east side, thus shutting off the whole of the Zuider Zee from the lagoons behind the Friesland islands. Two tidal sluices were made in the dike so excess water from the Yssel River in Yssel Zee would be discharged into the ocean without admitting sea water.

This dike carries on its top a fine concrete automobile road, a foot-walk, and a number of houses. A railroad will also connect Friesland and North Holland across the berm or ledge of the dike beside the automobile road. The water thus enclosed has an area of about 1,350 square miles and a depth up to 20 feet. Some 900 square miles, over a half-million acres, are to be reclaimed and the rest left under water to serve fishing and trade interests, which are well entrenched in the towns of the South Sea. The two smaller polders had been completed by April, 1941. When the four are occupied as fully as is the rest of the Netherlands, there will be space for about a half-million people. The waters left as Yssel Lake will be fresh in a few years, as soon as local drainage into the lake has time to dilute and remove the salt water over the sluices. Then it will have considerable value, particularly in dry summers, for irrigation and stock water. Many farmers along the present sea have been accustomed to use its brackish water for these purposes, to the discomfort of both plants and animals.

OCCUPATIONS

Agriculture. Agriculture is at once the chief occupation of the people and the basis and incentive for most other home work. During recent centuries many old, shallow lakes have been filled by natural processes, and others impounded, drained, and converted into possible agricultural land; but when all is counted which in any way has become good land, only about two thirds of the 12,500 square miles of the country can be used for rural work. In the east from Groningen, south to the river plains, and again south and east of the Meuse, are thousands of acres of high fens, now occupied by heaths and shrubs but once well forested. The soils are peaty, or made of clayey till of glacial origin. Trees grew on them and, when old, were blown down; their rotting logs covered the ground, checking the run-off, until the soil became so sodden that trees could not grow and lower vegetation took possession.

The usual method of reclamation in these fens consists of several steps, first burning off what will burn readily, then planting marsh buckwheat, one of the few possible crops which seems to improve the soil and help pay expense of further work. At this stage much labor is necessary. Fen colonies are established around the best patches of land; here the men carry on the reclamation work and the women do intensive diligent cultivation of the small patches. Ditches are dug for drainage and transportation; peat is cut, dried, and carried away on the canals as the first money crop; branch canals are cut, and the harvesting of the peat proceeds. Wagon roads are almost impossible, and therefore all communication is by the canals; hence the spread of population, villages, stores, and intensive agriculture follows the waterways. Limestone, clay, and sand form bases for lime-burning, brick-making, and glass-blowing with peat for fuel. Potatoes can be grown as the land improves, but they are of poor grade and are made into starch and syrups. Many communities with flourishing groups of people have thus sprung up in the last century or two in these high fen areas. Much remains yet to be reclaimed. The Pekela and Stadskanaal regions, 15 to 20 miles southeast of Groningen, are perhaps the most typical developments.

The sand dune areas occupy the west coast from near The Hague north to the Texel, and include considerable, though diminishing, areas in Drente, Overyssel, Gelderland, and North Brabant. These eastern areas are rem-nants of sand areas, beaches, and fluvio-glacial deposits, which have not been conquered yet by vegetation. They are being planted to selected forest trees, as have been similar areas in the Landes of France, with some suc-cess. The coastal dune area varies in width to a maximum of two miles. Nearly everywhere it restrains the sea from drowning North and South Hol-land ("Hollow"- or "Low"-land); but where waves break through, dikes have been built of stone. The northern section of this area is retreating landward before the waves and wind. Along the eastern side where fresh water seeped, there once grew much substantial forest. Unfortunately this has been mostly cleared; nothing takes its place, and so the dunes migrate more freely.

Grasslands for the 2 million dairy cattle are found both in the Groningen region and in the low clay polder country where drainage is most difficult. Fifteen to sixteen inches of drainage permits the grass to grow well, but root crops and fruits require drainage twice as deep and thrice as expen-sive. Although butter and cheese are made in both areas, the tendency is for butter to dominate in the more continental Groningen climate and for cheese to lead in the west where temperatures vary less.

The polder areas are a characteristic type of farmland. Pumps, formerly wind-driven, now mostly gasoline-driven, lift the water from the lower canals and sumps to the higher ditches, or in dry weather return the water

Row on row and bed on bed of hyacinths and tulips in endless tints blossom in the Netherlands polders near Haarlem. (Courtesy of Society for Making Holland Better Known Abroad)

A polder used for pasture, showing three farmsteads and their windmills. (Courtesy Netherlands Information Bureau)

to the land. Thus the soil, though 3 to 15 feet below sea level, is rendered cultivable, but it is often wet, soft, and loose. This type of land reclamation and utilization began about 1550. Cattle and the dairy industry flourish on many polder areas. If the ground is dry and firm enough, the cattle are allowed to go out and crop their own grass; but in some places they would destroy more than they would eat, and there they are kept in barns or floored yards and fed hay from the polders, or in some cases are equipped with broad-bottom boots to wear as they walk about on the grass. Canals extend between the fields, and both canals and steep-sided dikes serve as fences for cattle. A short length of portable fence set on the bridge across the canal completes the pasture fencing.

Many polder-farmers build their quaint houses on the slopes of the dikes where the better-drained soil can be cultivated with a hoe. Canals contain discolored water or are often covered with duckweed, and sometimes they give off odors. They cannot have limpid or sparkling dancing water. Polder-

Edam cheese market, Alkmaar. A fine old gate and drawbridge across a canal still persist.
(Courtesy of Society for Making Holland Better Known Abroad)

farming, whether in cattle, sheep, hogs, or poultry or strawberries, vegetables, oats, hay, or tulip bulbs, is by all odds the commonest type in the Netherlands and must of necessity continue to be so; agriculture must continue to be the great industry of the people.

Nearly one third of the agricultural products, many of them after some manufacturing, are exported, including flowers, bulbs, eggs, butter, cheese, potato flour, and vegetables. Such export is partly credited to the consummate care and attention bestowed upon purity and standardization of quality. It is possible, also, because of the strong quality of much Dutch soil, the favorable position of the Netherlands near countries of considerable purchasing power and high standards of living, and the first-class means of traffic at the disposal of merchants.

Since the humic soils and moist climate of the Netherlands make a poor grain country, the people import large supplies of wheat. They buy fertilizers and raw fertilizer materials also.

Fishing. The North Sea and South Sea support many fishermen, and thousands of fish are drawn from the 4,800 miles of canal and hundreds of miles of rivers. Salt-water fishing is mainly for herring, which are salted in the northern towns and sold fresh in the southern cities. Some of the inland fisheries use a two-year process of curing the catch, which furnishes a choice product for the trade but has its difficulties, inasmuch as fish may be caught under the stimulus of a high price and sold at one third as much two years later. Nearly two thirds of the annual catch is exported.

Factories making crystal glass and earthenware at Maastricht. (Courtesy Netherlands Information Bureau)

Manufacturing. With so little mineral wealth and even a meager supply of coal the Netherlands has never made the industrial progress of her coal-mining neighbors on every side. Abundant clays lead to a very large brick industry and almost universal use of bricks for buildings. Potteries make some fine jars and blue Delft chinaware. Salt is prepared by the brine process in Gelderland, where salt water is evaporated with peat fuel. The leading industries, however, rest on agricultural products. Cheese, butter, condensed milk, sugar from a million tons of beets, and millions of bulbs and blossoms move out to foreign markets, as well as fish and the products of cotton, linen, and woolen mills, which use mostly imported fibers. Diamonds from Congo and South Africa were cut and polished in seventy Amsterdam establishments before World War II employing 13,000 skilled workmen.[1a] The only geographic relations of this industry seem to be its following in the wake of the banking and jewelry business which came logically to a commercial center, and the possible later connection with Dutch exploration and settlement in Africa. Making of hydraulic machinery is demanded by the polder pumping requirements, and such machinery is replacing the windmill.

Paper factory of van Gelder & Sons at Velsen, using canal service. (Courtesy Netherlands Information Bureau)

Commerce. A coastal people with difficult agriculture and good fishing, the Dutch became most logically a seafaring people. Ship-building has been and still is important at Flushing, Rotterdam, Amsterdam, and several smaller places. A country that floats thousands of barges, tugs, and motor-boats on its canals, and other thousands of motor- and sail-boats on its inland and border seas, uses 5,000 fishing boats, and maintains a commercial fleet operating between its cities and the valuable Republic of Indonesia in the Far East and with colonies in northern South America must be classed as a ship-builder, and as commercial. While only 5 per cent of the imports and 9 per cent of the exports are with former Dutch colonies, the list of items exchanged with them is long and characteristic; imports include spices, coffee, sugar, tobacco, indigo, rubber; exports include machines and tools,

[1a] The industry is returning to the Netherlands.

Oil docks, tanks, and loading racks at Amsterdam. (Courtesy Netherlands Information Bureau)

Inside of warehouse on pier, showing crates and boxes ready for shipment. Rotterdam. (Courtesy Netherlands Information Bureau)

textiles, and northern foods. The fact that Java, a part of the Republic of Indonesia, is so densely populated explains in part the excess of exports over imports. Trade other than excolonial is largely with the immediate neighbors, for good geographic reasons. That with the United States is about equal to the colonial commerce.

CITIES

The mouth of the great river Rhine with its helpers Scheldt and Meuse, a place of transshipment between the great internal thoroughfare and the open sea, must of geographic necessity be the site of important cities. These would not be in the area of shifting channels but at the foci or corners of the delta. They could not be of equal importance or permanence, but no doubt would shift in relative significance as ease of access varied. In this delta there are four corners. The Hook [2] in olden times The Hague ('s Graven hage, "The Count's Hedge"), was formerly at the northwest corner, but at the present time the significant commercial town at this corner is Rotterdam and its entrance, The Hook. At the southwest corner Flushing (Flissingen) is the strategic place and is heavily fortified. At the northeast, Dortrecht, a town but a tenth as large as The Hague or Rotterdam, has suffered because on shallower waters and, in later years, on an island. The fourth corner is now in Belgium, and the great commercial city of Antwerp occupies the site, where its proximity to France adds to its importance.

The Hague (476,300) is one of the capitals, the Queen's residence, and has been given large international significance, since, by virtue of its position in a neutral or buffer state, it has become the home of the World Court.

Rotterdam (617,000) has the advantage of being on the Rhine, the great highway to the interior of Central Europe, with no locks, bridges, or winter ice to interfere with its use. It is the end of the journey for large ocean vessels and likewise the end of the journey for thousands of barges on the intricate network of Netherlands canals and for hundreds of steamers that ply the distributaries and the river. It is to the Rhine and the north side of the delta what Antwerp is to the Scheldt and the Belgian side. Inasmuch as ocean rates are just the same to Amsterdam, Rotterdam, Antwerp, and their neighbors, imports in bulk take the most direct route and are unloaded at Rotterdam. For this reason and because large vessels can go no farther up the Rhine, more than 65 per cent of the imports at Rotterdam are coal, grain, and ore. The same considerations do not affect outgoing goods which are not full shiploads. The harbor also handles a large quantity of transit trade that continues on small boats or railroads. The postwar

---

[2] The Hook of Holland is a sand point on the north side of one of the Rhine mouths, New Waterway. The Hague was at such a point when founded, but miles of sandy flats have been built between The Hague and the modern Hook.

unsettled political conditions in the Rhine zone no doubt react unfavorably on Rhenish (hence Rotterdam) commerce. Germany receives great quantities of colonial and other goods through the Netherlands and Rotterdam, but prefers to export through ports under its own control.

Half a dozen ports round the Zuider Zee, at one time prosperous commercial centers, have yielded to Amsterdam with its canals and are now known as the "Dead Cities of the Zuider Zee." They serve only local needs at present, handling butter, cheese, and timber for England and machinery and supplies for the agricultural industries in the vicinal polders.

Municipal housing project in Rotterdam, containing hundreds of apartments in close proximity. (Courtesy Netherlands Information Bureau)

Amsterdam. "To him that hath shall be given" certainly is true of Amsterdam. At first it was just one of many ports around the Zuider Zee, but it was made the seat of a royal palace and of several royal institutions, the location of a communal university and of the legislature, and the place where the king must be crowned, even though The Hague has the high court and the home of the king. Thus Amsterdam was set politically far ahead of its Zuider Zee rivals. It was probably on the best natural harbor around the Zee; and with its many political, educational, and business interests it drew a large population, which must have many local canals and warehouses for its own business. With these came manufacturing, which the rivals all lacked; hence Amsterdam (769,144) came into competition with Rotterdam and Antwerp. The Merwede Canal, leading south to the Rhine (Merwede-Waal) at Gorinchem, increased Amsterdam's business, but, nevertheless, larger ocean-going vessels could reach its rivals than could negotiate the Zuider Zee. To overcome this difficulty and make safer sailing, the North-Holland Canal was built from Amsterdam to the Texel Gate. It served the city and stimulated polder trade along the route. Neither canal solved the problem it was designed to settle; the former was crooked and required so much time that it offered no advantage to Rhine trade, and the latter simply extended the lead over the Zuider Zee rivals. Then

The Van Nelle tea and coffee factories in Rotterdam. A very modern plant. (Courtesy Netherlands Information Bureau)

came the North Sea Ship Canal with 31 feet of water directly west from Amsterdam to the sea. This more than doubled the tonnage of the city. Coffee and tobacco in bulk come directly here and stimulate the manufacture of both. Though still commercially far behind Rotterdam, it is the chief industrial center and largest city of the Netherlands. The canals have clearly demonstrated that the Zuider Zee can now be impoldered with little commercial loss.

Amsterdam [3] was a Hanse town and carries yet a hundred marks of

---

[3] Amstel is a stream that entered the Zuider Zee here, and the dam at its mouth for very early commercial purposes gave name to its city.

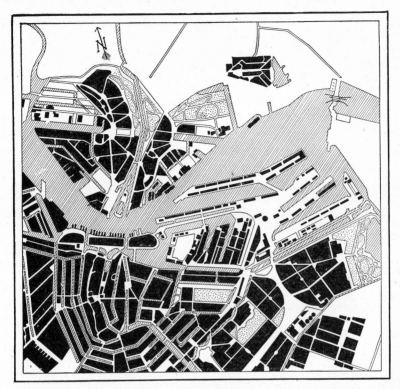

Details of Amsterdam canals. These are concentric around the core of the old city and are crossed by many radial canals. Modern docks, piers, and warehouses are situated in the northeast part of the city. Streets follow many canals as in Venice. (Adapted from detail Dutch topographic map)

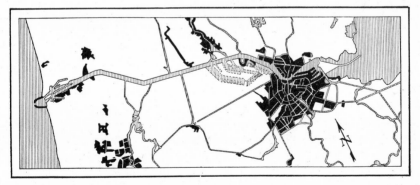

Nord Zee Kanaal, Amsterdam to North Sea. There are many docks and piers west of the city. (Adapted from Netherlands topographic maps)

that ancient glory. On a wide river mouth, it has six or seven semi-circular parallel canals concentric around the Ooster Dock, great plaza and central business section. These all are inside the great moat, once protecting the city wall whose space is now taken by a boulevard and street-car service. Some ten radial canals reach out across the semi-circular ones to the moat. Beyond all these are 25 to 30 miles more of city canals serving industrial or commercial plants. Along each canal is a street, often one on each side, and the streets are lined with tall (three- to five-story) business houses, all much alike, yet no two just alike. Under a hood from the top of every street gable a beam with hook and pulley projects over the street, and

The Netherlands salt industry at Boekelo, a village near the middle of the German border. Salt is brought up as brine and evaporated. (Courtesy Netherlands Information Bureau)

hand power (rarely some other form) still lifts bales and boxes of goods from boats or carts to the proper floor for storage, sale, or reshipment. While it resembles Hamburg and Venice in the abundance of its canals, it has been built in a much more systematic pattern than either. In building an addition to a city like Amsterdam or Rotterdam in this type of country, an unusual procedure is followed. An addition of 600 to 800 acres is laid out and given first of all a master canal dug by a floating dredge. No loaded wagons can move on the sands and muds of the addition. Cross and connecting canals follow, then barges bring in from Sweden or elsewhere paving blocks 5″ by 6″ by 10″ in size, of granite, quartzite, basalt,

Coal is mined from beds in strata near Maastricht. (Courtesy Netherlands Information Bureau)

City Hall at Middelburg, a town of 18,000 people. Old style of architecture; gas street light; large paving blocks, better in a soft soil. (Courtesy Consulate General of Netherlands)

and other hard rocks. Slag from furnaces is run into molds about the same size for building and paving blocks. The pavements with curbstones are then laid directly on the sand, but there is absolutely no drainage problem in these streets. With canals and streets made, building materials begin to arrive. Holes, cellars for houses, are dug and piles 50 to 60 feet long are driven down close together all round the hole, sawed off even on top and then covered with planks upon which the brick walls are laid. Sewage, water, and gas mains are laid through the yards but not in the streets. In the older parts of town multitudes of buildings may be found that have settled unevenly. All this is in close adjustment to a delta foundation for a city.

Groningen is a center of more than local importance, though it principally serves the northern provinces. The old city wall has been removed, and the large moat and other canals through the city are used commercially. A canal from Lauwers Zee to the Dollart passes through Groningen, and Delftzijl Harbor is its entrance.

COLONIAL POSSESSIONS AND INDONESIAN REPUBLIC

One cannot consider the political, economic, and industrial life of the Netherlands and leave out of the picture the Dutch East Indies and Surinam of South America. Sumatra, Java, most of Borneo, the Celebes, half of New Guinea, and scores of smaller islands constitute a great equatorial island empire. Agriculture is of two sorts: European, producing sugar, rubber, tobacco, coffee, tea, and cinchona for European and American markets; and native, producing primarily for home use rice, maize, cassava, arachides (peanuts), coconuts, sago, vegetables, sweet potatoes, soya beans, native tobacco, agava, and potatoes. In 1928 about one third of the colonial exports came from the native agriculture, and the proportion is increasing. Mineral wealth is great; petroleum and tin are at present the only items produced in commercial quantities; the iron ore, coal, gold, silver, manganese, and wolfram must await development of internal transportation, harbors, and mines where the minerals occur.

Teakwood is at present the leading forest product, though many other kinds of wood are found. A well-studied system of forestry is being established which will be a standard of excellence for equatorial forest care during years to come. There are great possibilities for water power, but development must await commercial or industrial needs.

These resources and their initial development suggest the lines of evolving commerce and the relations of the Republic of Indonesia to the homeland. The Dutch have worked out as progressive and efficient a system of colonial administration as any nation possesses. It includes a plantation system, trade connections, stable government, a health program, communications including postal, telegraph, wireless, motor, railroad, water and air services, financial and educational ministries, and a thorough study of crops, soils, resources, diseases, and climate of the Republic.

Following several earlier steps the richest and most populous parts of the Dutch East Indies became on July 1, 1950, the Republic of Indonesia, having co-equal status with the Dutch in the Netherlands-Indonesian Union. The three islands, Java, Madura, and Sumatra with an area of 218,365 square miles and a population of about 55 million people are included. This republic began in 1948 a five-year development program initiated with a $100 million purchase from the United States of machinery and other equipment.

QUESTIONS

1. The Netherlands has colonial possessions. Which will probably contribute more to industrial progress in the Netherlands, the home resources or those of the colonies? Discuss.

2. What does the setting up of the Republic of Indonesia indicate as to Dutch management of her possessions and the stage of development reached by part of them?

3. How do you look upon the reclamation for agriculture of the area of the Zuider Zee? Note the relative values of the area for agriculture and for aquiculture and commerce. Note the possible loss of the land again to the sea in such changes as occurred in the twelfth and thirteenth centuries.

4. "Agriculture must continue to be the leading occupation of the people." Discuss.

5. What kinds of engineers and machinery would one expect to find produced in the Netherlands? Discuss.

6. What geographic reasons can be given for the large commerce with immediate neighbors?

7. What reasons can be given for the development of the windmill in the Netherlands? What connections of the country have resulted in imports that may check its use?

8. What is a "Hanse" town?

9. The Netherlands has lessons to teach America in connection with our Mississippi problems. What are they?

CHAPTER 18

Denmark

But the Erl-King's Daughter dances still
When the moonlight sleeps on the frosted hill.
—VON HERDER

Position. The islands and peninsula of Denmark are centrally located in a remarkable area, from 50° to 65° north latitude and 10° west to 25° east longitude, where sea and land intermingle. The strategic values of such a position are apparent. These lands are stepping stones from Germany to Scandinavia, always dominating the entrance to the Baltic, and are central for fishing. In early times they were perched on the edge of civilization, and in later times they commanded the whole range of the two Hanseatic seas. From Hanseatic times to 1857 Danes continued the right and practice of collecting tolls from commerce, and Copenhagen still exercises much control over the Swedish and Russian butter trade. Danes have maintained continuous possession of Zealand for 2,000 years. In spite of the help of the Hanseatic League and certain inheritances from it, Denmark really never came into her own full political strength and unity until the League dissolved and Holland, her rival, became vitally involved with Spain.

As the size and draft of vessels has increased, the Little and Great Belts, both shallow, have become of less value to commerce and the deeper Sound has been used more and more. The Göta Canal across Sweden and the Kiel Canal across the base of the peninsula have weakened the position of Copenhagen, for the Kiel permits larger vessels to pass than does the Sound.

That Denmark has only 40 miles of land frontier as against 1,000 miles of water has given reason for navy and coast defense, but the west coast is so unapproachable that the Danish outlook has consistently been eastward, but not far east.

GEOLOGY

Geology in Denmark means interesting physiography but limited stratigraphy and mineral resources.

Surface. The land surface is of very low relief, from zero to 500 feet, and consists of plains or great rolling glacial features. Drift almost completely covers the Tertiary and Cretaceous rocks and is responsible for most details of topography, lakes, bogs, and the soils. In its last retreat the ice-front lay north and south throughout almost the entire length of the peninsula and left there a terminal moraine with sand and gravel out-

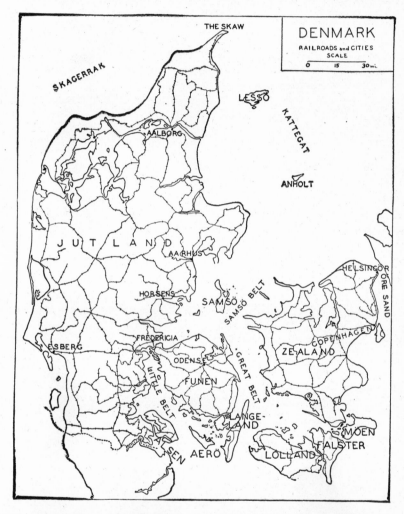

Danish railroads. Denmark is well served by railroads, to which the relief offers little obstruction. Towns are best developed on the coasts, but railroads make two or three inland places important. (Adapted from Danish government map)

wash along the west side. West winds piled the sand in dunes, making the "Deserts of Jutland," while the sags in the moraine became bogs and the bare rock-strewn moraine tops became heaths, all of which usually have been counted as waste lands. The islands, some 500 in number, are similar to the mainland. Not only is the land low and level, but the seas are

Morainic, heather-clad hills near Silkeborg, Jutland. Annually 40,000 to 60,000 Danish-Americans celebrate July 4 here in sight of the picturesque replica of the Lincoln log cabin. (Courtesy Danish Information Office)

shallow and their floors smooth. It is but an accident of time that modern man has come when the relative level of land and sea is as it is. Sea once covered much of the present land and also recently withdrew from most of the sea bottoms around Denmark but returned to its present levels. What vastly different economics would have evolved if either past condition had prevailed instead of the present one!

Soils in many parts are good, in some places excellent, usually wholly of glacial, fluvio-glacial, or recent marine origin. Post-glacial streams have done but little to drain or fill lakes, build deltas, carve valleys, or develop alluvial plains. The topography is very young. Soils have been cropped for a long time, and until the agricultural revolution they were badly impoverished in many places. About 76 per cent of the surface is cultivated, 9 per cent is in woods, 3 per cent is in roads and other non-agricultural uses, and only a trifle more than 10 per cent can be classed as wholly unproductive. Where bogs and lakes are being drained and sand areas planted to pines and beech, the forest and cultivated lands are being increased.

Mineral resources consist of clays and sands for brick, pottery, glass, and concrete construction; chalk, which is burned for lime for both building and agricultural uses; marl, made into cement; a little peat; low-grade coal; and the fine building stone and better coal from Bornholm Island, which is structurally a part of old Sweden. Its foundations are ancient crystalline granites and sediments under the drift. Extensive quarries are operated in its rocks, and its choice china clay is used in the famous porcelain works of Copenhagen. A bog-iron ore has been worked sparingly on the peninsula in places. Boulders from the drift are used for fences, for houses, and more generally for foundations. The people have made much of their limited mineral resources.

CLIMATE

Although oceanic in type, the climate has warmer summers and cooler winters than England, but neither extreme increases eastward because of the preponderance of water. Precipitation is sufficient for this latitude, 24 to 26 inches, but decreases eastward. A summer longer and a winter milder and shorter than in its Baltic rivals gives dairying an advantage in a shorter stall-feeding season. Grass is usually green, and sunshine is abundant enough to promote crop-growing and add to the cheer and beauty of the landscape.

PEOPLE

No known record of humanity in Denmark precedes the last melting of the ice sheet, but men apparently followed the ice-front as it retreated to the north. Such men were in the latest Paleolithic stage of civilization and lived only by the chase. They came when the land stood high enough so that they might cross dry-shod to Sweden. Later invasions of more advanced types of civilization brought proto-Neolithic and kitchen-midden people. As they came the Denmark region was lowered, seas were expanded, lands were restricted, and climate was ameliorated. Implements of horn and bone, so easily available from the wealth of wild life, were used more freely than almost anywhere else. The refuse heaps do not contain much from bony fish, but there is abundance of shellfish, more easily taken along the water's edge and in the lakes and streams. It seems probable that these people continued their development, by further adjustments to conditions and by learning from their neighbors farther south, until they attained the use of bronze, then iron; ultimately they became the Danish Section of the Teutonic Nordics. Many other Teutonic immigrants came to dwell among them and share their civilization. Oak coffins in Denmark preserve clothing, skeletons, and hair belonging to tall, fair, true Teutonic types from 3,000 years ago. Evidently these early people were as thoroughly convinced of the utility of good wood as are modern men. By de Geer's chronology the earliest dwellers in Denmark were there 7,000 to 9,000 years ago and the more sedentary kitchen-midden builders 6,000 to 7,000 years ago. There have been but trifling geologic changes since the latter dates.

The oldest historical source of Danish human distributions dates from the thirteenth century, and we learn that even then most of the present villages were in existence, a fact which testifies to a long previous agricultural occupation. A survey made in 1681-1684 shows that at that time fully 90 per cent of the total rural population abode in villages and cultivated the outlying soil in little tracts, scattered much as they were in England. Very few farmers lived on their farms, except in West Jutland where there were no villages at all and every one resided on his own land.

In the adjustments of the past century, great numbers of the rural villagers have built on their farms and now live near their work and have their stock, manure, seeds, and storage close at hand. This is a much more convenient and profitable situation now that security of life and property can be assured.

Four and one-quarter millions of people now make their homes in Denmark. About one fifth live in the capital; about one fourth of them live in eighty-five provincial towns and their suburbs, which range in population from 81,000 down to about 3,000; the rural villages number 500 ± and average some 700 persons each, and the actual residents of the farms number over 1,500,000. The urban population is increasing, although the number who serve agricultural occupations may not be decreasing. As will be shown, intensive specialization and coöperative marketing have settled in the villages and towns many whose whole activity is rural. In the census of 1921, 1,937,000 people were found to be thus in agriculture, horticulture, and forestry, with 221,000 more in traffic and commission businesses.

The thorough cleanliness of the people, a necessity for success in dairy-ing, their chosen specialization, has given them health and lowered the death-rate in forty years from over 17 to 11 per 1,000. At the same time the birth-rate has fallen from 30 to 19 so that the excess of births over deaths has been rather constant and has given them a steady, though small and decreasing, population growth. Stimulated by an invigorating though not severe climate and much outdoor work, the Danes have become a sturdy, hardy, virile people.

Market in square before the city hall in a Danish town. (Courtesy of Jonals Co., Copenhagen)

Proximity to Norway and Sweden and similarity of race, language, civi-lizations, culture, and climate have drawn the three countries together. The nodal influence of position has also functioned in keeping these three together and separate from other groups. Therefore at times all three na-tions have been under one administration, at other times some two have combined. Through the land connections came Christianity and later Lu-theranism, and liberal government, all of which passed on to the other Scandinavian countries. The Lutheran church claims 96 to 99 per cent of the people in each of the three countries. The governments are all constitu-tional monarchies and very democratic. All have much social legislation and uniform laws for sales, contracts, commercial transactions, and crimi-nal extradition. Nationalism is high in each, and while all are in close sympathy there is no tendency to federate or unite.

OCCUPATIONS

Agriculture. When fixed agricultural use of the land came, the Danes raised wheat, oats, hay, rye, buckwheat, and turnips. When in the middle of the last century, the great wheat lands of America opened up, intelligent, thoughtful leaders of Denmark decided they could make better use of their land by raising cattle, hogs, and green feeds, buying their grain foods of those who could grow them more cheaply. This has proven a much more

Red Danish dairy cattle, with water wagon. Denmark has about 3 million head of cattle, almost half for dairy purposes. (Courtesy Danish Information Office)

satisfactory geographic response to conditions than a tariff on wheat would have been. The Dane has found too that more cattle, milk, and butter can be produced on plow-land than on pasture. Since 1888 he has increased his cattle from 21 per 100 acres to about 33 in 1945 in spite of the war, a gain of over 56 per cent in 57 years. From 1861 to 1929 the number of cows doubled, the milk per cow trebled, and the butter-fat per cow quadrupled. Because of German slaughterings and deportation of stock, statistics have been confused since 1940; but recovery is steady and sure. Dairy cows and dairying have not yet quite recovered. Normally over 3 million hogs and over 28 million fowls are raised.

Mixed cereals (barley and oats) are grown to feed directly to cattle as a fodder. Root-crop acreage has been greatly expanded in order to have fresh cattle-feed in winter. For additional food beyond home crops, oilcake (cotton-seed, soya, and sunflower) and grains (maize, rye, and barley) are imported. Denmark probably raises as much grain under the new régime as under the old, and two or three times as much of root crops, and in addition the country has this enormous augmentation of stock.

Progressive Danish farmers reap grain with tractors and binders. (Courtesy Danish Information Office)

Reclamation of land for agriculture is still going on, though none can be recovered from the sea as in the Netherlands. Some commercial fertilizers are purchased ready for use, but even more are obtained in the raw, as bones and phosphate rock, and are manufactured in the coast towns. Grain growing is 80 per cent mechanized.

All this intensive dairying and attendant farming on small farms has necessitated coöperative buying and selling, sorting, grading, stamping with official guarantee of quality and quantity; and the result is the enormous export of butter and eggs to Britain, bacon and livestock to Germany, and cheese to America, in short, the establishment of a successful social and economic system.

Storage of cheeses. Each cheese is 3 to 4 feet in diameter and 6 to 8 inches thick. The one in the lower left corner has been cut. (Courtesy of Jonals Co., Copenhagen)

Coöperative dairy of a Zealand village. Ninety-one per cent of Danish milk goes through 1,400 such plants. In 1949, 312 million pounds of butter were made and about two thirds of it exported. (Courtesy Danish Information Office)

Forestry. Beech-trees predominate in the forest today, having replaced the oak of a century ago. The wood is used for tubs and barrels, for charcoal and for other purposes that fit into the closely knit dairy economy.

Manufacturing. There is little in the country that can be manufactured except the agricultural and very restricted mineral products. Ship-building has always been important and a natural response to the position and activities of the people. The capital has quite a reputation for the manufacture of clocks, watches, scientific and technical instruments to be used in navi-

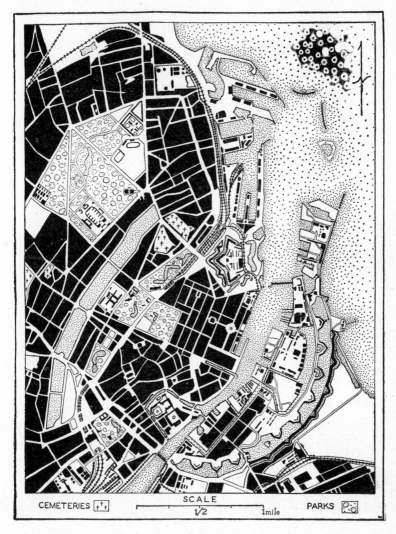

CEMETERIES   SCALE   ½   1mile   PARKS

Copenhagen. This city, the kaufman's or merchant's haven for centuries, was once a heavily fortified port and still maintains notable coast defenses. The picture shows only the port and the central part of the city. (Adapted from Danish government map)

gation and in the dairy industries, pianos, porcelain, leather, chemicals, sugar, tobacco, and artistic metal products. The manufacture of dairy equipment constitutes a natural leading industry encouraged by keen technical skill and a demand for the best.

CITIES

Copenhagen (Kaufman's Hafen or Merchant's Harbor) (927,404) has long merited its name. Its situation and connections have inevitably made it a trading center. For successful trading and toll-gathering it must have defenses, for which again its position serves admirably. A wall, double on the sea side with water-filled moats, and strong fortifications on hills beside

Danish eggs meet many a household need in many a town outside of Denmark. (Courtesy of Jonals Co., Copenhagen)

the city and on islands in front have long lent security to its shipping. Its walls on the sea front are still intact, but the wall on the land side has been demolished and replaced by railroads, parks, and buildings, which stretch far out into suburban sections. Seven thousand commercial airplanes came annually before World War II; twice as many since. Although Copenhagen is far to one side of the country, all railroad service builds up to it, as do industry, finance, government, and education. This is a natural result in a one-city country. Its museum is rich in prehistoric remains.

Odense (98,000), in central Fünen, is the most conservative town of its size in the country. It has lacked contact with the sea and has been "back-country" in the midst of Danish land and sea. Now it is on the through railroad which goes by hop, skip, and jump from Germany to Stockholm, running the length of Jutland to Fredericia, then over the ferry across the Little Belt, by train across Fünen, by ferry across the Great Belt, by train across Zealand to Copenhagen, and by ferry across the Sound to Malmö, finally by rail to Stockholm. This much-broken journey is necessary in such mixed land and water. Ten railroad lines reach out from Odense to coast towns on the island, and a ship canal to the sea now assures it more generous contacts with the world beyond. (See map, p. 387.)

Aarhus (114,000) is a similar railway junction in Jutland, advantageously placed on a good harbor, where it serves as export and import center for rural Jutland. Eighty seaports have been developed in Denmark mostly at municipal expense.

THE FÄROES, GREENLAND, ICELAND

Greenland and Iceland were named, shortly after their discovery, to misrepresent their geographic condition: Greenland, though ice-covered, to attract settlers, and Iceland, though a land of considerable rural promise, to forbid newcomers. Through a long history both islands have had affiliations with Denmark and Norway. Greenland supplies many fish and sheep. On the west side it has large reserves of cryolite, used in the manufacture of aluminum. Iceland is now independent, Greenland a Danish colony; while Iceland, Norway, Sweden, Finland, and Denmark have mutual peace and arbitration treaties. Icelandic language, literature, and government are unique, as might be expected on such an isolated island. Out of a population of over 140,000, 50,000 (estimate 1949) engage in agriculture, raising hay, potatoes, and turnips, and caring for 627,000 sheep. Exports are fish, wool, and sheep to Denmark, and imports are mostly food necessities. The Färoe (Sheep) Islands are bouldery, glaciated summits of ancient hard rocks that lift their heads above the sea to afford pasturage for sheep and bases for the operation of many Danish fishermen. Fishing captures 350,000 tons annually.

QUESTIONS

1. Compare the strategy of position of Denmark and the British Isles.
2. What are the essential differences in soils and rocks between Denmark and the Netherlands? Explain. What similarities are there in mineral resources? Explain.
3. What is involved in Russia's desire to possess Denmark?
4. Would Germany be interested in the problem of Russia's acquiring control of Denmark? Why?
5. Could Denmark be called a buffer state? Why?
6. Why should the Danes ever have invaded the British Isles?
7. Would Denmark have minority problems? Why?

BIBLIOGRAPHY

Annuaire Statistique, issued by Danish Department of Statistics (Copenhagen).

ARNESON, Ben A., *Democratic Monarehies of Scandinavia* (New York, D. Van Nostrand Company, Inc., 1939).

BERGSMARK, D. R., "Agricultural Land Utilization in Denmark," *Economic Geography*, Vol. 11 (April, 1935), pp. 206-214.

Census Reports, issued by Department of Statistics (Washington, D. C.).

Danish Ministry for Foreign Affairs and Danish Statistical Dept. (Copenhagen, The Government, 1943), annual.

FAIRGRIEVE, James, *Geography and World Power* (London, University of London Press, 1941).

Geografisk Tidsskrift (Copenhagen, Bind 33-34, 1930-1931).

Geological and Topographical Maps of Denmark, Danish Geological Survey, Copenhagen.

GEORGE, M. M., and DEAN, M. I., *A Little Journey to Holland, Belgium, and Denmark* (Chicago, A. Flanagan Co., 1931).

HACKETT, Francis, *I Chose Denmark* (New York, Doubleday, Doran & Company, Inc., 1940).

HANNAH, Ian C., *Capitals of the Northlands* (London, H. Cranton & Ousley, Ltd., 1914).

HART, J. K., "The Secret of the Independent Farmers of Denmark," *Survey*, Vol. 56 (June 1, 1926), pp. 312-315.

HINSLEY, F. H., *Command of the Sea* (London, Christophers, 1950).

HOWE, Fred C., *Denmark: The Coöperative Way* (New York, Coward-McCann Inc., 1936).

Land Utilization, 1929-30 (Copenhagen, Danish Department of Statistics).

LYDE, L. W., *Peninsular Europe* (New York, Longmans, Green & Company, 1931).

ROTHERY, Agnes, E., *Denmark, Kingdom of Reason,* (New York, Viking Press, Inc., 1937).

SCOTT, Franklin D., *The United States and Scandinavia* (Cambridge, Harvard University Press, 1950).

SHACKLETON, Margaret R., *Europe, A Regional Geography* (London, Longmans, Green & Company, 1942).

Summary Geology Denmark, 1928 (Copenhagen, Danish Geologic Survey).

WILLIAMS, Mary W., *Social Scandinavia in Viking Age* (New York, The Macmillan Co., 1920).

ZIMMERMAN, M., "Danemark" in Vidal de La Blache and Gallois, *Géographie Universelle* (Paris, Lib. Armand Colin, 1933).

CHAPTER 19

Norway

The one of the two who best can sail,
Shall rule o'er Norroway's hill and dale.
—ANON.

EARLY PEOPLES

Prehistoric men. The earliest people in Norway of whom we have record were hunters whose civilization was that of the New Stone Age, and who lived there probably 8,000 to 7,000 years ago. These people entered Norway from the south through Sweden as the last ice sheet melted away and gave them the opportunity to push farther northward. Bone seems to have been used more freely than stone for tools and ornaments, doubtless because reindeer and elk were common, whereas stone suitable for such uses is quite rare in Norway. Although there is no flint in Norway, these people had a few flint weapons and tools which must have been imported from Denmark, the nearest flint location. The early hunters were followed by builders of *kjökken möddingen* (kitchen middens), likewise without agriculture and domestic animals except the dog. They caught animals in the chase, gathered shellfish along the water's edge, and brought the bodies for food to the places where they had fire, piling the bones and refuse in heaps along the shores. Their attachment to place was so strong that some refuse heaps became several feet high, 15 to 20 yards wide, and one-fourth to one-half mile long. For a thousand years they continued this type of life and then adopted some sort of agriculture.

About 4,000 years ago bronze reached Norway, and implements of this metal are frequently found among the remains in southern valleys. The Iron Age came late in this far-off land, possibly 2,500 to 2,400 years ago, and from the south. At that time people were distributed much as now. Their settlements were strongly influenced by proximity to the sea, and intercourse between settlements was largely commercial. Forests and plateaus were great barriers to travel.

Roman period. The Roman influence began some 1,850 years ago and was never strong, but it may have invited the so-called National Migrations between A.D. 400 and 700. During the next century or two the ship-graves

399

seem to record the large and significant use of the sea that the people were making. Men were buried in large wooden ships with bones or offerings of horses, oxen, sheep, pigs, and chickens, a wide range of domestic animals which must have called for a rather fixed agriculture.

Viking age. Vikings first appeared about A.D. 800 and began that period of conquering, seafaring pirate life so characteristic and natural on such a coast as that of Norway. Their fishing and ship-building, commerce, and raids continued until the introduction of Christianity about 1050 to 1100; they ravaged all Atlantic coasts and entered the Mediterranean as far as Dalmatia. Ship-graves continue through the Viking age, and in some places the boats buried are identical with those built and used in the same valleys today. Irish relics establish the fact of trade with Ireland. Persian and Turkestan coins and relics in Sweden likewise suggest eastern trade or piracy through Norway at this time. Plenty of evidence exists that the Vikings were great traders and journeyed far.

The Norwegian is thus a direct descendant of Neolithic men, but no doubt has had many infusions of blood from other early sources. He has been working, playing, fishing, building, burying, subsisting, devising implements, trading with his neighbors far and near with increasingly apposite responses to his poverty-stricken mountains and fiord-indented coasts. In fact, he has become more closely related to his surroundings as he has approached his present status. "Their errands have accorded with the stage of civilization which, century by century, they have attained." [1]

SITUATION

Norway, for centuries the home of these successive races, and today the seat of a very progressive nation, is set far to the north, in the same latitude as the southern half of Greenland, Alaska, and northern Kamchatka, or farther poleward than any inhabited land in the southern hemisphere. It enjoys with Sweden much of the isolation of an island, since for most of the year it cannot well be entered by land through its northern continental connections. Its length, 900 miles, would reach from the tip of Greece to northern Rumania, from New Orleans to Milwaukee, a length that presents, when coupled with its topography and its climate, several difficult problems of government, internal communications, and national solidarity. Nearly one third of the country is within the Arctic Circle, the land of the midnight sun; but because of marine influences on climate it is saved from the inhospitable severity of Baffin Land. It is on no commercial highway but is between two "blind-alley" seas.

[1] A. P. Brigham, "Fiords of Norway," *Bull. Amer. Geog. Soc.,* Vol. 38 (1906), p. 9.

CLIMATE

Although in a latitude of meager insolation because of the low altitude of the sun and the great inequality of day and night throughout most of the year, the climate of Norway is so thoroughly marine that even at Bodö, latitude above 67° N., the monthly range of temperature is only from 26° F. to 56° F. and the rainfall is well distributed through the year with a total of

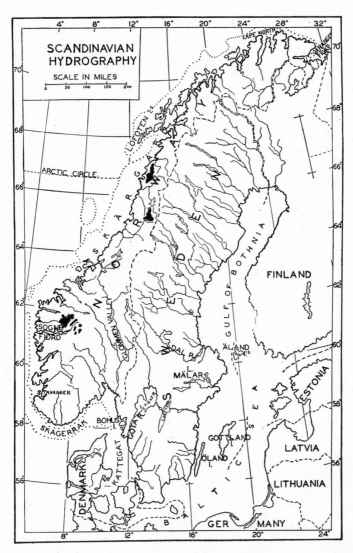

Lakes, rivers, and glaciers in Scandinavia. Black = ice caps; on Arctic Circle, Svartisen glacier; north of Sogne Fiord, Jostedalsbrae glacier. The dotted line near the coast is the 600-foot contour. (Adapted from *Oxford Advanced Atlas*)

30 to 35 inches. Winter snows lead to the expert use of ski and long snow-shoes. Altitude interposes severe climatic barriers between Norway and Sweden. While many summer days are beautiful, even in summer the clouds hang over the land and fill the fiords or scatter misty rain for days at a time; and the short winter days, when there is day at all, have sunshine at very low angles for only a few hours if clouds do not intervene. This gloominess is reflected more or less in music, poetry, and the spirit of the people.

Temperatures are so softened by the sea influence that even at Lofoten the winter temperature is 40° F. warmer than the average for its latitude, and no Atlantic harbor even to Cape North is ever frozen. Isotherms and isohyets run parallel with the coast. Grazing is possible along the coast all winter long, but so influential is relief in determining the temperature that winters on the plateau are very severe, and summer nights are always cool. Scores of ice caps lie on the plateau from south of Bergen to north of Tromsö, and the largest glaciers in Europe are here, Jostedalsbrae, 580 square miles, and Svartisen, 400 square miles.

Precipitation becomes very scanty on the high areas, but low evaporation greatly aids agriculture and forests. Forest trees over many hills are stunted and made very unsymmetrical by strong winds, but where they are protected in the gorges upstream from the fiords they attain excellent dimensions for use. Agriculture never lacks moisture. Hardy grains will mature near sea level in latitude 70° because of the very long daylight period in each summer day. The lack of sunshine up the slopes and the moisture always in the air have made necessary many unusual devices for drying hay.

GEOLOGIC AND PHYSIOGRAPHIC HISTORY

Rocks and rock structures. In Pre-Cambrian time a great mountain mass extended over much of Norway and southward to Scotland and northwestern Ireland. It certainly reached farther out in the Atlantic than the present Norwegian shoreline. Its erosion furnished sediments for lands farther east. Its roots are now schists, gneisses and slates, intruded by great and small masses of excellent granite and other igneous rocks. Through central Norway from south to north, and reaching the coast at many places, there are great areas of Paleozoic sediments, in certain localities much folded and faulted. Here and there these rocks are covered with glacial drift and recent marine, lake, and stream deposits. Because of meager mineralization there is very little metallic wealth in the whole country, and even the Carboniferous rocks are here barren of coal, oil, and gas.

Relief and altitude. Slopes are very old and gentle in almost all the upper parts, whether it be the lofty Kiolen Mountains or the tops of the low islands of the coast; but the lower slopes are generally much steeper, and some are nearly vertical for thousands of feet. Rock surfaces are con-

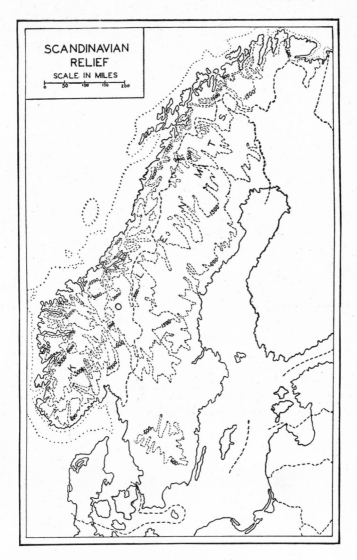

Relief of the Scandinavian Peninsula. Contours on land in dashes, altitudes in feet. Contour on sea floor in dots shows 600-foot depth. National boundaries in dashes. (Adapted from *Oxford Advanced Atlas*)

sistently stripped of soil and rock waste. Streams are generally short, swift, powerful, on the west side leading into the fiords or the sea, but longer and more nearly parallel in the south, where they lead into the Skagerrak. All are perennial; many have great fall, and although they are generally of small volume they have important power possibilities. Multitudes of lakes and glaciers conserve the water and regulate its flow.

Fiords and shorelines. Streams through ages long past reduced the land to a plain, probably more than once; then uplift occurred and deep erosion followed, making youthful valleys wherever the uplift was sufficient and ice cover did not prevent. Islands offshore have few youthful valleys or slopes among them, and large upland areas have not yet been rejuvenated. Probably several successive ice sheets covered the country. Valley glaciers or dependencies from the great sheets deepened, basined, straightened, and trimmed the slopes of many of the young valleys and produced the magnificent fiords. At many places the rock structure directed the streams in their work, and the resulting topography directed the ice in its carving. Changes

Characteristic Norwegian farming landscape. Drying grain and hay in an eastern valley. (Courtesy Royal Norwegian Information Service)

of level have occurred; great depression was followed by moderate uplift as the glaciers dwindled. The story is not simple, probably not all yet known; but some combination of the processes mentioned has given to Norway the most sinuous and magnificent shoreline inhabited by man. Its grandeur and beauty are enhanced by waterfalls, by the clear blue and green depths of the water, by the picturesque villages, homes, and farms dotted over the shorelines, beaches, and deltas, both those still under construction and those now finished and lifted from the sea. Moraines, lakebeds, outwash deposits, fans, and even the more secure talus slopes also furnish building sites; indeed, few houses occur in Norway except on these recent features.

Young valleys, fiords, and glaciers almost forbid land travel, so much so that the very name *fiord* comes from a root meaning "to carry." The fiord is the great common carrier. These same waters, and the lakes and streams, together with the thousands of miles of channels among the 150,000 islands of the skerry-guard or island fence (frontier), afford one of the finest fishing-grounds in the world. Lyde [2] comments on the "teeming waters and poverty-stricken hinterland, a nursery at once of seamen and of beggars." Such a land is not the place to develop a patriarchal type but an individualistic, a particularistic type, because every one is on his own, man and wife having similar and individual responsibilities, with neighbors far apart. Fishing, scattered farming, grazing with its seasonal transhumance and *sater*-life,[3] forestry, especially in such topography, are all occupations which set the character in the same direction. Out of this setting has come both the religious and the political Protestantism of Northern Europe, for most Scandinavians have been subject to similar occupational and topographic influences. Such a land and life must lead also to inequalities of wealth as different as that of a farmer of a tiny patch of land and of a ship-owner and master of commerce.

RESOURCES

As the British or the people of the eastern United States count resources, Norway is poor, but even poverty has its beneficial repercussions on a people.

Soils. Soils are so meager and patchy that 75 per cent of the country is classed as waste, about 22 per cent as forest and less than 4 per cent as cultivated. That cultivated portion is divided into 250,000 little farms, mostly of 3 to 25 acres each, and probably not one is rectangular, as so many are in America. Yet the cultivated land, 4,300 square miles, is inhabited by more than one third of the people.

Forests. About three fourths of the forests are conifers, and one fourth hardwoods—birch, beech, elm, and oak. The conifers are generally found high up the slopes and in the interior. Along the Glommen Valley trees are cut in winter and pushed into freshet waters in spring to float down to sawmills. All forests near the waters have been sadly depleted in the last century, and the people are just awakening to the necessity for reforestation and care of their forest resources. While much wood for building is imported, more than one third of the present cut is exported in the form of lumber, wood-pulp, and paper. Mechanical pulp is made in forested areas of abundant hydro-electric power (largely in the south), while chemical

[2] L. W. Lyde, *The Continent of Europe* (1924), p. 109.
[3] Dairymen who take their cattle to high mountain pastures for two or three months in the summer are called *saters* or *saeters*. They live in *sater*-huts, milk their cows, and bring milk down once a day, to make cheese or butter.

The upper end of a fiord. A three-funnel steamer at anchor.

pulp is made near the iron pyrite deposits in the Trondhjem region, from which sulphite is derived.

Minerals. Magnetite is mined in open quarries near Kirkenes on Syd Varanger off the Arctic coast, where the ore is crushed and oxidized to hematite by means of imported coal, separated magnetically and pressed, primarily by air exhaustion, into briquets for export. Narvik's never-frozen port behind Lofoten Islands exports Swedish iron ore from the Lapland fields of Kiruna and Gellivara and maintains an important codfish market for Norway fisheries. Iron is mined in several other places in Norway; copper is widely distributed (Lokken, Meldalen, Röros, Sulitelma), but is nowhere important. Norway is credited with 17 per cent of the world's

Inside a paper mill, showing paper, made from wood, being packed for export. (Courtesy Royal Norwegian Information Service)

molybdenum production from mines at Mandal in the extreme southern part. Building stones, granite setts or paving blocks, and marble are quarried in several places in the ancient rock areas. The limestone areas in the mid-west are worked for cement rock and for the basis of fertilizer and other chemical products (calcium nitrates, calcium carbide) by using the abundant hydro-electric power, imported coal, and free nitrogen from the air. These products are largely for export to England and France.

Power. Norway has developed about 1,500,000 horsepower at hydro-electric plants and still has six or seven times as much more available. When harnessed this will be a great boon to industry and commerce. Engineering plans are materializing to sell power to Central Europe. Water power owes its abundance and serviceability to several considerations: lakes and glaciers assist the heavy winter snowfall in conserving water for summer power, and long summer days rapidly melt the snow; lakes are mostly near the coast or fiord-heads and have narrow rock outlets specially favorable for dam construction and delivery of power to harbor towns; agricultural, fishing, forestry, and even mineral resources are usually so distributed as to be available for manufacturing in harbor towns.

Power station and its penstocks, up the forested slopes west of Oslo. (Courtesy Royal Norwegian Information Service)

Scenery. For many years English sportsmen have fished and hunted in Norway, but the tourist business is a new development. Its season is short, but the scenic treasures are so unique and are exhibited by such kindly and thrifty people that one may well predict an increasing number of tourists and the growth of winter sports.

MODERN PEOPLE

Centers. Three areas stand out conspicuously for their denser population. A strip along the coast, 300 miles long and about 20 to 50 miles in width, has the third largest town, Trondhjem (57,128), near its center and an average population density of about 20 per square mile, whereas all the surrounding lands are much more sparsely populated. This is a fishing

region and a market for the cod-fisheries of Lofoten Islands. It is also a
paper- and pulp-making region and contains the northern focus of the
country. It communicates with Oslo through the Glommen Valley. Because
of its remoteness Trondhjem was the last heathen capital and when converted became the first Christian capital of Norway.

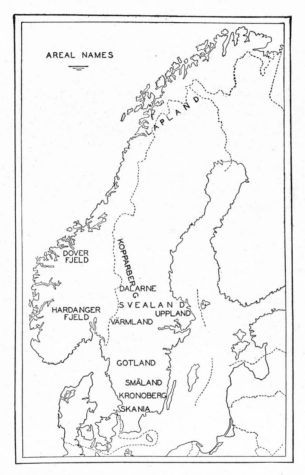

Areal names in Scandinavia. These are partly names of districts now recognized as civil and
political entities and partly names of old regions with no modern specific boundaries. (Compiled
from native sources)

The second area is smaller but more populous. It extends from the Sogne
Fiord southward to the end of the peninsula with a width of about 50
miles and contains the second town, Bergen (113,683), and the fourth,
Stavanger (50,320). Historic as well as physical advantages attach to the
Bergen region, for that town was a significant nodal point among Hanse
towns, was long fortified, has ship-building, engineering works, a university,

and is the center of the cured fish industry. It has associated industries in barrels, salt, and ice, while Stavanger cans the Norway sardines (sprats) and imports tin-plate and olive oil. Local forest products are used for barrels and packing boxes. A considerable rural population and many workmen in factories using local raw materials help swell the population.

The top of Norway from a summit peak. Slopes are forested or partly so. Snow mantles all. The advanced mature topography can be seen in the distance. (Courtesy Royal Norwegian Information Service)

The third area contains Oslo (427,500), the capital, and Drammen (27,100), which serve a rich rural, fishing, and lumbering population. Many scattered wood industries and much manufacturing depend on Oslo for labor and a market, and continental as well as oceanic connections are easy. While the area is in just the latitude of barren Point Chidley, north Labrador, it is the finest rural part of Norway. Oslo has a great university with several technical schools attached, the court, and diplomatic corps; it is in fact the center of the political and social life of the whole country. Most of the country outside these three areas has less than 10 inhabitants per square mile, with a most irregular distribution because of subarctic climate, relief control, and poverty of resources. The total population is

3,164,000 or about 25 per square mile, or 736 per square mile of cultivable land. This situation is greatly ameliorated by the development of fishing, commerce, dairying, and industry. The resources and opportunities are so distributed that every town is a water-side center, but only 25 per cent of all the people live in towns. All three centers belong to the lower story of the country. In Bayard Taylor's [4] words, "there are two Norways, one above —a series of detached, irregular masses, bleak, snowy, wind-swept, and heather-grown, inhabited by herdsmen and hunters; and one below—a ramification of narrow veins of land and water, with fields and forests, highways and valleys."

A Lapp cradle and baby with its mother. Note the reindeer-skin tent. (Publishers Photo Service)

Character. Probably Norway has the most homogeneous population on the continent, essentially Teutonic Nordics. The only non-Nordics are Lapps. Lapland lies across three countries, Norway, Sweden, and Finland, but more Lapps are in Norway than in both countries to the east. Lapland

[4] *Northern Travel* (G. P. Putnam's Sons, New York).

is more ethnic than geographic. Lapps are a Finno-Ugrian branch of the Mongols and because of their isolation here have undergone less intermixture than similar Mongols elsewhere. They were here in the Stone Age and for hundreds of years have been spreading southward, until recently increasing in number. Originally nomadic and engaged in reindeer husbandry, they are becoming settled in fishing and rural industries. Their tendency to migrate freely back and forth across the international boundaries and their tenacity for primitive customs and modes of life have introduced political problems. To their credit be it said, they pour into the stream of commerce and industry reindeer meat, skins, and bones, all of which contribute to the economic welfare of their countries. They seem to be making an interesting though unconscious geographic adjustment. Mongoloid, they were and are roundheaded; their hair was formerly straight and black, their complexion dark, but lately they have come to have chestnut curly hair and beards, and blue eyes. Superficially they do not look Mongoloid. Some 20,000 Lapps may be counted as residents of Norway; and in the extreme north, centering on Vadsö, there are also 8,000 Finns, who have recently drifted along the coast to their new home.

ACTIVITIES

Leading occupations. Agriculture is the leading industry and engages about one half of the people, at least during the farming season; even a fourth of the fishermen are primarily farmers. The tilling of the soil is seriously handicapped however by topography and climate, by scanty, difficult, stony soil, and by the persuasive invitation to become seamen. Not only is agriculture limited, but crops and methods are restricted. Short summers preclude many crops, but hay and pasture flourish. The drying of hay is accomplished by hanging it in handfuls on poles, or on wire frames like our grapevine trellises, or by spreading it over rock surfaces. Three times as much land is used for hay as for oats, and fully as much for oats as for barley and potatoes, while potatoes cover more land than all the lesser crops. Livestock consists of sheep, dairy cattle, reindeer, and swine. Growth of industrial life and improvement in transportation have increased the Norwegian's comfort; he imports 50 per cent of his grains and flour, 30 per cent of his fats and oils, his cotton for cloth, all his sugar and spices, and much of his fruit. There is not much chance to increase the acreage of crops and only a little to be gained by more intensive cultivation. Foxgrowing has been a profitable diversion and suggests possible lines of expansion. More change is to be expected by temporarily shifting farmers to industry, forestry, or fishing in their off season, or by developing the tourist trade, than by any change in agriculture.

Fishing and forestry are the next industries, often combined in the interior, and their geography has been sufficiently elucidated in other places.

Closely related to both is the ship-building for which many fiord harbors have been famous for hundreds of years. This industry requires the importation of lumber from British Columbia. Although Norway has only a comparatively small navy, there is a large and growing merchant marine. Norwegian sailors are among the best, and they not only man their own vessels but enter the crews of every shipping nation and are known in every important harbor the world around.

A fishing fleet in a harbor in Lofoten, an island group in northwest Norway. (Courtesy Royal Norwegian Information Service)

Exports and imports. As Norway gradually becomes somewhat industrial, commerce must grow. Foreign trade is nearly three times as large as it was in the 1930's and still imports have double the value of exports. Exports are based on water power as much as England's are on coal, with this enormous advantage, that use does not deplete the reserves. It seems that Norway is making as wise a use of resources, man power, and country in general as any people could do.

The characteristic exports fall into three groups very closely related to natural conditions. (1) Fish and fish products, based on a natural resource inexhaustible if wisely conserved, on the use of forest products for both boats and packing cases, and on the logical training and skill of the people, furnish a large item in domestic consumption and about one third of the exports. (2) Forest products (lumber, pulp, paper, and articles made of wood and paper), which come from land never capable of any crop but forests, and which use abundant power, pyrite, and convenient transportation, furnish 39 per cent of the exports. (3) Chemical and metallurgical products based on the abundant water power, air, and limestone resources and on the rather meager ore minerals, make up the third and perhaps most promising group of exports. Nitrates and other nitrogen fertilizers are coming into larger and larger use and can be easily shipped away from industrial harbor towns. The expense of quarrying and preparing the limestone to combine with the nitrogen is the only raw-material expense. In the development and export of hydro-electric power Norway is not as foolish as Britain is when she exports coal, or the United States when she exports

Fornehn Airport near Oslo. There must be some nearly level areas among the hills. (Courtesy Royal Norwegian Information Service)

oil. The export of butter and condensed milk helps pay for imported foods. The income from tourist trade will help buy food for tourists and keep up roads, build the 3,000 miles of automobile roads and similar mileage of railroads. Topography necessitates narrow roads with many curves and calls for ten railroad tunnels, each over a mile long, two of them nearly six miles long. Air service reaches most of the towns and moves thousands of passengers annually over its 93,000 miles of lines.

Her deep harbors, free outlet to the north, and peaceful traditions induced the inroad of the Nazis in 1940. Today she is recovering from destruction of her merchant and fishing fleet and the almost complete obliteration of northern villages and homesteads.

CULTURE

The Norwegian people are in the main a thrifty, frugal, courteous, friendly people; in religion tolerant. Literature has shown considerable originality and strength; art is mainly in wood and needlework. Architecture, likewise, is in wood, but stone is used in the cities (brick more rarely because of the scarcity of clay and fuel). Education is provided for all. Illiteracy in persons of school age and above is less than 1 per cent. Norway has produced several notable explorers, scientists, painters, authors, and musicians.

SPITZBERGEN

A group of islands, Spitzbergen, 350 to 680 miles north of Norway, has been explored by Norwegians and was granted to the flag by international agreement in 1925. It is destined to play an important part in Norway's economic life, for it has large reserves of coal (estimated at 9 billion tons), low-grade iron ore, and gypsum. All these are items much needed by Norway. Development of coal-mining, principally by foreigners, has gone on rapidly in the last two decades. These islands lie within the great fishing areas of the Greenland, Norwegian, and Barents seas and furnish an excellent base for the fishing industry.

QUESTIONS

1. Compare Norway with Italy. What are the contrasts and what the similarities?
2. Why were Norwegians and their relatives the first explorers to reach America? What are the reasons for the ephemeral character of their exploratory work?
3. What is the significance of the expression "Land of the Midnight Sun"?
4. How short is the daylight duration in Bergen? in Tromsö? How long is the longest night at Hammerfest?
5. Disregarding effects of clouds and refraction, which places have the most actual daylight in the year? the least? Explain.
6. What is the difference in the altitude of the noon sun in the parts of Norway most separated? How constant through the year is this difference?
7. Discuss the merits of Norway, Sweden, and Denmark as scenic and recreation lands.

BIBLIOGRAPHY

AHLMANN, Hans W., *De norska stadernas geografiska forutsällningar* (Ymer, 1917).

——, *Norges vattenkrafts forhallanden* (Ymer, 1920).

BERGSMARK, Daniel R., "Geography of Norway," *Bulletin Geographical Society of Philadelphia,* Vol. 27 (1929), pp. 283-299.

BOSWORTH, A. L., "Life in a Norway Valley," *National Geographic Magazine,* Vol. 67 (May, 1935), pp. 627-648.

BOWMAN, Isaiah, *The New World* (Yonkers-on-Hudson, New York, World Book Company, 1928).

BRIGHAM, Albert P., "Fiords of Norway," *Bulletin American Geographical Society,* Vol. 38 (1906), p. 9.

COON, Carleton S., *The Races of Europe* (New York, The Macmillan Company, 1939).

COOPER, Alfred H., *Norwegian Fiords* (in colors), (London, A. & C. Black, Ltd., 1907).

DENNIS, A. P., "Norway, a Land of Stern Reality," *National Geographic Magazine,* Vol. 58 (July, 1930), pp. 1-44.

DOMINIAN, Leon, *Frontiers of Language and Nationality in Europe* (New York, Henry Holt & Company, Inc., 1928).

ELTON, Charles, "Notes on a Traverse of Norwegian Lapland in 1930," *Geographical Journal,* Vol. 79 (January, 1932), pp. 44-48.

FITZGERALD, Walter, *The New Europe* (New York, Harper and Brothers, 1946).

GATHORNE-HARDY, G., *Norway* (New York, Charles Scribner's Sons, 1928).

GJERSET, Knut, *History of the Norwegian People* (New York, The Macmillan Company, 1927).

HARRIMAN, Florence J., *Mission to the North* (Philadelphia, J. B. Lippincott Company, 1941).

HUBBARD, G. D., "The Geography of Residence in Norway Fiord Areas," *Annals of the Association of American Geographers,* Vol. 22 (June, 1932), pp. 109-118.

HUNTINGTON, Ellsworth, *Character of Races* (New York, Charles Scribner's Sons, 1924).

KOHT, Halvdan, "Old and New View of Norwegian History," *Social Science Abstracts,* Vol. 3 (June, 1931), p. 829.

——, "Fur Trade in Norwegian History," *Social Science Abstracts,* Vol. 3 (July, 1931), p. 971.

KOHT, Halvdan and SIGMUND, Skard, *Voice of Norway* (New York, Columbia University Press, 1944).

LARSEN, Karen, *A History of Norway* (Princeton, Princeton University Press, 1948).

LORENTZEN, Öivind, *Norway, Norwegian Shipping and the War* (London, Oxford University Press, 1942).

NANSEN, Fridtjof, "The Strandflat and Isostasy," *Videnskapsselskahet skrifter 1 Mathematisk-natur, klasse,* No. 11 (1921), pp. 1-313.

Norway, Official Maps of Norway (Norway Geographical Institute, Oslo), occasionally revised.

Norway in Maps (Bergen, Norges Geografiske Oppmaling, 1947).

Norway Yearbook, 1938 and later (not strictly an annual), (Oslo, S. Mortensen).

ROTHERY, Agnes E., *Norway Changing and Changeless* (New York, Viking Press, Inc., 1939).

Royal Norway Air Force, *Little Norway in Pictures* (Canada, S. J. Reginald Saunders, 1944).

SCOTT, Franklin D., *The United States and Scandinavia* (Cambridge, Harvard University Press, 1950).

SIMON, Sir E. D., *Smaller Democracies* (London, Victor Gollancz, Ltd., 1939).

SVERRE-MORTENSEN and SKØIEN, A., *Norway Yearbook* (New York, Hafner Publishing Co., Inc., 1950).

THOMSON, CLAUDIA, "Norwegian Agriculture," *Foreign Agriculture,* Vol. 4 (Washington, D. C., 1940), pp. 65-94.

VOGT, Per, ed., *Norway Today* (London, George Allen & Unwin, Ltd., 1950; also Oslo, Forlaget Bok og Bilde, A/S, 1950).

ZIMMERMAN, M., "Norway," in Vidal de La Blache and Gallois, *Géographie Universelle* (Paris, Lib. Armand Colin, 1933).

Part IV

BALTIC LANDS (TRANSITIONAL CLIMATE)

GENERAL SURVEY OF BALTIC LANDS

As outlined in the general chapter on climate, the fourth section of this book deals with the present countries of the Baltic lands. This classification of countries in terms of the greatest geographic factor, climate, separates Sweden from Norway, but such separation facilitates recognition of a Baltic unity that has existed longer than the political affinities of the Scandinavian countries.

All the countries in this group border the Baltic Sea, drain almost exclusively into it, fish and travel on it, reach the outside world more upon its waters than in any other way, possess a climate transitional between the oceanic climate of the Atlantic coast and the continental climate of Russia, and have been completely glaciated. So far as soils and climate are concerned with products and enterprises, these states again are remarkably similar. The Baltic, their common waterway, occupies a basin which contained a fresh-water lake in late Pleistocene time and owes its present extent to a gradual, gentle warping-down of a stream-made surface which allowed the sea to spread in a shallow sheet over 160,000 square miles of territory much like its bordering lands. Depths of water rarely exceed 600 feet. Of course we should have more lands, more plains, if this warping had not occurred. Would a land area here be worth more than the water area?

CHAPTER 20

Sweden

When the waters were divided from the land
Sweden was forgotten.
—Native Lore

EARLY PEOPLES

The story of the occupation of Sweden by prehistoric groups and their development into the present citizenry is almost identical with that told for Norway (*q.v.*). Neolithic men may have arrived a little earlier, but they were of the same sort. Many more kitchen middens mark shoreline residence in Sweden than in Norway. Bronze Age men occupied Skania [1] long and well, while they were of less significance in Norway. The Iron Age, too, seems to have been better represented in Sweden, because there is so much better opportunity for hunting, grazing, and the early types of agriculture here. Both bronze and iron tools, weapons, and ornaments have been imported. There is no known evidence that any deposits of metal ores were worked in Sweden in these stages. Men were fishers, fighters, traders, and tillers of the soil, but not miners and metallurgists.

In the Viking age iron ores were mined, smelted, and manufactured into many tools, pincers, anvils, pins, weapons, and ornaments, even into helmets and coats of mail. Commerce with the east and south continued. Humble wooden dwellings were used, but no stone shelters and caves as in many central and south European countries, for there are no caves in Sweden.

SITUATION

Sweden occupies about 50,000 square miles more of the Scandinavian peninsula than does Norway. It lacks any direct contact with the Atlantic Ocean but has one good port, Gothenburg, whose commerce need not run the Copenhagen gauntlet. It does not reach so far north by 2°, nor stop so short in the south by about 3°, as does Norway, but its people feel the effects of the northerly latitude more because it is so well shut away from

---

[1] A province in southern Sweden. See map on p. 434. Those on pp. 401, 403, and 409 in the previous chapter are helpful in this chapter.

sea influences. As in Norway, so in Sweden, length and narrowness present many problems of administration and national solidarity, but fortune is kinder here than in Norway. Its position has made Sweden the northern jumping-off place of Teutonic commerce and has kept it face to face with Finns, Estons, and Russians, among whom it has not only a commanding, commercial interest but also has had a wholesome political, social, and scientific influence. Unlike her peninsula twin, Sweden maintained a precarious neutrality during both World Wars.

CLIMATE

Placed behind Norway with reference to the sea and prevailing winds, Sweden is sheltered from high winds, moisture, and the ameliorating temperature influences of the ocean so that winters are severer and summers

Eel-pout fishing in winter through a hole in the ice. Slow, lonely, but rewarding. (Courtesy Swedish Travel and Information Service Bureau, Inc.)

warmer than in Norway. This protection gives it a range of local climate more in keeping with its range of latitude and places stronger limitations on activities and crops in high latitudes. West Sweden along the Kattegat has marine climate, low temperature range, and rainfall of 35 inches, while

Kalmar in the east has continental climate, larger range of temperature, and rainfall of 13 inches. Sweden has more sunshine than Norway and less of fog and mist. The Gulf of Bothnia freezes over during many winters and its harbors are closed many months every year, but the waters of southern Sweden are rarely frozen.

GEOLOGIC AND PHYSIOGRAPHIC HISTORY

Ancient crystalline rocks, mostly of Pre-Cambrian age, make up the foundations of Sweden; Silurian rocks in the middle, higher, inland portion, and frequent patches of later rocks in the south give a little variety. Where these older bed-rocks are covered, the mantle is drift, alluvium, or lake deposits of Pleistocene and Recent ages. As the Baltic is approached from the mountains of western Sweden, literally hundreds of remnants of the older rock show through drift and water deposits like islands in the sea. These remnants are larger inland, just as are the islands landward in the skerry-guard or Skärgard. Alluvium and lake deposits cover many valley floors throughout all lower Sweden, half the surface in a coastal belt twenty to fifty miles in width, and many areas out across Gotland and Skania. Before the ice age the ancient rocks had been nearly base-leveled, probably more than once, until at least one peneplain with monadnocks was present to receive the ice. The surface had been strongly warped, upward in the west and downward in the east, with long, medium slopes between. The ice covered all Sweden probably more than once, sculptured the big valleys, shoved the residual mantle from most of the upland surface and added it to lowlands in Sweden and Germany, and during waning stages built moraines. The unequal deposition of drift, a little warping, and some ice erosion gave rise to many depressions, some fiords or fiord-like valleys with no sea but a lake in each, and scores of shallow lakes in the south. Thus hundreds of ice-modified valleys leading down from the international boundary are partly occupied by long, narrow, deep lakes. These valleys, if submerged by the sea as those on the Norwegian side have been, would be fiords; but slopes toward the Baltic are not so steep nor so much drowned, and in consequence Sweden has many times as much young plain with imperfect drainage as has Norway, much to the advantage of its agriculture, forestry, and travel. Lakes Wener and Wetter have inspired the construction of the great Göta Canal across the peninsula from Gothenburg to the Baltic. Islands—Gotland, Öland, and many small ones—are the summits of a land surface, like that of the adjacent mainland, which was largely submerged when the Baltic waters flooded the basin. Gotland and Öland, as the name of the former ("Good-land") suggests, are very attractive farmland. The moderate elevation in post-glacial time has brought to the surface much land, whose recent sediments had been worked over by the sea; but the greater previous submergence, which has not yet been wholly overcome by uplift, has given both mainland and islands an abundance of harbors which were adequate until the beginning of the nineteenth century.

Many river mouths are navigable a short distance; some are used a hundred miles inland; some open out into navigable lakes. Several cities, notably Stockholm, have taken advantage of islands in streams or lakes, or of narrow places in streams, to put up a defense for government or commerce.

RESOURCES

As a check on the natural resources and the opportunities in Sweden, note that its area is quite a little larger than the whole of the British Isles, Ireland included, but its population is only one eighth as great. It has no city much exceeding a half-million, whereas in the British Isles there are seven such, one of which has 30 per cent more people than all Sweden. Both countries are fundamentally agricultural; but the British Isles have vastly more that is not agrarian civilization than Sweden's resources can ever make possible, unless some wholly new economic basis be found.

Soils. Sweden may be divided into a large northern and a small southern part. The boundary is roughly on the 60° parallel, turning northward as it nears the Baltic. North of the line there is relatively more ancient, resistant rock, and bouldery, glacial drift, hillier topography, more mineral wealth, greater forest area, and more water power, with a much less favorable climate. South of the line there are more lakes and larger ones, much more of plains and recent lake and marine deposits, a more propitious climate, and therefore better-matured soils, and easier outlet to seas and other lands. Lakes may be found in every stage of filling, even to actual workable peat fields. Hillside bogs are common in the north where soils are waterlogged. None of the soils of Sweden are old residual ones, but all are closely related to glaciation, melt-water work, and deposition in waters that invaded the land during its temporary lower stands. In many places the soils are rich, even over-rich, in humus.

Forests. Sweden is one of the forest states of Europe. Forests, estimated at nearly 40 billion cubic feet, cover nearly 55 per cent of the land. This means that Sweden has more than five times the average per capita forest acreage of all Europe and more than ten times that of western Europe. The annual cut has now come to exceed the growth, and the government is responding with regulations and a system of forestry adapted to the physical conditions of the country. The export of lumber in its various forms of partial or complete manufacture amounts to about one half of the cut.

Zon recognizes four types of forest region. (1) Northern birch forests are above the altitude of 1,500 feet, rising to above 3,000 feet in Dalarne, Lapland. (2) The northern coniferous region occurs below the birch and covers thousands of square miles in the north. Its trees are dominantly pine and spruce, with birch, aspen, alder, and willow. (3) The southern coniferous area is a continuation southward of pine and spruce extending up slopes to the birch-forest altitude, but has in its territory many oak, elm, maple, and ash trees. (4) The beech region in the south is largely cleared now for agriculture, but where preserved it furnishes splendid beech, oak, and alder. The ancient dense forests of Småland have been completely cut over. Above the birch forests are beautiful stretches of heaths, and through all the forests are lakes, bogs, peat areas, and bare rock patches. Most of the vegetation shows peculiarities due to the recency of its migration from south and east as it followed back the retreating ice edge.

The forests of Sweden are extensive because climate and soils are more satisfactory for forests than for agriculture. The lumbering operations are closely related to geographic conditions. Trees are felled in winter; the logs are trimmed and piled near the streams while ice and snow cover all the land. When freshets come with the spring thaw, the logs are rolled into the water and floated down to more than fifty mills at the harbor mouths of Baltic streams, where they are cut into boards, railroad ties, mine props, and stove and locomotive wood, or ground into pulp or paper, cut into matches, distilled for their tar, pitch, resin, alcohol, and acetone, or burned into charcoal. Even the sawmill waste is thus used. Sweden has been in the lumber market hundreds of years, and there is no geographic reason why it should not remain there.

Minerals and rocks. Wealthy compared with Norway, but poor compared with Britain, Sweden's mineral resources are limited to few kinds. Iron ranks first. About one tenth of the production comes from a strip of country extending east and west from Värmland to Uppland, just north of the great lakes; and the rest comes from enormous reserves of good ore among ancient crystalline rocks. The mines are at Kiruna, far north near the Norwegian boundary, and at Gellivara. These places are connected by rail with the never-frozen port of Narvik in Norway and the Swedish port of Lulea, ice-bound for half of each year, on the Baltic. Because the central field is so conveniently located for home use and the Lapland field is so remote, government restrictions on export greatly favor the northern fields. Kiruna ore is exceptionally rich, abundant, and clean, but too high in phosphorus for the furnaces of Britain; hence it is shipped to Germany, where the basic method of reduction is more commonly used.

At Falun in the southern mineral zone, copper has been mined so long that the local *lan* or province was named Kopparberg, but the greater values are now in pyrite, with small amounts of gold, selenium, lead, and bismuth. Sweden is credited with 1 per cent of the world's zinc output from mines at Ammeberg. Coal and fire-clays occur in thin beds in Skania. Many fine building stones are quarried in localities where water transport to the cities is easy. Granites, porphyries, marble, and sandstones serve most satisfactorily. Sweden has over sixty varieties of very choice marble and serpentine marbles, white, gray, green, blue, pink; seventy-five kinds of granite, coarse,

In Spring and summer logs are floated down rivers from forest to sawmills near the coast. They look like matches floating in a pool. (Courtesy Swedish Travel and Information Service Bureau)

fine, red, pink, gray; more than twenty-five porphyries; over thirty dark rocks, some with lustrous play of colors; gneisses in abundance; and fifteen to twenty slates, with many sandstones and limestones. The influence of all this rock on buildings and architecture is strong. Since, in spite of such abundance and range of rock, most rural and village houses are of wood the latter must also make a strong appeal. As wood is exhausted here and there the use of stone increases; and where clays are plenty, some whole towns are built of brick.

Open-pit workings in the Kiruna iron ore mines. In the Lapland of Sweden, north of the Arctic Circle. (Courtesy Swedish Travel and Information Service Bureau, Inc.)

Power. In early days wood and charcoal power and heat were commonly used. Some charcoal is still used to smelt the iron ores. A country so rich in wood logically uses wood on local steamboats and railroad locomotives, but with so little coal any considerable industrial development awaits hydro-electric power. The latter is used in mining, metallurgy, the nitrate and other chemical industries, the manufacture of forest products, and the homes as frequently as in Switzerland. It should displace wood and coal on locomotives as completely in all Sweden as it has in the south. Lakes, winter snow, and ice caps, a few of which drain to Sweden, together with considerable fall on most streams and a meager coal supply, combine to make Sweden's water power important. Three to four million horsepower are available for nine months, and at present about one third of this amount is developed in plants much concentrated on the Dal and Göta rivers.

Scenery and sports. Scenery is not as grand as in Norway, but is more varied and more available for lingering visits. More inland lakes, falls, and streams encourage fishing, boating, and camping. Much more forest and grassland make hunting very attractive. Snow and ice in winter have led the Swedes to invent sail-skating, skiing, ice-yachting and tobogganing, while the many streams and lakes have made popular such summer water sports as rowing, canoeing, sailing, and swimming. Clubs for the various sports are well organized.

Tourists find interesting, attractive, and stimulating not only the scenery and climate but the architecture and museums of prehistoric specimens, and enjoy the courtesy of the kindly people. A definite effort is now being made to capitalize these resources.

MODERN PEOPLE

The present inhabitants of Sweden, like those of Norway, are Teutonic Nordics, probably the tallest nationals in Europe, very fair, long-headed, long-faced, blue-eyed, lineal descendants of the peoples who have carried forward the various stages of culture in the land for some 10,000 years; but they have been taught many things by their neighbors, have been invaded, and have received new blood repeatedly. These intrusions have been usually wholly Teutonic and largely Scandinavian. As in Norway, so in Sweden, Lapps of Mongolian strains entered the country thousands of years ago from the east along Arctic lands. Finns too, and a few Russians, have immigrated in later years. Lapps, 7,000 persons in all, are scattered widely in the northern states and rarely constitute more than a small percentage of the people in any locality, while the Finns have congregated in lumber or mining localities and remain well segregated.

The distribution of people is very largely a response to geographic factors. Greater altitude and relief and severer climate keep the population density very low in the northwestern third of the country. The Baltic shoreline and its bordering plains are so much more attractive, and the lumber mills give so much better employment, that the mean density is some ten times as great along the coastal strip as in the higher lands toward Norway. The whole Kattegat coast seems to have a similar influence. A strip of lands some 25 to 30 miles wide along this coast has decidedly higher density of population than adjacent interior lands. Harbor facilities and transportation in general, as well as fisheries, are strong factors in the population problem. Industry with its numerous laborers accompanies adequate transportation, and agriculture not only may be more intensive on the plains near the sea but must be so to supply food for the larger commercial, industrial, and fishing centers. The Bohus Islands north of Gothenburg make excellent fishing and naval channels and add to the attractions of this coast. The same shoreline influence continues across all the south end of Sweden.

The whole area south of parallel 60°, because of its levelness and better climatic combination, carries a population several times denser than even the coast strip north of the Dal. A strip across the peninsula, with numerous

Taking fish to market in summertime, at the village of Ulvön. (Courtesy Swedish Travel and Information Service Bureau, Inc.)

lakes and water connections and great adaptability for transportation, agriculture, fishing, and industry, supports as dense a population as the Kattegat coast strip. Rich forests occur here, and many of the great match factories are in this belt. Stone quarrying and cutting follow the crystalline outcrops, and their products travel to the cities on the cheap water routes.

Three areas of densest population surround the three cities. The Stockholm-Uppsala region is the most important; Gothenburg (349,145) northward is the second, and Malmö (189,232) to Helsingborg the third. Many factors combine in each place to draw the people into these areas. At first defense was extremely important. Now perhaps the harbor facilities for trade rank first. Industries based on local and imported resources gather around good harbors, and all the attendants of modern business—bankers, brokers, wholesalers, insurance men, administrators, shippers, and the employees of a score of little industries subsidiary to the great ones—help to swell the number of people in any such center.

Air view of modern apartment buildings at Ribershus, Malmö. (Courtesy Swedish Travel and Information Bureau, Inc.)

Swedish people, owing to the character of their country, its shorelines, and its position, have been more in contact with German, Danish, and Russian people than have Norwegians, a relationship which has contributed much to their spirit, culture, and interests. Literature, art, music, and even architecture all carry marks inscribed by these contacts.

ACTIVITIES

Agriculture and forestry are easily the supreme occupations. Half the people live on farms, and nearly one third get all or a considerable portion of their subsistence from the forests and dependent industries.

Agriculture. In most parts of Sweden the distribution of arable land is so patchy that farms are small. Work upon them is arduous and largely done by hand, so that one man cannot tend a large farm even if one could be had. The trend is generally toward intensive farming. For both these reasons holdings are small and for the most part are owned by the farmer. About 12 per cent of the country is devoted to tillage and pasture, a percentage six times too large in the north, but as much too small in the south. Still, agriculture does not produce nearly enough food for the semi-industrialized people. The farm crops comprise, for climatic reasons, only the hardy cereals—oats, rye, barley, a little wheat—and quick-growing or resistant vegetables—potatoes, root crops for cattle food, and in the far south beets for sugar. Many garden vegetables can be grown. Hay occupies more acreage than any three planted crops, because the wet, stony soil and moist

Drying hay on racks in northern Sweden. Timber, grazing, and tillage are intimately intermingled over the old glaciated topography. (Courtesy Swedish Travel and Information Service Bureau, Inc.)

climate cause a luxuriant growth every year; but these very factors introduce harvesting problems. Hay is cut by hand or small one-horse mower, raked and hung by handfuls on poles or trellis racks for days to dry. It never becomes parched, as hay often becomes in dry continental climates. Electric driers for hay are coming into use. These pasture and meadow conditions and the pressure of population lead to a growing dairy industry in which 2,500,000 cattle and 1,700,000 hogs are a normal animal population. Since the Stone Age, cattle-rearing has been characteristic. From Uppsala to Tralleborg and back to Vener Lake, except in the Stockholm province, the number of cattle is nearly equal to the number of people; a large proportion are dairy cattle. These and the swine use the great bulk of the agricultural output for food.

Forests. The distribution and care of forests is closely related to climatic factors, relief, mills, and markets. Some of these items were discussed under "Resources, Forests." Since snow cover remains longer in forests than in the open, logs are hauled out on sleds to streams or even to mills. Streams and lakes become either a frozen highway for the logs on sleds or a waterway for the logs in rafts. Snow also prevents, if it stays long, the deep freezing of the ground in spite of the cold winter. Fortunately for lumbering operations, the forests are ordinarily very monotonous, lacking variety in species. Because the boundary between birch and conifers approximates a contour line strips of coniferous growth penetrate far up the valleys between birch areas on the divides, and the latter sprawl as fingers among the conifers. Government forest reservations (conifers) occupy lower and lower levels northward.

Sweden not only has worked out rather carefully adjusted forest regulations but has coöperative unions for organizing the cutting, manufacturing, and marketing of the timber.

Manufacturing. Sulphite paper-pulp is made in the Falun copper-mining region by using the sulphur produced from its 1 per cent of the world's pyrite output. Mechanical paper-pulp, paper, and paper articles are made in hundreds of mills throughout the southern third of the country and along the Baltic coast, where power and transportation are available.

Electrification of rural homes and small industries reaches about 95 per cent, although many mills stand just where they did when they used water power direct. Small mills on many power sites grind grains for man and stock. Even windmills do some grinding in the plains portions. Rye is thus ground for the farmer's rye bread. Beet sugar is made where the beet is most easily grown, notably in Skania where are more than half the sugar factories. This local industry has almost stopped the importation of sugar.

Among industries, textile manufacturing has become the leader. Sweden has the power, skill, labor, and a considerable market, but must import all the cotton used and about half the wool. Cotton factories are concentrated primarily in and around Gothenburg, to which the cotton can be shipped, while woolen mills are widely distributed because half the raw wool is produced in Sweden. Jute and linen are also manufactured in a group of mills near Gothenburg, which use mostly imported fibers but supply mostly a local market. Tanneries and leather industries are profitably and economically set in Sweden, but the business in the aggregate is small. From the household evening or winter work of making tools, furniture, kegs, and baskets, practised through many generations in close adjustment to the geographic factors of raw materials, power, and market, have come many small factories, each making one or more kinds of articles and employing a small number (average twenty) of workmen. There are, for example, eleven basket factories, fourteen cork factories, importing sheet cork from Portugal, and a number of fish-tub plants. Quarrying and dressing of stone, based on the great wealth and variety of stone, have made rapid development in recent decades and promise a profitable future. Exports of stone in recent years have reached as high as four to five millions of dollars and have included several choice granites, porphyries, slates, and marble. Earthenware, tile stoves, crockery, chinaware, brick, and glass, all ceramic products, in the aggregate make a large contribution to local consumption and a small item of export. More than half the glass plants are concentrated on a granite area in the province of Kronoberg, where the quartz from weathered granite furnishes a part of the raw materials.

A glaciated country in the latitude and climate of Sweden may be expected to have generous supplies of peat, and Sweden is no exception. It is estimated that no country in Europe except Russia has so much peat, and the government as well as private enterprise has been experimenting in the preparation of it. The reserve is placed at the equivalent in fuel value of 4 billions of tons of coal. The charcoal industry is today, however, far more important than peat preparation. It is estimated that the charcoal output reaches $10 million annually. Much of this sum represents savings from sawmill and lumbering wastes, but probably three fourths of it represents charcoal made from forest wood. Not only the large supply of forests and sawmills and the requirements of the iron-works stimulate this industry, but so also does the lack of other fuel. Charcoal steel and electric furnace steel are the finest types made, and Sweden is forced to use these methods or import coal.

Sweden's large industries, aside from those using forest products, follow the iron- and steel-making. The value of this group of products reaches $75 million to $100 million annually and includes machines, implements, vehicles, boats, ships, and all high-grade iron and steel goods. The output does not nearly meet the local needs, and yet it furnishes a considerable item in the country's exports.

Chemical industries flourish in Sweden and add more than $10 million to the gross income of the country. Their list of products includes sulphuric acid from pyrite, fertilizers (both phosphate and nitrates), chlorates to be used on match-heads, explosives, dyes, and paints.

Electric power generation and dependent industries are most concentrated in the forest and foothill belt of country just north of the lake district —Uppsala to northern Kattegat. Their distribution continues south along the latter coast and north along the Baltic, where water power is fundamental in Swedish industrial life.

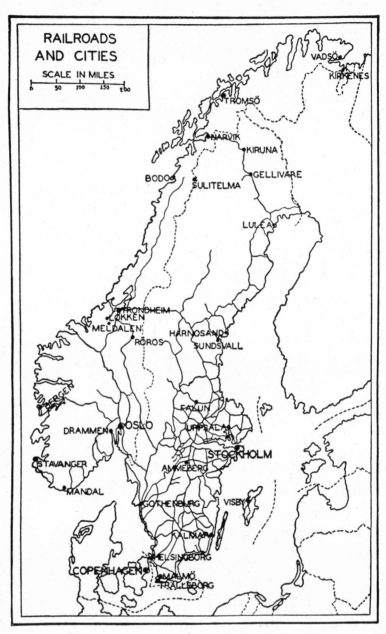

RAILROADS
AND CITIES

SCALE IN MILES

0   50   100   150   200

VADSÖ
KIRKENES
TROMSÖ
NARVIK
KIRUNA
BODO
GELLIVARE
SULITELMA
LULEÅ
TRONDHEIM
LØKKEN
MELDALEN
RÖROS
HARNOSAND
SUNDSVALL
BERGEN
FALUN
DRAMMEN
OSLO
UPPSALA
STAVANGER
STOCKHOLM
AMMEBERG
MANDAL
GOTHENBURG
VISBY
KALMAR
HELSINGBORG
COPENHAGEN
MALMÖ
TRÄLLEBORG

Railroads in southern Sweden are supplemented by several canals and by excellent automobile roads. (Adapted from *Oxford Advanced Atlas*)

COMMERCE AND TRADE

It is probable that amber, collected along Baltic shores and carried far to the southeast, was the first export from Sweden. Perhaps bronze was the first import to help dislodge the primitive culture of the New Stone Age in Sweden. Copper ores were discovered at Falun in the thirteenth century, and mining is supposed to date from about that time. Copper soon entered Swedish export lists, and for 200 years these mines were the largest copper mines in Europe and much of their output was sent all over the continent.

Forest products account for fully 40 per cent of the total exports; northern ports, such as Sundsvall and Härnosand, ship mainly pulp and timber, and southern ports, such as Kalmar and Gothenburg, ship chiefly furniture and wooden articles. Britain, France, Germany, and Denmark are the greatest buyers, since they have long since well-nigh exhausted the timber resources of their forest lands. Iron ore is a large item in the export trade; 85 to 90 per cent of the 150 million tons mined is sent away to Germany and England in exchange for coal, machines, and other manufactures.

In 1931 total exports and imports were about a half-billion dollars each, and 60 per cent larger in 1947-1949. Swedish harbors received 30,000 vessels of 16 million tonnage, about half of which were Swedish. There are over 10,000 miles of railroads. The Lulea-Narvik line and all lines south of Stockholm are electrified—a fine expression of the utility of water power. Fish are used extensively for food and are exported to southern countries.

Swedish air service, centered on the capital, reaches all important towns, and both French and British lines connect with Sweden.

CITIES

Stockholm (736,600), the capital, and the glory of the country both historically and in its setting and architecture, was founded by Birger Jarl (or Earl) about A.D. 1250 on a site that had been fortified somewhat before his time, though to little purpose. Towns and castles had already occupied commercial and strategic places on the inland waters of the Mälar Sea; but no adequate defense guarded its entrance. Two narrow channels, Norrström and Söderström, and three islands in midstream form the gateway to the whole beautiful embayment. Stadholmen (City Island), which separates the streams, bore the original fortress and carries today the unique, fascinating old city.

To reach the gate by water one may start inward from the Baltic anywhere among the hundreds of islands of the Swedish Skärgard, for all ways lead to this one gate. Once through it, water routes spread over Mälar Sea among islands and peninsulas and up many streams 30 to 75 miles beyond the gate to a score of terminals. The crossing at the gate is one of the narrowest and most advantageous in the whole expanse of the Mälar system.

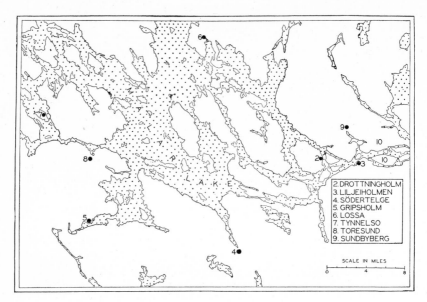

City of Stockholm and environs.

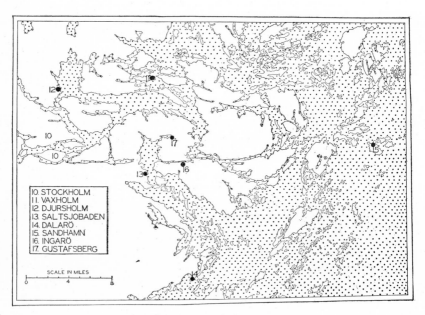

(Adapted from Swedish topographic maps)

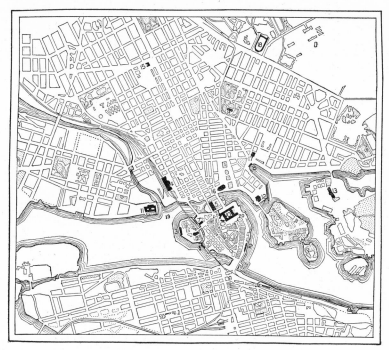

Stockholm. All the city except the part on the small islands in midstream is comparatively modern. 1. Boat Landing: Steamers to Gripsholm. 2. Boat Landing: Steamers to Finland. 3. Boat Landing: Steamers to Göta Canal. 4. Central railroad station. 5. Parliament House 6. Train to Saltsjöbaden. 7. House of Nobility. 8. Boat to Saltsjöbaden. 9. Riddarholm Church and accessories. 10. Royal Palace. 11. City Hall. 12. National Gallery. 13. Northern Museum. 14. Royal Library in Public Garden. 15. City Library. 16. Royal Opera House. 17. Royal Dramatic Theater. 18. Stadium. 19. Norr Strömmen. 20. East Lane Street. 21. West Lane Street. (Adapted from tourist map)

First, defense from pagan raiders across the Baltic, second, commerce with all the coming Baltic neighbors, and beauty all the time were the powerful geographic factors that put the fortress, castles, church, walls, and drawbridges at the present site of Stockholm.

Commerce could not fail to grow, until today it has become much more significant than defense. Beauty has been enhanced by buildings and made available by boat, bus, and tram-car. The seat of government, royal homes, museums, parks, and the long line of accessories to a capital and a commercial center have contributed to make Stockholm one of the finest of European capitals and a city of nearly three-quarter-million happy, busy people.

Because of its location it became one of two (Visby was the greater) notable Hanse towns controlled by German merchants; and until Gustavus Vasa in the sixteenth century broke the power of Lübeck, Sweden was allowed no trade beyond the Baltic. This strange restriction limited the naturally commercial, industrial city of Stockholm. Afterwards commerce expanded over wide limits and industries began to furnish products for trade.

The old town on the largest island consisted of a walled area surrounded by two convex walls meeting at the south end and joined at the north end by the Palace-Castle of the builder, thus enclosing an oval 1,000 by 600 feet. Inside were buildings for the use of soldiers and officers and for business purposes. Outside along the walls were *Öster lang gatan* and *Vaster*

Riddarholm Church and parts of the old town with its curved streets. The palace and government buildings are to the left of the church. The picture was taken from a building near the south end of the island. See map on p. 437 (Courtesy Swedish Travel and Information Service Bureau, Inc.)

lang gatan (East and West Lane streets). Then came many narrow streets, 4 to 10 feet wide, radiating from these lanes. Today these streets are occupied by many business blocks crowded above by tenements and below by stores full of souvenirs and modern wares of a hundred kinds. The small island, Riddarholm, to the west, has the old church and palaces of knights. These old buildings with their quaint iron-work and crooks remind one strongly of the medieval times from which they survive.

Because the city is on islands and hills of various heights, streets intersect on different levels, and railroads curve around or tunnel through hills. They must reach the water and must emerge on the uplands to serve their clientele. The railroad from the south comes in through a tunnel 1,000 feet long, crossing the streams and island on a high trestle. As short cuts from one street level to another, men move up and down long straight or spiral stairs or ride in out-of-door elevators as in hilly Lisbon.

Saltsjön is the name of the salt waters that lead out in many channels to the Baltic. On one channel, at Gustafsberg, a fine porcelain works has been built; on another the famous water-sports resort, Saltsjöbaden; on another a large paper mill and the arsenal and garrison town of Vaxholm; while toward the west up Mälar Lake are Drottningholm, an exquisite site for the royal palace, and Gripsholm, a castle of old, so situated as to guard waterways and contribute to history.

The beautiful slopes and islands of Mälar are used for summer homes, and some of the shores of islands and mainland near the city have been developed for harbors, equipped with docks, piers, and warehouses; but both pleasure and business may still be greatly extended.

Visby, at present ruins and roses, on Gotland Island, was perhaps the most important trade and defense town during the middle ages and Hanseatic days. Gothenburg served in a similar capacity, but being on the mainland it has entered into a period of modern prosperity, while Visby is mainly a relic of former power and glory.

QUESTIONS

1. Discuss the policy of exporting so much iron ore, considering the various geographic factors such as density of population, use of iron, amount of coal and other resources.

2. Compare the building materials of Sweden and Denmark.

3. How wide geographic connections did Denmark need to establish, compared with Sweden, to build its substantial palaces and edifices?

4. Compare Stockholm with Hamburg or Venice, which like it are cities on mingled land and water, with respect to forms, site for a city, salt- and fresh-water problems, uses made of elements of the site, and adjustments that may yet be made.

5. At the Chicago Fair in 1893 Sweden surprised many with her attractive, efficient tools and machinery for sawmills. Why should Sweden excel in such machinery?

6. What change in significance of geographic factors may have occurred in recent times in the Scandinavian Peninsula (a) to make the people decide not to have the same king? (b) to call forth a larger commerce between the two states?

BIBLIOGRAPHY

ANDERSSON, Ingvar, *et al., Introduction to Sweden* (New York, Bonnier, 1949).

APPLETON, J. B., and MITCHELL, Sybil, "The Forests and Lumber Industries of Sweden—A Study in Economic Geography," *Bulletin Geographical Society of Philadelphia,* Vol. 30 (1932), pp. 163-181.

ARNESON, Ben A., *Democratic Monarchies of Scandinavia* (New York, D. Van Nostrand Company, Inc., 1939).

BLANCHARD, W. O., and VISHER, S. S., *Economic Geography of Europe* (New York, McGraw-Hill Book Company, Inc., 1931).

BOWMAN, Isaiah, *The New World* (Yonkers-on-Hudson, New York, World Book Company, 1921).

CHILDS, Marquis W., *Sweden: The Middle Way* (New Haven, Yale University Press, 1938).

CLASSEN, Ernest, English ed., *The Northern Countries in World Economy* (Helsinki, Otava Publishing Co., 1937).

COLLINDER, Björn, *The Lapps* (Princeton, Princeton University Press, 1949).

DOMINIAN, Leon, *Frontiers of Language and Nationality in Europe* (New York, Henry Holt & Company, Inc., 1921).

GEORGE, H. B., *Relations of Geography and History* (Oxford, Clarendon Press, 1924).

GOTTMANN, Jean, *A Geography of Europe* (New York, Henry Holt & Company, Inc., 1950).

GRAVES, Ralph A., "The Granite City of the North," *National Geographic Magazine,* Vol. 54 (1928), pp. 403-441.

HERLITZ, Nils, *Sweden, a Modern Democracy on Ancient Foundation* (London, Oxford University Press, Humphrey Milford, 1939).

JONASSAN, Olaf, *Jordbruksatlas över Sverige* (Stockholm, Hoijer Björkman, 1937)

LYDE, L. W., *Continent of Europe* (New York, The Macmillan Company, 1924).

———, *Peninsular Europe* (New York, Longmans, Green & Company, 1931).

MYRDAL, Gunnar, *Population, a Problem for Democracies—Sweden* (Cambridge, Harvard University Press, 1940).

NÄSSTRÖM, Gustaf, *Swedish Antiquities* (Stockholm and New York, A. Bonnier, 1941), in Swedish.

OLSEN, Alma Luise, "Sweden, Land of White Birch and White Coal," *National Geographic Magazine,* Vol. 54 (1928), pp. 441-484.

POSSE-BRAZDOVA, Amelie, "Country-House Life in Sweden," *National Geographic Magazine,* Vol. 66 (July, 1934), pp. 1-64.

RIPLEY, W. Z., *Races of Europe* (New York, D. Appleton and Co., 1899).

ROTHERY, Agnes E., *Sweden, Lands and People* (New York, Viking Press, Inc., 1938).

SANDSTRÖM, Gösta E., trans. (4 editors, many authors), *Swedish Arts and Crafts* (New York, Royal Swedish Commission, 1939).

SCOTT, Franklin D., *The United States and Scandinavia* (Cambridge, Harvard University Press, 1950).

SHACKLETON, Margaret R., *Europe, A Regional Geography* (London, Longmans, Green & Company, 1942).

SIMON, Sir E. D., *Smaller Democracies* (London, Victor Gollancz, Ltd., 1939).

"Soul of Sweden; by an English Visitor," *Living Age,* Vol. 334 (January 15, 1928), pp. 119-127.

STOMBERG, A. A., *A History of Sweden* (New York, The Macmillan Company, 1931).

Swedish General Staff Maps (Stockholm).

Sweden Yearbook (Stockholm, Almquist and Wiksells boktryckeri, 1921 and later numbers), not strictly annual.

Sveriges Geologiska Untersökning publications (Stockholm).

WILLIAM-OLSON, W., "Stockholm, Its Structure and Development," *Geographical Review,* Vol. 30 (1940), pp. 420-438.

ZIMMERMAN, M., "Sweden," in Vidal de La Blache and Gallois, *Géographie Universelle* (Paris, Lib. Armand Colin, 1933).

ZON, Raphael, and SPARHAWK, William N., *Forest Reserves of the World* (New York, McGraw-Hill Book Company, Inc., 1923).

CHAPTER 21

Finland

Silent conifers—black nights shedding,
Birches slender, white, and gleaming.
—FOLK SONG

PEOPLE AND GOVERNMENT

Ancient people. In Finland one finds increasing evidence that people have emerged from Asia in human waves. The earlier waves brought the Lapps from the east into the northern parts of Finland and Scandinavia, where they found true Scandinavians already well established. The Lapps dwelt in the interior in winter and near the coast in summer, but they never fell under the influence of the intricate coast-line. They subsisted by the chase, and, caring for a few dogs and reindeer in a most primitive way, they remained in the Stone Age until they traded with more advanced people. Even to this day very few of them reside by the sea; rather, they wander over the interior mingling with the Finns, with whom they frequently intermarry. This intermarriage eliminates the Lapps, for Finnish women will rarely marry a Lapp. The men are considered very worthless compared with Finnish men or even with Lapp women, who do most of the work. About 2,000 Lapps now live in Finland in four colonies, one in the far north, three near the Arctic Circle. Their distribution in Finland, Sweden, and Norway is no doubt partly due to the pressure of later comers, but there seems to be little evidence that the sea ever effectively invited them to become navigators, explorers, or merchants.

Recently there have been found in northern Finland and adjacent Norway chipped stone implements believed to represent Paleolithic people who lived along the water on a moraine now elevated nearly 200 feet above the sea. Other chipped flints and bone, and the remains of a sort of dwelling such as Lapps now build, are found in several places, for example, on Fisher's Peninsula and farther south near the Norwegian-Finnish boundary.[1] Whether

---

[1] Dr. Tanner of the Finnish Geologic Survey dates the older remains 5,000 years ago and the younger at 3,700 years ago. He connects them with elevated shorelines and the geochronologic work done on varved clays. He feels certain that the people were the lineal ancestors of present Lapps and followed the ice in from Asia and North Russia.

or not these represent the ancestors of present Lapps and also of other Mongoloid strains, as seems wholly possible, they are relics of a nomadic people who dwelt part of the time by the sea (summer) and part of the time inland (winter), migrating with the reindeer, just as the northern colony of Lapps has long been doing.

The second wave of immigration from the east (possibly two waves) contributed the Finns, another Finno-Ugrian branch from Asiatic Mongoloid stock which now has large Nordic infusions.[2]

Lapps and Finns today do not at first glance suggest Mongol stock, because they are fair with blue to brown eyes and light, somewhat curly hair, whereas a modern Mongolian has black, straight hair and black eyes; but the shape of head (brachycephalic), the scanty beard, and the stolid, reliable personal characteristics all suggest ancient Mongoloid connections. Are their fair hair and skin and blue eyes due to the far-northern geographic conditions of light, shelter from sun, and long indoor season, that have bleached their hair, skin, and eyes (modified their pigmentation)? It has been suggested that Finland has been a center of dispersal for European peoples, but from a geographic viewpoint such an interpretation seems to be impossible. In post-glacial time, no race would have time to develop sufficient pressure to crowd out waves of migrants. Rather it has been a retreat for people crowded out of more favorable places.

Present population. Whatever was the origin of its people, Finland, considering its position, possesses today a remarkably homogeneous population. Of its total of more than 3,900,000 people, some 350,000 are Swedish, located along the west and south marginal plains; 5,000 are Russians, in large part refugees; less than 3,000 are Germans, well scattered for business reasons; and some 2,000 are Lapps. If a line be drawn from the head of the Baltic to Lake Ladoga approximately along the railroad from Kemi to Sortavala, dividing the country into two equal parts, 90 per cent of the people will be in the southern half of the territory.

But such a general statement does not describe the distribution of the people. Details show many responses to local conditions. In all parts of the country, both north and south, streams and lake shores are very influential in increasing the population density, and railroads following valleys have augmented the advantage of stream connections. The influence of the water rises as its transportational value increases. It is effective on lake and river

[2] Finns are said to be "first cousins to Magyars, forty-second cousins to Turks, Mongols, and Manchus and of no relation to the Lapps." This close relation to Hungarians intimates a more or less synchronous arrival about the ninth century A.D.; but scattered Finnish remnants over much of northern Russia witness to the almost complete Russification of Finns once occupying much of that area. Early references to the Finns describe many tribes in northwestern Russia, where each valley became a tribal homeland before the influence of Russia became strong. Under that pressure the Finns later became a compact mass in the present Suomi (Marsh) land. Thus "Finnish" comes to be a culture type of strong Asiatic color imposed on a race of Nordic-Tatar mixture.

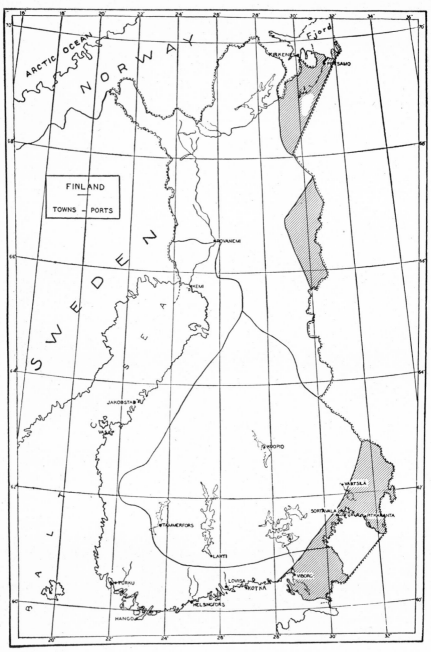

All towns of Finland are ports on lakes, rivers, or the surrounding seas. Shaded areas were lost to U.S.S.R. (Compiled from various maps)

when frozen in winter, as well as in summer. All sea-shores freeze more or less in winter, and ice close to the mainland has some transport value, but for ocean travel none. Islands are not avoided but are well occupied. The rural people are drawn to arable land along waterways. This distribution in relation to water is remarkably well shown both on village and town maps and on rural maps. Forest, swamp, bog, and tundra are almost absolutely free of towns even in the southern part, while offshore islands possess a number of towns built in response to the attraction of salt-water fishing.

Stadium at Helsinki, amid university buildings. Finns believe in sports at beaches, on playgrounds, and on skiis and skates, as well as at the Olympics. (Courtesy Finnish Consulate General in New York)

The capital Helsingfors (Helsinki) had 359,813 people in 1949. The next largest town is old Turku (Abö) with 99,274; then comes industrial Tampere, with about 95,753. Only five others exceed 10,000. These eight leave over 3,000,000 people for the small town, village, and farm—really a large proportion.

Government. Situated between different races, the Finns long have been a bone of contention. Their forests have tempted, and their industry and independence have disturbed, their neighbors. In very early days the Finns seemed to have lived in little groups with no real solidarity or central government, until their Swedish neighbors in the twelfth and thirteenth centuries began to notice them and make efforts to remove their superstitions and savagery by pressing upon them the Christian religion. Coming from the west, their Christianity was such as to make it subject to the Reforma-

Mannerheim Street, Helsinki, named for a recent president of the country. Note trolley car lines, auto lanes, broad sidewalks and parking strips. (Courtesy Finnish Consulate General in New York)

tion and ultimately to Lutheranism instead of to the Eastern Church. For almost 200 years Sweden intermittently devoted neighborly attention to these Finnish people; and the more they did, the more certainly did expanding Russia feel the need of Finnish territory and the Finns. In 1323 a treaty between Sweden and Russia set and sealed the boundary between Russia and the Swedish province of Finland nearly where it was in 1939, from the Gulf of Finland through Lake Ladoga and northward. Its northern extension was of little significance. Then for 400 years Sweden contributed security, laws, government, the Reformed religion, agriculture, education, and a large measure of liberty and self-government.

As Finland prospered, so much more did Russia covet it and fight for it, until in 1809 it was ceded to Russia, but with its constitution, laws, religion, and liberties well intact and guaranteed. Finland became a grand duchy of Russia. This condition existed with rising waves of nationalism until the Czarist régime collapsed in 1917, when Finland proclaimed her independence, adopted a republican form of government, and elected a president. Since then the state has been making rapid strides in internal improvements and external relations. The long years of Swedish tutelage have given Finland a western outlook not one whit weakened by a century under Russian rule.

Russia's aggression in and before World War II resulted in treaties that deprived Finland of Viborg and all she had of Lake Ladoga with considerable well-developed land from the Gulf of Finland as far north as Kuopio. Finland also lost a patch of border territory much farther north and all the state of Petsamo with the harbor of Petsamo. Russia obtained a base on Porkkala Peninsula near Helsinki. Ten per cent of Finland's population transferred west across the new line. The eastern or Russian boundary follows fairly closely the divide between the streams of the Baltic and White seas.

GEOLOGIC AND PHYSIOGRAPHIC HISTORY

General survey. Finland belongs to that great ancient crystalline rock area of which Scandinavia is a part. It was reduced to old age eons ago by erosion, was submerged in part several times in Paleozoic time, and was given sediments which also have been subsequently much eroded. Then the great continental glacier spread over all, removing mantle rock to neighboring states east and south, and depositing drift over Finland in a manner wholly systematic with reference to ice but equally unsystematic with reference to streams. Although in myriads of places the bare rocks show through, a mantle of drift covers much more surface; two great concentric festoons of marginal deposits sweep across the southern part from Hango to Lahti, then eastward and northward, past Saimaa Lake and Värtsilä toward the Russian boundary, while scores of radial eskers run from northwest to

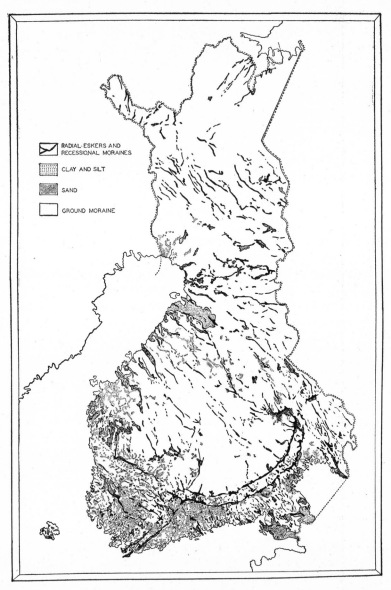

Glacial features of Finland suggest the source of the ice to have been Scandinavia. Two great concentric moraines and many radial eskers outline the pattern. Lake clays, silts, and sands assist in solving the glacio-chronology. (Adapted from *Atlas of Finland*)

southeast; clay or silt covers thousands of square miles of low coastal lands, and gravels and sands spread along the valleys. The old rocks display a grain or structure, but not continuously across the various kinds of material; however, glacial erosion and deposition have so thoroughly impressed their northwest-to-southeast trend on the country that lakes, islands, marshes, peat beds, many streams, forests, grasslands, and even the human distributions respond strikingly to it.

These deposits have so profoundly interfered with the normal flow of waters and have done it so recently that lakes and marshes, rapids and waterfalls indicate the extreme youth of the topography and contribute infinitely to the charm of the landscape.

NATURAL REGIONS

Marginal Plains. Bounded by the sea on one side from Torneo to the Russian frontier, and by the 500-foot contour line from Torneo River more or less parallel with the coast again to the Russian boundary near Lake Ladoga, there is a lowland region marked by absence of lakes and by ancient hard rocks covered with clay and sand deposits, some of which are recent marine beds, others glacio-fluvial. This crescentic zone has a higher percentage of arable land than any other natural region, a greater density of population, all the harbor towns and salt-water fisheries, a large proportion of the best water power, and most of the hardwood timber. It spreads out beyond the actual continental shoreline, including the many islands, even to the Rocky Ålands with many a patch of productive soil. Here 90 per cent of the Swedes in Finland live in two areas, one along the Bothnian shore each side of Vasa, the other extending from Åland Islands to Lovisa.[3] Along the Bothnian portions, this region has the strung-out type of community group found along valleys, whereas the Gulf of Finland portion has the clustered type of habitation found on broader arable lands. The Bothnian section is half peat bog, the highest proportion in Finland.

Central Lakes Region. Lying more than half surrounded by the Marginal Plains, this region occupies a third of the whole country, is a little higher than the plains, and contains a large proportion of the 40,000 lakes, particularly those chained together. It is the portion of Finland most meriting the term *amphibious*. The southern side is limited by the outer festoon of marginal glacial deposits, which in turn marks the falls on many streams and sharply sets off the storage portions of streams from the flowing, power-producing parts. In this region roads must bend around hill areas and avoid marsh and lake, or must climb up over the hills. Because of the patchy distribution of arable lands, bog, timber, and lake, the rural houses are scattered, and there are no cities. Kuopio (25,000) near the center and

---

[3] These Swedish areas are relics of a larger pre-Finnish Swedish occupation of the land and are not, like Greek fringes in the Near East, due to more recent immigrations.

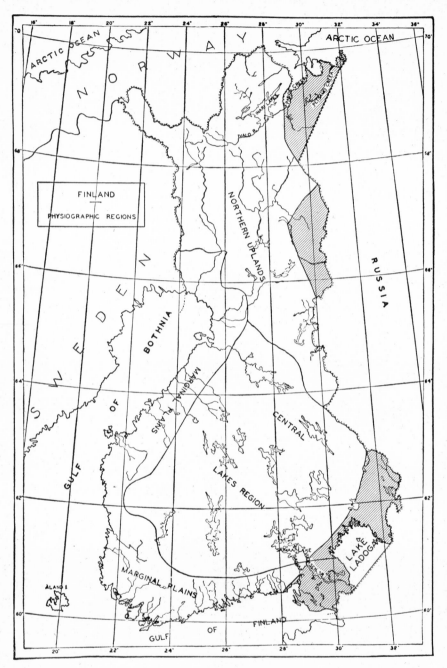

Physiographic regions of Finland are related to glacial features (lakes and moraines) and to the general altitude and relief. (Constructed from various maps in *Atlas of Finland*)

Tammerfors (Tampere) near the southwest margin are the only towns of note. Kuopio is in the richest inland scenic area of Finland and has a match factory and a flour mill, more because it has the raw materials than because of power. Water power is very limited in the Central Lakes Region.

In this region as well as in the plains, the railroads use wood for power fuel, necessitating enormous wood-piles at the stations. Wood is piled in

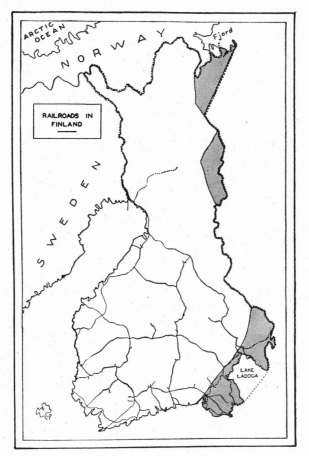

Railroads form a valued net in the southern half of Finland. The most northern branch reaches to the Arctic Circle and is supplemented by automobile service to the Arctic coast. Shaded areas as in other maps of Finland. (Adapted from *Atlas of Finland*)

long cords, seven or nine cords side by side, with a few inches of space between to ensure thorough drying; and with the middle cord highest a roof of sticks is put over the whole pile to keep it dry. In much of the wooded land, the fences are made by placing two posts side by side a few inches apart every 6 to 8 feet along the line, then laying small trees well limbed out and slanting between the pairs of posts, big end down. This makes a formidable barrier, solid and as durable as birch or pine poles.

Upland Region. Finland is nowhere high except in the extreme northwest arm. Occasional hills reach 2,000 feet, and along the Norwegian border several areas exceed 3,500 feet. The Upland Region as a whole presents a very old, grandly rolling surface, rising towards the divide in the mid-eastern boundary, and even higher northwestward, entirely across the country to the tip of the northwestern arm. Probably more than 50 per cent of these uplands have an altitude between 650 and 1,000 feet and a local relief of less than 200 feet, with slopes of less than 1° (25 to 100 feet per mile). Many lakes adorn the topography, except in the higher parts where the surface is divided between moor, peat, and marsh. Cultivable land is limited to 5 per cent, and that is near the streams or lakes. Much of the swamp land carries pine or spruce forest, and the drier areas birch. Although some of it is pastured, as a whole it looks barren and unfruitful.

A station on the auto-post route from Rovaniemi to Petsamo. Chauffeur and tourist alike find rest and food. Shocked oats in the distance. (Author's photograph)

Since 50 to 80 per cent of the land is forested, forest products are the chief values. Nearly all houses in this and the Central Lakes Region are of wood. So great is the fire hazard that at every house a big wooden ladder leans against the wall and two or more buckets of water sit at its foot. The severity of winter calls for double windows, which would be covered with frost if the air between them were not kept dry. Moss, cotton, and even cups of sulphuric acid or of calcium chloride are placed between the sashes to absorb the moisture.

The Upland descends toward the Arctic and becomes a little more hilly, with more real waste land, less timber, and many lakes, of which Inari is the largest. Pasvik Creek has a deep valley, cut through a high-level delta, with some interesting productive plains. Pasvik River after leaving Inari Lake leads through three narrow lakes with beautiful falls between; the boats which traverse the lakes are taken from the water on a truck which rolls on a railroad over the land between the lakes so as to avoid the falls. This stream leads down to tidewater at Boris Gleb (Koltta Köngäs) and to Kirkenes in Norway. This Upland Region is so far north that very moderate hills reach above the timber line; conifers disappear first as one ascends the slope, and the deciduous trees become very scrubby and dejected in appearance. The summit height of 1,300 feet on the auto road, from Rovaniemi northward, is in the zone of timberless heath and marsh.

Grain and root-crop fields and meadows of the Backly Farm. (Courtesy Finnish Consulate General in New York)

Gulf of Bothnia. This region, as large as any of the three land regions, is obviously not a drowned valley but a stream-carved land warped down until the sea covers it. The floor of the Gulf is as truly a peneplain as any of the land about it. Floor slopes are remarkably gentle. The water attains a depth of 700 feet west of the Åland Islands and again near the Swedish side 170 miles farther north, but generally it is less than 300 feet deep. Since continuously fed by fresh-water streams, snow, and rain, and connected with the ocean by only the Belts and Sound of Denmark, all shallow and narrow, the waters of the Gulf vary in saltiness from about one tenth that of sea water in the north to one fifth in the south. Because of inflow of heavy, salty sea water below and outflow of fresher waters at the surface, the bottom is more salty than the surface. Its total salinity is, however, so slight that marine fish do not flock to its waters, and fishing is limited to a number of brackish-water forms and to salmon that go up the streams to spawn.

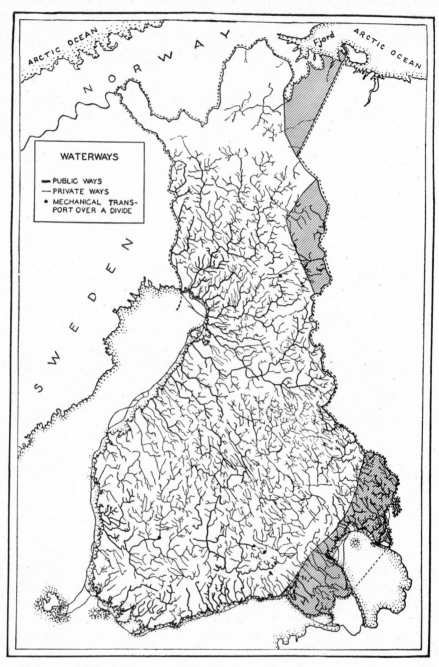

Waterways of Finland. These are used extensively in the open season. Many of these heavy lines pass through lakes. Water routes along the shores connect river highways. Many divides have mechanical facilities for the necessary portage. (Adapted from *Atlas of Finland*)

Because the waters are so fresh, they freeze easily. In a normal winter all harbors are closed by fast ice, frozen to the lands and docks, and the northern basin is completely frozen over. The southern basin is open in the central part in mild winters, but is closed with drift and pack ice in severe winters. All this has disastrous results on commerce and fishing.

Tides are feeble at the entrance of Bothnia, but high and low water, partly due to tides, partly to winds and rate of inflow, differ in the far northern part by about 10 feet. Currents of the surficial circulation flow into the gulf on the east side and out on the west. These, with the differences in level, keep the waters in good condition. The narrow Gulf of Finland shares all these conditions of salinity, freezing, currents, and change of level and is more like the northern than the southern basin. Thus, although the Gulf of Bothnia has excellent harbors at frequent intervals and free communication with the ocean, its entry into commerce is much restricted.

VALUE OF SITUATION

Some advantages and many disadvantages attach to the situation of Finland. Lying between two very different races and nations, it has been influenced by both and marks a transitional zone; but its different racial origin has minimized the impressions, and the waters west, versus land frontier east, have given Finland a western outlook, involving social, political, religious, and even intellectual characteristics.

This land has the distinction of holding the most poleward nation of the earth, although the domains of several others reach a few degrees nearer the pole than Finland. Of no other can it be said that the polar circle cuts it nearly in halves. Nor does any other land find its equatorward boundary so far from the equator. Finland lies between 60° and 70° north, beginning at the latitude of northernmost Labrador and continuing well into the latitude of Baffin Land. Though in high latitude, the climate is tempered by the ocean, but marine influences are minimized by the great Scandinavian barrier. Finland is so low that even with these barriers to marine influences its average temperature is 10° above normal for this latitude. Ice-breakers are able to keep southwestern ports open most of the winters. Inland waters freeze and furnish excellent, level, hard highways; even marsh becomes easily passable. In a lower latitude, glaciation would not have been so severe and agriculture would have fewer encumbrances, but winter sports would be less attractive and forests less important. Perhaps isolation is the most severe penalty placed by situation, and this is mollified by generous water connections.

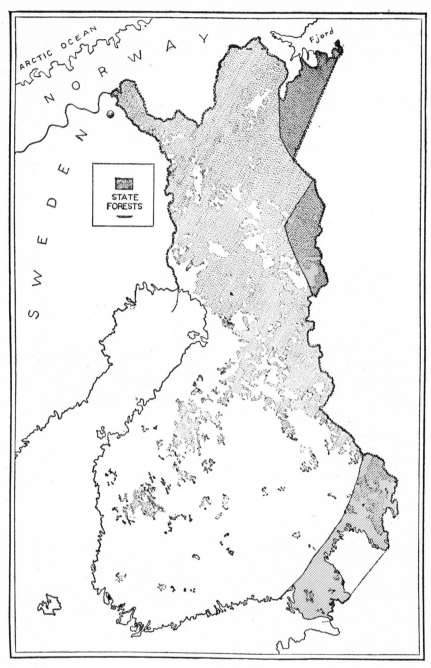

State forests are almost continuous in the northern half of Finland. Many private forests, not shown here, occur in the southern part. (Adapted from *Atlas of Finland*)

AGRICULTURE

With about 60 per cent of the land covered by forest and more than a third covered by marsh, peat bog, tundra, heaths, or moors there is little left for crops; there would be even less were it not for the fact that thousands of acres are marsh or bog, with a good stand of forest growing on them, a part of which is merchantable. Agriculture and pasturage occupy each some 4 to 5 per cent of the land with little chance to extend the acreage. But in spite of scanty, poor, glacial soil, an unpropitious climate, and a short growing season which forbids many fruits and crops, agriculture is the chief bulwark of the country's economic life and is in its several forms the main business of more than half the people. A little wheat is grown in the south,

The Finnish tundra; thick vegetation, 6 or 7 inches high. This is the shrub that bears the golden berry. (Author's photograph)

rye as far north as the Arctic Circle, barley and oats even farther north, though most patches in many summers are cut green or in the milk and dried on trellises for hay. Potatoes, next after rye the most important item in human diet, cannot be planted much before June 1, and are ready to dig in early August. They are grown in all latitudes, as also are turnips, cauliflower, onions, and many flowers, but sugar beets are restricted to the southern plains. In warm weather mushrooms can be picked in any latitude and form an abundant article of food.[4] Hay and pasture are common. Dairying is gaining in importance. Cattle, sheep, hogs, and horses constitute the important livestock, with cattle accounting for about half the total. One

[4] On the seventeenth of September I was invited to a dress dinner in Kirkenes, Norway, on the northern coast. Our meal consisted of three or four wines from France and Spain; carrots, cauliflower, turnips, peas, potatoes, cranberries, all from local gardens; Russian canned black peas, French asparagus tips, coffee, and sugar from afar; but fish, pork, beef, whipped cream, and cake, all local. All guests spoke English though but two present were born to it. Finns and Norwegians numbered nine.

hundred thousand reindeer feed in the Uplands. Coöperative societies flourish where individual effort is a constant struggle.

Wild berries of the heath family are abundant. Blueberries and blackberries, both much like American blueberries, are common. A rather insipid fruit resembling our cranberry in appearance is called a redberry, but the pride of the heath is the golden berry, much like a large huckleberry but yellow. These fruits are all picked from low shrubs a foot or so in height and enter extensively into Finnish diet.

INDUSTRIES

While more people are engaged in agriculture than in all else combined, forestry and forest products produce the largest income. Finland's climate and soils are better adapted to forest than to anything else, and it has a larger percentage of land under forest than any other European country.

A log drive down the Kymi River. Note the boom made of logs chained end to end, set below the floating logs to catch them. (Courtesy Finnish Consulate General in New York)

Manufacturing employs about 17 per cent of the people, and is largely occupied in woodworking, textiles and machine making. The great lumber, paper, and pulp mills are along the inner border of the Marginal Lowlands at the power sites—cutting logs, sawing lumber, making furniture, wooden utensils, and ships, grinding wood-pulp, and making paper, matches, bobbins, pegs, boxes, barrels, and plywoods. Sawmills are in these places and

The paper mill at Äännekoski, about 100 miles west of Kuopio. (Courtesy Finnish Consulate General in New York)

Copper mines and reduction works at Outokumpu, near Lake Ladoga. (Courtesy Finnish Consulate General of New York)

on the coasts where both power and floated logs are available. Tammerfors manufactures cotton, woolen, and linen goods for local markets, makes leather boots and shoes, and assists in the woodworking industries. Helsinki has engineering works and machine-shops, metal-working, printing, baked goods, and modern housing; it is the capital, the business, social, and educational center. Tobacco is imported and most easily processed in the

Weaving a *ryijy* (rug) on a vertical loom. (Courtesy Finnish Consulate General in New York)

coast towns, Jacobstad, Abö, and Helsinki; sugar and syrup works are mostly in coast towns also. Stone-quarrying, lime-kilns, and cement works are found along the sea, where coal for preparing materials and burning cement and lime can be imported and where the finished product can be shipped wholly by water to west European countries.

Mineral resources other than stone are not notable. Gold is found along

Ivalo River in the north; lead, zinc, and copper occur in the crystalline rocks of the southwest and copper in more satisfactory quantities near Outokumpu, in the southeast. Nickel in large quantities is known in the plateau country near the Arctic circle. Good iron is found in the northwest. Pyrite is mined for sulphur to be used in chemical pulp in several scattered eastern places. Not one of these metal products is sufficient for export. Some of the copper and nickel mining is now in territory taken over by U.S.S.R.

COMMERCE

Imports and exports are almost equal in value; but because the exports are so bulky and heavy, vessels depart much better laden than they arrive. All coast towns export sawn lumber and lumber products, about 80 per cent of all exports; and England receives as much as the Netherlands, Belgium, and France combined. Helsinki, Abö, and Vasa import foodstuffs, machinery, and other finished manufactures but export little. Only 4 to 5 per cent of the people engage in commerce.

It is surprising to find such civilization and culture in so high and unpromising a latitude, possessed by a race so meagerly represented in Europe. A large part of their success is due to their native ability and perseverance. They have been favorably situated to receive the stimulus of the West and the help of the Swedes. Their climate, while severe, is as stimulating as their resources are discouraging. Agriculture cannot produce food sufficient for the people; therefore, manufactures must be developed, but care must be taken not to manufacture and sell too rapidly exhaustible resources such as forests, but rather to increase the value of materials in manufacture by use of the great supply of water power and skilled labor. A larger development of industries based on stone and ceramic materials is possible.

QUESTIONS

1. Why is Finland not considered a "buffer state".
2. Discuss the fact that Finland's temperature is 10° above normal for its latitude. Note the causes and effects of this.
3. Finland prints choice books on its own home-made paper. Why? English is taught to all public-school pupils for seven years. Why? Is there any significance in the latter? Why not teach Russian or Swedish?
4. If Finland, with exactly the same relief and dimensions, stood 1,000 miles farther east, what difference might this make with the country's water power? with its agriculture?
5. Finland buys coal from Belgium and England, burns clay and marble (instead of limestone), makes thereby millions of bags of cement at the water's edge, and sells the cement in the Netherlands and Denmark. Discuss this commerce and industry in the light of national conservation and self-sufficiency.
6. Finland exports paper-pulp, paper, and lumber. Is this practice self-destructive? Why?

BIBLIOGRAPHY

Atlas of Finland (Helsinki, Otava Publishing Co., 1925).

BELL, H. M., *Land of Lakes* (Toronto, Ryerson Press, 1950).

BOWMAN, Isaiah, *The New World* (Yonkers-on-Hudson, New York, World Book Company, 1928).

BURNHAM, R. E., *Who Are the Finns?* (London, Faber & Faber, Ltd., 1946).

CLASSEN, Ernest, English ed., *The Northern Countries in World Economy* (Helsinki, Otava Publishing Co., 1937).

COLLINDER, Björn, *The Lapps* (Princeton, Princeton University Press, 1949).

ELLISTON, H. B., *Finland Fights* (Boston, Little, Brown & Company, 1940).

Foreign Commerce Weekly, U. S. Dept. of Commerce (Washington, D. C., Government Printing Office). Began in 1940-41. Look up data under country, commodity or department in weekly contents.

GRÄNÖ, G., *et al.*, *Suomen Maantieteen Käsikirja* (Helsinki, Otava Publishing Co., 1951).

International Trade Office. International Reference Service. Vol. 5. Many papers, Finland No. 65 (Washington, D. C., U. S. Government Printing Office, 1948).

JACKSON, John H., *Finland* (New York, The Macmillan Company, 1940).

KENDREW, W. G., *Climates of the Continents* (Oxford, Clarendon Press, 1942).

KEKONI, Karl, "Ports of Finland," *Economic Geography*, Vol. 8 (July, 1932), pp. 217-244.

LEINISKÄ, I., ed., *Finland Yearbook* (Helsinki, Oy, Tilgmann, Ltd., 1939-1940), others later; not an annual.

MCBRIDE, Robert Medill, MEDILL, Robert (pseud.) *Finland and Its People* (New York, Robert M. McBride & Co., 1925).

MCCALLIEN, W. J., and MCCALLIEN, C., "A Scientific Excursion to Finland," *Scottish Geographical Magazine*, Vol. 48 (March, 1932), pp. 94-98.

Moody's Governments and Municipals (New York), annual.

NORDENSKIÖLD, Erland, "Finland, the Land and the People," *Geographical Review*, Vol. 7 (1919), pp. 361-376.

NUMELIN, Ragnar J., *Some Aspects of the Geography of Finland* (Helsinki, Government Printing Office, 1928).

RUPPERT, Arthur, ed., *Bauern und Helden, ein Finnlandbuch* [Peasantry & Heroes] (Leipzig, Lühe-Verlag, 1944).

RUSSELL, W., "Some Aspects of Modern Finland," *Scottish Geographical Magazine*, Vol. 46 (March, 1930), pp. 90-92.

SCOFIELD, Edna, "Finland's Farm Refugee Problem," *Geographical Review*, Vol. 31 (1941), pp. 148-150.

SEDERHOLM, J. J., *et al.*, *Finland—Country, People, and Institutions* (Helsinki, Otava Publishing Co., 1926).

SHEARMAN, Hugh, *The Adventures of a Small Power* (New York, F. A. Praeger, Inc., Auspices Institute of World Affairs, 1950).

VAN CLEEF, Eugene, *Finland, the Republic Farthest North* (Columbus, Ohio State University Press, 1929).

———, *Finland, the Republic Farthest North* (Columbus, Ohio State University Press, 1929).

WOODS, Mrs. E. G., *The Baltic Region* (New York, E. P. Dutton & Co., Inc., 1932).

VIDAL DE LA BLACHE AND GALLOIS, L., *Géographie Universelle, Finland* (Paris, Lib. Armand Colin, 1933).

CHAPTER 22

Estonia, Latvia, Lithuania

Will you wear my jewels and my yellow amber?—FOLK SONG

Riga, the window of the Baltic.

I'm sowing the rue; the mint and lily I am sowing.—FOLK SONG

Introduction. In 1940 these three ethnic units, Estonia, Latvia, Lithuania, were incorporated into Russia and made political units in the U.S.S.R. without a vote or consultation, although it is reported that before their incorporation they requested Russian protection from the German-Nazi armies occupying their lands, a threat long abated. Their position in the Soviet Union is not recognized by the United States or by a number of other nations. Here they will be discussed in a chapter before the U.S.S.R. is taken up.

The rocks. On opposite sides of the Gulf of Finland the rocks and geology are quite different; on the north are ancient, hard crystallines; on the south, Paleozoic stratified sediments, dipping gently southward so that the oldest emerge in the points of the rocky north coast of Estonia and the younger, ranging in age from Cambrian to Tertiary, outcrop in more than a dozen belts extending east-west across all these countries. So simple are the structure and succession that obviously they have never been much disturbed either by folding or by vulcanism, and therefore little of mineral value has ever been put into them, though several of the beds themselves have value.

Crossing Latvia from Estonia to Lithuania, one everywhere traverses Devonian rocks lying in nearly horizontal layers. These undisturbed sedimentary beds are commonly covered with glacial drift and recent alluvium.

In the simple stratigraphy, limestones, dolomites, gypsum, shales, and more limestones overlie the heavy-bedded sandstones and outcrop here and there from beneath the drift. Beds of old lakes, filled with clay, marl, and sand, furnish materials for brick, tile, cement, and marl dressing for sour soils. Limestones and sandstones are occasionally quarried for building, especially near Riga.

Permian sandstones overlie the Devonian on the Lithuanian border, while in succession in the direction of dip, southward, younger rocks occur, laid down through Jurassic, Cretaceous, and early Tertiary time, the beds

463

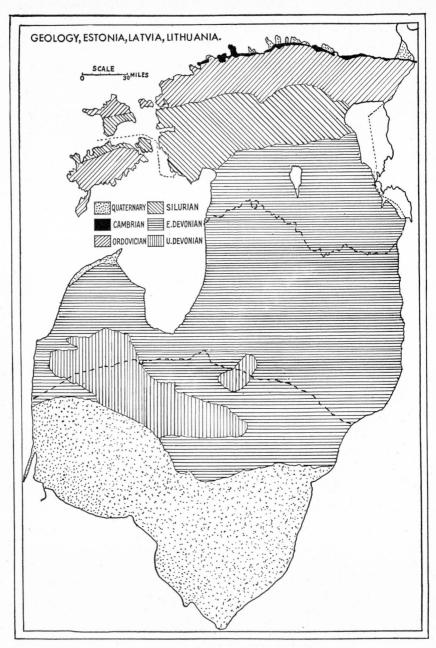

Geologic map of Estonia, Latvia, and Lithuania. See the symbols on the map. Cambrian is the oldest, and outcrops along the northern coast among patches of Quaternary sands and clays, the youngest. Cambrian descends under Ordovician; Ordovician in turn goes under Silurian; and Silurian under Devonian. In the southern part, the drift (Quaternary) is so thick that the older rocks below are unknown. South of Lithuania, Tertiary rocks are known near the surface. (Adapted from government and other maps)

of the latter underlying fully half of Lithuania. Chalk and sandstones alone contribute to the slender mineral resources.

Ice work. Before the first advance of the great continental glacier, streams had reduced the rock topography to old age and nearly to sea level. Two or three successive sheets of ice spread across the country; but, because the land was nearly level and the ice had spent its erosive power farther west, the glacier accomplished very little except to interfere with drainage and cover the rocks imperfectly with waste. In the last withdrawal the ice-front halted so as to build an end moraine, crescentic round Kovno, Lithuania, and just inside the southeast national boundary; the next halt strung a second moraine from near Libau (Liepaja) in Latvia southeast nearly to Kovno and then northeast to the former moraine; the third pause in the recession of the ice was responsible for another crescentic moraine just south of the northern Latvian border from Jonikis to Birzai.

Till plain and moraine north of Kovno. This area supports a horse-breeding farm. (Courtesy Lithuanian Consulate General)

The crescentic moraines marking the margins of two ice lobes, as shown on the map of glacial features, divide Latvia into two basins (east and west), which can also be recognized in Estonia. The lobe areas are separated by interlobate moraine extending from Krustpils to the northwest through the South Livonian Heights, or "beautiful Livonian Switzerland," of Latvia. This moraine topography furnishes the best-drained agricultural land in these states. Outwash deposits outside of them and eskers inside of them furnish gravels and sands of economic significance, much used for road-bed in a land where at times roads become impassable without such cover. The ice ponded streams and caused pro-glacial lakes, one near the Kurisches Haff, another along the Niemen, and four radiating west, north, and east from Kovno. Another lake occupied a broad area round the head of the Gulf of Riga, and still others were in northeast Estonia. Present lake beds are shown on the map of glacial features. Beds of extinct lakes consist of rich clays not yet well drained. The uneven deposition of drift is responsible for many kettles and marshes now filling with rich black soil or peat for fuel. In spite of all these disturbing elements, the land is remarkably level, too level today for the best agriculture. In future generations when drainage has wrought its normal changes, more land will be agriculturally available and all will be better drained.

The interlobate moraine continues northward into Estonia and marks the highest land in the three republics. Depositional glacial features are so significant in the landscape northward across Estonia that this republic can be divided into three physiographic regions on the basis of the dominant glacial features: (1) the Esker Region in the north and northwest; (2) the Drum-

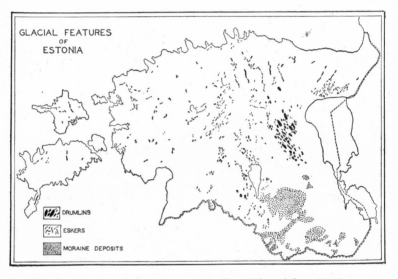

Estonia: glacial features. Moraines, eskers, and drumlins. (Adapted from Estonian government maps)

lin Region from Lake Peipus to the Gulf of Parnu (an arm of the Gulf of Riga) and south to the Latvian frontier; (3) the Moraine Region in the southeast. The highest land is a moraine summit, 1,060 feet, near the southeast boundary; very little of the surface is over 500 feet, and almost every acre except where marshy is usable for forest, grass, or cultivation.

The Northern or Esker Region is a trifle the largest and includes a margin along the Gulf of Finland with very few of the characteristic esker forms. Ice deposits are meager in this margin, and the bed-rock is close to the surface. Glacial till covers the rest of the region. It is strewn with long, narrow gravel ridges, literally hundreds of them, more or less radially disposed as if made beneath two ice lobes, one central in the Lake Peipus basin and one near the west coast, the Gulf of Riga lobe. The large islands in this gulf mouth, Oesel, Dago, and Moon, have the same layers of rock and similar drift cover, eskers, and general relief.

The vegetation of the Esker Region is such as would be called in America the park type; wooded meadows with scattered forest patches among open glades. Farther east, in a strip from the north coast at Loksa to Parnu, there is more of forest and moor with less of farmland. Still farther eastward,

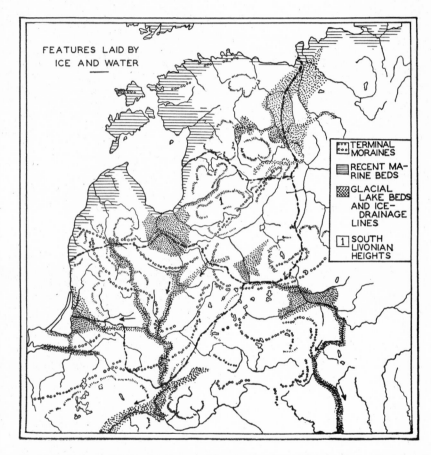

Glacial features of Estonia, Latvia, and Lithuania. Moraines, lakes, marine sediment, and fluvio-glacial valley fillings. National boundaries in dash-dot lines. Arrows indicate direction of glacial water flow. (Adapted from E. G. Wood's *Baltic Region*)

farmland is again more abundant and agriculture prevails. Possibly the underlying rocks help to give expression in feeble east-west ridges, but all are mantled with drift and good soil. The whole eastern half of this Esker Region is well broken by multitudes of eskers giving dry ridges for roads and dwellings and providing a wealth of sand and gravel for road surfaces and building purposes.

No finer display of drumlins is known than these in central Estonia. They are broader than those of central New York and dominate the landscape just as much. They cross the finest agricultural land, and their backs are

Place names in Estonia, Latvia, and Lithuania. (Compiled from Finnish government maps and various other sources)

very systematically divided into farms for all crops that need good drainage on a till soil. River deposition, modified by wind and wave work, has furnished a broad, level area, around Parnu Bay dotted with dunes of sand on the south side.

Although the whole of Estonia is agricultural, this section and the third are preëminently so, raising rye, oats, barley, and a little wheat, the first and last for bread, the others—with potatoes, turnips, and beets—for cattle and sheep food. Potatoes are eaten and also made into starch and alcohol. When winter approaches the root crops are gathered and piled in long windrows in trenches, after which they are covered with straw and then earth until safe from frost. Dairying finds a larger place each year in the rich pastures, while butter for export, meat, bacon, and eggs all come from the dairy farms, where swine and poultry follow the cattle for food. This type of farming puts back on the farms much valuable fertilizer from the stables and restores the strength of the land. Flax also is grown more each year for both the fiber and the linseed oil. When the oil has been pressed from the ground seed, the oilcake makes excellent stock food.

Rural scene in southern Estonia. (Courtesy Consulate General of Estonia)

The zone of greatest glacial deposition occupies the rest of the country and extends the agricultural region. Some of the most beautiful scenery in the land is here, south of Tartu. Lake Worts lies between the Drumlin and Moraine areas, and scores of lesser lakes dot the Moraine country. While possessing as beautiful a mingling of land and water areas as Finland, this region has a decided economic advantage because most of the land is productive.

Stream work. All description suggests the shortness of post-glacial time, a fact confirmed by the counted varves of clay found in successive lake-beds strung along through Lithuania and through Sweden, even to the Norwegian borders. Streams have been unable to carve more than small, youthful valleys through till plain and lake-bed and have rarely cut down to bed-rock. From a general altitude of 600 to 1,000 feet in Lithuania the topography gradually descends westward and northward past the moraine loops of Latvia and drumlins and eskers of Estonia. To the streams and their insufficient performance as well as to the glaciers may be credited the fortunes of agricultural effort. Drainage is still a youthful net instead of a group of more mature dendritic stream systems; yet the waters are hardly sufficient naturally, and certainly not enough under control, to furnish a suitable commercial, rural canal system. Neither have the waterways much power value. The Memel in the south and Daugava (Dvina) in the central part are building deltas in the Baltic Sea and Gulf of Riga respectively from the readily removed loose drift all over the surface of the republics; but surface erosion is rarely a conservation problem. The carving of valleys is rather a benefit because it promotes better drainage of many marshy or wet areas.

The busy harbor of Tallinn, Estonia. (Courtesy Ahlfeld)

Shorelines and harbors. Headlands along the north coast are rocky, usually defended by limestone, and protect several deep bays such as those at Paldiski, Tallinn, Loksa, Kasmu, and Kunda. East of the latter the shoreline is straight and usually cliffed, having no good harbors. The Narva (Narova) River, flowing from Lake Peipus but receiving several tributaries and working with the Luga in Russia, has built a delta into the gulf. The Rosson, a distributary, connects Luga and Narva across the mutual delta. At the mouth of the Narva a harbor is being developed to serve the industrial town of Narva (24,200), situated at the great falls which are able to furnish power enough for nearly all local industry.

The west coast, including the shores of the islands, is generally low, sandy, and marshy, with shallow waters. Haapsalu occupies a rocky point on a bay of the same name. From that town there is considerable trade with the islands, which involves the collection of their dairy products for export. The commodious Parnu Bay is too shallow for the largest boats, but the mouth of the river is used by many lesser ones. Several excellent bathing beaches have been developed between Tallinn and Parnu. Although Peipus Lake, about 100 feet above sea level, is an excellent reservoir for Narva power plants and a fine source of fish, its shores have gentle slopes and its harbors are suitable only for small boats.

Tallinn (formerly Reval) (146,000), a market town with a harbor adequate to make it important in Hanseatic days, has been obliged to deepen its well-protected harbor, and in winter ice-breakers must ordinarily be used; it is a valuable port for Russia and the best in the three republics. Because the Gulf of Finland freezes for four months in the winter, boats can go into it only a little farther than Tallinn, making the Tallinn-Narva-Leningrad railroad doubly important in winter. Baldiski, or Baltic Harbor, a little nearer the open Baltic waters, does not freeze in winter; Parnu on the west coast is well protected, but much dredging and construction are necessary to make it of service. Kunda and Narva serve the north coast; Tallinn and Kunda maintain ship-building. Tallinn's business section now has a cluster of skyscrapers.

About half the shoreline of Latvia is along the great Gulf of Riga. Along the eastern side of the gulf little cliffs and gentle slopes, interspersed with slightly drowned river mouths, used as small harbors, characterize a rather simple, straight coast. Around the head of the gulf the streams, notably the Dvina, have brought in much waste, easily eroded from the drift plains they drain, and have built a delta of sandy marsh-land, lagoons, and sandbars. This delta forces the city to stand back 6 or 7 miles from the coast in a location improved by sandbar islands in midstream. The great sandbar, southwest of the Dvina mouth, possesses the finest bathing beach on the Baltic, one extensively used in summer both by the Letts and by tourists from the south. Low, sandy shorelines with bars and lagoons continue along the west side of the gulf; therefore, no towns of any significance occur beyond the famous Riga beach. Windau occupies the banks of a stream that seems to have but little delta. Libau stands astride a break in a large sandbar, through which a stream enters the sea. Thus Libau has an advantage over Windau, whose harbor is continually shoaled by river sediments. Both are connected by rail with the interior and have advantages over Riga in severe weather.

The 60 miles of shoreline granted to Lithuania is all lowland consisting mostly of drift, lake clays, and other non-resistant materials. The waves and north-flowing currents of the Baltic have thrown up a long sandbar, Kurische Nehrung, extending from near Koenigsberg, now Kaliningrad, Russia, to

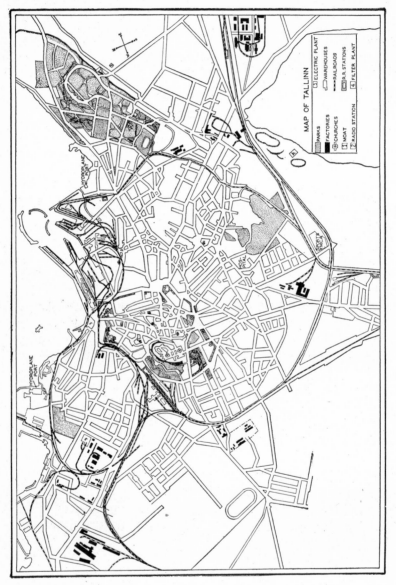

MAP OF TALLINN

ELECTRIC PLANT
WAREHOUSES
RAILROADS
R.R. STATIONS
FILTER PLANT
PARKS
FACTORIES
CHURCHES
MOAT
RADIO STATION

HYDROPLANE PORT

SPORTS MKT.

HOSPITAL

HYDROPLANE PORT

Harbor facilities, railroads, old castle and moat, modern industrial plants. (Adapted from tourist advertising)

Memel and enclosing a broad bay, Kurisches Haff. Such a long, slender bar is peculiar to this part of the Baltic coast. While but partly in Lithuania the Nehrung is commercially connected by steamers and ferries with the mainland and Memel. Its sea margin is a ribbon of clean, snow-white, even-grained, fine sand, patterned with flexible, intricate wave lines and long wind-made ripples, backed by myriads of dunes, free at first and tufted with dwarf broom, salsify, and sea-lavender, but farther back fixed and covered with pine trees.

Into the lagoon flows the Niemen (Memel or Russ) River, the most important stream mouthing on the coast from the Dvina (Riga) to the Vistula (Danzig). It is rapidly filling the north end of the bay; but the chief port is at the open end of the bay opposite the north end of the bar, where silting of harbor is relatively slow. From Memel north there is scarcely a break in the low, straight shoreline, nor has it any economic value.

The Riga Strand in summer. (Courtesy Latvian Consulate General)

Towns and cities. Besides Tallinn, Estonia has Tartu (Dorpat) (67,000) beautifully situated on moraines and along the banks of the Ema. It is a commercial center for surrounding rural and forest interests, supports an excellent university, venerable but modern in equipment and methods, and because of its position has attractive ruins of castle and palaces.

Riga (393,211) was a Hanse town and still preserves fragments of the old wall which guarded a score of tiny blocks surrounded by narrow, crooked streets. The old town borders the stream at a suitable bridge site. Over the old bridge many quaint vehicles, ancient and modern, roll in continuous procession. In old Czarist days Riga was the greatest timber market in the world. The growing city is taking advantage of its many stream channels; and docks, basins, and slips are being constructed among well-planned piers and warehouses. Parks adorn the city in every direction. It is well served by railroads. Its commercial development has been long under way, but will need much more care. In the new Russia it may again become a significant lumber market.

Dvina (43,000), a trifle more than one-tenth as large as Riga, is a significant commercial center, a railroad junction point, a fortified city, and servant to an active rural region. It is so strategic that both Latvia and Lithuania have wanted it. At the junction of three languages it has four names, Dvina, Dvinsk, and Daugavpils, and as a relic of German Knights' occupation, Dunaburg.

Ancient German church ruins in Tartu. Why brick? Part has been restored for the library of the University of Tartu. (Courtesy O. Haidak'i)

Vilno (Wilno) (200,000), the capital of Lithuania since 1942, was the capital in Lithuania's great days before the country was annexed by Russia in 1795. This city is a junction point for railroads from Leningrad and Moscow to Warsaw with Libau connections. It is a market for lumber, cattle, flax, and wool, and the seat of an ancient, well-modernized university.

Kovno (Kaunas) (182,000) has a position commercially strategic at the junction of three streams, one flowing north from Grodno, one west from Wilno, and one south, which unite and flow to the Baltic coast south of Memel. This city must soon become a railroad center as well as a river junction. Kovno is becoming a modern town. Picturesque moraine, covered with trees, almost surrounds the city, and substantial modern residences are constantly rising on these attractive slopes, to which well-built streets are being extended. Few towns could be expected in a land almost exclusively rural like Lithuania, but scores of quaint market villages with their little churches, planted over all the country, meet the needs of the people as religious and barter centers.

Memel (36,000), at once a seaport and a terminus for canal and railroad, has two approaches to its own rural and its foreign hinterland. One railroad leads north, then east through a break in the moraine across good agricultural lands and into Russia; the other leads southeast to Tilsit, thence northeast to Dunaburg and to Russia, both thus bidding not only for national trade in lumber, skins, flax, eggs, and meat but for much additional lumber and forest products from Russia.

Old, narrow street and church, Riga. (Courtesy Latvian Consulate General)

Soils. In general the soils are the products of the weathering of glacial drift, either unmodified or sorted and laid as sands and clays along streams or in lake beds. Many of the latter are now peat beds and as valuable for peat as for soils. Only occasional patches of soil are developed from the exposed rocks below; hence true residual soils are rare. Most of the land consists of plains; some is rolling enough to have sufficient drainage; much of it needs draining; and nearly all needs lime, which is easily prepared from the limestone underlying half the drift area. Phosphate rock is scarce and is imported. Gypsum beds are worked for soil dressings. The well-stocked dairy farms furnish good stable manure for the drift farms.

Resources. Estonia has the richest, most abundant, and most easily worked oil shales known. They outcrop at very low angles for many miles near the north coast, and are stripped and drift-mined and roasted for their oil, tar, and other fuel and chemical products. Limestones and shales are worked near-by for cement, and pulverized oil shale is blown into the kilns for fuel, while the ash (shale) falls to advantage into the cement mixture. Clays and sands are abundant; peat is worked in many places; amber has been a common article of commerce for ages. Phosphorite is quarried northeast of Tallinn and made into fertilizer but is not sufficient for home needs. The forests and forest products enter generously into the foreign trade.

Raftsmen carry much freight on the Nemumas (Memel) River. (Courtesy Lithuanian Consulate General)

Trees are felled in winter, and the logs and lumber are floated downstream on spring floods. The output of dairy products, bacon, and eggs has doubled since the independence in 1918. Fish, especially anchovies, are abundant.

No coal or petroleum is known in any part of the three republics; peat is common; the oil shales yield several oil products. The land is too level and has too scanty rainfall to have much water power. Twenty-five thousand horse power has been developed, mostly at Narva. Windmills are used some; but peat, wood, and imported coal are the mainstays for power.

The real resource is soil and the rural and forest products grown upon it. About one fourth of the land is forested, and twice as much is cultivated. Soils are strong and cultivation easy, thus ensuring an annual crop of grass, stock foods, flax, oats, rye, barley, potatoes, and wheat, in descending order of importance. The greatest activity is agriculture, a close response to topo-

Oil shale strip mines, Kohtla, East Estonia. An overburden of 5 to 6 feet of earth is here removed. (Courtesy Consulate General of Estonia)

Entrance to mines where oil shale lies a few feet deeper than at strip mines. Kohtla Järve. (Courtesy Satrap)

graphic and climatic conditions. Crops are grain and vegetables grown for home use and these crops are being slowly replaced by dairying, a better adjustment and a more profitable occupation.

Industries. Industries are, in the main, such as rest directly on the natural resources in agriculture, forestry, and quarrying and are increasing. Sugar beets yield sugar; flax reduces to linen, linseed oil, and oilcake; the dairies yield butter; forests yield board lumber, wood-pulp, and widely known three-ply plywood. Potatoes are converted into alcohol, starch, and glucose. From oil shale there are derived oil, tar, and the bases for small chemical industries, but the chemical industries are not carried far.

No great industrial development is probable though there will be an increase no doubt in the manufacture of foodstuffs, glass and other ceramics, lumber, and paper-pulp products. As stock-breeding and the dairy industry develop, leather-making and related industries will increase. Industry, as it comes, stands on a firmer basis than if it rested on some exhaustible mineral resource, for crops and forests are continually renewable, and clays, sands, and chalk are inexhaustible.

Transportation, commerce, imports and exports. Position is the key to both the political and the commercial history of the Baltic states, all three of which are between Russia and the sea. Three through lines of broad-gauge railroad lead from the three ports, Riga, Windau, and Libau, back across the country and into Russia. The Dvina, navigable for barges and small power-boats, has been floating nearly a million tons of goods in recent years, one third to one half of which is in transit from Russia. If the Baltic States and Russia make the most of the true geographic opportunities and of their mutual relations, these railroads, rivers, and harbors are sufficient to maintain prosperous commerce between the Baltic, with its external connections, and the great continental interior as a hinterland.

Butter, meats, eggs, and flax products go to Germany and England, but more to Russia. Lumber, woods, wood articles, paper, and pulp from the forests are of about the same value. Potatoes, potato alcohol, and other potato products, cement, plain cotton fabrics, hides, and some wool and flax goods are shipped out. Flax and its products make a valuable money crop. A unique product of Memel is amber, a fossil tree-gum found in beach sands and worked up into various ornaments for the trade by a well-equipped amber factory.

Roads are easily built and maintained. The 4,400 miles of railroad were owned by the states and now by the U.S.S.R. In the north most of them now use shale oil for fuel. This insufficient railroad net is supplemented by a much more extensive net of improved automobile roads and thousands of miles of dirt roads. The rivers Ema, Narva, Parnu, Dvina, and Memel are all navigable for small craft and receive larger Baltic vessels at their mouths. These and many lesser streams, all in youthful post-glacial valleys, transport logs and invite fishing.

A necessary import is cotton, from which the Narva mills make most of the cotton goods needed in the country. Coal, petroleum, and salt are imported. Raw wool, fish, and fertilizers are needed to supplement the home products, and metals, machinery, leather, and chemicals to meet the failure of home industries. At several ports are iron and steel mills using imported coal and iron ores. Other imports are flour, grain, sugar, machinery, and farm implements, the latter stimulated by agrarian reforms and technical rural education.

Lithuanian farmers are fond of ornate porches. Note well-sweep at left. (Courtesy Lithuanian Consulate General)

People. The people are in three small groups corresponding to their nationalities: Estonians (Ests) and Latvians (Letts) long under Russian rule, but with western outlook, and Lithuanians for centuries a strong nation. At times Lithuania spread its authority over a belt of land reaching from the home base on the Baltic to the Black Sea. At other times it was engulfed by Polish rulers who extended their power to the Black Sea. Thus the Lithuanians differed from Ests and Letts in having had extensive experience in self-government. Letts and Lithuanians are considered to be of Indo-European stock, while Ests are Finno-Ugrians in both language and lineage. The three languages are distinct, though those of the Letts and Lithuanians are related to the south and west European tongues.

The Ests were Christianized from the west and 75 to 80 per cent are Lutheran in religion. Because of Russian contacts 15 to 20 per cent belong to the Orthodox Church. Sixty per cent of the Latvians are Lutheran, indoctrinated by Scandinavian teachers, about 20 per cent Roman Catholic, and 20 per cent Orthodox Church. Because of Polish contacts Lithuanians are largely Roman Catholic. All three states were overrun centuries ago by German "missionary" barons (Teutonic Knights), who planted in all three a feudal system that was fostered by the Russians when they were in the ascendancy but opposed by the people when they had their independent national life.

Probably the Estonians are the most distinct of the three and are least mixed with unrelated neighbors. Probably Lithuanians are least distinct for they have spread over Russians and mingled with Poles and Germans for several centuries.

Future. These three groups of people have had enough of western contacts through Danes, Swedes, Germans, and Poles to become troublesome subjects of Russia. The people of all three republics are being deported in large numbers to the depths of the U.S.S.R. in an effort to scatter them and break up their unity.

Typical granary of a Lithuanian farmers' coöperative. (Courtesy Lithuanian Consulate General)

As independent units from 1918 to 1940 the three states were developing industries, such as processing rural products, ceramics, wood-working, and stone-cutting. Their farmers were becoming a land-owning group with mechanized and coöperative farmwork. Universal and higher education were fostered and the western freedoms respected.

Their geographical position on the Baltic makes them a highway between Russia and the western sea ways. Commerce and change of transportation methods at their Baltic ports are necessary for their modern existence. Under Soviet control such commerce offers little benefit to the small states, but the ports are too valuable for Russia to give up their ownership or at least their use.

QUESTIONS

1. Why are the ethnic boundaries so sharp between Russians and the Letts and Ests?

2. What are the opportunities for the development of lime, cement, and other ceramic industries in the three Baltic states?

3. Discuss the geographic implications of the statement that cattle-raising and dairying are increasing at the expense of plow-land; that forests are increasing. Are these changes good conservation?

4. Compare the relative importance of Latvia and the Netherlands. (The latter is only about half as large as Latvia.)

5. From a geographic point of view, should the Baltic States strive to become industrial? Why?

6. It is true that Riga, Tallinn, and Memel were among the great lumber markets of the world. Why? Should they be again?

7. Can you see any particular difference in strength or nationalism, in vision or purpose, when you compare Lithuania, which has had a long active independence, with Latvia and Estonia, countries which never had very much independent experience? Discuss.

8. Why was amber so notable an element in very early Lithuanian commerce? Why was the trade with the Levant and Near East rather than with western Europe?

BIBLIOGRAPHY

BILMANIS, Alfred, *Baltic Essays* (Washington, D. C., Latvian Legation, 1945).

———, *Latvia as an Independent State* (Washington, D. C., Latvian Legation, 1947).

CHASE, Thomas G., *The Story of Lithuania* (New York, Stratford House, 1946).

COON, Carleton Stevens, *The Races of Europe* (New York, The Macmillan Company, 1939).

EICHHOLZ, Alvin C., *The Baltic States, Estonia, Latvia, and Lithuania,* Commerce Trade Information Bulletin 569 (Washington, D. C., Government Printing Office).

EKIS, Ludvigs, *Latvia Economic Resources and Capacities* (Washington, D. C., Latvian Legation, 1943).

Foreign Commerce Year Book (Washington, D. C., Government Printing Office).

HARRISON, E. J., *Lithuania, Past and Present* (New York, Robert M. McBride & Company, 1922).

———, *Lithuania* (London, Hazell, Watson & Viney, 1928).

JACKSON, J. Hampden, *Estonia* (London, George Allen & Unwin, Ltd., 1941).

JURGELA, Constantine R., *History of Lithuanian Nation* (New York, Lithuanian Culture Institute, 1948).

Latvia (Washington, D. C., Latvian Legation, 1942).

Latvia (Washington, D. C., Latvian Legation, 1943).

OLÈNS, Peter Z., *The Teutonic Knights in Latvia* (Riga, Lamey, 1928).

WOODS, Mrs. E. G., *The Baltic Region* (New York, E. P. Dutton & Co., Inc., 1932).

Part V

THE UNION OF SOVIET SOCIALIST REPUBLICS (CONTINENTAL CLIMATE)

CHAPTER 23

Russia: A General Survey

The whole purpose of the plan is to make a nation of conscious workers
out of a nation that was a lump of sodden, driven slaves.—DURANTY

Introduction. Outside the United States no better place exists than Russia in which to study the interaction of region with region. Even though plains predominate, there are as many types of regions as are possible anywhere between polar seas and latitude 40° north. There is tundra desert in the north temperate and Arctic zones; continental interior desert in the south central section, some irrigated, some non-irrigable; there are great coniferous and deciduous forests with rainfall ample to maintain them in their north temperate latitude. These forests spread over plains in the west and over much rougher, mature to mountainous lands in the Caucasus area and southward. There are grain and grass lands of the Ukraine region grading into plains too dry for any fixed grazing in the Caspian Steppe. There are temperate and subtropical fruit lands, cotton-growing areas, and flax lands. There is a wide range in mineral wealth including diversified fuel supplies, and metalliferous and ceramic raw materials. There are seaports on the Pacific, on the Baltic, and on the Arctic shore in northwestern Europe.

This diversity of conditions and resources plus diversity of race, peoples, and language has all been incorporated under one government. The elaborate five-year economic plans and other movements have done much to unite these unlike areas and interests with one great national purpose. Forest products from northern and Caucasus forest are shipped to wheat lands; dairy products to forest areas and tundras; golden berry preserves to general agricultural lands; coal to iron-producing regions, and iron and copper to coal regions; petroleum to industrial and residential cities; sugar from the beet soils and farms in Ukraine to all the rest of the country; and the consumer goods from industrial cities to all the republics of the Union.

Such an exchange of products is an excellent response to the geographic situation. The five-year plans have endeavored to plant industries where they could flourish, wheat and collective farms where they best produce, and highways where they could best serve in the transfer of commodities from producing areas to the consuming populations. It is one of the ele-

485

ments of the Soviet strength that this interdependence has been recognized and fostered.

The federated socialist republics of the Russian Soviet constitute in theory probably the best current illustration of this sort of working interdependence. According to its constitution it is a voluntary union, and member republics, except the Russian S.F.S.R., can withdraw at their pleasure.

When it comes to trade relations between the Soviet Nation and other nations, the problem is somewhat different from that between regions or republics within the Union. There are no innate difficulties in the way of pleasant relations and large movement of goods to and from U.S.S.R. The scare raised a few years ago of "dumping" and "discrimination" has never risen to a reality. Some barriers to trade, such as tariffs and favored nation clauses, are raised by foreign nations but these are no more serious than between any other two nations. The real problem relates to the fact that trade must be between individuals and firms in other countries and the government itself of Russia and its representatives. The trade of Russia is all in the hands of the government through the People's Commissariat of Foreign Trade for both buying and selling. This Commissariat maintains Trade Delegations in the fifteen or more countries with whom most of the trade is carried on. Foreign companies and individuals trade with this Commissariat and not with Russian companies or individuals. This constitutes a real difference in the mechanics of trade with Russia, but it has worked for 25 years and when understood it is not a serious barrier.

Area and population. The U.S.S.R. (Union of Soviet Socialist Republics) comprises 8,473,444 square miles and stretches across two continents, from the Baltic Sea eastward across Asia to the Pacific Ocean. European parts of the Soviet Union occupy about 1,800,000 square miles and contain 133,000,000 people (estimate) considering natural increase, war losses, and additions of people annexed during and since World War II. This European part is a gently rolling to level, low plain with the old Ural Mountains bordering but not barricading about half of the east side and the young, rugged Caucasus stoutly defending half of the south side; yet the authority of the Union has spilled through, over, and around the Caucasus to include in modern Russia Transcaucasia, an area south of the Caucasus as large as the Caucasus. The expanse of European Russia is roughly a rectangular area about twice as long north and south as it is wide, containing nearly one half the land of Europe and more nearly one fourth of the people.

Present frontiers. Of all the Russian frontiers the Arctic Ocean is probably the most formidable. Alexandrovsk on Kola Bay is never frozen, but the mouth of the White Sea is closed by ice nearly nine months, and eastward the Sea is seldom open. The broad Pechora mud delta with shifting distributaries has been artificially improved and renders valuable service a few months of the year. The Urals as relief features have little barrier value, but as they receive more snow in the north and hold it longer than the plains on either side, they are difficult to cross in winter. More than two centuries ago, when the development of Siberian Russia was beginning, Russia had ceased to use these mountains as boundaries.

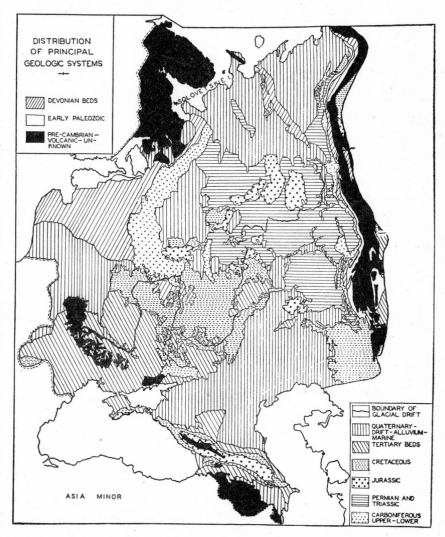

DISTRIBUTION
OF PRINCIPAL
GEOLOGIC SYSTEMS

DEVONIAN BEDS

EARLY PALEOZOIC

PRE-CAMBRIAN—
VOLCANIC—UN-
KNOWN

SOLOVETSKIE I.

ASIA   MINOR

BOUNDARY OF
GLACIAL DRIFT

QUATERNARY—
DRIFT—ALLUVIUM—
MARINE
TERTIARY BEDS

CRETACEOUS

JURASSIC

PERMIAN AND
TRIASSIC

CARBONIFEROUS
UPPER—LOWER

Geologic map of the U.S.S.R., European part. (Adapted from an atlas issued by the Geodetic Committee of the U.S.S.R., 1929-1931)

South of the Urals, gently rolling topography and plains spread to the Caspian and Aral seas. The Caspian has been a passable highway for many centuries. Although the shallow, brackish north is closed by ice for two months, the deep, salty south part is always open, and regular steamer routes cross it. The southern shores are steep and rugged but have harbors. Since it lies between deserts and mountains, there is little need for commerce on the Caspian, and it makes a good boundary.

The Black Sea, except in its northern, less salty, shallow embayments, is navigable all the year and serves as an excellent commercial highway and a friendly boundary. Its outlet through the Bosporus gathers many lesser routes, such as those from Odessa, Kherson, Sevastopol, Rostov, Novorossiisk, and Batum, across the border to the outside world. Rocky headlands on the Crimea and the northeast coast afford sites for defense, few of which have been fortified. Lesser promontories at the gate of the Azov and near Odessa have been occupied. All in all, the Black Sea is a good boundary both for commerce and for defense, and Russia has long coveted complete control of it and of its outlet. Greek traders colonized several harbors of the Black Sea. In pre-Christian centuries pirates sallied forth from the Caucasus coast, where ship-building timber was accessible and seclusion was free, to rob both on the Black Sea and on the Mediterranean, and to raid adjacent lands. Other corsairs recognized the value of the Dardanelles and Bosporus not only as a trade route but as a choice location to prey upon trade. Even the Dniester furnished Scythian buccaneers who ravaged the shores and commerce of the Ægean.

The western boundary, as laid by Russia and her treaties, starting at the northern Danube distributary follows up the Pruth River beyond Cernauti, leaves the river, jumps twice across the Carpathians to bring the Ruthenian tip of former Czechoslovakia into Russia, then proceeds across plains between U.S.S.R. and Poland to the Baltic just west of the old Prussian city of Koenigsburg, and follows the sea north until it becomes a land line over hills and among lakes between Finland and U.S.S.R. to Norway and the Arctic Ocean. This western frontier nowhere has any real defense barrier value. Much of the way it is an ethnic line, as against Rumania and Poland, but less satisfactory against Hungary. For many miles it is drawn for Russian security reasons, as along the Finnish frontier, where large blocks of Finns and Karelians are unhappily on the Russian side of the line.

Taken all in all, the frontiers have been wisely chosen. In the Caucasus and Transcaucasian regions forty nationalities and peoples with many non-Slavic languages were included in Russia; they are small groups which would have been troublesome outside a large state and are probably better off in Russia than in Turkey or Persia. They think so, at least. But the prime reasons for including these lands in Russia were probably not so much the choices of the occupants, as the facts that Russia had included them for several generations and that Russia much needed the mineral wealth of the region, particularly its oil and manganese. Rich supplies of timber in the mountains near sections wholly timberless are another advantage of the present southern boundary. The nature of the boundaries and the necessity, imposed by situation, of trade with and through neighboring states have called for treaties of non-aggression and peace with at least ten nations. Trade agreements have been framed with a score of nations. All border nations of European Russia can be reached easily by water.

Rivers. The large unity of plain is augmented by a radial river system. Out from the Valdai Hills to the Gulf of Finland flows the Lovat-Volkov-Svir-Neva river system draining several of the larger lakes. The Dvina flows west to the Gulf of Riga. The Dnieper and Don gather south-flowing waters and deliver them to the two embayments of the Black Sea. The mighty Volga sends three great branches into the Valdai Hills and leads the waters from the east slopes to the Caspian Sea. So low are the divides at the heads of these rivers that canals have been constructed to connect the Volga through Lakes Ladoga and Onega with the Baltic and through the Northern Dvina with the White Sea; a new, more direct, large canal connects the Baltic with the White Sea at Soroka. A canal connects the Sukhona branch of the Northern Dvina through small lakes, Yoga River, and other streams with Sheksna River to serve Moscow and to connect the capital city with Baltic and White seas. The Dnieper has canal connections near its sources with the southern Dvina, the Niemen, and the Vistula. Thus freight can go by a 6-foot waterway from White Sea or Baltic to Caspian or Black. Canal building and river canalization greatly augment river navigation. Large investments have been made in recent years to improve rivers, mechanize river harbors, and build wharves, docks, warehouses, grain elevators, river craft, and shipyards. About 3,500 river ports were recognized in old Russia, and many new ones are now constructed every year. River steamers bear over 50 million tons of freight in a year. No wonder railroad construction has gone slowly in a land where overnight deliveries are not demanded. The commercial value of rivers is enhanced by the very low grade of the streams, their slow flow, great length, and arrangement; but it is restricted by the shallowness of water at all seasons due to scanty rainfall of the regions through which they flow, by the decrease in size of the Volga, Ural, and Don as they flow into dryer regions, and by the long closed season in winter.

The extremely low grades of Russian rivers and their correspondingly slow flow mean shallow valleys, marshes, and miserable drainage over thousands of square miles, with floods in snow-melting and rainy seasons. This leaves the land temporarily unfit for agriculture and modifies the type of natural vegetation. Trees in such places are water-loving sorts, tamarack, willows, and others which are not drowned by excess. In spite of these difficulties the rivers serve the people generously. The northern Dvina system has over 300 docks for its boats. The Dnieper has over 500 and the Volga over 800. The number is increasing all the time because of dredging, canalizing of rivers, and harbor improvements.

Many elements of the climate have been described in the general chapter on climate. Suffice it to say here that the climate is severe enough to freeze the streams for many weeks of the year until, since they are so level, sledding is quite as possible on them when frozen as boating is when thawed. The snow cover over large portions of the plain makes winter travel even easier than spring and late fall travel, when the roads are often muddy, or summer and early autumn travel, when they are choked with clouds of dust.

Natural vegetation. The natural vegetation presents far more diversity than does topography, rainfall, or temperature. It responds to both temperature and precipitation. Coniferous forests grow in the north, where, although rainfall is not great, the temperatures are never high enough to cause great evaporation and low humidity. The mixed coniferous and hardwood forests occur south of the coniferous belt in a wedge-shaped area, narrowing eastward because the decrease of temperature eastward spreads the coniferous forests farther south and because a similar decrease of precipitation eastward makes the conditions difficult for any kind of trees. The grasslands thus expand eastward and pinch out the hardwood forest belt between the widening coniferous and grassland areas. Grasslands occupy a belt, narrow north of Odessa but widening rapidly to the meridian of Stalingrad (44° to 45° E.). Here precipitation becomes so light that even the quick-growing grasses have trouble; and around the Caspian in a crescentic belt 100 to 250 miles wide swings a semi-arid to desert area more than half below sea level, nearly all very level and covered with recent sea and alluvial deposits. The Caucasus and Transcaucasian states carry 25 to 50 per cent hardwood forests with a great variety of other vegetation, including conifers, grass, and mountain-top tundra. The Urals have mountain-top flora also. This clings lower and lower on the slopes northward until it merges into a broad tundra belt along the Arctic, which narrows westward as the moderating influence of the Atlantic on the climate becomes more effective.

Natural vegetation has been modified by man; in the prairie or grasslands, the grass has been replaced by wheat, rye, and lesser cereal crops; the mixed coniferous-hardwood forest has been cleared in great patches to make room for a variety of northern crops, pasture, cities, and industrial shops. The influence of natural vegetation is strongly reflected in many of the geographic regions described below.

History of growth and expansion. Many Slavic tribes in the early centuries of the Christian Era occupied the central part of what is now European Russia. The earliest major federation of tribes was in the north, where the Novgorodians began to coalesce for purposes of defense. The founders of the city of Novgorod, built in the fifth century on the site of an earlier city, selected its site, for its strategic significance, on the banks of the Volkhov, 2 or 3 miles below Lake Ilmen. Here grew up a fortress with wooden, turreted walls, a fishing town, and a commercial center in the great coniferous forest. These northern tribes were distinctly the "Forest Folk," for they resided along streams and lakes of the western forested plains.

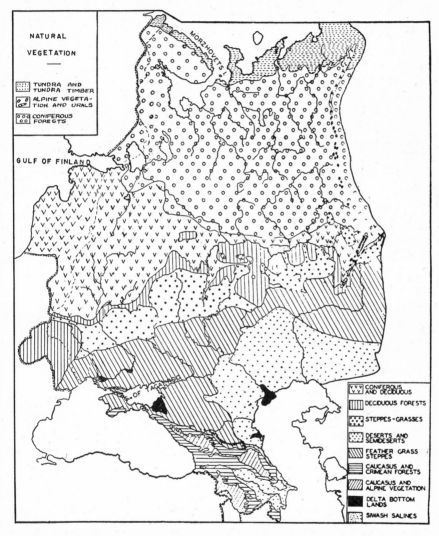

The natural vegetation of European Russia seems to be closely related to climate and to determine in part soils and land utilizations. (Adapted from atlas issued by Geodetic Committee of the U.S.S.R., 1929-1931)

South of the Novgorodians other tribes developed a national conscious-ness or solidarity, but it was not until the tenth or eleventh century that they could first be called even the Muscovite Kingdom. They built on the river bank among the deciduous forests the early wooden stockade, which later became the inner stone wall and defense, the Kreml (Kremlin) or keep of Moscow. These tribes also were "Forest Folk." Farther south the "Field Folk," who occupied great open spaces in sparse timber areas, began to coalesce by the fifth century and built Kiev on the Dnieper in A.D. 430. It is probable that Scandinavian influence was important in both the organization and the building of the commercial towns in the north and in the south; but the Muscovites, in the center, federating a little later, seem to have acted on their own initiative, perhaps under foreign aggressive pressure.

Three lines of foreign influence of enduring significance reached these tribes in their early development. In the ninth century Nordic conquerors overran many of them and gave them an example of military activity and organization which they have never discarded. Predatory expeditions carried on in this new spirit took the Russians to Byzantine lands, and they were persuaded to adopt the Orthodox Church form of Christianity—more formal and less helpful than the Western or Roman form. Four hundred years after the Nordic contacts were given them and 300 years after they had fallen under the religious sway of the Mediterranean race a crushing invasion came across the open Caspian plains from Asia, that of the Tatar nomadic hordes. These people depressed rather than elevated the Russians, taught them nothing of value comparable with the military and religious civilizing elements received from the west and the south. Out of these ingredients poured into the Russian mold in the Russian environment grew the early Russian spirit and civilization. One wonders what there might have been had the Roman Catholic and Reformation religions permeated the Slavs; and Tatar and later Turkish influence been missing.

While these central lands and tribal groupings lay close together, with free intercommunication as possible as in modern times, their people did not combine at once. Although these lands were also open to plains on the west and southwest, occupied by other tribes, language groups, and nations, there was little intercourse with them. Russians kept their faces eastward.

In the closing decade of the twelfth century the Russian kingdom reached from the Carpathians to the Arctic Sea. The Novgorod confederation of earlier times had completely collapsed, and its people, Slavs, were being absorbed by the Muscovites. Lapps and Finns, who in previous centuries had become segregated in lands to the north, were moving westward to their present homes—evidence that the topography was no barrier. A Tatar kingdom lay across the southeastern plains.

By this time expansion had become a conscious habit. It was motivated by strong desires for an open port, for diversity of topography, and for a larger range and quantity of resources, but not for political power nor for control of other people. Rarely has so geographic an urge accomplished so much.

Between 1690 and 1740, under Peter the Great, Russia's expansion was more rapid. During these years the St. Petersburg area was acquired and the new capital was founded on the gulf. Finland had already been incorporated; Estonia, Latvia, Lithuania, and the territory of the Don Cossacks had also been absorbed. Early in the last century the Crimean state yielded, and some Transcaucasian states were gathered in. The plains people were conquering the mountain tribes. Thus a group of Slavic tribes in 1,300 years had spread, absorbed, consolidated, unified, and interbred until a rather homogeneous race occupied most of the great Russian plains. The incorporation of border states of diverse peoples on the Baltic, in Crimea, and in and beyond the Caucasus was accomplished in order to have commercial seacoast and available mountain resources. But no such amalgamation as had occurred in the plains could take place with this fringe of nations. Geographic conditions were quite opposed to it. Independent mountain people mix very slowly among themselves as well as with outsiders. West-facing peoples on the Baltic were never Russianized, although many means were used to this end, especially in Finland.

The Urals were no barrier to Russian expansion eastward into Siberia, as the last 400 years have demonstrated. Nor were the plains between the southern Urals and the Caspian Sea a barrier to frequent invasion from Asia. Nomadic tribes came in more easily than settled peoples went out over these steppe grazing lands. Russia has thus always had to bear the brunt of defense against Asiatic hordes who would overrun Europe. Tatar and Turk, Avar and Hungarian have all come in at this gate, though the great Turkish expansion came south of the Caspian and Black seas.

South and West European peoples had made so much progress and were so well set in their lands with their faces westward before the Russian tribes were ready to expand and to become nations and kingdoms, that the Slavs could make little headway against them, even though there were no physical barriers to overcome. Slavs early crowded into Bohemia and Poland and, with their western contacts there, far surpassed their Russian relatives, so much so that they were long ago called Western Slavs in distinction from Eastern and Southern Slavs. When the great church line was drawn, both West Slav peoples, although Christianized in part from Byzantium, became Western or Roman Catholics; the Russians and South Slavs, having received their Christianity wholly from the eastern nations, became Orthodox Church or Greek Catholics. Eastern Slavs have been inhospitable to westernizing influence, and have preferred Asiatic contacts and ways, to which they have always been exposed. Thus Western Slavs have been buffers between West Europe and Russia.

Russia's war and revolution losses. During the Russian revolution in 1917 Finland declared its independence, and as World War I closed Poland demanded and was granted its independence. The Finns had long associated with Swedes more than with Russians and had learned western ways.

Many Swedes live in Finland. Poland, though Slavic, had been under western governments in large part for over 100 years or since its partition in the late eighteenth century. Polish independence cost Russia an area of about 75,000 square miles containing many Russians as well as Poles. This area came back into Russia at the close of World War II, partly into White Russia, partly into Ukraine.

The Ukrainians in the south have often wanted to become independent, but because of position, affinities in language and race, and because of Russia's great need of Ukraine agriculture, the Ukraine is still in Russia. Georgia was kept in the Soviet Union only by force of arms. Georgia is one of the larger mountain states whose ideas of freedom were mountain-born, primitive, and individualistic. Now from this mountain group has come the master of all Russia—Stalin.

The people. Compared with the other half of the continent, the population of Russia in Europe has a remarkably simple distribution and composition, a small number of languages, and homogeneous social habits and culture. If the Caucasus states be omitted, the comparison is even more striking.

As the upheaval of almost every occupation subsided after the revolution of 1917, 80 per cent of the people were rural, but during the operation of the five-year plans farm work was mechanized and otherwise organized requiring fewer workers to till increased acreage with larger production; and industry increased drawing more and more people into the towns and cities. Thus when the Second World War came to Russia, less than 45 per cent of the people were in rural occupations including planters, grazers, fruit and fibre growers and nomadic groups. No reliable figures seem to be available for European Russia alone, but it is probable that the rural percentage is still declining. Larger numbers are continually drawn into industry, transportation, lumbering, building, education, and other professions.

Russians (Great Russians) cover about three fourths of the country, or nearly all the area between latitude 51° and 62° N., and include half of the European U.S.S.R. population. White Russians [1] occupy a forest and agricultural district on the Polish border between the Western Dvina and the Pripet marshes, and number some 10 millions. Ukrainians, mostly in the southwest, number nearly 40 millions, and occupy the best rural lands of the country—the blackearth plains. All three speak similar dialects of the Russian language. The typical Russian is an Alpine, short of stature, brachycephalic, roundfaced; has a short nose with low bridge, eyes brown or blue, rarely black, chin not pronounced, lower jaw heavy and more massive than the usual Alpine type, hair brown to fair, stiff but not coarse or straight. The White Russian, as the name suggests, is fairer, also a little taller, than the Great Russian; whereas the Ukrainian, having mingled much

---

[1] White Russians are so called because of their fairer complexion and have no relationship with the Czarist exile group.

with the neighboring types, departs farthest among the Slavs from the Great Russian. He is darker, a little shorter, not as broad-headed, and often partakes of Asiatic characters. Probably his darker skin is due to his more sunny location and to admixtures of Mediterranean and Mongolian blood.

In the northeast Volga plains and the borders of the coniferous forests between Perm and Gorki there are patches and sprinklings of Finns, remnants of the Finnish tribes that occupied most of northern Europe in early Christian centuries. In Karelia Finnish people predominate. These Karelians are more Russianized than the Finns of Finland, because closer to Russian authority, and they generally speak Russian. A similar group also occupies areas around Leningrad. There are Lapps in the Kola Peninsula as in Finland and Scandinavia. Other sections of the Finno-Ugrian family are the Permian branch (Zyryans, Permyak, Votyak), numbering 900,000 in the Pechora and upper Kama river basins and between the Vyatka and Kama rivers. These show their Oriental racial connections and culture even more than the former branches, probably because not so far or so anciently removed and because less mixed with Russian blood. The Volga branch contains the Cheremise and Mordva (linguistic) and ethnic groups in the Volga plains (Oka River to Ural Mountains) and numbers 1,770,000 people. Like the northern branches these are more or less nomadic cattleraisers, but many of them have settled into a crude agricultural practice under the stimulus of the plains and the pressure of adjacent Russians. A few Voguls and Ostyaks reside in the valleys of the Urals and live by nomadic grazing and by fishing. About 5,000 of these are on the European side of the mountains and three times as many on the Asiatic side. Samoyed peoples, only a few thousands, roam over the tundras from the White Sea eastward, caring for their reindeer or fishing from streams and embayments of the sea.

The Altai, or Turanian, family migrated into southern Russia, and now tribes and groups of them occupy alone or with Russians many areas in the Volga Basin, Crimea, and Caucasus; in the latter they are mingled with the Caucasians. Some authors call them Tatar-Turks. The largest, best-defined Turanian unit is that of the Bashkirs in the Ufa plains and the foothills of the southern Urals. They number about 700,000 and are engaged in agriculture and grazing, in part nomadic. The Nogays west of the lower Volga, miserable nomadic grazers (36,000), the Kumyks of Northern Daghestan (50,000), Tatars and Karaites of Crimea (123,000), Azerbaijan Turks in Azerbaijan (1,000,000 or more), and other Tatars known locally as Tats on the south coast of Crimea (60,000) all belong in this Turanian or Turkic sub-family in southeast Russia. Considerable numbers of Kirghiz care for their wandering herds on the dry, salt plains along both sides of the Ural and Volga rivers and have little competition. They probably cover more acres than all the other Turanians, but less effectively and completely. All these tribes are related by language, Turkic or Turanian, and by racial ties, Mongolian, though many of them are far from pure stocks.

The Kalmuks spread over a large section of the steppe plains south of Stalingrad. They are true Mongols with a Mongol dialect, who arrived in the Volga plains 300 to 400 years ago. After 100 to 200 years many wandered back to Sungaria, leaving wretched remnants to roam about among a more sedentary, capable population of more remote Asiatic origin.

Germans came generations ago on invitation of the Russians to promote trade and industry. The largest group of Germans (about 450,000) occupied an area in the Saratov region but they have been mostly deported and are scattered in far Siberia north of the Amur River. Swedes, Letts, Lithuanians, and more numerous Rumanians are scattered or grouped in the western and southern parts. The last-named people actually predominate in four areas north of Odessa. Greeks (200,000) scattered along the Black Sea coasts prevail in three areas north of Azov Sea. Poles (1 million) were scattered among the Ukrainians and White Russians before the recent treaties were written, and some have migrated into Poland.

In the Caucasus and Transcaucasia, besides the Mongoloid groups already mentioned, may be found a number of entities speaking Indo-European tongues who are neither Slavs nor Tatars. They are called Japhetics, Caucasians, and, in part, Iranians. If the name "Caucasian" be restricted to people speaking Indo-European languages and belonging to these Caucasian tribes, that would be the best name for them all. Georgians (1,800,000) are the largest group today, living in west Transcaucasia and engaged in general and pastoral agriculture. The second largest group are the Armenians (1,500,000), a simple Christian folk in villages and on farms. A third group are the Ossetti (260,000), engaged in pastoral agriculture on valley slopes of the south side of the Caucasus. Kurds and Persians also dwell in villages and on farms in these valleys. Two small groups yet remain. For many years Jews have enjoyed sanctuary in Russia. As the Germans advanced in World War II, a million or more were removed to an area of safety in a Jewish state already well established. This is situated in a large curve of the Amur River in and around the modern city of Birobijan. The relatively few Gipsies (61,000) wander freely from place to place, parasitic nomads.

History of peoples. There seems little doubt now that the Muscovites were Alpine tribes, broad-headed, dark-complexioned, who had come out of Asia, probably because of climatic pressure (desiccation), along the south Caspian-Black Sea-Asia Minor route into the central European mountains. After centuries of evolution there they were squeezed out by the expansion of the Nordics, possibly of the Mediterraneans also, and moved nomadically from the mountains eastward to the Polish Galician plateaus, and then to the south of the Pripet marshes (more of a barrier than were the Carpathians) into the highest lands of the Russian plains southwest of

Moscow, then to the Valdai Hills and the Moscow region. Some believe another stream of these people wandered from the mountains down the Elbe and Vistula and joined their fellows by going north of the marshes. Those coming by the northern route preceded the Muscovites and became the Novgorods, who were already a federation of tribes before the Muscovites began to organize. The Novgorodians reached out for commerce and for the furs of forest animals. The Muscovites, in more open country and a more temperate climate, were military and agricultural. These virile people, centrally located on a boundless plain, became the nucleus and power of the Russian race, nation, and culture.

Ukrainians are a fringe of Muscovites, augmented by later Alpine dribbles and admixtures of Mediterranean stock. They do not differ notably from the Great Russians, but speak a different Russian dialect and because of contacts and more frequent Western infusions are more progressive, westward-looking, and independent.

By the time the Muscovites were leaving their mountain homes for the plains, Finnish tribes, more recently from Asia, were occupying the upper and middle Kama and Vyatka river plains during their slow, trickling movement to northern Russia, Karelia, and Finland. They were associated with the Cheremisses and Votyaks, who remained in the less attractive eastern forests. The coming of the Muscovites stimulated the Finno-Ugrian tribes to move more rapidly to their future (present) homes.

Finno-Ugrians, as was stated before, have made their way westward from Asia for thousands of years, not as persistently or abundantly as Russians have invaded Asia but sufficiently to account for the pagan tribes known in northern and northeastern Russia. Other Asiatics, Turko-Tatars, have for many centuries entered southeast Russia from Asia. Sarmatians, Scythians, and Huns have made their homes here; and out of a residue from the Huns probably descended the Bulgarians, who were divided and expelled by the Khazars in the seventh century. A part of the Bulgars were thus driven north to settle and blend with Slavs in the Kama Valley; the other portion migrated toward the Danube and, likewise mingled with Slavic blood, became later the founders of the Bulgar nation. When southeastern Europe was overrun by the Turks, these southern parts of Russia received their share of Turkish blood and became Mohammedan, which religion they retained; but they forcibly expelled the invaders, so that only remnants remain.

The mountain tribes and nations in the Caucasus seem to merit the name "Caucasians proper." They are not fundamentally Slavs, Tatars, or Semites. They represent tribes and peoples forced to the protection and isolation of mountain fastnesses many centuries ago. The study of their ethnology, religion, and culture, even of their languages, has not gone far. The languages seem to be Iranian. One guess is as good as another, but it is reasonable to believe the people are Indo-Iranians, who have retained tribal peculiarities through the centuries because of mountain isolation and have only recently been exposed to external, progressive, expanding influences.

International and Siberian relations. Siberia [2] never has held quite the same relation to Russia in Europe that a colony, protectorate, or dependency holds to France or England. The Russians have simply overflowed into contiguous territory for many generations, into territory that no people in comparable culture or civilization were occupying.

For many years Siberia was best known as a penal region for political and other offenders; hence it became settled with many of Russia's brainiest and most thoughtful, aggressive, and resourceful leaders. It is no wonder that rapid and long steps have been taken in Siberia toward developing the country. Later Siberia was appropriated as a part of the Russian expansion program. The trans-Siberian railroad gave a great impetus to all forward-looking movements; and the territory, when really crossed, gave to Russia the three geographic advantages she long had sought—an open, free, ocean port, mineral resources, and diversity of topography.

And so it comes about that one cannot and should not think Russia without thinking Asiatic as well as European Russia. This has become strikingly more true in recent years as the Union of Soviet Socialist Republics has come into being. That Union consists of sixteen republics.

1. Russian Socialist Federated Soviet Republic.
2. Ukrainian Soviet Socialist Republic.
3. Byelorussian or White Russian S.S.R.
4. Armenian S.S.R.
5. Georgian S.S.R.
6. Azerbaijan S.S.R.
7. Karelo-Finnish S.S.R.
8. Estonian S.S.R.
9. Latvian S.S.R.
10. Lithuanian S.S.R.
11. Moldavian S.S.R.
12. Uzbek S.S.R.
13. Turkmen S.S.R.
14. Tadjikistan S.S.R.
15. Kazakh S.S.R.
16. Kirghiz S.S.R.

The first-named republic differs from all the rest in that it is a federation of many lesser political units and is the only one which may not separate itself from the U.S.S.R. It contains nearly 70 per cent of the total population and about 78 per cent of the area. Bordered on the west by the Gulf of Finland, Finland and Karelo-Finnish and other Republics to Ukraine, and on the south by Georgia and Azerbaijan in the Caucasus, it stretches to Bering Strait and the Pacific. On the south it touches Kazakh, Mongolia, Man-

[2] Siberia here connotes Asiatic Russia and not the group of provinces sometimes called the Siberian area.

churia, and Korea; on the north it reaches the Arctic Ocean for 159° of longitude. Less than 25 per cent of it is in Europe.

The second and third republics are large; occupy portions of the European plains and have large, active populations. The fourth, fifth, and sixth

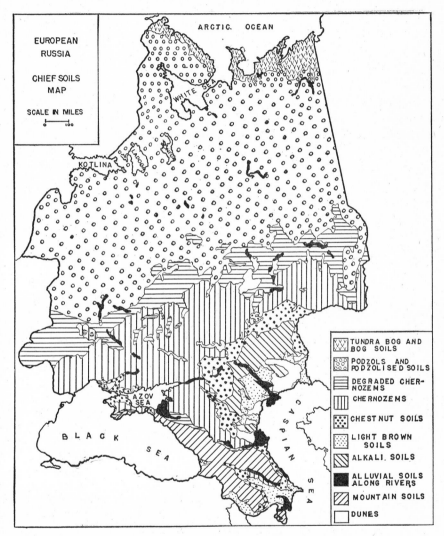

Soil types of European Russia, somewhat generalized. (Adapted from atlas issued by Geodetic Committee of the U.S.S.R., 1929-1931)

are small and diverse, and lie in and south of the Caucasus. The seventh was set up after the recent war with Finland to include the fragments of Finland acquired at that time and the Karelians (related to the Finns) who reside east of Finland. Numbers 8, 9, 10 correspond with the three Baltic states for many years parts of Russia, but independent states after the treaties of World War I. The eleventh is a province obtained from Rumania after World War II. The other five are wholly in Asia along the southern highland border of U.S.S.R.

The census of 1939, the last made public, reveals that Great Russians constitute about 58 per cent, Ukrainians over 16 per cent, and White Russians, 3 per cent of the population. This census recognized 49 nationalities incorporated into the population and nearly 2 million persons from other national groups residing in the Union. The list of republics makes clear that the government has recognized many ethnic or language groups in setting up its subdivisions. Each of the eleven in Europe stands for at least one language or dialect, several of them comprise two or more. Some thirty units were gathered into Russia when the Caucasus and Transcaucasia were annexed. Russian is taught in all the schools and the various language groups may have their own languages taught also. Russia has been generous with her minorities in many respects. The five large minorities in European Russia are Georgians, Armenians, Tatars, Jews, and Azerbaijan Turks.

Russian resources in Siberia are vital to Russia's evolution. Of the forests of the Union, 71 per cent are in Asia, and almost all of these belong to the government. Both coniferous and hardwood lumber and forest products are exported, much to the advantage of the exchequer and the balancing of the national budget. Cotton, to meet a considerable portion of textile demands, is grown in southwestern Asiatic Russia. The furs of the Russian trade are now largely from the animals of the Asiatic Russian forest.

Minerals in great variety and abundance contribute to Russia's welfare. Coal and lignite, gold, copper, iron ore, and many lesser metals are available, some with very large reserves. Two thirds of the potential water power is in Asiatic territory; by estimate only 20 million horsepower can be developed in European Russia. If it were not for these Asiatic reserves, the progress of the Union must needs be slower, and the level possible of attainment would be considerably lower. These eastern resources are rapidly playing into the economy of the state and will no doubt do for Russia for a generation or two what American land, forest, and mineral reserves have done for the United States. But when the limits are known and are being visibly approached, the effects will be similar to the same approach here. Russia needs everything but natural resources. The government is essaying a herculean task, the uplift of an illiterate, backward people, repressed for generations, to real life and national self-sufficiency.

In measuring Russia's international relations, Asiatic as well as European resources are considered. Exports of forest products, mine timbers, paper-pulp, and lumber have great possibilities which are already beginning to show. Here, the east Asiatic forests are of notable significance because so near the growing Chinese markets. The export of wheat is looked upon with great hopes, for millions of acres in the Ukraine, in the

Manych, in the Volga plains, and in the Donetz Basin, as well as areas in southern Siberia, have suitable soils and sufficient rainfall to ensure a crop nearly every year. Very little of the manufactured goods is made for export. The people are finding many items "made in America" or in England or Germany better than those made at home. This has been especially true of machinery, watches, automobiles, and tools. Thousands of foreign engineers and artisans were brought in during the time of the first and second five-year plans to set up the industries of Russia, and many carloads of machinery to make machines, tractors, grain drills, and automobiles have been imported.

Places in northern Russia. This map should be referred to often in reading Chapters 23-26. (Adapted from several sources)

Actual figures for production in extractive and manufacturing industry are difficult to get for Russia. Latest figures obtainable are for 1938 and were published in 1946. In March, 1948, the government issued some results of production in 1947 showing the gains in that year over 1946 for twenty-four major industries. These had gained on an average of 22 per cent, which lifted production back to the level of 1940.

Exports and imports vary much from year to year. Exports exceed imports about half the years, but on the average keep very close to the latter. Figures for 1913 to 1938 were given in rubles and were converted into dollars approximately by dividing by 5. Rate of exchange is fixed arbitrarily in U.S.S.R., because rubles are not sold on foreign markets or allowed to leave the country legally.

In Czarist days Russia held only a tenuous connection with world trade.

Not until the turn of the century did the total turnover, exports and imports, exceed $2 billion a year. Even today U.S.S.R. trade is but a very small percentage of world trade, far from comparable with its relative area or population. At no time since 1913 has Russian foreign trade been as great as for a few years before that date.

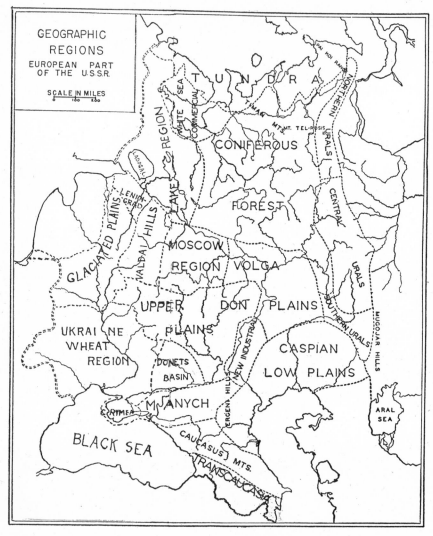

Geographic regions of European Russia. Regional boundaries in dash lines. (Constructed from atlas issued by Geodetic Committee of the U.S.S.R., 1929-1931)

Trade with Germany led in 1913, but in postwar years trade with Great Britain has led with U.S.A. a close second. China has been third with about half as much trade as U.S.A. Netherlands, Belgium, and Germany appear as fourth, fifth, and sixth, but all three combined fall far short of the trade with U.S.A.

Leading exports [3] have been wheat, timber, and lumber, furs, flax, manganese ore, beans, and fertilizer. More important imports [4] were machinery (boilers, etc.), non-ferrous metal goods, and precision instruments.

Regions. The administration in U.S.S.R. has done a prodigious amount of redistricting, changing of names, and regrouping of provinces into sixteen republics and several minor national divisions called Autonomous Soviet Republics and Autonomous Areas or Regions. The minor units are mostly Asiatic and like the Republics are divided into oblasts, okrugs, krias, raions, and other units usually of a local character. Boundaries of these divisions and subdivisions are said to be "racial or geographic," but they are usually far from having any relation to the fundamental physiographic, climatic, resource, and occupational factors upon which geographic regions are usually based.

There seems, however, to be good geographic basis for subdivisions of European Russia into a score of regions. Regions along western side in the maps have been enlarged to include recent additions to Russia. Some boundaries are fairly definite, though most are transition zones; but each region as mapped and named here has a unity of some sort. Description and discussion of European Soviet Russia will continue under regional headings as follows:

Northern Regions

1. Tundra; skirts Arctic coast; too cold for crops and trees
2. White Sea Commercial Region
3. Lake Region, Mining and Forests; Extractive
4. Coniferous Forests; Extractive
5. North Ural Mountains, Forest, and Tundra

Central Industrial Regions

6. Leningrad Industrial and Commercial Region
7. Moscow Region, Leading Industrial Area
8. Valdai Hills Region, Agricultural and Industrial
9. Middle Urals Region, Mining and Industry

Central Rural Regions

10. Glaciated Plains, Rural Region
11. Upper Don, Rural Area
12. Volga Plains, Agricultural Region

Southern Populous Regions

13. Ukraine Wheat Region
14. Donetz Industrial Region
15. Middle Volga New Industrial Region

[3] Wheat nearly $60,000,000; timber and lumber products $56,000,000; furs $26,000,000; beans $4,600,000; manganese ore $6,100,000.
[4] Machinery about $76,000,000; non-ferrous metal goods $51,400,000; precision instruments, tools, etc., $4,400,000.

Grazing Lands

16. Southern Ural Grazing Region
17. Caspian Low Plains Grazing Lands
18. Manych Cattle and Farming Lands

Southern Mountainous Regions

19. Crimean "Riviera"
20. Caucasus Mining, Forestry, and Farming Region
21. Transcaucasian Rural Industrial Region

QUESTIONS

1. Why would a Tatar kingdom flourish southeast of the Muscovite kingdom in the twelfth century?
2. A French anthropologist wrote, "To the conquerors the lowlands and valleys; to the conquered the mountains." Is it true? Why?
3. Why did the great Turkish expansion into Europe come south of the Caspian and Black seas?
4. What are the advantages and disadvantages for regional self-sufficiency applied to Russia? for interregional commerce?
5. From a geographic point of view what can be said of need for and conditions affecting commercial air transportation in U.S.S.R.?
6. What other possible grounds are there for Alpine race expansion into the Russian plains as suggested on pages 496-497?
7. What products are probably shipped to Leningrad and the interior through the new Baltic-White Sea canal?
8. Why should Siberia have been long a penal region?
9. Why have Karelians and Finns become more progressive and forward-looking than their relatives, the Cheremisses and Votyaks?
10. Compare and contrast eastward expansion in Russia and westward expansion of U.S.A., as to methods and reasons, and as to values attained or results.
11. Discuss Russia's "urge to the sea." Consider older ideas and recent plans. What plans can you suggest which would be fair to Russia and to other nations?
12. Much of Europe seems to be gathering into east and west divisions. Discuss some probable or possible effects of this trend on the commerce and industry of U.S.S.R.

BIBLIOGRAPHY

Atlas of the Industry of the U.S.S.R., 6 vols. (Moscow, The Geodetic Committee, 1929-1931).

BADDELEY, John E., *The Rugged Flanks of the Caucasus,* 2 vols. (London, Oxford University Press, 1940).

BALZAK, S. S., *et al.,* Russian eds.; HARRIS, Chauncy D., American ed., *Economic Geography of the U.S.S.R.* (New York, The Macmillan Company, 1949).

BARMINE, Alexander, *One Who Survived* (New York, G. P. Putman's Sons, 1945).

BAYKOV, Alex., *Soviet Foreign Trade* (Princeton, Princeton University Press, 1946).

BERDIAEV, Nikolai A., *The Russian Idea* (New York, The Macmillan Company, 1948).

BERG, Lev S., *Natural Regions of the U.S.S.R.* (New York, The Macmillan Company, 1950).

BILMANIS, Alfred, *Baltic Essays* (Washington, D. C., Latvian Legation, 1945).

BLANCHARD, W. O., and VISHER, S. S., *Economic Geography of Europe* (New York, McGraw-Hill Book Company, Inc., 1931).

BOWMAN, Isaiah, *The New World* (Yonkers-on-Hudson, New York, World Book Company, 1928).

BRIDGERS, Emily, *Arts in the Soviet Union,* University of North Carolina Lib. Extension Pub. Vol. 12, Nos. 3, 4 (Chapel Hill, University of North Carolina Press, 1946-47).

BUCK, Pearl, *Talks About Russia with Masha Scott* (New York, The John Day Company, Inc., 1945).

CARMAN, E. Day, *Soviet Imperialism: Russia's Drive toward World Domination* (Washington, Public Affairs Press, 1950).

CARR, Edward H., *Soviet Impact on Western World* (New York, The Macmillan Company, 1947).

CHAMBERLIN, Wm. Henry, *Russia's Iron Age* (Boston, Little, Brown & Company, 1934).

————, *Russian Enigma* (New York, Charles Scribner's Sons, 1944).

Commerce Reports, Numbers 14-26, April 6, 1931, page 7 f., "Tariff Changes" (Washington, D. C., Government Printing Office).

Commercial Handbook of U.S.S.R., U.S.S.R.-Amer. Chamber of Commerce Washington, D. C., 1936 and occasionally later. Title varies. Yearbook, etc. Pub. also by G. Allen & Unwin, Ltd., London.

CONDOIDE, Mikhail V., *Russian-American Trade* (Columbus, Ohio, Bur. Business Research, Ohio State University, 1946).

CRANKSHAW, Edward, *Russia and the Russians* (New York, Viking Press, Inc., 1948).

CRESSEY, George B., *Basis of Soviet Strength* (New York, Whittlesey House, McGraw-Hill Book Company, Inc., 1945).

D'ALMEDIA, P. Comena, "Russia," in Vidal de La Blache and Gallois, *Géographie Universelle* (Paris, Lib. Armand Colin, 1932).

DAVIS, Jerome, *Behind the Soviet Power* (New York, Reader's Press, Inc., 1946).

DEAN, Mrs. Vera (Micheles), *United States and Russia* (Cambridge, Harvard University Press, 1948).

DEWAR, Margaret, *Soviet Trade with Eastern Europe, 1945-1949* (New York, Royal Institute of International Affairs, 1951).

DOBB, Maurice, *U.S.S.R., Her Life and People* (Toronto, University of London Press, 1943).

EARLE, F. M., "Mechanization of Agriculture in U.S.S.R.," *Economic Geography,* Vol. 7 (July, 1931), pp. 297-307.

EAST, W. Gordon, "The New Frontiers of the Soviet Union," *Foreign Affairs,* Vol. 29 (July, 1951), pp. 591-607.

FIGDOR, Carl, *Geographische Untersuchungen im Raume der Sowjetunion* (Vienna, Touristik-Verlag, 1947).

FISCHER, John, *Why They Behave Like Russians* (New York, Harper and Brothers, 1947).

FISHER, Harold H., *Russia and America* (Claremont, California, Claremont College, 1946).

Foreign Commerce Year Book (Washington, D. C., Government Printing Office).

GOLOMSHTOK, Eugene A., "Old Stone Age in European Russia" *Trans. Amer. Philosophical Soc.*, Vol. 19 (1938), pp. 454-460.

GORER, Geoffrey, and RICKMAN, John, *The People of Great Russia* (New York, Chanticleer Press, Inc., 1950).

GRAY, G. D. B., *Soviet Land* (London, A. & C. Black, Ltd., 1947).

GREGORY, James S., and SHAVE, D. W., *The U.S.S.R., a Geographical Survey* (New York, John Wiley & Sons, Inc., 1946).

——, *Land of the "Soviets"* (New York, Penguin Books, Inc., 1946).

Guide Book to Soviet Union, compiled by A. Rado (Berlin, Society for Cultural Relations of the Soviet Union with Foreign Countries, 1929).

HEYMANN, Hans, *We Can Do Business with Russia* (Chicago, Ziff-Davis Pub. Co., 1945).

HINSLEY, F. H., *Command of the Sea* (London, Christophers, 1950).

HOLME, K. E., *Two Commonwealths* (Toronto and London, George G. Harrap & Co., Ltd., 1945), Vol. 2.

HRDLICKA, A., *The Peoples of the Soviet Union* (Washington, Smithsonian Institution, 1942).

HUBBARD, Leonard E., *Soviet Trade and Its Distribution* (London, Macmillan & Co., Ltd., 1938).

Information Bulletin, The Great Stalin Five-Year Plan (Washington, D. C., U.S.S.R. Embassy, 1946).

IVES, Vernon, Russia [Juvenile], (New York, Holliday House, 1943).

JASNY, Naum, *The Socialized Agriculture of the USSR: Plans and Performance)* Palo Alto, Stanford University Press, 1949).

JOHNSON, Hewlett, *Soviet Power* (New York, Modern Age Books, 1940).

KENDREW, W. G., *Climates of the Continents*, 3rd ed. (Oxford, Clarendon Press, 1942).

KERNER, Robert J., *The Urge to the Sea* (Los Angeles, University of California Press, 1942).

——, *The Russian Adventure* (Berkeley and Los Angeles, University of California Press, 1943).

KUEHNELT, Leddihn E., "The Petsamo Region," *Geographical Review*, Vol. 34 (1944), pp. 405-417.

LAMONT, Corliss, *The Peoples of the Soviet Union* (New York, Harcourt, Brace & Company, Inc., 1946).

LAZERSON, Max M., *Russia and the Western World* (New York, The Macmillan Company, 1945).

LEIMBACH, Werner, *Die Sovjetunion, Natur, Volk, und Wirtschaft* (Stuttgart, Frankhsche Verlagshandlung, 1950).

LOVELL, Maurice, *Landmen and Seafarers* (London, Toronto, George G. Harrap & Co., Ltd., 1945), Vol. I.

LOVENSTEIN, Meno, *American Opinion of Soviet Russia* (Washington, American Council on Public Affairs, 1941).

MANDEL, Williams, *Guide to Soviet Union* (New York, Dial Press, 1946).

MARBUT, C. F., "Agriculture in the United States and Russia; A Comparative Study of Natural Conditions," *Geographical Review*, Vol. 21 (October, 1931), pp. 598-612.

MIKHAILOV, Nikolai, N., *Land of the Soviet* (New York, L. Furman, Inc., 1939).

——, *Soviet Geography* (London, Methuen & Co., Ltd., 1935).

Mineral Industry, An Annual (New York, the Scientific Publishing Co.).

MIROV, N. T., *Geography of Russia* (New York, John Wiley & Sons, Inc., 1951).

Moody's Governments and Municipals (New York, Moody's Investor's Service, annual).

MOSELEY, Philip E., *Face to Face with Russia* (New York, Headline Series No. 70, Foreign Policy Association, Inc., 1948).

NAGY, Ferenc, *The Struggle Behind the Iron Curtain* (New York, The Macmillan Company, 1948).

NAZAROFF, Alexander I., *Land of the Russian People* [Juvenile], (Philadelphia, J. B. Lippincott Company, 1944).

NORMANO, J. F., *The Spirit of Russian Economics* (New York, in coöperation with Russian Econ. Inst., The John Day Company, Inc., 1945).

PARES, Sir Bernard, *History of Russia*, 5th ed. (New York, Alfred A. Knopf, Inc., 1947).

PARKER, Ralph, *How Do You Do, Tovarish?* (London and Toronto, George G. Harrap & Co., Ltd., 1947), Vol. 3.

REYNOLDS, J. H., "Nationalities in the U.S.S.R.," *Geographical Journal*, Vol. 73 (April, 1929), pp. 370-374.

RIPLEY, W. Z., *Races of Europe* (New York, D. Appleton and Co., 1899).

ROUCEK, Joseph S., *Central Eastern Europe* (New York, Prentice-Hall, Inc., 1946).

SALISBURY, Harrison, *Russia on the Way* (New York, The Macmillan Company, 1946).

SHABAD, Theodore, *Geography of U.S.S.R.* (New York, Columbia University Press, 1951).

SHOTWELL, James T., and LAZERSON, Max M., *Poland and Russia, 1919-1945* (New York, King's Crown Press, 1945).

SIMMONS, Ernest Jo, ed., *U.S.S.R., A Concise Handbook* (Ithaca, Cornell University Press, 1946).

SNOW, Edgar P., *The Pattern of Soviet Power* (New York, Random House, Inc., 1945).

SOROKIN, Pitirim A., *Russia and the United States* (New York, E. P. Dutton & Co., Inc., 1944).

Soviet Union Facts, Descriptions, Statistics (Washington and Moscow, Soviet Union Information Bureau, 1929).

SPECTOR, Ivar, *An Introduction to Russian History and Culture* (New York, D. Van Nostrand Company, Inc., 1949).

Statistics of Russia's Agriculture, U. S. Dept. of Agriculture (Washington, D. C. Government Printing Office), recent dates.

STEWART, Marguerite A., *Land of the Soviets* (St. Louis and Dallas, Institute of Pacific Relations, Webster Publishing Co., 1942).

STEVENS, Edmund, *Russia Is No Riddle* (New York, Greenberg, Publisher, Inc., 1945).

SUMMER, B. H., *A Survey History of Russia* (New York, Reynal & Hitchcock, 1943; London, Gerald Duckworth & Co., Ltd., 1944).

TIMOSHENKO, Vladimir P., *Economic Background for the Postwar International of U.S.S.R.* (New York, Russian Economic Institute, 1945).

TULAIKOV, N. M., "Agriculture in the Dry Region of the U.S.S.R.," *Economic Geography*, Vol. 6 (January, 1930), pp. 54-80.

TURIN, S. P., *The U.S.S.R., An Economic and Social Survey* (London, Methuen & Co., Ltd., 1944).

U. S. Treaties, Commercial Relations No. 179 and No. 215 (Washington, D. C., Government Printing Office, 1941).

VAN CLEEF, Eugene, "The East Baltic Ports," *Geographical Review,* Vol. 35 (1945), pp. 257-272.

VERNADSKY, George, *A History of Russia* (London, Oxford University Press, Humphrey Milford, 1944).

VINTER, A. V., with IOFFE, A. F., *Twenty-Five Years of Power Development in the U.S.S.R.* (New York, American Russian Institute, 1943).

WELLES, Samuel, *Profile of Europe* (New York, Harper and Brothers, 1948).

WILLIAMS, Albert R., *The Soviets* (New York, Harcourt, Brace & Company, Inc., 1942).

———, *The Russians, Land and People* (New York, Harcourt, Brace & Company, Inc., 1943).

YUGOW, A., trans. by N. I. and M. Stone, *Russia's Economic Front for War and Peace* (New York, Harper and Brothers, 1942).

See additional bibliography after last chapter on U.S.S.R., Chap. 29.

CHAPTER 24

Northern Regions

Her forests huge,
Incult, robust, and tall, by nature's hand
Planted of old.

—THOMSON

1. TUNDRAS

Characteristics of the region. A treeless coastal strip, 50 to 150 miles in width, extends entirely across northern Russia from Finland to the Ural Mountains. It averages twice as wide east of the White Sea as west of it and thus comprises 75,000 to 80,000 square miles, or more area than Ohio and Indiana combined. It is broken into two parts by the White Sea entrance and nearly broken again by the sandy, muddy delta and the changing distributaries of the Pechora River.

The topography is as monotonously level as that of any Russian region, yet in detail is not as smooth as in some other parts. Shoreline features consist of dunes, beaches, sandbars, offshore islands, and on both sides of the entrance to Cheshskaya Bay low, rocky headlands; but none of these features have value for defense, harbor, bathing, and other uses to which such features are put in more salubrious climates. Outside the Urals the region has no altitude above 500 feet, except a small area where the roots of the base-leveled Timan Mountains approach the coast west of the Pechora.

Geologically, the surface is among the most recent. Glacial drift with occasional moraines was laid over a peneplained surface; upon the drift, except where too high, later Quaternary marine sediments were spread by the Arctic transgression. Considerable high, uneven to rolling areas of drift are not covered or leveled thereby. The rolling areas are better drained than the rest and are therefore the choicest for human use. Higher areas of older rocks also are not covered by marine deposits. Patches that thus escaped are in the Urals and Timan mountains and a bar of Pre-Cambrian rocks stretching obliquely across the Kanin Peninsula. East of the White Sea the peneplained surfaces consist mostly of late Paleozoic rocks; in Kola they are of Pre-Cambrian. The surface also is a little higher and more uneven in Kola. So recently was all this drift and marine surface made, and so slowly do streams with slight gradients erode, especially

509

where bound by ice and frost half the year, that marsh and bog cover much of the tundra. The soil survey classifies all under two heads, "dry tundra and bog tundra soils, but on the south side it grades into podzolized soils still swamped."

Ural glaciation covered the tundra east of the Pechora, and consequently the land is rougher than that west of the Timan Mountains. On their south slopes, where protected from winds and more exposed to sunshine, hills of drift and dunes of sand have higher types of vegetation, which assure forage for reindeer and white fox when other tundra food fails. Flood-plains of streams are annually inundated, partly because the rivers thaw first at their headwaters; therefore they are poorly adapted to navigation. The Kanin Peninsula formerly was separated from the mainland by a channel which boats used until 200 to 300 years ago, but the water is not continuous now. A little dredging to deepen the trench would aid fishermen in getting from the Gulf of Cheshskaya and coasts eastward into Mezen Bay and the White Sea ports.

Climatically, the weight and depression of high latitude are always upon these lands. This Tundra Region has 12 to 16 inches of snowfall in the year and is covered by snow 200 to 225 days, longer and more deeply in the Kola Peninsula and Urals, where the land is a little higher. Total precipitation for the year ranges from 15 to 20 inches; the larger figures prevail westward. Humidity is reported to range from 56 per cent to 70 per cent except during precipitation. Absolute temperatures of −48° F. are experienced frequently in the eastern part. In all these climatic items is clearly seen the marine influence, which is tempered in the west by the drift of warm Atlantic waters but unmodified in the east.

Tundra vegetation includes no trees that look like trees. Low, stunted growth of species that do well in more favorable climates stand sometimes a foot high, with thick branches several feet long spreading in every direction flat upon the ground. These subdued trees are surrounded and often partly covered by mosses, lichens, and heaths, grown in a thick, tangled, interwoven mat of stems and roots, and adorned in season with showy flowers followed by many sorts of edible berries somewhat like blueberries and huckleberries. This mat of vegetation grows in water-logged soil, which is frozen in winter many feet deep. In summer a foot or two of it thaws, but it never drains and hence is absolutely uncultivable. Precipitation and humidity are ample for trees, but cold, wind, and the perpetual ice below forbid their growth. Only plants that can grow in the thin soil layers that thaw in summer can prosper.

The geographic landscape is monotonous in relief, in vegetation, in its winter snow cover, in its wild life, and in human habitations. It is a region of low subsistence level and meager opportunities. In summer the coastal parts are teeming with birds—ducks, gulls, and other migratory fowls—which nest everywhere in the low vegetation and feed upon the berries as long as they remain. All the year a few wild fur-bearing animals roam over it.

Resources. Peat, the richest and most characteristic resource, occupies a little of the Kola and large areas of the eastern half. It is estimated that, on the average, 12,000 to 25,000 tons of peat could be cut from every square mile east of the White Sea. Coal in the western flanks of the Urals has been of great help to transportation and to growing industries. Tens of thousands of birds and birds' eggs could be taken in summer and packed for markets elsewhere; feathers and down, bird waste for fertilizer, and

Northern tribesmen driving reindeer teams on the edge of the tundra. (Courtesy Sovfoto)

berries are other products available but used only by the natives. Magnetite iron ore is mined in two areas west of Kola Bay, one very near Murmansk. In each area two artels or labor units are working when the climate is decent enough for work to proceed normally. Lead and zinc are known on Vaigach Island, an island section of the Ural structure, but the severity of the climate so far has forbidden all development. Iron ore and petroleum are known in this east Pechora Valley.

Labor resources are meager. Most of the tundra east of the White Sea has no permanent residents. Along the Pechora many small, miserable settlements give a density of 25 to 50 per square mile. In the delta is another squalid cluster of houses, and two similar colonies appear farther west near the coast. In the Kola Peninsula the people, concentrated along the coast and very sparsely scattered over the interior, give a census density of about one per square mile.

No fuel is available except the peat, drying conditions for which are limited to a part of the summer. No water power can be had except on the Tuloma, which flows from a large lake to Kola Bay. A plant here furnishes light for Murmansk and power for a machine-shop employing forty to fifty workers. This current is valued at $30,000 per year, Murmansk has over 117,000 people, 3,500 of whom are listed as engaged in industry. The winds are strong and steady enough to serve for power, but Russians have only suggested their use.

People. Russians greatly predominate on Kola Peninsula, but they dwell along the coasts and in the towns of Kola Bay. Lapps, Karelians, and Finns occupy the interior. Russians also predominate east of the White Sea as far as the Timan Mountains, and beyond them the Zyrians greatly exceed all others. The Russian census says the birth-rate of the Kola exceeds the death-rate two and one-half times, being 41 to 45 per thousand. Literacy at present stands a little above 50 per cent in Kola towns and coast settlements, but a little below 50 per cent in rural parts. Lapps possess reindeer; fifty head keep a family of four or five persons and require 4 or 5 square miles. The mean population density of the whole Tundra Region (less than one per square mile) is comparable with that of the Northern Coniferous Region where limited by too much forest, and with that of the Caspian Low Plains where drought excludes people. In all three areas subsistence is difficult, holding the level of culture low. Schools exist, but no colleges, cathedrals, printing-presses, or newspapers; and chapels are rare. Administratively the tundra connects with three units. The Kola Peninsula belongs with Leningrad of the R.S.F.S.R.; from the White Sea beyond Pechora it affiliates with R.S.F.S.R. through Archangel; a small eastern portion is in Komi, the Zyrian Autonomous Area.

Occupations. The industries of the tundra are quite exceptional. Most of the manufacturing is done in the homes and consists in the making of leather and dressing of furs, making boats and clothing, felting hair for overshoes, and shaping bone and horn. Limitations—the lack of wood—prevent woodworking and finishing in every form. Electrification of industry has gone far. Although Murmansk commerce consists of many items, only its magnetite iron ore is a tundra product. Its herring from the coasts and salmon from the streams have a good name. Fish products find their way into the Russian interior. The trade in herring and leather products is aided by the railroad from Leningrad, even though the marshy ground over which it runs is troublesome in summer. The ice-free Kola Fiord opens to the warm Arctic Sea.

Fishing occupies a larger proportion of the people than in any other region except the four towns, Archangel, Astrakhan, Leningrad, and Rostov; east of the White Sea the proportion falls off about half. Next to fishing probably comes the raising of reindeer. These animals are kept by native herdsmen who lead their droves over the moss-covered areas in summer and let them dig through the snow to the moss in winter. Very little provision is made for feeding the reindeer; even in winter they browse for themselves. This occupation, together with the chase, engages the Lapps of the Kola Upland, the Zyrians east of Timan Mountains, and some of the Russians. These industries lead to seasonal migrations and, to some extent, seasonal shift of industry. In winter half the people are occupied with household industries; some are handling lumber floated down in flood season from the coniferous forests to the south; others are packing fish caught in the streams and the sea. It is a strange life, yet one very closely related to the physical conditions. The Eskimo of America are the only other group that would live comfortably in the Russian Tundra.

2. WHITE SEA COMMERCIAL REGION

Its unity. The White Sea embayment comprises waters, mostly brackish, which lie upon lands as smooth as the surrounding plains. No part exceeds 500 feet in depth, except portions of the western arm. If uplift should reestablish the White Sea area as land, which certainly was its status not many millenniums ago, its surface could be traversed in any direction as freely by auto roads and railroads as it is now crossed by tracks of water craft. The land in the region as outlined exceeds 500 feet altitude only in parts of Kola Peninsula. The sea has four arms or embayments, one in the Tundra Region, one, Kandalaksha Bay, extending west partly isolating Kola, and two broader ones spreading southeastward. Islands dot the south one, Onega Bay, and the great northern Dvina pours its muddy waters into the other, Gulf of Dvina. Where the border of the White Sea Commercial Region crosses the neck of the sea the water is not more than 30 miles broad.

The geology resembles that of the Tundra Region. A peneplain across ancient crystalline rocks on the west side and across Devonian and Carboniferous rocks on the east side was covered first by glacial drift, then by Quaternary marine sediments, except where too high to have been immersed by the boreal transgression which rose 200 or 300 feet higher than the sea today. Recent stream and wave erosion has bared the older rocks along coasts and valleys; the same processes have furnished waste for alluvial and beach deposits, notably at the mouths of the Dvina and Onega rivers.

Mineral deposits consist of mica, apatite, feldspar, and nephelite (the last two valued for their potassium and kaolin content) at the head of Kandalaksha Bay in the crystalline rocks, and of common salt, gypsum, and strontium salts in the later rocks east and south of Archangel. Sands and clays are abundant but not worked. Native fossil fuel is limited to peat; some coal is imported for heat and steam, because of the difficulty in drying peat. Wood is extensively used on the railroads and to a limited extent for domestic heat.

Politically, the region lies partly in the Kola administration but mostly in the Archangel province of R.S.F.S.R. The people are Lapps and Karelians on the north and west and Russians on the south and east where things are being done. Russian fishermen occupy the south Kola coast.

Products. Coniferous forests in natural condition cover all the land area, and their products constitute an important factor in the commercial life of the region. Lumber and logs are floated down the Dvina in rafts, and the logs are sawed in great mills run largely by electric power. The lumber and tar from the pines appear in British and continental markets. Much lumber was exported from this area before Leningrad was built.

These coniferous forests occupy podzols matured with forest cover, soils satisfactory for agriculture. The high-latitude climate restricts many crops, but roots and other quick-growing vegetables are grown for local use; oats furnish forage for cattle, which do well on many pasture clearings around the coasts. Fish from White Sea and all Russian Arctic waters are dried and salted at Archangel and Onega and shipped to the interior. They even find their way to the great fairs at Gorki (Nizhni-Novgorod). The Mezen, Dvina, and Onega rivers pour large supplies of fish food—organic matter—into the White Sea and in consequence attract valuable herring fisheries.

Grain, both wheat and rye, comes from two southern sources to this export point. From the plains among the headwaters of the Obi it is floated down the Tobol and Tura and even the Irtish to the Siberian railroad at Tyumen, where elevators transfer it to cars. It then goes by rail to Kotlas on the Dvina and by barge to the port, Archangel. The reach of the port is extended farther by the double-track, broad-gauge railroad south, which has replaced the old single-track, narrow-gauge road. This line extends to Vologda, where it connects with a Siberian-Leningrad line, also directly with Moscow. An all-water grain line serves the lower and middle Volga grain lands. Barges and steamers make their way up the Volga, Kama, and a small improved tributary to the Katharina Canal and down a branch of the Vichegda to the Dvina at Kotlas, where they join the fleets loaded at Kotlas and proceed to Archangel. Another canal connects the west branch of the Dvina through the Volga-Neva system with Leningrad. These river routes are much restricted by winter ice.

Archangel and its seaway. Archangel, a strategic seaport on a strategic sea, is the capital of the province of the same name in the R.S.F.S.R. It stands about 25 miles from the sea, up the distributaries of the Dvina. The harbor has been dredged to 21 feet; yet it must be dredged anew every summer because of the active delta-building of the river. The province embraces 221,000 square miles and over 500,000 people; the city, essentially a commercial center, has grown rapidly to a population of over 281,000. Its largest industry is sawmilling. A large electric plant furnishes power for the mills, for light, and for harbor machinery. Fixed and floating docks and rows of warehouses have been built since the new régime. A tram-car serves its citizens, and a good military motor road has been built to Leningrad. Recently from Archangel sailed the intrepid Schmidt, hoping to open up a freight route through the Arctic Sea to the Pacific. In some mild years such a trip and commerce are possible.

One may count 150 islands among the ramifying and interlacing Dvina distributaries. Only one channel is improved for navigation. Aquatic birds in enormous numbers possess these islands and waters during the summer breeding season. The shelter of these delta channels and the adjacent forests made possible ship-building, and for many years Archangel has been a naval base—Russia's first (and for many decades, only) seaport. In a single recent year 300 foreign vessels were loaded with lumber. The largest ocean steamers afloat can enter the harbor, nearly 100 at a time, and they are served by up-to-date harbor machinery. Foreign ships from many different countries call at this port.

One might be familiar with the problems involved in the commercial use of the mouths of the Rhine or Thames and still find many surprises at Archangel. River and harbor and the White Sea out to the ocean are completely closed by ice three to four months every year. The river thaws upstream first, goes into flood before the delta is thawed, and pours down upon frozen islands and channels not only sand and mud but ice in great quantities with only a frozen sea to receive them. The situation has been described from the point of view of the usual river harbor engineer as "a mess." Because of its narrow neck and shallowness, together with its supplies of fresh water and the high latitude, the White Sea never could free itself of ice except for the help from outside generously supplied by the drift of warm waters from the north Atlantic. Ice-breakers operate in the sea for a month or two in the fall before the cold becomes too severe, and begin to hammer on the ice cover in the spring to accelerate the break-up and open navigation. But for the work of these powerful machines—boats —the sea would be closed usually for six months.

Up the Dvina about 50 miles stands Kholmogory, rebuilt as a modern town on the ruins of the famous old fortified site. Although off the railroad, it has excellent river communication, and it has become famous for a choice breed of dairy cattle introduced from the Netherlands long ago by Peter the Great. The success of the enterprise is a sample and promise of the large possibilities for future development and utilization of the luscious pastures that take the ground when forests are removed.

Onega, on the Gulf, Bay, and stream of the same name, has little opportunity to rival the capital city. Its river is much shorter and smaller, and has no canal connections across divides; its sea is shallower and more island-studded; and it has no railroad. It has the same heavy coniferous forests, has good fishing grounds, and is about 50 miles farther south, as well as farther inland, and its stream does not shoal the waters as rapidly, but at present these advantages have not been capitalized. As the lumber industry develops, Onega may increase in importance.

The old convent on the island of Solovetskie has, in the new régime, become a federal prison—possibly a better adjustment to conditions and needs.

3. THE LAKE REGION

Description. Continuous with Finland in foundation rocks, in recent drift, in topographic expression (altitude, lakes, moraines), in coniferous forests, in climate, and in people, the Lake District extends to Lakes Ladoga and Onega. Beyond these large bodies the same topography prevails to Rybinsk, Vologda, and the Onega River; but underneath the characteristically glacial topography of this extension, the rocks are not crystalline; they are Devonian and Carboniferous beds dipping gently southeast. Between Rybinsk (139,011) and the great lakes are thousands of acres of level, alluvial plains in a hundred patches representing filled lake beds—filled, while the lakes farther north are not, because exposed longer to sedimentation since the ice left them. Much of this region would probably have been in Finland when it became a national entity, had not the Murmansk railroad been built. The western boundary conforms much of the distance to the divide between Baltic and White Sea drainage.

Most of the Lake Region belongs in the Karelo-Finnish Socialist Soviet Republic, which has a population of nearly 500,000 people. No towns of note have developed in the region. The capital city is Petrosavodsk (70,000) on the west shore of Lake Onega and on the railroad. It is a local market and distributing center.

Products. Forest products (lumber and timbers for many uses as in mines and ship-building, staves, box flats, pulpwood) constitute a large item in the output of the Lake Region. Logs and lumber are floated down all the streams. Some are shipped to Murmansk for export, others to Leningrad for local use. Fish and game of many kinds are taken and shipped mostly to Leningrad. The coasts of the White Sea and Kandalaksha Bay have such excellent waters, harbors and lumber that fishing and ship-building are the chief occupations. Thousands of tons of herring are taken annually on Kandalaksha Bay and shipped to Russian industrial centers for food. Many are canned in modern plants, but a large proportion travels as fresh fish. Men not only fish in the streams for salmon and in the coast waters for herring but sail out to the Arctic and even to Spitzbergen and Novaya Zemlya to fish. The women, accustomed to coast rigors, often assist in local fishing. Broad banks for many miles off the Arctic coast are favored fishing-grounds. In the category of game also come many fur-bearing animals, whose pelts are shipped to Leningrad or to foreign markets.

Iron and copper are found in workable quantities in the area of crystalline rocks, with mines opened near the railroads in several places. At Khibinsk, a village in the north near Murmansk (117,054), apatite deposits estimated to contain 500 million tons have recently been explored, and development has begun. Sulphide ores near will assist in the reduction of the apatite to proper fertilizer composition. Already export of raw apatite and super-phosphate has begun. Barite is mined near to and east of Onega Lake in the Devonian and Carboniferous rocks. Rocks of many kinds, granite, marble, and sedimentary, have been quarried and shipped from their respective areas. Sands and clays, even fire-clays, are dug and shipped out to be manufactured.

Workmen of the Kirov apatite mines with a drill for drilling holes in the ore preparatory to blasting. (Courtesy Sovfoto)

Other occupations. The Karelians carry on such types of agriculture as are possible in this far north region. Some cattle are raised on the meadow clearings, and a profitable dairy industry is possible in many parts. The Lake Region should be classified as one engaged in extractive industries, lumbering, agriculture, mining, fishing and the chase, with no manufacturing except peasant household industries. It is so well served by railroad and water transportation that even such manufactures are diminishing.

Many of the lakes and connecting streams furnish water transportation, and the axial railroad from Baltic to Arctic, although not a first-class road, serves to connect most towns with outside cities and countries. It reaches several White Sea ports also. While the road stands up well under traffic in winter, so much of it crosses marshy land, impossible to avoid, that it is precarious in thawing summer weather.

A canal, 143 miles long, completes water connections between Soroka, on the White Sea at the mouth of the Vig River which drains Vig Lake, and Leningrad on the Baltic. The canal connects the improved Vig River and Onega Lake, using natural waterways wherever possible, and is described as containing nineteen locks and fifteen dams with twelve floodgates. It greatly shortens the water route from the White Sea to Leningrad, but inland water travel was possible before by way of Archangel, the Dvina River, and its tributaries. Lakes of the Lake Region provide ample storage both for the canal and for hydro-electric power. Natural resources, in forest, fish, furs, and mines, supply cargoes; sawmills, paper and cellulose factories, and woodworking, chemical, metallurgical, and boat-building plants have developed along the waterway.

4. THE CONIFEROUS FORESTS

Situation. In the northeast part of Russia, occupying the basins of the northern Dvina, Mezen, and Pechora rivers, lies the great Coniferous Forest. It is bounded on the north by the Tundra Region, on the west by the White Sea Commercial Region and the Lake Region. It extends east to the Ural regions and south to the Moscow and Upper Volga regions, which are, in the natural vegetation categories, parts of the deciduous forests. Over these 360,000 square miles spread almost virgin forests in the open density characteristic of forests such as are known in Canada. Moderate rainfall, cool enough temperatures to prevent drought by great evaporations, some winter precipitation conserved in ice and snow to be liberated by spring melting, a climate too severe for many crops and for general agriculture—these are the conditions favoring such great, uniform, open forests.

Scotch pine and spruce predominate, but in the east are found fir and the deciduous larch, together with pines, birch, aspen, and, locally, alder. Several Siberian species have migrated over the Urals into Europe. The white bark of the birch, the ever-twinkling leaf of aspen and birch, together with the aspen's brilliant leaf color in autumn, add to the beauty and break the monotony of the somber-needled green of spruce and pine. Broad-leafed trees mingle in the southeast part along Kama River.

With reference to climate the Coniferous Forest is spread along both sides of the mean July isotherm of 64° F., but in winter the January isotherm of 8° F. and 0° cross the region nearly from north to south. In summer, rainfall and sunshine, the latter for long-day periods, stimulate growth; in winter, snow, sifting down among the trees, makes a uniform blanket over the ground, which prevents deep freezing, and melting in place in the spring adds to the vernal precipitation moisture enough to ensure a reasonable annual growth. This region contains the choicest coniferous forests of Russia, but the most difficult to work and to send to market, so that the growth, fortunately for the future, is about twice the annual cut.

The Timan Mountains anticline with a syncline on each side extend across this area, which was well baseleveled before the ice age, then mantled with drift, and more recently veneered in all its lower portions by marine sediments. Thus the geology is simple, but difficult to decipher because of forest and recent rock cover.

Soils are the true coniferous forest, podzolized types, clays and light loams, of relatively youthful profile but amply productive for forests and for high-latitude crops where the trees are removed. Thousands of square miles are swampy and flooded with water. Rivers are the greatest transportational blessing of the foresters. True, the high latitude and poleward course are restrictions, for the rivers are frozen from six to eight months a year and are not valuable for power. Railroads skirt the region from Vologda to Archangel and cross the southern part from Vologda to Vyatka and Perm. Two others cross the Bashkir portion of the region, and a stub line from Vyatka penetrates the forest to Kotlas, where the Dvina becomes navigable for larger boats. Distance from the Atlantic restricts construction, but Finland and Sweden in the same latitude have much more railroad mileage than has the Coniferous Forest Region.

When the Novgorodians of northern Russia spread eastward, they journeyed through this Forest Region, passing from the plains lying between Leningrad and Moscow of today, down the Sukhona River to its junction with Vichegda River, then up that stream in a course 600 miles long in latitude 59° N. to 62° N. as far as the Urals. Later they penetrated the Urals and went into northern Siberia to begin its development. One does not comprehend some of the difficulties involved in such a migration until he realizes that it took place in the latitude and rigors of Hudson Bay and Alaska.

Resources. Resources other than the forest are scarce or not yet known. In these 360,000 square miles limited quantities of coal, bituminous and anthracite, are known along the upper Pechora River; gas and iron ores are found in the central part of the southern margins; on the southern limits notable occurrences of phosphorite are available for fertilizer products. They are worked near Vetluga. Of these resources the iron alone is manufactured, and that only in small furnaces for local use. Gypsum and calcareous shales of Permian age abound along the Sukhona below Vologda; and, near Totma, Peter the Great in the early part of the eighteenth century developed a great salt industry. Salt and furs were for many years the only exports of this forest region. Both are now relatively and actually of less importance than formerly. Under the growing pressure of other industries and the increasing scarcity of wild life in the west, the hunting of fur animals, so important one or two centuries ago, has gone in large part through the low Urals into Siberia. Many furs are still taken, however, in these coniferous forests. In value of pelts taken the fur-yielding animals stand in the following order—squirrel, wolf, ermine, hare, fox, skunk, bear, marten, lynx, wild-cat, sable. Ruthless hunting has almost exterminated the sable. Game laws are now in force, and fur farms are occasionally being established. These forests are capable of producing large income from furs if the wild life is properly protected.

At present this forest area is a one-resource and therefore a one-industry region.

Tractor pulling sled loads of logs out of the coniferous forest. (Courtesy Sovfoto)

Occupations and crops. Lumbering, the leading industry of the region, is now carried on extensively through all the western part, where the railroad can assist in moving the logs to Archangel. Great quantities of lumber are cut along the Dvina and its tributaries, Pinega, Vaga, Sukhona, and Vichegda. These rivers constitute the efficient highways in the Dvina basin and carry millions of logs to the city. Few sawmills operate where the trees are cut, but in Archangel twenty-five well-equipped modern power mills saw 70 per cent of the entire value of timber exported through White Sea and Arctic ports. Vologda has even more mills and contributes more lumber to the Baltic ports. The railroads from Kotlas and Vyatka carry lumber for home use into the less forested areas south and west. Trees in the state forests are designated for cutting to the amount of two and one-quarter billion cubic feet [1] per annum, but less than two thirds of these are cut; and the proportion cut in other forests is lower still. In all European Russia the cut (7 billion cubic feet) is less than half the annual growth, and the proportion is lowest in the Coniferous Forests because they are least accessible. Sixty-six cubic feet per capita is kept for home consumption. Sweden uses nearly twice as much per capita.

Large quantities of logs are normally exported to Germany. Boards and railroad ties, nearly 50 per cent of all lumber exported, go to Great Britain, Belgium, Holland, and France. Pulpwood constitutes nearly one fifth of the export, and mine timber makes up the rest. White Sea ports send away about one sixth of the Russian lumber export and Baltic ports one half.

Cereals (barley, rye, and oats) together with flax and hemp are grown in many clearings, especially along the streams. Cabbages, potatoes, and other leaf and root crops are grown solely for home use. Recently grass and lucerne and a little wheat have been added to the crop list. Cattle-raising is increasing, and many farmers are branching out into dairying. Picking wild berries, Arctic bramble and whortle berries in the far north and raspberries and currants from the luxuriant undergrowth in many coniferous forest areas, adds to the variety of diet and occupation. Jam is now made from golden berries, and they might be canned in commercial quantities.

Fishing and hunting of migratory birds furnish seasonal employment for a number of people, but the transportation restrictions make these activities purely local. Bee culture was once an interesting occupation in some parts of the Coniferous Forest Region, but it is now nearly abandoned.

Little villages or single houses strung along the streams and lake shores reflect the relatively great importance of water communication. A few people live on sunny, well-drained slopes of morainic hills, avoiding cold, wet lowlands and bogs. Their crops grow faster than elsewhere and have ten days more of time than anywhere else to ripen before early frosts. Peasant industries in the homes or in village shops take up a part of the winter time of many people. All the manufacturing serves local markets, except that of homespun linen bags (flour-sacks) sent to the fair at Gorki near the southern border of the forest region.

Road and railroad building would be simple on the level lands and never disturbed by the difficulties besetting their construction and maintenance within the tropics, but other difficulties arise here. The season for building is short unless it extends into the winter. If done then, thawing weather often shows the road to have been built on covered ice or on frozen bogs; or its foundations thaw and slump. Even the best of summer-built roads are threatened by freezing and thawing, because good drainage is almost impossible. Water transportation is much preferred and is good with boats or rafts in summer, and with sleds on the ice of streams in winter. Kolvinsky Reservoir, flooding a broad area of plains, has been con-

[1] Cubic feet multiplied by twelve gives the board feet.

structed to provide generous water storage and commercial connection between the upper Kama, Vichegda, and Pechora rivers.

The people in the western part of the region are mostly Russians; Zyrians predominate in the east; Bashkirs are most numerous in the southeastern neck of the forest area. About half the region is the Autonomous Area of Komi; most of the other half belongs to the R.S.F.S.R.; Votyak, a small Autonomous Area, centers round Izhevsk (nearly 200,000); the Bashkir Autonomous Soviet Socialist Republic covers a little more than the southeastern neck. Little urban population exists except in these southern parts, but the region has a few towns which merit description. All are on streams in order to be assured of a means of transport.

Cities or towns. Kotlas is strategically placed at the junction of the Sukhona and Vichegda rivers and thus at the head of the Dvina. It was a fur-collecting town and a transit station for lumber en route to Archangel from the interior forests. Then came the railroad overland from Vyatka, a thriving town on the main line which stretches from Leningrad through Vologda, Perm, the industrial and mineral-bearing Central Urals, and on east across Siberia. Now this line gives an outlet south for the forested interior, and also, much more to the point, an inlet for wheat from Siberia to nourish the lumbermen, boatmen, fishermen, and others scattered along the rivers. Other lines reach out to Siktivkar and into the forest.

Velikii Ustyug stands 50 miles or so up the Sukhona from Kotlas. Here the great sandy Yug pours its waste into its master stream and at times nearly throttles commerce; yet both streams serve populous, industrial forest valleys. A town must occupy this place to help collect and distribute goods and to serve the men in commerce who are delayed by the sand. *Velikii* means "great," but the population is not more than 25,000; *Ust* means "northern," and together they mean "a large northern town at the mouth of the Yug." Houses are one-story wooden structures built from the forest products—a vicious fire hazard.

Ust-Sysolsk is a Zyrian town of 5,000 people at a big turn and junction point on the Vichegda and serves an active, growing river commerce in furs, logs, and other forest products. It is a station on the crooked through river route, Vologda to the Northern Urals and northern Siberia, and is the administrative center for the Autonomous Area of Komi.

Ust-Tsylma (2,000) grew at a big turn in the Pechora. Founded in 1542 by the Novgorodians as they developed the profitable fur trade of the Coniferous Forest, it has since been a trading center of wooden dwellings and storehouses. It is called the extreme northern limit of people, though it is not as far north as the Arctic Circle. Finland and Sweden have many towns and activities farther north. A difficult overland road uniting Ust-Tsylma with Mezen is far preferable to a journey down the Pechora and round the headlands by sea. The road passes a group of abandoned silver mines, a busy center many years ago. Merchants of Cherdyn on the Kolva, a feeder for Kama River, ship grains and manufactures from the Volga country by river all the distance upstream, work them through the new canal and Kolvinsky Reservoir, and take them down the easy but crooked, circuitous Pechora to nourish woodsmen, trappers, and fishers who live along every tributary stream and the Pechora itself. While the river is very serviceable, violent and treacherous winds on its lower reaches often hold up boats for days. These little settlements help make the forest profitable, and the river transportation makes its development possible.

Near the southwest corner of the region stands Vologda (102,000), the key to the Coniferous Forests and all they contain. The town occupies a secure site on the Sukhona where it is still navigable. A few miles upstream the river flows from a lake connected by canal with the Sheksna and by the Sheksna and other canals with the Volga system and with the Svir system leading to the Baltic. Eastward the waters belong to the Dvina system. Ivan the Terrible saw the strategy of the situation and in the middle of the sixteenth century made Vologda a capital. It is now an important railroad center, having the Archangel road, the through east and west line —Leningrad to the far east—and two direct lines to Moscow. Besides the usual crops mentioned for this latitude, much flax is grown and a lively butter industry has developed. The town was marked in the first five-year plan for large expansion in commerce and manufactures. A large electric-power station helps to make it an important lumber milling center, a maker of farm tractors and lumbering equipment. It has long been famous for its lace and for its fur market.

Izhensk (198,000) is the capital of Udmurt Autonomous Republic and the main center of iron and steel industries; machines, lathes, precision instruments, small arms, and motorcycles. The iron ore comes on the Tama River from mines in the Urals.

Ufa (246,000) is the capital and center of the Bashkir Autonomous Republic. It is a railroad and river center connecting with the Kama-Volga system and shares in the great industrial Ural complex just east of it and in the very important lumber industries supplying western Europe.

5. NORTHERN URALS FOREST AND TUNDRA

The northern Urals are separated from the southern by a rich mining region now thoroughly industrialized. They reach from latitude 61° N. almost exactly north to latitude 65° N. where stands Mt. Tel-Posis (5,500 ft.), the highest point in the area. The range angles northeast, then northwest, and continues in the Pai Koi range, and Vaigach and Novaya Zemla islands. Structurally, the northern Ural Mountains consist of one master fold and two to three subsidiary parallel wrinkles involving Pre-Cambrian schists, igneous rocks and a whole section of Paleozoic beds. So far as known no mineralization has occurred, but good coal is mined in the western flanks and makes a real contribution to the economic life farther west.

Most of the northern Urals was glaciated during the ice age and contributed drift to the plains westward. Only one valley glacier remains to the present. Old rounded mountain forms rise 2,000 to 3,000 feet. They are not high enough to appreciably increase precipitation over that of the Pechora plains, but in summer they call forth a perceptible rain shadow in the Obi Valley on the east.

While not lofty, the northern Urals are high enough to reach above the timber line in this high latitude and bear more or less continuous Alpine and tundra vegetation throughout their whole length. Coniferous forest, feathering out toward the summits, clothes both slopes of the range. Fur animals are taken more freely and abundantly in the mountains than in the plains to the west, because human habitations are rare, and lumbering operations have scarcely commenced anywhere within the region.

In striking contrast with the development of the Central Urals, no towns or even villages have been built in the Northern Urals. Voguls and Kami, Finno-Ugrian tribes, and the Nentsi and Ostyaks, both Samoyedes, occupy the flanks of these mountains and hunt over their slopes. The Finno-Ugrian men are short, often of blond complexion; occasionally they have herds of reindeer or cattle and live a migratory pasture-seeking life. The Samoyedes differ from the Finno-Ugrians in having dark, straight hair, sallow skin, broad, flat faces, and oblique, narrow eyes, and live a similar herdsman's life. Hides are the only products that ever get to market from either the animals of the chase or those of the herdsmen.

While the Northern Urals have great quantities of excellent stone and are clothed extensively with primeval coniferous forests, growing on excellent, youthful, podzolized soils, they are probably the most backward region in European Russia. Their inhabitants are there because no one else wants to occupy the forests. No one considers the forest worth cutting, as long as great forests equally valuable but more accessible, are scarcely touched. The region is the home of many fur animals and these relic remnants of a backward race, and has no promise of being more. Climatic barriers inherent in the latitude effectively check all native progress.

QUESTIONS

1. What chance has Onega to rival Archangel?
2. Discuss the strategic value of the White Sea.
3. State any commercial or subsistence relations existing between the Lake Region and its neighbors.
4. Why have Finland and Sweden, in the same latitude, so much better railroad nets than has the Coniferous Forest?
5. Why is Ust-Tsylma such a lonely, rare town here in the same latitude as many towns in Sweden?
6. In what ways may the Coniferous Forest Region coöperate with adjacent regions?

CHAPTER 25

Central Industrial Regions

From the Kremlin walls, from the vast white walls,
From the Kremlin walls, from the towered walls.

—Folk Song

6. LENINGRAD INDUSTRIAL REGION

Situation. The Leningrad Industrial Region is probably the smallest but one—the Crimean Riviera—of the Russian geographic regions as defined in this work. This region consists of about 16,000 square miles of plains with one great city, Leningrad; both area and city are strategically situated, politically and commercially, and they have become therefore industrially significant. On the Gulf of Finland, an arm of the Baltic, the city occupies a section of the highway from the capital and the great Moscow Industrial Region to the Baltic. By the Neva River with its navigable canal connections, not only with Lake Ladoga but with the great Volga system and the Northern Dvina system, the region may have easy water commerce with the grain regions and the sheep and cattle pastures of the south as well as with the important coniferous forests of the north and the hardwood forests to the southeast. At the present time railroads provide speedy communication with rapidly developing Finland, with the Arctic coast at Murmansk, with Archangel and the northern coniferous forests, with Moscow and all the southeast regions, with Ukraine, with the Baltic republics, and with Germany. Russia's objection to exporting through other nations directs considerable commerce, which is destined for water transport, through Leningrad and the Leningrad Industrial Region. Other Baltic ports may now come into larger service.

Geology. Cambrian limestones, much masked by drift and alluvium, come to the surface around Leningrad, along the south shore of the Gulf of Finland, and on the south shore of Lake Ladoga. The structure parallels that in the Baltic states. The more resistant Lower Carboniferous beds mark, with higher topography, the eastern limits of the Leningrad region. Many patches and strips of alluvial and lacustrine sediments effectively conceal the bed-rock. One of these patches comprises Lake Ilmen, by far the largest lake in the region, and an equal area of abandoned lake-bed.

Where lakes and streams have not sorted the drift, a more or less complete drift sheet mantles the bed-rock and, with the sorted areas, furnishes thousands of acres of excellent agricultural soil as well as providing raw materials for lively ceramic industries producing brick and tile for building, drain tile, plain crockery, and insulating patterns. In many of the lake-beds that have reached the bog stage, extensive and valuable peat deposits are developed for power and fuel purposes. For a few miles from beyond the Estonian border, the Ordovician beds carry an oil-yielding shale, from which the distillation products supply a very small percentage of the needed fuel of this region. But more significant are the Silurian beds, which produce a small escarpment, responsible for the Narva (Estonia) water power, a steep grade on the railroad at Trotsk, formerly Gatchina, and the rapids in the Volkhov River. Sediments carried out by the Neva River have been built into a low mud-and-sand delta at the head of the Gulf of Finland. Strong winds driving from the northwest occasionally push water up over the margins of the delta to a depth of several feet in the city streets. Around the delta region is a level Quaternary till plain, nowhere more than 400 feet above sea level and meagerly dissected by infant post-glacial streams, but not flooded as is the delta.

People. The region was attractive to neither Finn nor Slav until the people rose above the hunting, grazing, and purely agricultural stages. Both races, however, lived in the region, grazing cattle over the rich meadows among the dominant forests and fishing in the waters. When need for commerce arose, the first center was Novgorod, a trading post at the outlet of Lake Ilmen, where the Volkhov River starts toward Lake Ladoga and through the Neva River to the Baltic. A commercial city could not grow normally on the mud marsh and bog near the sea and the low, muddy shores could not well be defended; so Novgorod grew. It had, in addition, the marvelous advantage of easy access to interior cities, for the severest part of the journey from sea to interior lay between Novgorod and the Gulf of Finland.

The significance of the general site later occupied by Leningrad, as well as its difficulties of access, were early recognized. Situated near the mouth of the Neva River and at the very place where the Baltic Sea penetrates farthest into the lands, the place was of commercial importance to medieval merchants trading by the Volga route between northern tribes and the Greeks and Arabs. Then it became a contested spot for Russians and Swedes. To Russia it meant an outlet for Novgorod and central Russia; to the seafaring Swedes it was the key for their continental trade. The Swedes first defended it in 1300 with the fortress Landskrona, which the displeased Novgorodians shortly destroyed. Three hundred years later the Swedes, again in possession, built a new fortress, and for a century Swedish wharves, factories, and shipping held sway in this normally Russian territory. Finn and Novgorodian Slav continued to occupy these lowlands. Swedes and

Muscovite Slavs crowded in, and the Novgorodians were absorbed. Today, Great Russian and Finn or Karelian occupy the land.

In the northwest quarter of the Leningrad region the density of population exceeds 375 per square mile, and forms of intensive utilization include agriculture, dairying, household industries, and several town factories. Population in the southwest quarter ranges from 60 to 120 per square mile and includes fishermen as well as farmers and gardeners. Two or three notable old towns also remain. The southeast half of the area sustains a population of 25 to 60 per square mile, mostly engaged in rural activities carried on from village residences. In remote rural sections handcrafts still supply over 90 per cent of the locally needed industrial products and 1 to 3 per cent of the people engage in peasant household work. Home industries have been more fully replaced in the western half than in the eastern, a comparison which shows the strength of urbanization on an old, traditional, strongly entrenched industrial method.

In this region two thirds of the people live in towns and one third live in the rural villages and on the farms. A dozen villages exceed 1,000 in population; many are smaller, dotting the plains at frequent intervals. The winter climate encourages seasonal migration of labor from the soil in summer to the shop and factory in winter, an institution well established in the old régime but disturbed in the new. It will be interesting to see the relative strength of a geographic influence and a ukase.

Leningrad (3,191,000). In the first years of the eighteenth century the Czar, Peter the Great, began to aspire to marine connections, a seaport, a city of nations, and commerce with the outside world. Seated in his capital at Moscow he looked to the Gulf of Finland as his nearest coast-line. In 1703 were laid the first stones (fortress of Peter and Paul) of the new capital and commercial emporium. Stones and piles were necessary, for the muddy site was as miry as that of Amsterdam. Schlüsselburg, a Swedish fortress on the shores of Lake Ladoga, guarded the outlet of the lake— Neva River—and the route to Novgorod. The fortress of Kronstadt, superseding Landskrona, was begun by Peter but was completed only after several interruptions and renewals of building activities. Admirably situated to defend the new venture and at the same time to control the entrance to the Neva, Lake Ladoga, and the trade with Novgorod, it occupied the island of Kotlina in the midst of the narrower part of the Gulf of Finland and about 20 miles from the new city. Of course the new capital must be called St. Petersburg, or Petrograd—now, in the same spirit, Leningrad. This city was not built for a naval base alone, but for a winter palace, a center from which to foster foreign commerce, and to develop the resources of the thinly settled, backward frontier plains with their agricultural life. Spars, planks, and naval stores were easily derived from the pine forests in the hinterland. Ships of those days could reach the city piers with little difficulty. The mild winters and ample rainfall of the plains permitted the making of beautiful gardens; construction was favored by the presence of lumber, limestone, travertine for cement, and clays for brick; unique palaces, churches, art galleries, and administration buildings arose rapidly. Before Peter died in 1725 the population of his capital had become 75,000.

The rural region back of the city contributed to its growth, and the city stimulated the evolution of the farmer communities. Foods were needed for the city, wool and flax fiber, lumber and other building materials, horses for the droshkies and for many clumsy freight wagons. Water resources drawn from the hills to the eastward supplied the city's needs. A bathing beach was developed along the north side of the gulf near Sestroretsk; clay and gravelly islands, strewn with little lakes and rounded verdant hills, were animated by many summer tenants.

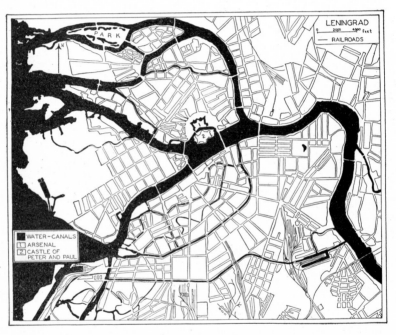

Leningrad. Note waterways and railways, and their interrelations. (Adapted from Soviet and British Admiralty charts and maps in a *Guide Book to Soviet Union* [Berlin, 1929])

The many canals connecting the city and harbor with rivers to the White and Black seas were begun early in the city's history. In 1851 the railroad to Moscow connected the new and old capitals. Commerce and industry grew. Many products passed through the city, and manufacturing commenced on a small scale, in order to add value to the goods. Filatures prepared and spun flax and wool, and other mills wove cloth. Metallurgy in numerous establishments handled ores from within the land as well as from without. Paper-making and glass, tobacco, and brick manufacturing flourished. Sawmills worked up logs floated to the city. Boots and shoes of both leather and rubber became important products. Scarcely an industry was lacking in the city. In commerce, manufactures, glory, pomp, intrigue, and religion, St. Petersburg became the greatest capital city of northeastern Europe.

A distressing break in the industrial and commercial life of the city came during the depression of civil war and revolution, and again in the seige during World War II. The capital with all its trappings was moved to Moscow after the Revolution of 1917, and the city, now Leningrad, in spite of geographic advantage declined 30 to 40 per cent in population and much more in its activities. But restoration has arrived. So close is the city to the flax fields that the hum of scores of linen mills may always be heard. The fur market has revived, and $30 million worth of furs change hands here annually—in some years twice as much. Squirrel skins rank first; fox, hare, ermine, sable, marmot, and many others here enter world commerce. Every old industry returned, and scores of new ones have arisen, including meat-packing, fancy woodworking, and the finishing of many food products from flour, sugar, oils, and fruits. With the return of industry foreign commerce is increasing, but not government pomp.

The plan of the city takes advantage of the delta topography and distributaries of the Neva River, five of which enter the Gulf of Finland within the present limits of the city. The great castle or fortress stands on the west side of the main distributary, and behind it the arsenal. The palaces, administration buildings, museums, and university are on the east side. A great canal encircles these and many other buildings on an area of 2 to 3 square miles, with lesser canals, easily constructed in soft, level lands, serving many business houses. Most buildings are necessarily supported by scores of great piles driven down into the mud and sand. The streets, or Prospects, radiate from the administration center with concentric cross streets in ever wider semi-circles.

Slips, docks, warehouses, and piers for marine commerce were constructed at the start and have been multiplied and enlarged in many parts of the city. When railroads came, some of them reached the docks, but even now none of them enter *the city* or reach within one and one-half miles of the palaces on the river. The greatest harbor development is on the south side of the city, where water and rail lines interdigitate, where the great Petrograd Canal (27 feet in depth) reaches out 17 miles to deep water at Kronstadt; and where lumber docks and wharves are thoroughly modern and fully mechanized. The entire Gulf of Finland is dotted with lights and other aids to navigation, and ice-breakers strive to keep it open extra months in fall and spring when nature, if left alone, would close it.

Today Leningrad, no longer the capital, has many relic features; palaces are museums, or orphanages and asylums; government houses are factories and tenements; industry has multiplied and commercial opportunity has been seized; and both manufacturing and trade have grown. As Finns are residents in the rural parts, so Germans, Jews, Poles, and Letts have flocked to the city until Leningrad is as cosmopolitan as any Russian city except Odessa. Literacy is rising and has reached more than 80 per cent in the Leningrad Region. While the city population declined tremendously when the capital was moved and domestic strife upset all programs, the population in 1931 was estimated at 2,228,300.

The extraction, drying, and collecting of peat in the Leningrad region is mechanized. Here one tractor pulls three machines which turn the peat to promote its drying. (Courtesy Sovfoto)

Resources. As connections are demanded for a commercial region, so resources are imperative for an industrial region. The Leningrad Region mines no coal, or iron, or any metallic ores. For fuels and power it uses more peat than all else combined. Vegetable substitutes are used half as much as peat, wood 20 per cent as much as peat. Petroleum finds very small use because of the great distance to Russia's fields and the aversion to importing. In the west corner the same shales found productive in Estonia yield oil and gas when roasted; but the area is small, and both output and reserves are of little significance. Wood is still used on railroads. Communal enterprises and water transportation together use nearly as much wood as do the railroads, and the factories nearly as much as all other users combined. Much of the wood comes from local birch forests, which cover half the region, and from pine and fir patches toward the east where the climate is severer. The lumber industry is so stimulated by its proximity to great coniferous forests and hardwood areas that it maintains forty to seventy factories of which one fourth are sawmills and veneer and plywood plants, one fourth make finished lumber, and half devote their energies to paper-making. Matches are made in the towns. The Leningrad Region has access to and uses more water power than any region outside of the Caucasus, and from this power has come a high development of electric lighting devices. The industries of the city are as completely electrified as those of any Russian region, and a small area of 2,500 square miles around the city is more highly industrialized than a similar area around Moscow.

Fishermen of a collective farm pulling in a seine on the Neva River near Leningrad. Notice the sheds along the river bluff in which the fish are processed. (Courtesy Sovfoto)

The limestones and dolomites furnish a basis for the building trades. Limestone and calcareous tuff, with peat for fuel, feed a large cement industry in many towns. Bauxite, aluminum ore, at Tikhvin and hydro-electric power from the Volkhov stimulate a growing aluminum industry; sand sustains a flourishing glass industry in the city; and clays, the brick and tile industry in the small towns. Ocher for paints comes from residual deposits over some of the limestones.

Aside from fisheries of the Arctic regions and the sturgeon fisheries of the Caspian the Leningrad Region has the largest per capita and total fish production of any region, all of which comes from local waters.

Next to actual possession of resources upon which to build industries comes the opportunity to import raw materials needed. Leningrad imports coal from other countries as well as from other regions within the Union, notably from the southern part of the Moscow Region. Lumber comes from the coniferous forests, iron from the Lake Region, apatite for fertilizer works from Khibini in Kola, flax from the Valdai Hills, wool from the southeast. Wheat, shipped from the south, supplies large modern flour-mills; rubber and tobacco manufacturing became established long ago because crude rubber and raw tobacco could be imported to this coast city easily to employ native labor. Moscow, the nearest competitor, has about one fourth as great a rubber industry. Meat-packing prospers in both Leningrad and Moscow, with large modern plants. Distance to the tobacco fields of Crimea and Caucasus handicaps the tobacco industry, and, coupled with the strong feeling against importation, it may drive Leningrad's tobacco manufacturing to the land where tobacco grows.

Regional significance. All in all, the Leningrad Region is today just what it is best suited to be, commercial first and industrial second. In industry it is second only to Moscow; in commerce it excels all northern and western regions. Its foreign relations are much what the founder of the chief city desired, when he planned a place where Russian and West European could meet. Its industry is not built on its own resources and power but has risen because of the commerce and trade passing through and the resultant necessary change in means of transportation.

7. THE MOSCOW INDUSTRIAL REGION

Situation. An approximately rectangular area about 300 miles on a side, with no notable physical limits, surrounds the city and capital, Moscow, which stands far to the western border of the area. Important cities in the region with recent population estimates from recognized sources are Kaluga (90,000) at the southwest corner; Kalinin, formerly Tver (217,000), makes railroad cars; Rybinsk (140,000) makes river boats and printing-presses; Kostroma (125,000); Gorki (650,000), the former Nizhni-Novgorod, famous for fairs and manufactures; Tula (275,000) and Ryazan (96,000) process farm products; Yaroslavl (300,000) makes linens, synthetic rubber and tires; Ivanovo (290,000) uses peat to generate electrical power, makes chemicals; Serpukhov (91,000); these are a part of Moscow's industrial family. Each and many lesser towns have gained as much as 100 per cent in the last twenty years. Central in European Russia, both historically and geographically, the Moscow Region is an admirable place for a capital area and a capital city. In the modern régime much has been done to emphasize its central position by the development of radial railroads and the improvement of its waterways. The Baltic-Moscow canal was enlarged just before the Second World War.

Physiographically, the region is on a plain which descends gently from the Valdai Hills eastward, from altitudes of 600 and 700 feet to about

200 feet. Great rivers drain the plain eastward, the Volga in the north and Oka in the south, with the lesser Moskva and Klyazma in the central part. So low is the grade of the rivers that floods are frequent and severe. Where the Cheksna and Mologa come into the Volga near Rybinsk, great areas are inundated in high-water times, because the turn in the river retards the flow. A similar turn at Kostroma causes floods to broaden the river and to make an island of every swell or hummock, always decked with a village, a farm-house, or a little patch of timber. The simple old topography of the plain lends itself to a fine modern system of automobile roads connecting all important centers with the capital.

Geologically, the region may be looked upon as a shallow structural basin having younger rocks in the central part. No surface forms attest the structure. The region may be divided into two sections, a northern half where the Recent and Quaternary deposits more effectively mantle the older rocks, and a southern half where the cover is thinner and the outlines of the older geology can be deciphered. In the northern half southwest of Rybinsk a large area of Jurassic beds furnishes the clays for the pottery and china industry; north of Moscow a Cretaceous area does the same. East of Kostroma are Cretaceous beds of some value for lime, and east of Ivanovo, the center of the cotton industry, is an area of Permian beds of little value. Along the Volga between these Cretaceous and Permian areas are Jurassic rocks, which furnish phosphorite for fertilizer works and chemical industries.

South of Moscow an area of Jurassic rocks yields limestones and phosphorite, and east occur the sands that make the great glass factories possible. Farther south Carboniferous rocks are exposed and supply the lignitic coal of the Tula-Kaluga section, and farther east Permo-Triassic beds seem to be the sources of the iron for many furnaces. Everywhere the Quaternary and Recent clays, sands, and gravels are abundant. The Moscow region is admirably situated geologically for its splendid, varied industrial development.

People. Moscow is the modern name for a city built by the Moscovites, or Muscovites, who inhabited the central Russian plains in the very early days of the Christian Era. These people have been the most powerful, aggressive, and progressive of all Russians except possibly Ukrainians. They have been more warlike than the latter and have spread their governmental jurisdiction far and wide over the surrounding lands. Their distance from other nations and races has kept them a purer stock than many other Slavs and has restricted their intercourse with more progressive people beyond the Russian borders, from whom outlying Slavs have absorbed many ideas. Within the region are one great city of about 4,137,000 people, the several industrial cities named at the opening of this regional discussion, and thirty more sharing in the urban activities of the region; 150 villages of a more rural character give a mean density of rural population of over 100 per square mile. The rural population lives largely in the villages of 5,000 and under. This distribution is a response principally to need of protection on the plains, but partly to the growth of the *mir* type of social organization.

Literacy in the Moscow Region is increasing and already exceeds 80 per cent. The birth-rate is almost twice the death-rate, a fact which speaks well for climate, food supply, and modern sanitation.

Resources. Several of the geologic resources were mentioned in the paragraph on geology. No notable mineral wealth occurs in the region, but many minor deposits are developed. The lignitic coal in the south is good lignite and constitutes the largest reserve of coal in European Russia outside the Donetz Basin. Peat, at least one fifth as abundant as coal, furnishes its proportion of the fuel and is the cheapest producer of steam.

Soils of the region are podzolized clay-to-light-clay loams with large areas of sandy soils east of the city. In the south half of the area the soils grade into leached chernozems, as the coniferous forests give way to deciduous and the mean temperatures become a little greater. In all the region they are generally of glacial drift origin. The soils are young and because derived from drift will doubtless be long-lived.

The climate of this region partakes of the continental type more than does that farther west. Snow usually covers the ground 150 days of the year and attains at times depths of 16 to 24 inches; cloudiness exceeds 50 per cent most of the year and in winter mounts to 80 per cent. With the shortness of the days (six hours in December) characteristic of the latitude, this gloom becomes somewhat depressing. Sufficient rainfall for all crops that can stand the shortness of the growing season and the severity of the winters, together with the long days of sunlight in summer, make many crops possible and give to the Moscow Region a remunerative agriculture. For the best dietary results it should be heavily supplemented with subtropical fruits and spices, products of lands outside the Russian frontier.

Oats, rye, and barley are the leading cereals; wheat is grown sparingly; but the region does not lie in the major producing area of any cereal. It has too severe a climate. It does lie in the hemp- and flax-producing areas as well as in the apple belt. Cattle, sheep, and swine for food and horses for draft animals are raised in large numbers; pasture and hay with other forage crops occupy large areas of the farm lands. The vegetables cultivated are root crops such as turnips, rutabagas, carrots, beets, onions, radishes; or leaf crops, including lettuce, cabbage, and cauliflower, all of which do well. Small fruits—raspberries, blackberries, strawberries—and trees such as crab-apples, apricots, and plums all resist the weather and do well when planted and cared for, but enough fruits are not yet raised for local needs.

The entire Moscow Industrial Region is naturally a forest region, coniferous in the north and transitional toward deciduous in the south. Heavy cutting through two or three centuries, however, has reduced the actual forest to somewhere between 20 and 40 per cent of the area, depending upon the distance from the city and the railroads. All main lines seem to run through lanes wholly cleared of forest. Even between the railroads the low hills are only dotted with scores of small forest areas of pine, spruce, fir, and birch and, in the south, of oak and other deciduous trees. There yet remains enough timber for most of the lumber needs of the region. Whereas the state possesses most of the forests of northern Russia, in this area the scattered patches, trees from which are needed by the local farmer for fuel and shelter, are administered by the People's Committee of Agriculture.

Industries. Industry in Russia is divided by the census and the government into two classes, Census or great industry and Household or peasant industry. The former is new, and even under the so-called non-capitalistic régime has grown greatly in the last 10 to 15 years, because the government has assumed the rôle and responsibility of the capitalist and invests heavily in transportation and such industrial plants as it deems necessary. Peasant industry is carried on in the homes or in small enterprises in rural villages and small towns, and although not more than one third to one half as efficient per capita as in the factories it still persists in the cities side by side with the great federal industrial establishments.

Whether a plant or industrial set-up shall be classed as domestic-peasant-household or be counted as a census or great industry is determined by the size of the establishment, measured sometimes in workers, at other times in output or investment; but it does not depend upon the kind of raw material nor upon the nature of the finished product. In some cases an industry is so small that in no city does it assume census industry proportions; in some cases the nature of the industry lends itself best to the household type of work; in others it is simple to concentrate the work into a census industry establishment. [1]

The Moscow Region has more manufacturing than all the rest of Russia. State ownership of industry has gone further in this region than in others: 5 per cent is coöperative; less than 3 per cent is privately owned; over 90 per cent is owned and operated by the state. Federal authority is strong around the capital.

---

[1] Census industries as listed in the reports of the government are (1) iron, steel, manganese (black metals); (2) fuels; (3) gold, silver, platinum, lead, zinc, copper (colored metals); (4) machine-building (electrotechnical and agricultural machinery); (5) lumber and wood-finishing; (6) salt; (7) chemical industries (basic, lacquers and paints, soaps, rubber and chemico-pharmaceutical); (8) flour-milling; (9) vegetable oils (linseed and sunflower); (10) beet sugar; (11) tobacco and liquors; (12) leather and leather goods; (13) textiles (cotton, flax, hemp, jute, wool, silk); (14) extraction and finishing of minerals; (15) ceramics; (16) power (hydro- and carbo-electric); (17) mechanical engines (steam, gasoline, and alcohol).

Household or peasant industries are listed similarly as (1) extraction and finishing of clays, stones, etc.; (2) metal industries (smithing); (3) wood-finishing; (4) foods and condiments; (5) finishing hard materials of animal origin such as bone, horn, hoof, leather, and furs; (6) textiles; (7) toilet articles.

Climate and proximity to hills and lakes suggest reasons for the smaller use of water power in this region than in the last, and the lesser distance to the oil fields in the southeast may explain the larger use of petroleum for power. The urgent need for power compels a more extensive use of peat here than in all other regions combined. One can see that some pressure must be exerted on a region no better endowed naturally than this to make of it a first-rank industrial region, and this pressure the government exerts wherever the conditions offer any promise of success. Industry is more electrified in the Moscow Region than in any other in spite of its comparatively meager water power. Lignitic coal, mined extensively in the southern reaches of the region, and peat, which can be taken from a thousand bogs, are both converted into electric power. Wood from many forest areas and petroleum imported from the Caucasus Region both encourage industry. But when all are put to the best use and production is at its height, the Moscow fuel production is little more than 5 per cent of that of the Donetz Basin.

Iron, mined from four deposits east of Moscow and smelted in six furnaces near the Cretaceous limestone outcrops, utilizes a favorable combination of materials. Thus produced, the iron goes to Moscow and is made into machines for local factories; or it goes to Kolomna and Sormovo to supply locomotive works, freight-car shops, and tractor factories; or to the docks on the Volga, where the fleet of steamers is continually recruited. The ceramic and chemical industries, based on the clays, sand, and pyrite in the northeast section, flourish in several centers in and round Ivanovo, and their products take river steamer at Kineshma (80,000), on the Volga. Jaroslavl makes rubber tires and brakes, manufacturing cord, rubber, and asbestos for them. Ivanovo was made a linen manufacturing center by Peter the Great and still prospers, supplied with fiber from the thousands of acres of flax to the west. Cotton manufactures share the labor and shipping facilities, but the raw cotton must be shipped in from Asia (Siberia) or foreign lands. Serpukhov, south of Moscow, is also in the girdle of spinning and weaving towns so well set as to raw materials, climate, power, and market. Orekhovo-Zuevo (100,000) is one of a number of highly industrialized towns east of the capital engaged in textile manufacture. Its chief product is a wool drugget, often red, to capture the rural or peasant market. Vorsma and Pavlovo have long been famous for their locks, keys, cutlery, and surgical instruments. Tula in the midst of the coal-fields manufactures arms, and samovars of copper and nickel, while around it are acres of horticultural plots and rows of nursery stock, the center from which goes a large supply of young trees for reforestation and ornamental planting.

Gorki was founded in 1221 at the strategic junction of the Oka with the Volga, about 250 miles east of Moscow. The upper city with its Kremlin and most of the attractive residences occupies a hill, or bluff of the river, nearly 400 feet above the water. The lower part, spreading along the Oka and Volga, contains banks, wholesale stores, and other commercial institutions of the city. The river district occupies low land between the rivers and consists of the factories, a large harbor development with great warehouses, and the ground and buildings of the Fair, directly connected with the city by a bridge across the Oka. Formerly known as Nizhni-Novgorod, it was for many years among the most distinguished commercial centers of Slavdom. Dry-docks and yards for boat-building occupy a section of the

An automatic machine-tool line drilling holes in beams for freight cars in a plant at Moscow.
(Courtesy Sovfoto)

river front; hundreds of great river steamers are here constructed, many having a draft of 20 to 25 feet and a length of 400 to 500 feet. Men from Persia, India, China, and other eastern countries came to buy and to sell and gave to this city a cosmopolitan and Oriental flavor rare in Europe. More than a hundred years ago the commercial importance of the Fair began to decline. Railroad construction contributed to its loss of prestige, and the Suez Canal disturbed its commerce notably; but, except for the years of civil war, the Fair has opened annually about August 1. Gorki manufactures window-glass, tools, kitchen utensils, agricultural machinery, and zinc products. It has an automobile plant producing annually 100,000 cars. Rural peasant industries are especially well maintained here because of their outlet in the Fair. They are strong in woodworking, the finishing of wood, and toy-making, a specialization favored by the proximity of the great coniferous forests. The city has been long a notable cultural center and is the birth-place of several statesmen, authors, and musicians. Besides its admirable water transportation facilities three railroads meet at the city, one of which reaches to the Siberian road.

Suzdal, an ancient capital of commerce and religion, stands a few miles north of Vladimir, about 110 miles northeast of Moscow on the Kamenka River, a branch of the Klyazma. It so well expressed the trading motive and spirit of the older Russia that even though it is now only a district town it may find place in our survey. Founded before Moscow, Suzdal was a factory in the Hudson Bay Company sense, a center where furs and other products were gathered for shipment to cities, and where supplies were distributed to the hunters, trappers, and farmers. Its buildings were of wood from the adjacent forests and were massive and strong. It became, in 1125, a center of religious education for northeast Russia. Its Kremlin still stands; and beside it the great trading square and the monastery of 1207, one of the oldest in Russia. This is the type of town that prospered in the early Russia where wild animals and the forest, dotted with primitive independent agriculture, provided the basis for subsistence, and where heathen natives furnished the opportunity for pious expansion of religious and educational ideals.

Kostroma, another Volga city, rises in terraces from the water front. Contrary to the usual geographic adjustment, the residential area is in the smoky, dusty eastern part. The urge for water transportation directly from and to the mills seems to have been stronger than the desire of the residents to live on the windward side of town. One great linen plant in the western part along the river employs 11,000 workers. Other linen plants and metal workings share this area. Thousands of acres of potatoes are grown in the sandy plains north and east of Moscow, and Kostroma shares with Jaroslavl the task of converting many of them into starch and even into syrup.

Moscow. In all the chronicles of Russia, the first mention of this flourishing, once aristocratic, industrial capital was about 1147, when it was only a defenseless villa with its appurtenances on the gently rolling glacial-till plain beside a humble stream (Moskva River), a way station between Suzdal and Kiev. The river, here about 600 feet wide, is divided by a crescentic sand island ¼ mile wide by 2 miles long. Furthermore, the river here makes a group of three sweeping meanders, like the Seine at Paris, thus offering three areas nearly surrounded by water. The old fortifications were first a wooden stockade with towers, placed beside the river and between the Neglinka and another lesser tributary. Moskva and these tributaries served as moats for the fortress. This wooden wall was succeeded by a great stone wall, which surrounded the Kremlin with its palaces, cathedral, churches, and arsenal. This Kremlin has been stormed, burned, and rebuilt several times. It was built not on one of the meander tongues but on the outer or cutting side of the river opposite the toe-cap island. Later a stone wall was built to surround the Kremlin and about twice as much adjacent city area—the Kitai Gorod (White City). A second great wall, the "Chinese Wall," was erected concentric with the first and a half-mile outside it, extending horseshoe-like from the river around the city to the river again.

Moscow, the present capital city. Note the Kremlin triangular area in the central part and the first, second, and third walls, mostly demolished. The great Moskva River winds about in the plains. (Adapted from a *Guide Book to Soviet Union* [Berlin, 1929])

And at a later date a third longer circular wall, an earth rampart with a radius of 1½ miles, surrounded the second, enclosed much more city, crossed the river at two points, and included most of the island and a square mile of city that had grown within the meander loop opposite the Kremlin. Fortified monasteries and suburbs stood outside the earthen wall and guarded every radial highway. Only remnants of these walls, save that of the Kremlin, may still be seen at several places along their respective circuits, but boulevards follow their former courses, and a circum-urban electric tram-line follows the outer one completely around. The city now reaches in every direction 2 to 4 miles beyond the largest wall circuit.

To account for a great city in the midst of the central Russian plains one must note that in the early days the land was a forest wilderness where the only routes were waterways. Portages thus became significant and route intersections doubly so. This would apply not only to commercial and colonizing journeys but to political missions as well. The Volga for centuries furnished a great highway for Tatar invasion as well as for Tatar trade; and its tributary, the Oka, was frequently an alternative route for travel from Nizhni-Novgorod to Smolensk, Wilno, and the Baltic, preferred to the colder Volga route via Riga or the Gulf of Finland. Then the Moskva led half-way from Middle Oka to Volga, and their respective tributaries bridged the gap, save for a short portage. Moscow is on this connecting route as well as on the navigable Moskva. Further, a great highway for boats and for vehicles led along the Klyazma; and the Moskva, bending northward where Moscow arose, approaches closely to this highway. It was no accident that the villa, then the Kremlin, and later the city were located at this intersection of routes. Important in colonizing movements and then in trade journeys, central for the Great Russians and nearly as well centered for European Russia, it is so far in from Russian frontiers that only the more violent of external foes reached it—even Napoleon and the Nazi armies were so far exhausted when they arrived that their victorious arrival became a dismal defeat. Its very internal protection made Moscow somewhat of a refuge from alien marginal pressure. Its economic, colonizing, and then political significances increased as its routes were used. No doubt the House of Prince Daniel [2] was a factor in the rise of this capital, for it seemed to know how to embrace and develop advantages of position. In later decades canals have connected rivers over portages, and railroads have contributed tremendously to the growth of the hub at the center of the spokes.

The great meander curves of the river give about 15 miles of river front on each bank, whereas a straight river through the city would yield less than half that frontage. Monasteries, palaces, and many fine buildings in the massive, plain Russian style occupy intermural grounds. Most of them are now used for government offices, museums, and other public buildings. Factories and mills abound in the borders of the city, but residences and shops fill in the space among the public buildings and old walls or boulevards. A geographic city profile or landscape here as in many Russian cities must now include new types of office buildings, apartment and residence halls, radio palaces, technical schools, and "palaces of culture

[2] Prince Daniel of Moscow (1261-1302) annexed to his domains, by force and purchase, many towns and villages.

and rest." Eleven railway lines, none of which get within the outer wall, connect the city with all parts of the Union, although no road connects with any other across the city. Moscow is a terminal on each line. A belt line crossing the river four times connects all railroads in the outskirts of the city. Many miles of modern artistic subways serve the city's traveling public. A ship canal connects Moscow wharves with the Volga 80 miles north near Kalinin. Moscow is also the center of the nation's government air service radiating to all cities of note in the U.S.S.R. and of a dozen lines leading directly to as many important European cities. Moscow's industrial plants, forming a circuit around the city but not penetrating within the old, outer, earthen wall, are admirably served by the railroads and operated by current from a great high-tension net connecting a score of hydro- and carbo-electric plants. Industries, like the railroads, arrived too late in the history of the city to get far within. This does not, however, exclude the household industries, which still rank well in the city.

Motor works and many plants for making machines take the iron from the steel mills east of the city. Makers of farm implements and machinery draw on the same sources and on the forests for raw materials and supply the rural workers throughout the region. Flour-mills use local rye and wheat as well as Ukrainian products and supply the large local market. Mills grind the flaxseed shipped from the Valdai Hills, Ukraine, and Moscow regions and press the linseed oil, used in paints and in linoleum factories, from the oilcake, which becomes stock food. Beer is made from barley brought from White Russia, and liquor, starch, and syrup from local potatoes. Moscow ranks second in the shoe industry, making with Leningrad about 90 per cent of all Russian factory shoes; it is an important leather center, utilizing local hides and leather as well as supplies from the southeast cattle regions. Moscow is preëminently a textile center, making over 80 per cent of all Russian factory textiles.

Cotton is brought from the warm south Siberian cotton lands and imported from the United States to supply the city's spindles and looms. Wool is essentially home-grown and is gathered far and wide over Russia for Moscow's fabrication. Localization here of skill and market seems to be the strongest factor, but the fact that small parcels of both wool and silk goods contain large values must be an additional reason for such centralization in both lines as is here found. Silk is imported to supply the silk-mills, notwithstanding Russia's desire to furnish all its own raw materials. While there has been much effort and considerable success in industrialization, weaving persists in the homes. Cotton and especially silk manufacturing make large use of the household loom and peasant skill.

The city for centuries was a typically proud, aristocratic capital and still maintains many marks of early splendor in buildings and boulevards, but the modern metropolitan aspect of industry, commerce, and government without pomp and parade so greatly overshadows the older glory that the appearance of the latter occasionally startles one. Much has come to the city because it was, and is again, the capital of a great nation.

8. THE VALDAI HILLS REGION— AGRICULTURAL AND INDUSTRIAL

Position. Consult Geographic Region Map, page 502, for the location, size, and shape of Valdai Hills Region. The area is twice as long as wide, embracing 57,000 square miles, equal to Illinois. The region has a definite western boundary for some distance in the feeble scarp or cuesta of the lower Carboniferous strata, which dip eastward and disappear under Quaternary sediments and drift. Southward, even the cuesta goes under Quaternary beds, and scattered lakes and lake-beds testify to the marked youth of the surface. The region as here outlined contains more land to the southeast than the Valdai Hills, properly speaking, but land better described with the hills than with any other region.

Topography. While the Carboniferous bed-rock gives form and altitude to the region, nearly all detail is due to glaciation and post-glacial erosion. Drift, often in well-developed moraine, mantles the bed-rock, conceals preglacial old topography, and holds multitudes of lakes and lake-beds now filled with organic matter or drained by meager post-glacial erosion. The largest lake, Lake Seliger, covering about 100 square miles, sprawls among moraine hummocks near the highest summits of the Hills, and like other lakes and streams furnishes a large supply of fresh-water fish. The moraines culminate in Kamennik at 1,073 feet and in these heights arise the Volga, Dvina, Volkhov, and Dnieper rivers.

No purer Russian stock occupies any region of Russia than that in the Valdai Hills. The Great Russians spread up through this rural land, but neither Tatar from the east nor Finn and Est from the west seems to have contributed much to the population. Why? The present population averages about 65 per square mile.

Resources. Coal, in part lignite, in part anthracite, is worked in the northwest, and the Moscow coal area extends into the southern part. Peat is found and worked in every quarter, but particularly from the central part northward. Forests cover 20 to 30 per cent of the region, and lumbering has scarcely begun in them. Conifers dominate in the north and yield to deciduous trees in the south. Brick and tile clays are very extensively used, particularly in the north. Fire-clays supply refractory linings for many furnaces. As a region, the Hills are second to the Moscow Region in both products as well as in chinaware, glass, and cement. These industries are relatively new and largely state-owned, but 58 per cent, a large proportion for such a rural region, is carried on in the homes. Few large plants for any industry have been built in the region. Borovichi in the north is far-famed for its diagonal or twill cloth, also for ceramics, sulphur from pyrite, coal and paper.

Agricultural products outvalue all other resources, and rural workers outnumber all others combined. Commerce and government claim less than 5 per cent each. Only 5 or 6 per cent of the people migrate seasonally for work.

Flax-growing leads all non-food crops. The flax belt extends entirely across the hills and into both the White Russian and the Moscow Region. Flax is threshed among the hills and some of the seed is ground and pressed for linseed oil, but all the fiber and a large proportion of the seed go to the mills of the Moscow Region, or of Leningrad.

A common rural type of transportation. Note that three horses are used to pull a small wagon; also the heavy winter garments.

Smolensk (160,000), the only city in the region, is an ancient center with all the advantage of a site on the Dnieper as well as of nearness to the northern tribes and states. Much of its former river trade and all its east and west commerce have been taken over by the railroads, three of which serve the city.

Regional significance. The Valdai Hills, even with their coal and peat resources, never would have become industrial but for their position on the highways from Moscow to Leningrad and Moscow to Warsaw. Even so, the southern part is but little industrialized, while the northern shares generously with both bordering industrial areas. As a forest and food-producing region, it is of much help to the industrial centers. As a grower of flax and to a much less extent of hemp, it has long played a leading part in European life. Its flax fiber was shipped to Ireland for many generations to be manufactured by the much more skilful Celts.

9. CENTRAL URAL MINING AND INDUSTRIAL REGION

Boundaries. This region is a little larger than the last and probably more specifically set off from its neighbors. Its unity attaches to its mountainous structure, its mineral wealth, and its altitude, about half that of other parts of the Urals. Geologically, it is a part of the late Paleozoic fold that rose on the 60th meridian east, but it differs from the extremities of the fold in being more complex, especially in having more intrusions of granites, porphyries, trachytes, and diabases, and possessing more complicated folding of the strata, and much greater width than either extremity. Mineralogically, it has been signally blessed with gold, platinum, iron ore, manganese, copper, chromium, nickel, pyrite, zinc, and arsenic among metals; salt, barite, magnesite, corundum, asbestos, talc, graphite, tripoli, and phosphates among non-metallics; coal (anthracite, bituminous, lignite), oil shale, and peat as fuels; and marble, granite, limestone, cement rock, and sand among building materials. Gold in placers and quartz veins is still worked, but the platinum seems to be nearly exhausted. The Central Urals are less of a barrier than either the northern or southern parts. Summits in this region rarely reach 4,000 feet, and many broad mature to old valleys are below 650 feet. Topography is so old that one can cross by train and not sense the mountains at all. The boundaries of the region are set on the east and west where the strata cease to be folded, and on the north and south where the rich mineralization dies out. On the north this occurs at about 61° N. and on the south at about 53° N. The region averages about 150 miles in width.

Forests. Coniferous forests persist a little farther south in Central Urals than in the bordering plains, because on the mountains and in the continental interior the climate becomes too severe for the deciduous trees; hence the Central Urals are predominately coniferous with but a transitional sprinkling of deciduous species in the south. Primeval forests thickly covered all when man began his occupation of this region. But mining, building, railroad construction, and in later years wood-pulping, the development of power, and other wood-consuming occupations and industries have entered the field so that nearly half the region is cleared and devoted to pasture, meadows, and cultivation.

People. A borderland, a mountain land, to say nothing of a land of mineral wealth, is liable to have a lawless, mixed population; and the Central Ural Region is no exception. Tatar hordes have crossed the mountains many times, left relic colonies in the valleys and tribes of grazers on the hills with Bashkirs reaching to the western slopes. Slavs have surged up and over in a more or less continuous stream ever since Siberia became a penal asylum, until Great Russians and other Russians of the wilder or more restless sort make up more than 50 per cent of the population. The pioneer, prospector, frontier types of Russians are the most numerous. In recent decades mining and construction engineers have taken their places among the rest; and, since the Republic was established, industrial engineers, builders, manufacturers, railroad men, and many types of administrators have arrived. Thus the population has become cosmopolitan, energetic, virile, not lawless so much as progressive, and withal a productive group of people.

Industries. Agriculture engages about half the workers; industry (census and household) employs many, while commerce comes third; mining and lumbering, once foremost, have been pushed to subordinate ranks. The rise of industry came late, partly under the stimulus of the first five-year plan. In recent years local water power, coal from Karaganda, and petroleum from the Caucasus and Perm fields supplement local coal reserves and abundant peat supplies.

Mineral industries of the Mid-Urals arose in the nineteenth century and stimulated many cities. Iron from local sources in a score of places along the mountains has called for twenty-six furnaces. Manganese with the magnetite in the south contributes to manganese steel, and abundant limestones aid the smelting. The iron industry in the Central Urals is not surpassed by that of the Donetz Industrial Region.

Hundreds of workers mine and manufacture lead and copper. Reserves of the latter are estimated at 10 million tons. About ten salt mines in the extreme northwest of the area produce annually $100,000 worth of salt, both common and potassium salts, to be used in packing hides and furs and to be shipped to the Moscow area for domestic uses and chemical industries. Solikansk potassium deposits supply fertilizer plants and export potassium to other European countries and America. Flour-mills in Sverdovsk and Cheliabinsk grind wheat, shipped from the southeast, to be used by the workers in the Central Urals. As a home industry, boot and shoe making flourishes because hides, tanbark, leather, and a strong market are all in the Central Ural Region.

Since so much of the industrial development is very recent, it is strongly governmental and in the census industry class. Small industry employs about 35 of each 1,000 persons and is largely rural. Very little hydroelectric power is developed. Streams are small and winters are severe, but the fall in the streams is quite sufficient for any use the region now has for them.

Towns. These Central Urals have seven towns of urban type and over sixty villages of 1,000 to 5,000, but no cities. Cheliabinsk (275,000) a district town in the southeastern corner of this region, lies well east of the Ural axis and has large deposits of brown coal worked in open cuts which are estimated to have reserves of 400 million tons. It borders on the Asiatic wheat fields, for which it manufactures tractors and other rural machinery.

Zlatousk (100,000) has a beautiful river situation at the southern border of the Central Ural Region; it has a famous side-arms factory, a blast
furnace and iron foundry employing 15,000 workers, and ceramic plants
using many hundred workers. Local iron, coal, and clays enter into these
industries.

A skillful gear maker prepares equipment for a new power station. (Courtesy Sovfoto)

Sverdlovsk (426,000), the Ekaterinburg of pre-Revolution days, founded
over 200 years ago as a station on the way to Siberia, has now become the
center of the Central Ural Mining Region. It has a copper electrolytic plant
using local ores. The Trans-Siberian railroad passes through the city, and
four other roads connect it with neighboring and distant towns, with mining
centers and lumber-mills, so that its heavy machinery can be shipped to
tractor and combine-harvester factories and to steel-mills.

Perm (285,196) enjoys an attractive river site on a bluff of the Kama,
below which are wharves stretching several miles along the river. Three
streams with as many highways converge on the city from the northern

part of the region. Permian and Carboniferous rocks with their rich coal-fields spread south and east of the city. Copper was discovered many years ago and petroleum recently; both contribute to industry in Perm. At the head of navigation it has large boat-building docks. Phosphate rocks from the borders of the Coniferous Forest Region, fuel, and sulphide ores make possible the important superphosphate works, and multitudes of milking machines made in Perm go to the dairies of the Volga Plains.

Nizhnii Tagil (160,000) marks the contact of porphyries and basic rocks in the district, and has obtained great wealth from alluvial platinum deposits along many streams and lake shores. Copper-zinc mines occur north of town, and metallurgical and machine-building works reduce the ore and make electrical and other machines. Enormous reserves are claimed for the locality, and consequently an active future.

Magnitogorsk (150,000) and Verkhne-Uralsk (20,000) are iron and steel towns on the upper Ural River in the midst of great reserves of easily worked titaniferous magnetic iron ore, and fifty miles southwest from the Bakal mine, which furnishes an abundance of brown hematite equal to the best Swedish ore. Magnetite reserves are estimated at 200 million tons. The iron and steel industries spread over the lower slopes of the old hills, with a plant complete in every respect. Eight or more open-hearth furnaces are in operation. Coal is imported from Karaganda in exchange for iron ore; hence both places have smelters. Coke-ovens in several modern batteries serve the steel-mills at Magnitogorsk. Rows of tall storage tanks for gas from the coke-ovens constitute a part of the geographic landscape. Magnitogorsk is a planned city. It spreads up the hills from the plains in a great semicircle with radial and concentric streets; peripheral areas have more rectangular blocks where topography permits. Its population is increasing rapidly as subsidiary industries arrive to absorb the iron and steel made here.

Handicaps. The Central Ural Region has a severe climate and is far from other centers of population, yet its mineral wealth is so varied and so great that an industrial status seems secured. The agricultural opportunities are limited, as are those of northern Labrador in America, by the characteristic high-latitude, continental climatic conditions; yet it is a region much more favored than many places in similar latitudes, so that hardy cereals, root crops, leafy vegetables, and the hardy bush fruits are grown. The need of importation of wheat is met by the product of fields to the southeast. Other warmer-climate products should be imported, even from beyond Russian borders, to make balanced rations and a balanced budget.

QUESTIONS

1. In these four regions how serious a handicap on industrial development is the high latitude and corresponding climate?

2. Compare and contrast the Moscow Region with the Birmingham, England, Region and the Belgium Industrial Belt as to possibilities for great industrial evolution.

3. Why do canals and rivers play so important a rôle in Central Russian commercial activities? Of what significance is their presence and importance to railroad development?

4. Which of these four regions has the best natural foundation for a strong industrial region? Explain.

5. To what extent should any of these four regions draw on other regions of Russia for resources or raw materials? on other nations?

6. What is the geographic answer to a proposal that a nation buy as little of other nations and sell as much to them as possible?

7. What are the reasons for thinking that Gorki will maintain the position of Nizhni-Novgorod as the seat of a great fair?

CHAPTER 26

Central Rural Regions

We the millet seed in the field have sown.

—Folk Song

10. GLACIATED PLAINS

The region. A more or less rectangular unit of Russian *desiatins* [1] lying along the western border from the Leningrad Industrial Region southward to Ukraine can be called the region of Glaciated Plains. It is about 510 miles long north and south, about 160 miles wide in north half and 275 miles wide in south half, and includes about 110,000 square miles. The increased southern width represents a section of Poland and the northern part of German East Prussia annexed to Russia at the close of the Second World War.

From lakes Ilmen and Peipus southward the underlying rocks are Devonian strata, dipping gently southward at first, then rising southward until Silurian and Cambrian beds may be seen near Minsk. In the southern half of the region, alluvium, drift, and lacustrian deposits cover the bed-rock so completely that the underlying structure is almost unknown; but outcrops are of frequent occurrence in the northern half, and limestone is quarried in several places. The region was peneplained before the ice age; but glacial deposition greatly disturbed the simple pre-glacial drainage patterns. In their intermittent retreat, the glaciers left many concentric moraines with their hummocky surface, scattered boulders of Scandinavian rocks, and abundance of sand and gravel. Gravel is so abundant and so widely distributed in the northern part as to make agriculture difficult and forest the best-adapted vegetation. Here coniferous forests were almost continuous before Great Russians and Karelians cut clearings for farms, pastures, and rural villages. Deciduous trees predominate in the south until one reaches the morainic divide in the higher, drier surroundings of Vitebsk, Mogilev, and Minsk, the capital. Included are the Pripet marshes, where 20,000 square miles are so ill-drained that moor and morass prevail. These swamps are being drained and healed of their menace to health. Agriculture is

[1] Units of land. One *desiatin* is about 2.70 acres or 109 ares (metric).

PLACE NAMES — SOUTHERN RUSSIA

On this map may be found most of the towns and other places in southern Russia mentioned in Chapters 26-29. (Adapted from several sources)

everywhere backward and difficult; valuable forest is almost wanting in this marshland. A little bluff on a branch of the Dnieper River in the southeast corner of the region is occupied by Gomel (145,000). Where the Devonian rocks occur in the north there are many sink-holes and lost streams, but the subsurface drainage is yet as imperfect as that above. Many lakes have been filled with vegetation and now present only wet lake plains.

The people. Most of this region is occupied by that stock of eastern Slavs known as White Russians, with a population density of 25 to 125 per square mile. The lower figure generally obtains in the south, whereas on the higher land containing the three centrally placed towns the figure rises to 175 per square mile. The region contains the northern part of East Prussia with Koenigsberg, now Kaliningrad (368,433), and a large part of pre-War II northeast Poland with the old city of Wilno, Vilnyus now (209,000). Many Poles and Germans in these annexed areas have migrated to their respective homelands, leaving Russians in possession. Both Eastern and Western churches fought for supremacy here. White Russian individuality is less a result of dialect or race than it is of western influence and long separation from the rest of Russia.

This region is believed to be the most rural of all European Russia, its urban percentage standing at about 13. The good health and vigor of its people are manifest in the birth-rate of about 41 per 1,000, which, with a death-rate of 16 to 17 per 1,000, explains the rapid increase of population. The backwardness is nurtured by a literacy of only about 50 per cent. Both may be accounted for by the frontier situation, the need of drainage, meager resources, primitive communications, and the consequent vigorous, out-of-door life.

The resources. Lakes in the north are the basis for a lively fishing industry, but the streams, in spite of natural reservoirs, furnish scanty power. In the region as a whole, forests are the greatest natural resource and account for the frequency of heavy wooden houses and for the export of tar and pitch, produced as a peasant industry. Thousands of logs are floated down the Dvina to Riga for export. Hemlock and oak furnish tanbark and thus assist the tanning industry, which in turn supplies the leather for an active peasant leather industry.

Aside from the limestone, clay, and sand, the region is most poverty-stricken in minerals and rocks. Sand is used in a half-dozen glass factories and clays in more brick plants. The absence of coal, oil, gas, iron, manganese, salt, and copper must mean very little industrial development. Peat is plentiful and is used for fuel; wood is used with it for manufacturing and power; coal from the Moscow Region supplies the railroads. Besides these items much substitute domestic fuel is used, such as weeds, trash, and brush.

Soils are excellent, still immature, formed of the subforest podzolized clays and sandy loams in the north, with sandy soils and large areas of peat bogs in the south. In detail the lakes and bogs occur on the concave

A part of the Pripet Marshes near the old Polish border. (Courtesy Sovfoto)

sides of moraines, while sand and gravel flats occupy the convex sides where outwash was spread by melt-water as the moraine was built. On these sandy soils the forests flourish.

Forest cover and resources are carefully conserved by an excellent system of cutting and planting. Planting is mostly of coniferous species. In the forests, bears, wolves, elk, and European bison furnish excellent hunting and a small fur trade.

The crops. Very little is raised beyond the local needs. Almost 10 per cent of all northern crops is flax, which is grown everywhere. After threshing, the flax is shipped to Moscow and the Valdai Hills for manufacture, and the seed goes to Moscow to have its oil expressed. Hemp is grown in the southern part for export to Ukraine. No flax, linseed, or hemp enters local industries.

The rainfall of 22 to 24 inches, augmented locally in the high midlands by relief to 28 inches, is ample for agriculture in this latitude, where evaporation is not great and the growing season is short. Root crops for both man and beast abound. Cattle and sheep find pasture in summer and eat beets and turnips in the winter. Butter and cheese are produced as abundantly as in Ukraine; more of both are made in this region, in spite of its small size, than in both the Upper Don and the Volga Plains.

The industries. The industrial population of the whole area ranges from 10 to 20 per 1,000, but near Pskov it rises to 30 to 50 per 1,000. In and around Vitebsk (172,000) and Minsk (240,000) about one third of all industry is of census type, but through rural parts the proportion is much less; peasant industry comprises 92 per cent of the total for the region. Manufactures use the crops and native products; there is no metal-working or machine-building even for rural purposes, no beets or beet sugar, no basic chemical industries; flour-milling is of peasant type only. Clays near Minsk supply a large brick industry, and local grains serve distilleries and breweries. Minsk owes much to its position on a highway intersection, the value of which increased when railroads were built from Warsaw to Moscow and Ukraine and from Leipaja to the interior of Russia. But before the railroads came, Minsk was the capital of the White Russians, the seat of an old university, and a religious center for Jews, Catholics, Eastern Church, Protestants (Lutherans), and Moslems. A little lumber is sawed and plywood made, but there are few finished wood articles. Vitebsk maintains a clothing factory and knitting mills of note, using local wool. Barley is grown in the northern section, and the grain is made into beer. Hides in many places are made into leather, and much leather is shipped to more industrialized regions. The people of the region do not make even their own felt footwear, a common industry in the interior. Among articles made in the peasant workshops are clothing, toilet articles, foods, condiments, and ornaments of horn; there is not enough of anything except leather goods for local demands. Because of these items of production and industry, commerce remains indifferent. The high barrier in the central part of the region never was high or continuous enough to check intercourse across it. The short routes to the Baltic were never significant except for the shipment of logs from Vitebsk down the Dvina. Stream-directed commerce south from Minsk, Mogilev, and Gomel converges on Kiev, while a canal above Mogilev (99,440) connects its river with the Dvina at Vitebsk. With short portages over divides a water route serves between Novgorod near lake Ilmen and Istanbul, via Smolensk and Kiev. Wheat was and still is

Village on a Minsk highway. (Courtesy U.S. Dept. of Agriculture)

shipped from the south through Smolensk and across this region to Novgorod, but in olden times Moscow could starve its rival, Novgorod, by intercepting its vital food stream. This throttle hold helps to explain why Novgorod came to depend on Moscow.

The niche in Russian economy. This glaciated region not only is rural but must so remain. It does export logs, and should continue to do so; it may develop phases of the lumber and wood-pulp industry. It can best fit into evolving Russia by increasing leather production, dairy products, and lumber until it can buy manufactures and share in education and other advantages making for higher standards of living.

11. UPPER DON RURAL PLAINS

The region. This rural region contains about 160,000 square miles spread in a triangular area over the upper Don Basin. About two thirds of it is drained by the Don and one sixth each by the Oka of the Volga system and the Desna of the Dnieper system. The average altitude does not exceed 500 feet. In the south and in the Oka valleys most of the plain is below the average; but the cities, Kursk, Bryansk (87,473), and Orel in the west and Penza in the east, occupy lands over 500 feet in elevation. Two thirds of the floor of this region consists of Cretaceous rocks with more resistant Paleocene capping them in the south and east, and with Devonian showing through the younger rocks in the north central section near the coal-fields of Tula. All formations are nearly horizontal. The drift and some of the bed-rocks are weak and permit the carving of many youthful valleys; but because relief is feeble, valleys are never deep. Moraines trail away from the Valdai Hills toward the southwest, across the western part of the region and on south to Kremenchug in Ukraine. Though feeble, the relief had marked directive influence on the ice flow. The higher western portions restrained it, while on each side the lowlands allowed it to flow far south. In the central lowlands the ice spread in a great lobe 240 miles wide and 275 miles long, almost to the Donetz Basin. Again the hills east of this lobe, held up by the Paleocene rocks, stayed the ice flow and gave its eastern margin a north-south direction for 450 miles, from the Don near the mouth of Khoper River to the Volga River east of Gorki. This lobe in the Cretaceous Don Basin much resembled the Scioto lobe in Ohio.

Rocks and minerals. Glass sands and china clays in the western part extend the ceramic industry of the Glaciated Plains a few miles into this region. Fire-clays foster manufacture of refractories; tripoli supplies abundant abrasives; ferruginous clays make mineral paints. Eight occurrences of iron ore are known, and magnetic anomalies northeast of Kharkov suggest another body. No coal is known; yet one iron-mill smelts and casts iron, and other mills are contemplated. Abundant limestones provide ore flux, carry small values of lead ore, and contain rich, though not used, beds of phosphorite. Quartzite in the central Cretaceous is worked in two places for refractories. The glacial deposits, rich in gravel and sand, are used sparingly for roads. This region has very little mineral wealth upon which to build industries; agricultural opportunities are so much better that rural occupations must be expected to prevail.

Soils and forests. Except in a few small areas soils have reached maturity. In the northwest, Orel to Ryazhsk and eastward, soils are strongly leached, clayey, and loamy chernozems. A broad strip south of this one, extending from Kursk and Donetz region to Tenza, has a rich, deep chernozem with spots of podzolized soil on top. The southern portion of the region has mostly chernozems passing, in the extreme south, into chestnut, clayey loams, subarid to steppe, which bear spots of alkali. Where the glacial lobe advanced in the lowland, soils are deep, dense, and poorly drained by a network of tributaries of the Don; on the highlands on each side unglaciated soils are in the main permeable and permit free infiltration of water and satisfactory drainage.

The western end of the region has abundant deciduous forest with scattered conifers. All the central part is prairie steppe of varied grass types. In the southern part the steppe prairies are covered with colored feather-grass. Although the forests have been greatly depleted by cutting and occur only in little patches, becoming few and small eastward, a rigid forestry system prevails. Deciduous planting has begun. Building and fuel uses of wood are important. Fuel wood is, however, used sparingly; farm refuse, weeds, stubble, and fence-row brush constitute the leading fuel substitutes. Near the glacial borders many relic plants left by glaciation tempt the botanist.

Agriculture. In this region of extensive plains the rural population and rural activities make up over 92 per cent of all. Russia as a whole is 83 per cent rural. Moisture adequate for general agriculture falls in all parts— 20 to 22 inches; and almost all unforested land is good for cultivation or meadow. Spring wheat does well in the northern parts of this area with rye, potatoes, and other root crops. Winter wheat in the south with barley, grapes, plums, and prunes supply most of the peasant needs. Wheat is a large export item in the vicinity of Tambov, from which place trainloads depart to Saratov and Moscow. Many windmills grind the grain, and in recent years there has been frequent construction of grain elevators in small towns along the railroads. Hemp is grown over all the region, most abundantly in the northwest, but nearly all is shipped to other regions to be manufactured. Openings in the forests in the Tambov plain frequently have flourishing apiaries. Horses and sheep are the commonest livestock, and in dry summers they are driven from the south and east far north for pasture. Transhumance of horses is rare in Europe.

Industry. Manufacturing is concerned almost entirely with work on food and clothing materials. Flour and beet sugar lead but are insufficient for local markets. Hides are tanned but are shipped to Moscow to be manufactured. A few woolen goods are produced, and Lipetsk makes chains and anchors for river boats, of local iron ore. Saguny boasts a larger egg production than any other place in Russia; a near-by town is famous for its blacksmiths; others excel in the dressing of hides, in clothing, or in toilet articles. A little rural area between Orel and Tambov (121,300) is the second lace-producing center in Russia, rivaling Vologda. Power for industry is scarce; water power perhaps is least available; coal is mostly imported. Industry labors under severe handicaps, most of which are due to geographic conditions. Roads are often deplorable. Good roads are being built easily and cheaply. The Don and Oka rivers are connected by a canal southeast of Tula. Railroads ramify well but miss the towns because of anti-railroad prejudices. Towns that permitted such roads to enter are stimulated in commerce and increased in size.

Cities. A rural region has little opportunity to develop cities. Voronezh (330,000), the largest, and the capital in a plains district of the same name, is surrounded by the best black earth of the land, and is served commercially by the Voronezh River, which enters the Don just below the city. Three railroads reach it and help the large rural population of its district. It is famous for its jams, butters, fruit juices, pickles, canned and dried fruits, and canned vegetables.

Kursk (120,000) on the Seim River, a tributary of the Desna and Dnieper, is an ancient city, once ruined by the Tatars, but restored and fortified. It is on one of the old highways connecting Voronezh, Tambov, and Ulyanovsk (102,000), formerly Simbirsk. Orel (112,000) and Penza (160,000) are capitals and chief centers of rural districts of the same names. Each is on a commercial stream and a railroad or two, and each has grown with its rural constituency. Penza, furnished power by an electric network, makes woolen clothing.

Inhabitants. The people of this region are Great Russians with a generous mixture of Ukrainians in the southwest and a few Mongoloid Turks, who came as nomads in the eastern part. (When Tatar nomads came to raid in this region, many of the Russians fled to caves in the limestone for safety.) Little Russians occupy the southern section, and their linguistic stock meets Great Russian at Pavlovsk on the Don. Outside of Ukraine the population density of this region is the greatest in Russia. While the death-rate is high compared with West European countries, the birth-rate (45 per 1,000) is almost twice as large, thus effecting a rapid increase in population. Literacy is increasing and now exceeds 50 per cent. Owing to the low percentage in industry, very few men migrate in winter for employment. Industry is mostly rural.

Regional relations. Most of the region is too dry to permit extension of forests. Practically every *desiatin* that is not forested is suitable for agriculture. A small portion of the southeast, however, should be left in permanent grazing lands as it is today. Mineral resources upon which to build heavy industries are almost entirely lacking. Forest products can be purchased in the coniferous and hardwood forests lying near on the north and west. Industrial products can be imported easily from the industrial Donetz Basin on the south and from the Moscow Region on the north. Therefore, it seems that this great Upper Don Region can best serve other regions of the Union by entering fully into an agricultural program, which provides meat, butter, cheese, milk, and eggs for more industrial regions, likewise fruits, vegetables, fibers, and wheat to send away. There is need for industries to refine agricultural products for home consumption, can fruits and vegetables for northern cities, and make tools, leather goods, brick and tile for home use.

12. VOLGA AGRICULTURAL PLAINS

The region. This region comprises 144,000 square miles in a crescent-shaped area lying east of the Moscow and Upper Don regions and approaching the semiarid grazing lands which surround the north end of the Caspian Sea. The Volga drains all except a small strip along the south side which is yielded to the Ural River. Much of the region is less than 500 feet above sea level. Scattered small areas north of Kazan exceed that figure. In the east about one fourth of the region also lies above 500 feet and culminates near Chkalov (173,000), formerly Orenberg, in old hills 1,300 feet in altitude. Northwest of Kuibishev, formerly Samara, near the Volga, another summit reaches 1,070 feet.

The geology is very simple. Horizontal Permian beds occur at the surface except in a few places where younger rocks cover them and in more numerous but smaller areas where the streams, in their youthful shallow valleys, have cut through the Permian to older rocks below. Toward the southeast both Triassic and Jurassic strata occur in considerable areas, and the former furnishes dividing highlands between the Ural and Volga waters. Glaciers left a drift cover only in the western end of the crescent, but Quaternary fresh-water deposits are spread widely both north and south of Kuibishev (400,000).

Resources. With this large range of stratified rocks no igneous rocks are known, and mineral deposits of economic interest are few and limited. In the Permian area north of Kazan there are abundant supplies of gypsum, and ground waters have dissolved parts of it, enough to develop many sink-holes, lost rivers, and collapsed caverns. Carboniferous shales, impregnated with asphalt, outcrop northwest of Kuibishev in the great river loop. Clay is used for brick round Chkalov, and oil is piped from Emba fields to Chkalov refineries. Fragments of chalk terranes of Jurassic age stand as isolated, rounded or conical nomadnocks above the general surface; hence they receive more rainfall and are tufted with timber. Phosphate rock is produced for fertilizer in several places. Copper sands in large areas of the east and northeast are estimated to contain 50,000 tons of copper; there is no known production. Glass is manufactured from local sands in several places, and gas is reported in the northeastern part. The usual fundamentals of great industry are nowhere produced in the region.

Forests cover much of the northern portions; deciduous trees are first in importance, but conifers are more frequent toward the northern frontiers. All forests except the coniferous fringe are of the park type and rapidly give place southward, where the rainfall diminishes, to varied feather-grasses of the steppes and finally to the gorgeous, highly colored varieties with long, plumose awns. A little forest planting has been done, and all forests are under a careful forestry system. The non-forested parts of the region are more than 90 per cent fit for agriculture.

Soils and crops. In the northern border of this region there is no soil boundary. The podzolized soils grade northward into those of the Coniferous Forests. Various chernozems or black soils of the central part make up the largest percentage of the area and grade southward into chestnut soils and subarid steppe soils of clayey loam with alkali spots, like those seen in the southern part of the Upper Don Plains.

Among the planted and harvested crops there are three somewhat peculiar to the region: flax and sunflowers each occupy about 6 per cent of the land, and hemp, grown generally throughout the region, covers about 2 per cent. Spring wheat, rye, and oats are the chief cereals. Grass covers probably half or more of the farmlands, and much of it is under the control of Asiatic Turks and Tatars. Grazing results in a large supply of hides and wool; but dairy industries have recently taken a strong hold, partly in response to the stimulation of national planning, and over 1,000 dairies are now operating under the most perfect conditions. State and collective farming is extensively developed, and the crops include grain, flax, sugar beets, cattle, sheep, swine, and dairy products.

People. Great Russians are the predominant racial type in this region, but where eastern contacts can be made a sprinkling of stock-raising, nomadically inclined Turks and Tatars occupies the grasslands. Mean density of population is generally 65 to 125 per square mile, increasing in the vicinity of some cities to over 175. Toward the Urals there is a large area having only 25 to 65 inhabitants per square mile. Birth-rates, death-rates, and literacy are in the same unsatisfactory figures as in the Upper Don Region.

Industries. Agriculture is almost the only occupation. Census industries claim only about 1 per cent of the people. Peasant industries include soap-making and tanning, but the making of clothing, including felt footwear, is most important. Flour-mills and sawmills are the leading types of factory. Kuibishev, at the river junction, is a grain, lumber, and consumer-goods market. It excels in flour-making. Near this city on the Volga and at several sites on the Kama, a system of great hydro-electric power plants recently installed furnishes power for neighboring industrial cities. The Volga is here frozen for about 170 days each year, but it yields millions of fish for the industrial Moscow region. Wool and flax manufacture, beet sugar making, and small woodworking industry are widely scattered. Ulyanovsk (103,000) has woolen, leather, and food manufactures. In the Tatar republic and under the stimulus of the great Gorki fairs, flax is made into cloth, flour-sacks, and matting for use and for sale at the fair. A new fiber, kenaf, has been developed as a substitute for jute, and excellent bags are made of it. Kazan (402,000) is a notable commercial city manufacturing chemicals, wagons, and typewriters, using electric power. Industry feels the stimulus of the Moscow Industrial Region on the west margin of the Volga Plains, but our boundary line for this geographic region places most manufacturing centers in the Moscow Region. In response to this situation about 5 per cent of the industrial workers migrate there for winter work. Hundreds of boats plying the Volga and its great tributaries move agricultural and forestry products in one direction and farm machinery in the other.

The beautiful Volga River, flowing through its agricultural plains, floats hundreds of steam- and motor-boats for passengers and for freight. (Courtesy Sovfoto)

Regional significance. As a neighbor of the Central Ural Industrial and Mining Region, of the Moscow Industrial Region, and of the Industrial Region on the Volga, this rural region will always have markets for its produce, and it will be able to purchase near-by to meet its needs. It seems to have no possibility of an industrial evolution. The absence of metal mineral wealth and of all fuel except wood and rural waste substitutes is a great handicap to industry. Rainfall is meager, in the south precarious, and water power consequently very limited.

QUESTIONS

1. Discuss the possibilities of future industrial development in the Glaciated Plains Region.

2. Discuss the uses of the water route between Novgorod and Istanbul via Smolensk and Kiev.

3. What determines whether the forests are coniferous or deciduous in these regions? What difference does it make to man which type of forest grows?

4. In the Volga Agricultural Plains, why should soap-making and tanning be widespread household industries?

5. Is there any advantage or disadvantage in the presence of rural regions in the part of Russia discussed in this chapter? Give reasons for your answer.

CHAPTER 27

Southern Populous Regions

Lo! in Kiev, the old and mighty town,
Reigned the Red Vladimir, the sun-blest prince.

—FOLK SONG

13. UKRAINE WHEAT PLAINS

The region. The Ukraine Wheat Plains Region of Russia has recently been increased by over 50,000 square miles, bringing its area up to nearly 200,000 square miles. More than half of the added area came from the prewar Poland, 10,000 square miles from Rumania when Bessarabia was incorporated in Moldavian S.S.R., and 5,000 square miles when Carpathian Ruthenia was ceded by Czechoslovakia. See the map of Geographic Regions for its position and shape. The new Republic of Moldavia and a large proportion of the Ukraine S.S.R. are included. Ukraine means "border land" or frontier, with reference to Muscovy and Novgorody.

The plains stand, on the average, about 500 feet above sea level, being lowest near the Black Sea and along the principal river, Dnieper. Gentle slopes rise from the lower levels toward the northwestern or Polish frontier and the Podolia Plateau in the west, where, beyond Vinnitsa, the summits reach 1,200 feet, than fall northward toward the Pripet Valley. In Pleistocene time the Fennoscandian glacier spread over 50,000 square miles around Kiev and toward Kharkov, Tarnopol and Lvov (317,700). River meanders have been deeply incised in the Tertiary rocks and drift of the region, making the granite falls of the Dniester at Jampol south of Vinnitsa (92,868); reaching the ancient granites on the Bug where quarries furnish paving blocks to Kiev and material for bridges, such as the great railroad bridge at Warsaw; exposing clay beds in many places, some of which near Kiev are extensively worked for brick; and cutting into ancient crystallines for 50 miles along the Dnieper to make falls and rapids with most attractive power sites.

Resources. The fertility of Ukraine has brought both good and ill fortune to the territory; while through the centuries its people have been well fed, its fields have attracted countless invasions. Soils are the most important resource of the region. There are many types of chernozems (black earths),

561

rich, loose, and light, blown too easily by the winds but usually of high fertility. Patches and strips of alluvial soil lie along the Dnieper, Desna, Dniester, Bug, and Pruth; such areas have a network of living and dead river channels with alternate marshes and sand-dunes. Podzolized soil areas underlie the small pine and deciduous forests of the northwest; stiff, clayey loams have developed locally in the south central part and along the Crimean borders. Black earths vary from 3 to 5 feet in depth, in some localities exceeding 20 feet, and everywhere are deep enough for general agriculture. Although forests are scrupulously developed and cared for, it

The Ukraine has been famous for hundreds of years for its black-earth plains and its wheat harvests. Women as well as men work at the harvesting. (Courtesy Sovfoto)

is nevertheless true that nowhere else in Russia is lumber more expensive. Forests become patchy and scattered toward the southwest, where they give way abruptly to prairies, covered naturally by varied meadow grasses. Toward the Black Sea and eastward both plumose and highly colored feathergrasses prevail.

Wild life of note is almost lacking, but the waters of the sea and of the rivers upstream to the falls are rich in food fish, enough for all the people. The Greek colonies established 2,000 years ago at the mouths of all these Black Sea streams were for fishing and trading—the same occupations as prevail today. Alders, willows, and reeds are very abundant at the mouth of the Dnieper, and the reeds furnish house roofs, shelter for cattle in tempests, fish meshes, and fuel. The economy of many families rests on reeds.

With the slight relief and meager rainfall of this region, water power can be valuable only in exceptional circumstances. The only possible locations for large power plants are between Dnepropetrovsk and Zaporozhie at the far eastern turn of the Dnieper, where a narrow valley and nine rapids over granite ledges take the place of the broad alluvial plains above and below. Ukraine windmills develop power for grinding much grain. Electric power developed from imported coal serves in many towns; Kiev, Kharkov, and Odessa have eight to twelve plants each, generating for public and private use, but mechanical engines are scarce.

A village maiden in Ruthenia, area acquired from Czechoslovakia in World War II. (Courtesy U.S. Dept. of Agriculture)

Clays for chinaware occur in the northwest; sand for glass is used in many places, and quartzite for refractories is produced in increasingly large quantities. Graphite and phosphate rock are quarried in the south, the latter from limestones in many localities. All these minerals are scattered in small areas. Iron in enormous quantities at Krivoi Rog (197,621), a hundred miles west of the power sites, and manganese at Nicopol (57,841) southwest of the gorges, are mined extensively, and Donetz coal is shipped to the wheat lands. Coal is used on railroads, wood in factories. Three times as much coal is used as all other fuels combined. Proximity to the oil fields and available water transportation have led to petroleum importation from the Baku field, but production of gas has not gone far, though some pools are known. Ukraine oil is produced at Voznesensk (285,000), 100 miles north of Odessa.

People. Ukrainians, a distant branch of Russians, greatly predominate; a few White Russians in the northwest and Great Russians around Kharkov increase this large Slavic majority. In the area round Berdichev, formerly Ossipevsk (66,306) the Jews formerly found refuge, but Russia kindly moved most of them to far Siberia, Birobijan, before the Nazi invasion. Germans and Gipsies are scattered widely; the Germans have settled in

A Ukrainian grain field, with a patch of sunflowers in the foreground. (Courtesy Sovfoto)

the cities and are engaged in industry or commerce, whereas the Gipsies as everywhere are wanderers. A few Turks and some other Mongoloid groups raise tobacco along the sea or tend cattle and sheep in the dry southern part. Ukrainians, remote from the capital and touching aggressive nations, are least sympathetic of all Russians toward the Soviet régime. On their more productive lands they never yielded to the *mir* system, but were always individualistic, independent in spirit. They had no sympathy with collectivism nor with such innovations as restrict the freedom they long have known. Their position athwart the lines of easy communication between Moscow and western Europe during the last decade was a fortunate geographic circumstance for the latter.

These Ukraine plains have the densest rural population in Russia. Even the small industrial population is largely rural, engaged in peasant industries. The total population in favored places, as near the Polish border, rises to over 200 per square mile.

Occupations. Ninety per cent of the people engage in rural pursuits. Great numbers take advantage of the fertile soils of the central, west, and north to raise winter wheat, sugar beets, and sunflowers. Wheat has by far the largest acreage and yields the largest item in income. In the more moist northern sections it constitutes half of the farm crop. Clover and lucerne,

Work of a Russian experimental farm. At the left is an ear of ordinary high-yield wheat, and to the right, a variety of branching wheat head that yields five to eight times as much as the ordinary kind. (Courtesy Sovfoto)

10 to 15 feet tall, make hay, a rotation crop, and green manure. Sunflowers are grown for fodder and for the oil of the seeds on 5 or 6 per cent of the cultivable land. Sugar beets occupy about another 5 per cent of the land and are manufactured in many mills northwest and northeast of Kiev. The south Ukraine plains grow barley for beer, and potatoes primarily for food are produced in every section. Hemp, grown across the northern uplands, stands 20 feet high and is manufactured into rope and coarse cloth in Kharkov and Odessa. Large numbers of hides, especially from the southeast, are manufactured into leather goods in the same cities. The vine does well in Podolia and gives its name to two towns there—Vinograd and Vinnitsa.

Inferior tobacco is grown northeast of Kiev. In the south under the influence of the sea tobacco matures better than elsewhere but never wholly satisfactorily. Here gardens of cucumbers, melons, onions, pumpkins, squashes, and small fruits prevail. Fruit trees—apples, pears, cherries, plums, and apricots—are abundant and prolific in the south and also for miles around Kiev. Fruit confections, using native sugar and fruits, are a staple product of Kiev. Dairy products are almost unknown in the markets of these plains, where they might be a very valuable money crop, but they require more intensive agriculture than the people now know. Tumbling weeds roll everywhere before the wind in the fall and are retrieved in great quantities for substitute fuel. Fishing in the Black Sea, on the delta flats, and up the Dnieper supplies a large element of the local food.

General view of a part of the forest shelter-belt system protecting the fields of the Institute of Agriculture of the black-earth zone. (Courtesy Sovfoto)

Manufacturing has been restricted by the supplies of minerals and other raw materials, but recent discoveries and developments hold great promise. The chief products are those from the rural crops mentioned and those demanded by the local market. Of the former, cigars and tobacco in Kiev and Ossipevsk, leather goods in Odessa, Kiev, and towns to the southwest, flour and other food products throughout all the region, and cooper products, baskets, and other wood articles in the northwest are leading items. Industries supplying local markets are the farm machinery and tool plants, boot and shoe industries which turn out nearly half the peasant-made boots and shoes of all Russia, factories which make threshers, harvesters, seeders, fanning mills, general machinery, and at Kharkov, electrotechnical machinery. In addition to the items enumerated, Kharkov makes a fine line of toilet articles, and the many scattered peasant plants of the region produce more soap than all the rest of Russia combined. This production seems to be related to the livestock industries which furnish the necessary fats. Basic metal industries will be mentioned under cities.

A general view of the machine-tool and assembling plant of the Kharkov tractor plant. It is a thoroughly modern plant. (Courtesy Sovfoto)

Among the occupations of the Ukraine Wheat Region transportation looms large. Railroads are more frequent than in any other region except the Moscow Industrial one; the master river with its tributaries, and the lesser rivers that reach the sea, together with the Black Sea itself, supply further facilities. Because the Black Sea is one of the best outlets to foreign lands, much transit trade moves both in and out through Odessa and other Black Sea ports. Passenger traffic is heavy, as shown by the carrying of over half a million people per annum on steamboats of the Desna and Dnieper rivers.

Cities. Kiev (846,000) is on a 300-foot bluff on the western side of the Dnieper River where it makes a large turn below its junction with the Desna River. As early as the eighth century the commercial importance of the situation was recognized by Variags (Northmen) and Greeks. First fortified against the Tatars, it was later held by Tatars, Russians, and Northmen, by Lithuanians, Poles and Russians, in succession. Largely a wooden city, it

was burned and rebuilt three times; for a time it was the political and religious capital of the Russians. When local rural interests became more
important than political prestige, the city became not only the meeting-
place of north and south in the great fair but the marketplace of a strong,
thriving rural state. The sugar industry has nourished the city for hundreds
of years. As a wheat market, a lumber distributing center, and a fruit market
the city has grown and prospered. Today, from the celebrated heights of
Askold occupied by the city proper, one looks down over the quiet river
and its great flood-plain, 10 to 12 miles wide, across the flowing waters, the
junction of the two streams, the abandoned channels, the marshes, and the
new factories and wharves. Other factories have grown up in the southern
and western suburbs, manufacturing sugar and railway equipment respectively. A knitting factory produces many knit fabrics. While far behind
Moscow and Leningrad, Kiev is the third city in Russia and is rich in
history as well as present significance.

    While it is not in the mining region, Kharkov (833,000) is near enough
to the coal of the Donetz and the iron of Krivoi Rog to have developed a
large machine-building industry and a commensurate, reciprocal trade in
machinery and rural products, indeed to have become the greatest economic
center of the Ukraine. Its industries produce not only locomotives, tractors,
and various farm machines to replace the age-old hand tools of the Russian
peasants, but several metallurgical products, sugar, flour, and food preparations, wool, hides, and furs. Bricks are burned with substitute fuel (farm
rubbish, weeds). Most of these industries except the production of machines
are in the hands of the people as home industries. The city possesses modern hospitals, museums, and business and educational institutions, has
gardens and long, shady avenues, and stands as a junction point on the
highway from the Crimea to Moscow in close contact with industrial Donetz
and rural Ukraine. Kharkov was founded about the middle of the seventeenth century and has therefore no long history, as have Kiev and Moscow,
but it is the industrial capital.

    Odessa (605,000) stands picturesquely on a plateau rising 150 feet
above the waters of the sea and dissected by local ravines. As remotely as
the Middle Ages a town had been built near the present Kherson and was
exporting cereals when the builders decided to fortify it. After consideration
the present site of Odessa was chosen, fortified, and opened for commerce.
So wise a choice was made, so commodious and sheltered a harbor was
prepared, and so generous trade conditions were established that the place
grew rapidly. Owing to its long open season and proximity to the productive
populous parts of Russia its development has gone forward steadily. The
regularly laid-out streets are wide, well-paved, and equipped with car-lines.
Seven great piers standing out into the sea are served by railroads, provided
with warehouses, equipped with loading and unloading machinery, guarded
by lights and buoys; all protected from the sea by great breakwaters two

miles long, and nearly a mile from shore. As a port Odessa carries on more export and import business than any other Soviet harbor on the Black Sea. This commercial importance has led to industrial activities in food manufacture and to the production of agricultural machinery. Sea salt is made in extensive evaporating pans near by. Since the city is in such frequent, easy communication with the marts of the world, it has a cosmopolitan population, including Poles, Greeks, Armenians, Germans, and all types from Russia, which engages actively in the business of the port. Odessa and Kherson (98,000) are the Russian outlets southward. They ship out wheat (a thousand cars a day in November and December), sugar, oil, and wool; they receive oranges, cotton, and petroleum. When the lands were uplifted for dissection in Late Tertiary time, gorges were carved which matured into steepsided valleys of useful width. More recent submergence has let the sea into them, and the streams have built deltas into the upper ends of the bays thus formed, while the sea has constructed sandbars across the mouth of each drowned gorge-valley. More than a dozen of these lakes are now strung along thirty miles of coast each side of the city, each lying at sea level, 100 to 150 feet below the uplands. Health and summer resorts surround coast parts of the city; curative sea baths and mud baths occupy the above decribed estuaries (*limans* of the Greeks), each with different properties because its waters are different.

Dnepropetrovsk (500,000) is an old town rebuilt, renamed, and industrialized by using borrowed coal from Donetz, iron from Krivoi Rog, manganese from Nicopol, and salt from the Bakhmut salt-mines at Artemovsk. In addition, this promising industrial city is on the Dnieper River within easy reach of the great power plant erected in the 1930's, demolished by Russians in the war, and recently rebuilt at Dnepropetrovsk. The iron at Krivoi Rog (198,000), 100 miles west, a siliceous ore which is very abundant and easily worked, is shipped to the steel-plants. Manganese ore at Nicopol (60,000) has no farther to travel. It comes from large deposits on the Dnieper a few miles below the gorges. Both iron and manganese are derived from the ancient crystalline rocks revealed in hundreds of places by the streams, which cut through the overlying Tertiary beds. These same ancient rocks are the resistant terrane into which the Dnieper is cutting. The recency of the course of the stream has permitted only gorges and rapids to be formed from Dnepropetrovsk to Zaporozhie. Much water power is being developed at the lower end of this 50 miles of river. The dam at Zaporozhie, raising the water about 125 feet and setting it back nearly to Dnepropetrovsk, furnishes power for rural as well as urban activities of 16 million people occupying 70,000 square miles, and irrigation for 200,000 acres of surrounding semiarid steppe. Industrially this hydroelectric power makes possible the adjacent aluminum plant using ores from Tikhvim and the Urals, the ferro-alloy furnaces, cement kilns, and chemical industries, all three drawing on local resources, and the nitrogen fertilizer

Dnieper Dam as it looked in the spring of 1934. This is one of the most important modern power dams and also aids navigation. (Courtesy Sovfoto)

plants. The power is also used at Zaporozhie (290,000) in a factory producing combine harvesters and other modern agricultural machinery to work the fertile fields of Ukraine. Large locks around the dam and up to the new level allow all river boats to go with safety from the lower to the upper Dnieper. Thus a tremendous hindrance to river navigation is removed and Dnieper towns are brought into advantageous connection with the sea and with world markets.

A warehouse of rolled steel in one of the iron works of the Dnepropetrovsk region. (Courtesy Sovfoto)

Other cities are Ossipevsk (67,000), a leading tobacco and grape-processing center; Kishinev (117,000), capital of the Moldavian Republic, an area containing a mixed population of Rumanians, Ukrainians, Jews, and Great Russians, an area whose possession has been much disputed; Lvov (317,700), 700 years old, always a commercial center, now also industrial, making chemicals, textiles, paper and wooden wares; Vinnitza (93,000) in the grape district; Nikolaev (170,000) on the embayed mouth of the Bug River, naval base, shipyards, railroad carworks; ships out grain, iron ore from Krivoi Rog, and manganese ore from Nikopol.

The Ukraine Wheat Plains, for centuries known to be wonderfully adapted to wheat cultivation and extensively used for cereals, grass, grazing, and fruits, are now as capable as any part of the Union of sharing effectively in the unfolding of industrial Russia.

Dnepropetrovsk has many blast-furnaces. This one, No. 7, produces 530 tons of iron **every** twenty-four hours. (Courtesy Sovfoto)

The Dnieper aluminum combinat. This plant was complete and ready for operation early in 1935. (Courtesy Sovfoto)

14. DONETZ INDUSTRIAL REGION

The region. Most of the portion of all Russia included under this heading (50,000 square miles) is drained by the Donetz River, a branch of the Don. Through a long history the unity of this area has been recognized in the name Don-bas or Donetz Basin. The eastern boundary runs so as to include all the Donetz coal-field and most of its dependent industry. Relief is greater than in many interior regions because the streams have cut down nearly to sea level. Some of these recent valleys are beautiful gorges whose mouths are drowned by moderate submergence, attested by the shallow Sea of Azov and by the many *limans* along its coast. These lakes are partly closed by hooked spits standing 5 to 10 miles out into the water, work of the winds and waves that often harass the fishing and commerce of the sea.

Geologically, the region is varied from simple horizontal strata of Cretaceous and later age in the north and west to simple, broad, east-west folds across the central part involving late Paleozoic rocks and the coal-beds, and on to ancient crystallines in a broad belt nearly across the southern part. This granite is a portion of the massif noted in Ukraine. Some of these central and southern parts were so high that the Quaternary submergence did not cover them. The region reaches north to the terminal moraine but has not been glaciated.

Resources. Most valuable of all resources are the rich, varied chernozems and the flood-plain soils along the Don and Donetz, although alkali spots make places unavailable for general agriculture. Salt in thick beds underlies large areas at workable depths. Kaolins and fire-clays for chinaware and refractory bricks, limestones for flux, calcareous shales for cement, gypsum, graphite, and even mercury are among the developed deposits. Iron is meager within the region, but the enormous Krivoi Rog reserves are only 200 miles west. Sands for glass and quartzite for refractories are abundant and of excellent quality. Water power could not be expected in a region of such low relief and meager rainfall.

Anthracite is known over three fourths of the folded belt and bituminous coal over the northern parts and western fingers. The coal cokes well and produces gas readily. Industrial development began in 1860. Now there are scores of coal-mines, producing 70 per cent of all European Russian coal output, and eight or ten smelters; railroads connect almost every mine with smelter or factory, with quarries and clay-pits in many places. Commerce by rail and sea extends to many quarters.

Vegetation and climate. While Donetz industries are a response to the resources, the vegetation coördinates more closely with the climate than with the rocks. No forests occur in the region save a few tufts of timber on summits high enough to intercept a little more than average rainfall; hence lumber must be imported from the north. It is as expensive here as in the

Ukraine Wheat Plains. Normally all the land bears steppe grasses, some rich plumose, other plumose and highly colored, all a response to the scanty rainfall. Precipitation over the region varies from 16 to 20 inches, with the summer fall about double that of winter. Snowfall is rarely more than 3 to 5 inches, but it often remains two to three months and furnishes to the winter wheat splendid protection against the icy blasts of winter and the freezing and thawing so destructive in a sunny winter. Even in this prosperous rural region climate is quite capricious. The native grasses feed multitudes of cattle and sheep, and over large areas are replaced by potatoes (5 per cent of all sown crops), by barley (more than 10 per cent), and by

Coal mining in one of the Donetz colleries. (Courtesy Sovfoto)

wheat, oats, rye, corn, and tobacco. Sunflowers equal barley in area. They are raised for forage, fuel value of the stocks, and for the oil of the seeds, some of which is shipped to America for a soap fat.

People. From the time of early nomadic outpouring from the plateaus of Asia into Europe, these plains have been portions of an important highway. Many burial mounds and saucer-like depressions attest the occupation of these grazing lands by early man, probably the founders of the Alpine Race. Nomadism is least changed today in the south and east, but many groups, even those of nomad habits, have fixed homes from which they wander.

The present people are classed as Ukrainians or Little Russians, and they include many Cossacks, products of the ancient highway environment—

fighting, nomadic, mounted citizens; but the people in general are able workers, engaged in active rural, mining, and manufactural occupations. Workers maintain many types of peasant industries, but industrialization, i.e., establishment of census industries, has only attained some 20 per cent in the more favored central part. The region as a whole is easily and naturally the most notable industrial center of the European part of the Union. In the more industrial part the people number 400 per square mile, in the northern part not more than 100, and in the eastern section as low as 25.

A rural landscape includes the rolling old hills, well mantled with soil but never concealed by forest, many small farms, but an increasing number of coöperatives, and not a few state farms where mechanization is complete and where the fields are prepared and crops planted and harvested with modern power machines. Villages of old-style thatched roofs dot the scene, and roads, often still of dirt, lead from one village to another. An urban landscape is much more modern. No cities are walled; streets have been straightened and paved; business houses are modern, light, and well built, factories with myriad-paned glass roofs stand apart among great stacks, towering cranes, mountains of raw materials, and spacious warehouses; steel-mills light up the sky at night and roar all day. Near the mills are the huge modern apartment houses, four to six stories high, the theater, clubhouse, recreation grounds, nursery, school, clinic, coöperative store, and kitchen. It resembles not in the least either old Russia or anything new in other lands. It is an architecture and plan unique in the world.

Cities. Rostov-on-Don (510,000) sends its fish products from the choice fishing grounds of Azov in great quantities to the industrial centers. The city is engaged in heavy industry, importing steel and coal from the furnaces in the central part of the region and turning out rural and fishing machinery. Its sands supply the glass factories with clean, abundant raw material. Its commerce includes tallow, wool, hides, tobacco, and wheat. The coming of the railroads stimulated its growth perhaps more than usual, for they put it in easy communication with Kharkov, Moscow, and the north, whence it receives lumber and whither it sends machinery; and with Baku and the east, with which it has an active trade in petroleum, forest products, furs, and skins. It is a home of the Don Cossacks where they have special privileges. The Don is subject to spring floods and has built a great delta in its *liman,* through which three navigable distributaries wander. Its waters above Rostov meander in ever changing channels which require constant engineering care. When strong winds, often serious on the Azov, blow down the gulf, they drive the water out and leave great strands of sand.

Voroshilovgrad, formerly Lugansk (215,000), on the Donetz makes freight and passenger locomotives and has many collieries; it is not to be confused with Voroshilovsk (55,000) 30 miles west and also possessing locomotive works. Both towns are named after a general of the U.S.S.R. army. Zhdanov, formerly Mariupol (222,000), on the Azov coast has a good harbor and a lively export trade, shipping away many products of the region. Makeevka, formerly Dmitrievsk, and Stalino (465,000), another locomotive center, are busy making and using the products of iron and steel furnaces and manufacturing machinery for other industries.

Artemovsk (56,000) nestles in the deep valley of the Bakhmut River and may be considered typical of several towns in the salt area. The mines produce over 80 per cent of all Russian salt and maintain many basic chemical industries, producing a large percentage of the chemicals of the U.S.S.R. Salt, gypsum, limestone, coal distillation products, vegetable oils, and starches go into the works, from which come soda, lime salts, fertilizers, a wide range of ceramic products, detergents, foods, alcohol, and drugs. The best clays in Russia here go into pottery, earthenware and choice china.

Taganrog (190,000) on Taganrog Gulf, really the estuary of the Don, has a more favorable commercial site than either Rostov or Zhdanov. It is far enough down the gulf to avoid the handicaps set for Rostov and is further favored by a 24-foot channel dredged the whole length of the gulf. The town is also in close rail communication with the industrial cities on the coal-fields.

15. LOWER VOLGA INDUSTRIAL REGION

The region. This unit of 30,000 square miles united by the ease of water transportation and the prewar German industrializing influence is set in the midst of expanding agriculture.

Earliest Tertiary to recent rocks underlie the region. Bluffs, continuously undercut and destroyed by the river, rise rather steeply on the western side of the Volga to heights of 1,000 feet. Stalingrad and Saratov are the chief cities. Plains everywhere less than 600 feet above sea level, spread eastward from the river. The region, as here defined, narrows in width from 125 miles in the north to 25 miles in the south. The alluvial plain, 5 to 10 miles wide along the river, is below sea level almost as far up as Saratov, but because the Caspian lies 85 feet below sea level the plain is as well drained as any such flood-plain. Because of aridity the river decreases in size from Saratov down. Its plains possess sandy soils, whereas the plains to the eastward have chestnut loam soils in the north and steppe clay loams with many alkali spots in the south. No timber grows in the region. Since the mean annual precipitation is less than 14 inches and is predominantly a summer rainfall, only grasses grow naturally in the north, giving way in the south to semi-desert coarse weeds and brush. Climate is capricious and often treacherous.

Resources. Soil resources have little value beyond grazing possibilities in so dry a region as this. Winter wheat has become the major cultivated crop in the broader northern part and sunflowers the second. Irrigation from the river here assists agriculture over broad areas, so that these plains are as intensively sown as any part of Russia, but irrigation possibilities also determine the southeast limits of cultivation. In the desiccating lakes there are medicinal muds and near them mineral springs. Some lakes have water salty enough to yield commercial salt on artificial evaporation. In the north are found cement marls, phosphate rock, gypsum beds, tripoli, and lead ores. No iron, coal, oil, or gas are known in the region, but shales with an oil content furnish fuel for part of the industries at Saratov.

People. Centuries ago Tatars wandered up the Volga to harass the Muscovites, but in return the Muscovites worked down the river and drove back their invaders. Tsaritzin, now Stalingrad, was founded by Russians in 1589 at a great turn in the river where, approaching within about 40 miles of the Don, it indicates a migration route across and up the Don. Great Russians occupy almost all this region except that part around Saratov, which has become the Volga German Republic with a German population of over half a million. These are the Germans who were deported to eastern Siberia as the German army advanced into Russia in World War II.

The density of population is extremely low in the southeast but rises northwestward from one or two nomads per square mile to over 125 permanent farmers. The narrow strip of higher, moister land on the west bluff of the river also has a high density. These figures do not include the cities. Industry outside the cities is very low and is almost entirely of the household or peasant sort. While the flood-plain supports diversified agriculture and in some places has a fairly dense population, so much land is marsh or is occupied by recent beds of migrating distributaries that the average density is not high.

Houses on farms and in rural villages are of wood or have a framework of wood with brush, weeds, and reeds for walls, roofed with reed thatch. The towns have been of a similar simple, cheap construction until recently, but Stalingrad has been largely rebuilt and many other towns have new, more modern sections, since World War II.

The people on the drier plains herd thousands of sheep, marketing wool and hides, but as yet they sell very little meat. On the river many engage in fishing, and their catch furnishes a considerable portion of the local diet. River commerce by steamer has been active. Now, as in the early days, wood comes down the river in rafts from the forest upstream, wheat and fish are carried back upstream, and salt is exported through Nikolaevsk from the rich supplies evaporated at Elton Lake, 100 miles southeast of the city. Here camels come into the picture. They transport salt and other products to the river cities and take supplies out to desert villages.

The flood-plain. The utilization of the flood-plain of the Volga in this section is unique, and in some respects is closely related to the cities. The

Post War II apartment houses in Stalingrad. Note Russian street cars and automobiles. (Courtesy Sovfoto)

river meanders continuously, developing new curves, altered channels, dead bayous, marshes, islands, and recently terraces on several levels above the stream bed. These habits of the stream make navigation uncertain, but thousands of boats carry merchandise up and down the river except when it is frozen. At Saratov navigation is closed about 165 days, at Stalingrad 148 days, and at the mouth only 109 days. In spite of this the river is a highway of the first order.

Stalingrad is reviving. This plant which makes oil pumps has reached the pre-war level of production. (Courtesy Sovfoto)

Wheat is collected and shipped on the Volga from Kamyshin opposite the salt market. Mustard, grown quickly when the spring rains come, is harvested and prepared at and around Krasnoarmieski. Cherries and apples excel prunes, peaches, and apricots along the valley slopes; watermelons are cultivated the whole length of the region in the sandy soils of the bottoms and are as highly esteemed over Russia as are Posey County, Indiana, melons raised on the Ohio bottoms in the United States. Fruit culture supersedes all else near Nikolaevsk, and grapes are the first crop at Dubovka above Stalingrad.

Cities. Stalingrad (450,000), is today a large, modern city rebuilt extensively from war's destruction. Workers' residence towns, vegetable gardens, and new factories spread along the river plains for miles. Its industries make high-quality steel from Donetz coal and imported iron ore from Dom-bas and Kusnetz; chemicals based on Elton Lake salt and local limestones; agricultural tractors and other rural machinery. Oil received by pipeline and boat is refined, wood from upriver is processed for many uses; wheat and stock-farm products are manufactured.

Saratov (380,000), not so hard hit by war as Stalingrad but fully as well recovered, is the center of many towns engaged in textiles of cotton, flax, and wool. From local products it makes flour, beet sugar, sunflower-seed oil, potato starch, cement, glass, and chemicals. Exchange of goods from river to rail transport gives it an important commercial aspect, and the large river bridge opens up the city to eastern commerce. Gardens, dairies, stock and poultry farms nearby furnish food. Since it stands in the midst of the winter wheat belt, new modern plants make the combine harvesters for Geant, the great state farm, and for many other farms nearby.

Commerce and connections. The river ensures commerce to both cities. Both have become industrial because they were first commercial. A railroad from Moscow to Kusnetz passes through Saratov and here connects with one from Astrakhan. Railroads from the Caucasus forests and mining regions and from the Donetz furnaces converge on Stalingrad, and a good line connects it with the Moscow region. These make an industrial center possible and with Russian determination to do things in spite of unfortunate location and limited resources the region will continue to be industrial.

For generations, even since the days of Peter the Great, a ship canal connecting the Volga and Don near Stalingrad has been discussed and planned. It is now completed, making a 40-mile link from river to river. The Don is 150 feet above the Volga, and the lowest *col* across the divide is 235 feet above sea level. The difference in level necessitates nine locks up from the Volga and four down to the Don. A supply of water at the summit requires care in a dry climate. This canal forms a valuable integrating unit in the great waterway system of the Union. A good railroad also connects the river routes.

QUESTIONS

1. What influence will the development of heavy industry on the Dnieper have upon the attitude of the Ukrainians toward the Union?
2. What physical unity is there in the Ukraine Wheat Plains?
3. What reasons can be given for the gradual disappearance of forests and the prevalence of grasses as one crosses Ukraine from northwest to southeast?
4. What more or less vital interrelations may exist between this region and some other regions of European Russia?
5. Will the industrial region newly centered in the Donetz Basin expand to wider limits? Why?
6. What possibility exists for the Donetz Industrial Region to enter world markets? What need is there for its products in Russia?
7. Which are more liable to enter world commerce, the products of agri-

culture in the Ukraine, of industry in the Donetz Basin, or of mining in the Krivoi Rog section? Why?

8. What advantages has Saratov for its industries over Stalingrad for its manufactures?

9. Why can the Don-Volga canal be considered a valuable part of Russia's inland waterways?

10. What advantage to western Europe during the last decade or two could accrue from the position of Ukrainians across the lines of communication between Moscow and the west?

11. Why do Sea of Azov and its *limans* freeze more than other Black Sea waters?

CHAPTER 28

Grazing Lands

Praise a great estate but cultivate a small one.
—VERGIL

16. SOUTHERN URALS REGION

The region. The Southern Urals have been often recognized as a unit region, differing from the Central Urals in having little diversity of mineral resources, though this difference may largely disappear as further explorations are made. The region differs likewise in having very little forest because of scanty rainfall. It may be delimited from the Caspian Plains and the Volga Plains by its mountain structure, although some of its topography is very old.

Geologically, this region consists of rather complex, folded structures involving ancient granites and other crystallines with recognized Devonian and Carboniferous beds on each side and undifferentiated Paleozoic and Permian beds on the west. After these beds and structures had been much eroded, Tertiary sediments were laid over many areas among the old hills in the southern and eastern parts. Quaternary material is scarce in the region because it was too high to be submerged when other regions were, and not high enough to have glaciers. Many low ridges sprawl and spread southward. Summits rarely exceed 1,600 feet, and all land consists of old rolling hills mantled with chernozem soils in the north and chestnut soils in the south which become more and more alkaline with increasing aridity.

The rainfall varies with relief from 20 inches (partly snow) on the hills to 8 inches on the lower parts. April is the driest month and July the rainiest. Thus the natural vegetation is colored feather-grasses in the north with occasional clumps of timber on the hills and plumose grasses in the south, giving place to wormwood and desert vegetation as the plains are approached. The Ural and its branches drain almost all the region.

People. This area was a line of expansion for Russia into Central Asia, used in preference to the more arid but more level land southward. The old, treeless topography offers little hindrance to travel, and the grasses furnish excellent food for horses, cattle, sheep, and camels. Russians have come to occupy much of the best lands, but there are many nomadic Kirghiz and other Mongoloid tribes wandering about with their herds and flocks. The country had to be redeemed from the Cossacks of Chkalov and of the Urals, not so much because they were Cossacks as because they interfered with legitimate pursuits by blocking the valleys from trade and raiding the developing center of Orsk on the Ural River. A railroad now runs entirely across the region, connecting Orenberg and Orsk with the outside world. This facilitates the export of wool and hides, the chief products of the region. State cattle farms have been established and on level lands there are several wheat farms.

So long as aridity characterizes the climate of the region, the dominant occupations will be grazing and restricted wheat culture. Abundant flowers encourage bee keeping and honey production. Placer gold is mined along many streams. Several deposits of chromic iron and one of nickel have been found at Orsk, and some millions of tons of bauxite have been mapped. Chkalov (175,000) is just outside the region but is its chief city and commercial center. Orsk (70,000) has a pipe-line for oil from the Emba fields, refineries for oil and nickel ore, a large electric power plant, and looks forward to development of commerce and industry commensurate with the needs of the region.

17. THE CASPIAN LOW PLAINS

Physical conditions. This region includes about 200,000 square miles of semiarid to arid plains, 10 to 15 per cent of which is below sea level, and no part of which is over 300 feet above sea level; nor is any part covered by more than 300 feet of Caspian water. The western border of the region is drawn on the mean annual rainfall line of 10 inches, essentially on a relief line of 650 feet, the top of the Ergeni Hills, which are due to the presence of more resistant, horizontal, Tertiary beds of the Manych Region. The north line approximately follows the curve of the same rainfall line but is not so conspicuously a topographic or geologic line until half-way across from the Volga River to the Ural, where Cretaceous beds cause higher, more hilly forms. The line is drawn for many miles just south of the Ural River where it flows westward, and then near Orsk it bears southward along the Mugojar Hills to the Aral Sea. The southern limit, more or less arbitrary, extends between the Aral and Caspian seas near the rim of the Miocene Ust-Urt Plateau, and embraces much of the Kalmuck Autonomous Area and the Kazak Republic of the Kirghiz Steppe. Although the Emba, Ural, Volga, and Terek rivers succeed in flowing across the region from higher, moister lands beyond, scores of streams completely disappear in the sands before reaching the Caspian. Their failure is a measure of the general aridity.

The plain is made up mostly of loess overlain with alluvium and the salty deposits of the Quaternary Caspian transgression. In the eastern fifth,

Cretaceous rocks not covered by later beds spread over the area. Recent alluvium makes up the marshy flood-plain of the Ural, several miles wide, and similar deposits veneer the Volga flood-plain, here 10 to 15 miles in width and entirely below sea level though not below Caspian level. The abandoned channel and the flood-plain now occupied by a row of lakes extend from Stalingrad southeastward to the Kuma mouth. The Terek delta occupies over 4,000 square miles of mud-flats; that of the Volga is perhaps half as large, and those of the Ural and Emba are tiny at the present Caspian level. Between the Volga and Urals stretch 25,000 square miles of alluvial plains, presumably delta built for the most part by the rivers when the Caspian was a few feet higher than now. On the Terek delta one can count a score of mouths and on the Volga at least five times as many. Hundreds of low, reedy islands divide the distributaries below Astrakhan into shifting streams, making it very difficult to map a shoreline. The situation is aggravated by the slight fluctuations of level of Caspian waters as the ratio between inflow and evaporation changes. It might almost be said that the whole Caspian shoreline along the plains is amphibious. The shallow waters lap upon the lowlands differently with every season and with the perpetual deposition by stream, wind, and sea current.

Surface. The surface, as the name of the region suggests, is a plain of oppressive monotony and unique character. Sand and clay, mingled with salt, blow freely with every wind; dunes are constantly formed and shifted from place to place. Streams that do not reach the sea, spread flood waters over great playas, where the water evaporates and leaves a crust of alkali or salt. At times hundreds of lakes dot the surface. Some lakes are very salty, other brackish; all fluctuate greatly. Some areas are marsh, brackish to saline, and variously filled with vegetation. Not only is salt in the waters and in the sand and clay, but it is in the air and blows about into everything. It collects on tents, on tufts of herbs like hoar frost, on one's clothing, and up one's nose.

Soils are classed as chestnut and clay loam on the subarid steppes, and as light brown along both sides of the lower Volga. Alkali soils, dunes, salinas, playas, and gypsiferous soils increase in frequency toward the sea. Gypsum hills rise above the general level as residual isolated knobs not covered when the Caspian invasion occurred.

Over this surface a cruel climate scourges the people and stock with bitter cold winds of winter, scorching heat of summer, dust storms any time, and for weeks at a time with a parching drought that is extremely disagreeable for all life. The cold of winter and dry heat of summer are separated by a short, showery, growing season in spring. Over the sands, or among the patches of grass there spring up quickly tulips, iris, hyacinths, violets, and clematis, creating a landscape of brilliance and incredibly varied color.

The wormwood, a hard, bitter shrub with slightly aromatic taste, struggles against the severe conditions of the more arid parts. If white, it signifies a clay soil; if black, a salty soil. It is used for fuel and from it are derived the oils used in absinth. Back from the sea where precipitation is a little more generous, grasses, not colored but plumose, cover the better soils of the plains and toss their graceful heads in the winds like great ostrich feathers. In the Caspian Plains there has been the least change found in Russia from spontaneous vegetation to crops and from nomadism to settled homes.

Along the Volga flood-plain where water is always available, patches of timber cover some 5 per cent of the land and mark the watercourse in a striking way. This river probably resembles the Nile in its life-giving qualities more than does any other river, though it has no fixed seasonal flood and flows through a much more seasonal climate. Willows, reeds, club- and bull-rushes, arrow-heads or *Sagittarius,* water-lilies, and lotus grow freely in many places, but very few crops are planted. More could be made of this great flood-plain with its perennial waters.

The Volga often overflows in May and June, covering its delta. When the flood subsides and the delta emerges as a green oasis amid desert sands, waterfowl swarm to the thousands of islands and intervening channels— ducks, geese, gulls, and even egrets. Fish in myriads swim the waters, and with the birds feed on the wealth of organic matter available. One unfamiliar with water in a desert can scarcely realize the concentrating power it exerts over life.

People. Into this setting of plain, river, shoreline, and sea, of sand, salina, storm, and grass has come man, as strange among men as is the land among lands, yet perhaps as fully adjusted to his unusual conditions of life as are the plants and beasts.

Mongols were the first of the present people to arrive. They were already accustomed to aridity and a nomadic life. Kalmuks occupy a large area south of Stalingrad and the Volga and live the normal miserable existence of sheep-grazers with no place to go when extended drought comes. They are passionate horsemen and love a diet of meat, meal, and tea with butter. A few Tatars and Kirghiz, another Mongoloid group, wander in the worst parts of this desert. All three groups keep the Buddhist religion which they brought with them; their dress is Oriental. Nothing exists here to change men or their habits of life. On the east side of the Volga the people are mostly Kirghiz. Their property is necessarily variable with the uncertainties of climate. Tempests of snow with freezing cold threaten the stock with death and often decimate the flock, if they do not exterminate it altogether. Camels are least accustomed to this severity of weather and perish at times by thousands. Sheep-raising is perhaps the best developed occupation and furnishes for market an annual crop of wool with a continual stream of pelts. To Urda, now called Khanskaya Stavka, the Kirghiz come twice a year to exchange their products for wheat, sugar, and tools. These nomads

Sturgeon are caught in the Volga and in the Caspian Sea. These fine fellows have just been removed from the net by Caspian fishermen. (Courtesy Sovfoto)

pass the winter in earth huts covered with reed roofs, but most of the year they dwell in tents of skins and mats, surrounded by their herds of sheep, horses, goats, and camels. Their water supply comes from wells and from pits at the base of sand-dunes. A beginning has been made of collective stock farms.

As the Tatars went up the rivers and came among the Russians in Muscovy, so the Great Russians have now come down the rivers and dwell along both streams and seacoast near the Mongols. The coast seems not to increase the density of population, but it appeals to Russian much more than to Kalmuk and Kirghiz. They build themselves houses of earth, grass,

The fish roe taken from sturgeon are pickled and packed in tubs for the market. (Courtesy Sovfoto)

and reeds and have more permanent homes than the Mongols, for their occupations are more sedentary—fishing, evaporating salt, making boats and fishing gear, preparing fish and caviar.

Fishing near the Volga and Ural mouths and up the former to Stalingrad is very important. Not only is it the principal European Soviet fishing center, taking half the total catch, but it takes also most of the salmon and sturgeon and supplies a very large part of the caviar. Caspian fisheries extend along both sides of the sea and look to Astrakhan for market. Kirghiz and Kalmuks have for years extracted salt from the waters of Lake Baskunchak east of the lower Volga. Evaporation was partly artificial; salt was dug by hand and drawn away in camel carts, much as at Lake

Elton. In recent years this lake has dried up, and modern salt works have been erected at Elton. Russians have put in large steam excavators and laid railroad tracks, and the salt is shoveled into cars to go to boats on the Volga. In spite of its enormous domestic supplies, Russia still needs to import salt. While salt is shipped from the lower Volga lands far into the interior, great quantities are used here to cure fish and hides.

Astrakhan (255,000) is an old city that is being rapidly enlarged and rebuilt in order to measure up to its opportunities as a river-mouth commercial center. Spreading over the plains of islands 20 to 25 feet above the water, it harbors many strange craft from other Caspian ports, and has a fine old bazaar near the water's edge. Fish canneries seal a million cans

Pyramids of salt, taken from the dry salt lake bed east of the Volga, awaiting shipment.
(Courtesy Sovfoto)

annually and care for tons of caviar from all the neighboring waters. Fish are taken all the year round, in winter through the ice—a hazardous business. They are shipped at all seasons by train from Astrakhan to industrial cities in the interior.

Besides the fishing and canning, Astrakhan has a large woodworking industry. Logs are rafted down to this treeless land and manufactured at the port into boards, furniture, boats and ships, buildings, boxes, tubs, and barrels. Sands in wasteful abundance around the city are being used now for glass, fused with petroleum for fuel, which arrives by water from Baku. Salt is evaporated at several places around the city. A score of suburbs, of 2,000 to 5,000 inhabitants, surround the city, entering into its industries and commerce. Machine-building for local industries occupies some of the towns. The lower Volga has a large state poultry farm, taking advantage of grain foods, dry climate for chickens, and abundant waters for ducks and geese. Fine fruit of the rich alluvial valley competes with the Crimea for markets in the heart of Russia. There is a large import trade in Persian and Armenian fruits, notably raisins, as well as in weavings and needlework. In the port the presence of Persians, Armenians, Turks, and other Asiatics shows the close relation between Astrakhan and Asia.

18. THE MANYCH REGION

Situation. The Manych, named from the relics (lake and stream) of the former connection between the Black and Caspian seas, lies between the Azov and the Ergeni Hills and between the foothills of the northern Caucasus slopes and the Don, and comprises about 55,000 square miles of plains. Surface rocks are a veneer of Quaternary, except near and eastward from Stavropol where the land maintains greater altitude because defended by more resistant, late Tertiary rocks. The surface is more rolling than much of the plains of Russia, but rarely uneven enough to prevent satisfactory cultivation.

Residual lakes occupy many miles of the old channel by which Caspian waters overflowed to the Black Sea. Many temporary lakes form when snow melts. A little interior drainage exists eastward, but westward waters come down to the Don and the sea or spread in marshy land near sea level on the Azov borders. Soils are black, rich chernozems in the west, becoming chestnut eastward and more argillaceous with increase of alkali spots toward the Ergeni Hills. These streams and soil conditions are brought about by the insufficient rainfall of 16 to 22 inches, the large figures prevailing westward and on the higher parts. Spring is the rainiest season. No forests can meet the climatic conditions; rank, colored, plumose grasses covering all the western and central sections become sparser and less colored toward the east, where they are supplanted by the desert wormwood, a bitter, hard, aromatic, drought-resisting weed or shrub taking the place of our western American sagebrush and greasewood.

People. Early Asiatic migrants into Europe paused in the Manych Region, as shown by the many tumuli or *kurgans* and saucer-shaped burial places. They, no doubt, were then nomads, as many have been for thousands of years. Little Russians or Ukrainians occupy most of the western third, a result of proximity to Ukraine and of the easy water transportation across Azov as much perhaps as of the presence here of agricultural conditions similar to those in Ukraine. Through the central and eastern parts Great Russians prevail, but as the aridity increases and grazing becomes more necessary Kalmuks and Tatars make up a dominant proportion of the population.

Occupations. The Manych is a rural region and must so remain. The Ukrainians of the western part are sheep-raisers who market tons of wool and many thousands of pelts. Hides go to the Donetz Basin to be tanned and manufactured. A peasant boot and shoe industry supplies much of the local market. Sheepskin coats, with the wool on, make as characteristic a part of dress here as does astrakhan in the drier plains of the last region. Pedigreed sheep imported from America form the basis for hundreds of flocks of the Manych and lower Caucasus. Sheep and shepherds are omnipresent. Sheep intestines for sausage casings to a value of $3 million per annum find their way to foreign lands.

Wheat in bags is brought in home-made wagons drawn by oxen from the collective farms to the grain-receiving station on the Don River. (Courtesy Sovfoto)

A continuation of the old nomadic cattle industry is found in the many herds of cattle on fenced pastures. State cattle farms supply meat to the industrial markets, and many peasant herds are producing butter and cheese. Ten mechanized creameries use 40,000 tons of milk annually. Horses are raised in the lower Don to mount the Don Cossacks.

The people have known for some time the crop possibilities of the western half of the region, but more than subsistence agriculture has come slowly. Barley is grown over all the region and occupies more than 10 per cent of all sown land. Sunflowers occupy as large an acreage in the western section, where their oil is expressed for local use in the towns. Flax takes

2 to 3 per cent of the cultivable lands, and rice, a well-established crop in the Kuban district, where great marshes occur, has become a state farm crop north of Krasnodar. Winter wheat has for generations been a profitable crop; the new régime has seen its great possibilities and has here enormously expanded the acreage. Geant, the largest state farm, is situated near Salsk on the West Manych River; its sown area is 780 square miles, or as much as a large county in Ohio or Illinois. Several other state farms in Manych are half as large. They raise wheat primarily, but also corn, soy beans, and, where suitable moisture occurs, rice. In the wheat fields teams of seeders, each planting twenty-two or twenty-four rows, sweep across the plains, each a team of five drawn by one tractor. Combine harvesters cut and thresh the wheat, each machine pulled by one tractor, and eight or ten harvesters chase each other *en échelon* back and forth across the fields. Collective farms also are numerous in the Manych.

Soap-making from animal fats has been established in some of the towns as a census industry, and flour-mills grind a part of the local wheat at Krasnodar. Fishing and fish-canning flourish along the Azov coast.

Cities and commerce. Rostov has been described in the Donetz Basin section. It maintains an intimate relation with the Manych both politically and industrially, for it furnishes much of the necessary agricultural machinery. Stavropol (85,000), is situated on the higher land in the southwestern section of the region and has become an important grain center. It suffers from the lack of water. Three streams come down from the mountains and unite close at hand, but because of climatic conditions they dry up in the summer. Leather and leather goods are naturally important Stavropol industries. The city has had some political and strategic importance and is now on the great commercial railroad from Baku and Grozny to Rostov.

Krasnodar (205,000), the leading city, is a commercial and political center. From it as a center the railroads radiate to the larger towns. It is the market for rice cultivated at the great state farm of Cherkars with its thousands of rice-paddies. Eisk, on the south coast of Taganrog Gulf, has a fine beach and has become a coast resort of more than local interest. The government proposes to restore the Azov-Caspian waterway by canalizing the Manych lakes and streams and extending the work down the slope to the Caspian. Locks covering about 100 feet will be needed. A branch canal connecting at Kropotkin with the Kuban River will add to the usefulness of the main waterway and to the trade of Krasnodar. The Manych Region is probably being changed by the Soviets as much as is any part of Russia.

QUESTIONS

1. Compare the lower Volga with the Nile. Why does it not bring about similar responses in man?

2. What industries and products would you suggest for new developments in Astrakhan? in the Volga Plains?

3. Would extensive improvements in harbor and river be worth while for Astrakhan? or for Stalingrad?

4. Note and discuss the difficulties and advantages in the restoration of the waterway between the Azov and Caspian seas.

5. What problems may arise as the natural grasses of the Manych are replaced by wheat and corn? Can you suggest a better crop than corn?

6. Why is the Manych so destitute of metallic mineral resources? Is it a lack which may some day be made good?

7. Will the state wheat farm probably be established in the Caspian Low Plains? Why?

8. How do you account for rice culture in the western Manych section? It is as far north as Ontario is north of Lake Erie.

CHAPTER 29

Southern Mountainous Regions

Scratch a Russian and you'll find a Tatar.
—Old Maxim

19. CRIMEAN RIVIERA

Character. The smallest and the most obvious unit, the Crimea, is a unique region, full of surprises, of historic interest, and of contrasts. The 45° parallel lies across it, but in spite of this high latitude its proximity to the Black Sea and to two great embayments gives its climate many charms, and where best exposed to the marine influences an attractive Mediterranean vegetation cover.

The total area of the peninsula probably does not exceed 8,000 square miles, less than one fourth of which consists of well-watered folded mountains whose summits attain 5,000 feet, and three fourths of which are barren desert plains. Exposed rocks in the plains are mostly late Tertiary, and in the mountains are Triassic, Jurassic, and Cretaceous strata, many of limestone, intruded by many little dikes and plugs of more recent igneous rocks. So recent is the intrusion and associated faulting that hot springs still occur in the Kerch section. The folded, eroded structures give cuestas on the north side with consequent streams in gorges through the hard cuesta-makers. Solution work has riddled some limestone layers until caves abound. One has more than 10,000 chambers on eighteen levels and merits the popular name given it, the "dove cote." These caves have been used as refuges and homes by prehistoric men, by Greeks, Jews, and Goths.

Plains just above sea level occupy the central and northern part of Crimea and continue eastward to the Azov mouth at Kerch. No drier, more desolate place occurs in the peninsula than the lower parts of these plains, while no more charming slopes and terraces can be found than those on the south side of the mountains. In early Quaternary time the peninsula was one third under water and hence was a small island, but more recent changes of level left it a larger island with only narrow straits between it and the mainland. Waves have now constructed a sandbar neck, the isthmus Perekop, 4 miles wide, which ties the island to the land; other sand construction between the peninsula and Ukraine nearly encloses a score of lagoons and salt marshes, part of which are known as the Siwash. These quiet waters support myriads of pelicans, cormorants, and swans.

Resources. Soils of the plains are chestnut loams, salinas, alkali spots, and sands, often blown into dunes; on the hills there are various types of brown mountain soils. Feather-grasses cover some of the plains, wormwood others, and mixed deciduous-coniferous forests cover most of the mountains. True Mediterranean vegetation with palms clothes the lower slopes

A garden in the Crimea, containing palms, ferns, yuccas, aloes, and many other plants. (Courtesy Sovfoto)

on the south side. Rainfall of 10 to 30 inches varies greatly with the altitude, as also does the vegetation. A small maximum of rain in July and a large one in winter suggest a climate partaking of both Mediterranean and continental characteristics. Severe erosion occurs where forests do not hold; hence, pastures over the mountains are meager. Rude and capricious winters prevail in the mountains. Snow may persist on their tops until May; then come the shepherds with their flocks of sheep to remain until fall, sleeping in little rock shelters for protection from cold nights. The south slope of the mountains is the Russian Riviera. Here winters are humid, not cold; summers are dry, not hot. Mountains, sea, beaches, beautiful vegetation, fruits, attractive climate, and sunshine combine to make this slope most charming and in keenest contrast to the monotonous, sandy, arid plains to the north.

To the resources of soils, forests, scenery, and climate, salt and iron are added. The former, with a valuable bromine content, is taken by both natural and artificial evaporation in the Siwash ("putrid sea") country and westward in a "dead sea" of beastly odors. The iron comes from the Kerch section, where the reserves are estimated at 1 billion tons, and where furnaces now produce annually a half-million tons of pig iron. Bituminous coal for the smelting is mined in the south near Kerch; limestone is quarried even nearer, and a little petroleum on the eastern tip of Kerch land serves active ceramic industries. Wind and hydro-electric power add to the natural resources. Sulphur comes from several volcanic points in the east.

Flourishing Black Sea fisheries. Members of a fishing collective taking dolphin off Yalta.
(Courtesy Sovfoto)

Occupations. Agriculture in many types prevails in the Crimea. No region has a higher acreage of sown land per capita. Over 10 per cent of the cultivated land is in barley; corn is an important crop; cotton and winter wheat do well on state and coöperative farms; tobacco is both grown and manufactured. Choice grapes for wines and for export in home-made kegs, apples, cherries, choice pears, peaches, prunes, apricots, almonds, chestnuts, gardens of vegetables and flowers, all are exuberant under the touch of Tatar horticulturists. Poultry, and sheep for hides and wool, are well-adapted livestock. The largest incubators in all Russia operate in this Mediterranean grain-growing climate. Dolphin and other fishing in neighboring waters give employment to many, and the canning of fish and meat is a lively industry. Imported tinplate is made into cans for a large Crimean canning industry, preserving fruits and vegetables. The mountain forests, the only timber for many miles, are carefully cut and conserved.

Cities. Crimea is a part of the Russian S.F.S.R. Simferopol (143,000), 2,000 feet up the mountains, succeeding an old Tatar town, carries on commerce in its cannery products and in fresh fruits. In the mountains of the vicinity stand many beautiful palaces now converted into sanatoriums for workers and peasants. Infinitely less salubrious are the environs of Sevastopol (112,000) on the west coast. It has a commercial bay 5 miles long, a railroad terminus, and connections across the isthmus with the rest of Russia. The great harbor shelters a fleet, a military and naval base, and a modern ship-building plant. Its waters furnish attractive sea baths and areas of oyster culture; its shores are decked with ruins of battles, sieges, and a succession of fires; its hinterland is desert. A dozen coast towns eastward along the foot of the mountains, among them Yalta, the chief health resort, contain palaces, baths, hotels, and fishing facilities; above them on the slopes cling the most enchanting gardens, magnificent marble palaces, and all the elements of the winter playground of the former aristocracy and nobility. The Czar's palace now serves as a peasant rest home. In the mountains above, one may hunt fox and wolf amid most exuberant life, both plant and animal.

In Greek days Feodosia was already a famous wheat market because of its easy access around the mountains to the wheat lands of the interior. Old ruins witness to its former importance. Beyond Feodosia Mediterranean vegetation disappears, and wretched desert reigns supreme. Kerch (105,000), at the end of the peninsula, maintains the iron, steel, ceramic, and related industries on a harbor where all boats in and out of Azov and the Don may stop. Its commercial importance is attested by the fact that it has been held by Greeks, Genoese, Tatars, and Russians.

People. Tatars and Great Russians share the peninsula. Tatars, 28 per cent, are the laborers as well as nomadic shepherds and fishermen, but many Russian peasants also dwell here. Sea borders and mountains contain almost all the permanent population, and the density increases on the mountains from the coast upward to more than 400 per square mile before the pastures are reached. Its outpost position on the Black Sea gives the Crimea a notable cosmopolitan aspect, particularly in its commercial and industrial cities.

20. CAUCASUS MOUNTAINS

Character. The Caucasus is the only region in European Russia having young, lofty, rugged mountains. This mountain area of 65,000 square miles is twice as large as Austria with its 6,700,000 people, 25 per cent larger than Greece with its 6,500,000 people, and more than four times as large as Switzerland with its 4,000,000 people, yet it has not more than 1,500,000 inhabitants. It extends so completely between Caspian and Black seas that it has always been a formidable land barrier; yet it has always been possible to get around it by water.

The Caucasus consists, geologically, of a great, massive fold stretching from sea to sea. In the western half a core of granite and Pre-Cambrian schist makes the summits; an ancient Paleozoic series of rocks outcrops centrally almost the entire length, and on each flank occurs an interesting section of Mesozoic and early Tertiary beds, all involved in the folding. It follows that these mountains are among the recent structures of the earth, made perhaps in mid-Tertiary time and not yet eroded sufficiently to be classed topographically as more than youthful. Peaks rise in many places above 15,000 feet, and Elbruz, the loftiest, scores 18,469 feet. Volcanoes are responsible for hot and mineral springs, where men have constructed medicinal and health baths. Hundreds of glaciers gather in the cirques toward the top and flow down below the snow line. No finer mountain scenery is known than that in the Caucasus.

The unity of the whole region inheres in the stratigraphy, structure, and topography, but not in race, religion, language, or any cultural item. We found much unity among the people of Greece, in old topography to be sure, and in Switzerland and Austria, both more like the Caucasus. This comparison raises the question, How long does it take a diverse people to become fused and to develop a unity of any sort?

Varied relief and altitude are responsible for great diversity of climate, particularly of temperature and precipitation. On the southwestern slopes near the Black Sea both summer and winter rainfalls are heavy, each exceeding 40 inches. Around the eastern end both summer and winter combined bring less than 20 inches.

Vegetation and soils witness to the climatic conditions. Only alpine and tundra floras can cope with the heights; conifers flourish on the upper flanks; below them gradually come in the mixed hardwoods and deciduous trees. Most timber fails below 5,000 feet except on the Black Sea slopes, where heavy forest mantles all slopes, even to the water's edge. Soils are mostly chestnut and brown earths and are so young that they resemble the parent rocks more than in any other part of Russia.

Resources. Forest trees are a valuable resource not only for local use but for export to the treeless, grassy plains to the north. From the days when pirates and Greeks built ships on the Black Sea-Caucasus coasts, these oak, beech, spruce, and pine forests have been important in commerce and industry. Here 50 to 75 per cent is forested, but not more than 10 or 15 per cent of adjacent areas has timber. Forests belong to the state and are developed and cared for, but are not fully surveyed.

Mineral resources are varied, but not comparable with those of the Central Urals. Limestones, marble, and many other building materials are quarried. Clays and Cretaceous limestones are manufactured into cement in large rotary kilns at Novorossiisk for export. Lead, zinc, manganese, magnetic iron ore, copper, gypsum, mercury, antimony, and sulphur from pyrite are among the mineral products. The Baku oil fields are included in the Caucasus region, although they are in Azerbaijan, a Transcaucasian state. Much more oil found in the Terek Valley is marketed at Grozny. Maikop (67,300), a newer field, adds to the Caucasus output. These three fields furnish two thirds of the power used in the vicinity, and pipe-lines, steamers and tank-cars take oil and its products to many distant factories and markets. Modern loading racks and tanks receive the oil piped from Baku to Batum and Tuapse on the Black Sea, and transfer it to tank-cars and to Black Sea and foreign vessels for export. Grozny oil is also piped 390 miles to Tuapse and is there refined and exported. In each field many refineries prepare the oil for local use. More than 1 million motor vehicles that travel the roads of U.S.S.R., and probably 50,000 tractors that energize the farming, need the oil and gasoline. Bituminous coal, known in small quantities for years, has recently been proven to be much more abundant than supposed. Reserves are estimated at 1 billion tons.

Available water power, equal to that of all the rest of Russia, is developed to only one-tenth capacity. Electric power is developed from gas and oil and transmitted to factory towns more cheaply than the oil can be piped.

The scenery and recreation possibilities in the Caucasus Mountains will some day make them a notable tourist playground. Fishing is excellent in many streams, a few lakes, and the Sea. Bear, wild boar, wolves, and mountain goats furnish the sportsman with an enticing lure.

Occupations. Besides the occupations suggested in previous paragraphs, agriculture claims the attention of many people. Three important crops, wheat, barley, and sunflowers, have become state farm specialties on the north slopes. Cotton to meet heavy demands takes a large acreage. Good tobacco grows along the Black Sea and is shipped to Odessa and Rostov. Flax and sugar beets grow on the northern slopes. Tea-growing marks the beginnings of a Mediterranean climate in the Georgian slopes; and around the northwest section of the mountains 25 million cans of fruit and vegetables are put up every year. Two good sheep and wool areas, one around the drier east end, the other in the province of Karachai on the northwestern slopes, produce hides and wool beyond local needs. Hides are tanned in the villages, but wool is generally sent away raw. Forests are systematically cut for lumber and paper-pulp, particularly above the Black Sea coast. Kefir, a fungus gathered in many places, curdles milk and makes the delicious, semisolid, cheese-like food called *yogurt* or *yhourt*.

Cities. With the great supply of fuel in the Baku district its chief city, Baku (810,000), the fifth city in the U.S.S.R., has become quite industrial. Refineries abound; sulphuric acid works use local pyrite; salt-works furnish material for chemical industries; quantities of petrol-electric power serve many small industries; glass is made from local sands; iron is imported to manufacture many machines for local use. Sochi on the Black Sea coast, largely rebuilt and much expanded, caters to a large tourist and health trade. The catching of flatfish has become an active collective industry. Novorossiisk (95,300) at the foot and end of the mountains has probably made the largest growth of any town in the region. It is an oil commercial center whence petroleum moves by rail to Stalingrad. Imports from foreign lands for the Manych and vicinity land here. Industries incident on such commerce are growing up rapidly. Grozny (172,500) is in large part a product of its oil business but owes much to its agriculture and lumbering. The abundance of oil fuel stimulates industry which is growing rapidly.

People. Many relic peoples were incorporated into Russia when the great Slavic empire expanded through the Caucasus. At least a dozen linguistic stocks are so included; Caucasians, Tatars, and Circassians occupy the western section, although Great Russians who have crowded in since the national expansion are everywhere in the majority. Mingrelians, more Circassians, Chechens, and the Northern and Southern Ossets dwell in the mountain valleys of the central section; Georgians spread far up into the valleys from their major habitat in the Rion River plains. In the eastern section, more Circassians, Tatars, and scattered Jews occur with groups of Lesghians, Persians, and Armenians. In the oil and industrial sections Russians of more recent arrival hold the strongest positions. These languages and nationalities differ more than those of the cantons of Switzerland that have been fused so effectively by outside pressure, and perhaps as much as did the city states of Greece that have required more than 2,000 years to evolve common bonds and a considerable unity of spirit. But the isolation of each group here is much greater than in Greece, and it has been effective in preserving languages, customs, traditions, dress, and many backward ideas. Modern means and necessity of communication plus modern haste may, however, soon synthesize these groups. Progress will be stimulated by the Russian advance into the mountains as much as by the coming of the tourist, who has worked wonders in the Swiss Federation.

Interrelations with the outside world and among these groups themselves are being more and more expanded by railroads, telephones, wireless, and the airplane. The old military and post route followed a primitive trail across the low pass, Darial (3,760 feet); today a highway and telegraph line lead over the pass. A railroad using a long tunnel is planned to connect Gori and Tbilisi on the south with Ordzhonikidze and the Terek Valley on the north. This line will link the two roads located on opposite sides of the Caucasus Mountains, which now meet only around the ends at Baku and Tuapse respectively. Airlines unite business centers on opposite sides of the mountains.

21. TRANSCAUCASIA

Character. An area as large as Illinois, Transcaucasia comprises three states in two great valleys and a mountainous tract: Georgia, largely in the western valley of the Rion; Azerbaijan, in the eastern or Kura Valley; and Armenia, in the southern mountains. Considerable portions of the first and second states extend up the mountains and were included in the Caucasus. The population, 5 million people, is nearly as large as that of Illinois, although there is no great metropolis.

Embankment along a Georgian stream in the Caucasus. This town is in the manganese mining region. (Courtesy Sovfoto)

Geologically, Transcaucasia is a complex of granites, diorites, diabases, tuffs, early Tertiary stratified rocks, and a large area of alluvium reaching up the Kura from its delta almost to Tbilisi. In the folding, faulting, and vulcanism, rocks of many other ages have been involved, but they are not widely exposed at present. Topography ranges in altitude from eighty-five feet below sea level in the Kura delta to over 10,000 feet in many mountain summits, and in character from recent plains of accumulation, dunes, and beaches to submarine mountains. Relief and exposure give remarkable ranges in the climatic factors; for example, rainfall varies from over 80 inches at Batum to 0 in the low Kura plains. October is usually the rainiest month. Soils present a wide range commensurate with relief, climate, and their vegetation cover. Alkaline and saline areas are too frequent in lower

Copper works in Armenia of Transcaucasia. A newly established workers' colony has an enriching plant and copper foundries. (Courtesy Sovfoto)

Azerbaijan, and mountain steppes with xerophytic vegetation occupy large areas in Armenia.

Resources. Forest resources are limited by relief and climate. Conifers clothe the higher slopes; beech, oaks, and other deciduous trees come in at lower levels, but all are very patchy and only about 10 per cent is forested. Near the Black Sea, on the other hand, rain-belt forests cover 50 to 75 per cent of the lands. All forests have become state properties and are operated under an efficient forestry system but are not yet fully surveyed. Water power is abundant and extensively developed.

The greatest mineral resource lies in the Chiaturi Valley, a tributary on the north side of Rion Valley, north of Kutias, which holds so great reserves of manganese that Russia produces more than half the world's output. These deposits are worked primarily for export, and their products go in great quantities to the United States. Copper in eastern Armenia, and in Georgia southwest of Tbilisi, salt on the Caspian shores, marble and granite in the mountains, and petroleum along the valleys are important products. Petroleum furnishes a large part of all fuel used. Clay, limestone, and sands are made into cement, ceramic wares, and glass, using oil as fuel. A volcanic tuff in Armenia has been used for buildings for many centuries. Armenian churches 1,000 years old still stand well preserved. The tuff is easily quarried, is lighter than brick, and can be sawed, nailed, or laid up with mortar. Lesser but significant minerals are ores of aluminum, chromium, and molybdenum, sulphur, pyrite, barite, tripoli, and gypsum.

Occupations. Agriculture leads all other activities. Perhaps sheep- and cattle-raising are its most important phases, but cotton-growing is spreading to meet the demands of Moscow Region textile mills and fruit and vegetable growing and canning are assuming important proportions; 40 million oranges are made into preserves annually. Sericulture employs 10,000 women in the mild sub-Mediterranean climate, and an equal number manufacture silk and wool into rugs, shawls, and tapestries in Armenia and Georgia. The people of the lowlands of Georgia, with their Mediterranean climate, grow tea, of which they prepare several million pounds for Russian markets, citrus fruits and grapes, tung-oil trees for lacquer, ramie (a fiber plant), cork oak, bamboo, and a number of plants for essential oils such as lavender. Great irrigation works in the Kura Valley are redeeming fertile desert soils to cotton, tobacco, vine, and fruit-tree culture. Many a farm here raises barley, sunflowers, and flax. Fisheries, canning and salting fish, and pickling caviar in thoroughly modern plants thrive in coast towns.

Cities. Tbilisi (550,000), also known as Tiflis, the administrative center for these states, is fortunately situated on the Kura River above the low alluvial, arid plains where the trans-Caucasus highway crosses the more important Caspian-Black Sea route. The divide above Gori, separating Rion from Kura plains, scarcely exceeds 2,000 feet, and the route over it has been used from prehistoric times. The city has some of the 151 hydro-electric plants, which in these trans-Caucasian states produce in the aggregate 400 million kwh annually. The oil pipeline, Baku to Batum, serves the city. Cotton, woollen, and silk fabrics, tobacco, chemicals, films, vegetable oils and fats, are among its varied products. Oil-producing and refining machinery, furniture, paper, and many wooden articles are made here. Tbilisi, farther north than Cleveland, has a cinema studio, but much of the film-making is done in a large domed building and not in the open.

Azerbaijan cotton breeding and experiment station, with staff director (black suit, center) and cotton breeder. This is an irrigated area. (Courtesy U.S. Dept. of Agriculture)

Erivan (200,000), capital of Armenia, serves a great alluvial, intermontaine plain, through which the Aras River flows to join the Kura near the Caspian. A branch of the Aras drains the great Lake Gokcha, which, over 3,000 feet above the city, furnishes a wealth of steady water power sufficient for many of the rug and tapestry mills of the city. Batum (72,000), a notable oil export town with modern equipment, spreads over the plains among acres of tea, luxuriant palms, rare eucalyptus, mimosa, oleanders, groves of tangerines, lemons, olives, and clumps of bamboo and maintains sea baths, health resorts, and busy silk-mills.

People. For ages the formidable mountain barrier of the Caucasus has forced army, caravan, and migrating horde through the highway of the Kura-Rion valley. Led by the water of the Aras, Asiatics who rounded the southern Caspian came into this valley. For thousands of years early races passed through. Greeks, Scythians, and Huns found the route; then from the northeast appeared Turks and Mongols. All streamed down from Persian or Iranian plateaus on their way to Europe, leaving fragments lodged here and there in isolated valleys until one is not surprised to read in the Russian census that over fifty nationalities reside in Transcaucasia. They are a varied lot, separated for ages by topographic and climatic barriers, by ignorance, prejudice, and superstition bred of isolation and poverty; but now being leavened by a generous sprinkling of Russians, removed from the separateness of centuries, and put upon the highway of auto roads, radio, and plane, of common schools, colleges, and agricultural and industrial experiment stations.

QUESTIONS

1. Note the figures given for the Caucasus in comparison with Austria, Greece, and Switzerland. What interpretative comments can be made?

2. Of what real geographic significance will be the trans-Caucasus railroad? Compare with the first transalpine railroad.

3. What place in the world's economy do you think the people of the Caucasus will take? the people of Transcaucasia? When? Use analogies with other people.

4. What difference would it make in Caucasian progress if their mountains were as bare of minerals as are the Pyrenees? Make other comparisons and contrasts between the two mountain regions as to setting, people, and values.

5. Under what circumstances would the Crimea become a battle field? See Crimean War, 1854-55, in the encyclopedia.

6. Why should Perekop be heavily fortified?

BIBLIOGRAPHY

ARMSTRONG, Hamilton F., *Tito and Goliath* (New York, The Macmillan Company, 1951).

BALZAK, S. S., *et al., Economic Geography of U.S.S.R.* Russian edition about 1939, trans. by R. M. Hankin and O. A. Titelbaum; American edition, Chauncy D. Harris, ed. (New York, The Macmillan Company, 1949).

COON, Carleton S., *The Races of Europe* (New York, The Macmillan Company, 1939).

Europa, Encyclopedia of Europe (London, Europa Publications, Ltd.), annual.

FITZGERALD, Walter, *The New Europe* (New York, Harper and Brothers, 1946).

KONOVALOV, Serge, ed., *Russo-Polish Relations* (Princeton, Princeton University Press, 1945).

McCORMICK, Thomas C. T., ed., *Problems of the Post-War World* (New York, McGraw-Hill Book Company, Inc., 1945).

NEWMAN, Bernard, *The New Europe* (New York, The Macmillan Company, 1943).

SHACKLETON, Margaret R., *Europe, A Regional Geography* (London, Longmans, Green & Company, 1942).

Statesman's Yearbook (New York, The Macmillan Company), annual.

SUPER, Margaret L., *Poland and U.S.S.R., Last Quarter Century* (New York, Sheed and Ward, 1944).

WELLES, Sumner, ed., *An Intelligent American's Guide to the Peace* (New York, The Dryden Press, 1945).

Part VI

CENTRAL STATES
WITH TRANSITIONAL CLIMATE

CENTRAL EUROPE PROPER

The six states grouped under the caption Central Europe Proper as shown in the chapter on Climate have a transitional climate, neither marine nor continental, polar nor Mediterranean. None of them touch the ocean, though two of them border on large embayments, the North Sea and the Baltic. They form a large rectangular area containing every type of topography in Europe and nearly every mineral resource, strong soils, great forests, and a wealth of water power, extending over nearly 400,000 square miles and, according to the census of 1946, supporting 124 million people. Moreover, the climatic conditions combine to give to these lands the finest working conditions in Europe after those of the coast states, with satisfactory agricultural temperature and rainfall.

With considerable physical unity, there is diversity of race, language, religion, and cultural attainment. Four of the states are held by the Alpine race, two of which are Slavic; one is largely Nordic; and one is Magyar. All the languages except that of the Magyars are Aryan tongues. All the nations have been Christianized; some of the people are Protestants, some Roman Catholic, and a few belong to the Orthodox Eastern Church. The Christian or Church culture came to these mid-European people late in European history, and phenomenal progress has been made in most sections. The Great Schism, which developed before 1500, laid a line or zone between eastern and western Patriarchates of the Catholic Church. Those on the east are designated the Orthodox Eastern Church; those on the west, the Roman Catholic Church. The line ran through this group of the states. On opposite sides of the line the people participated in the activities, education, and spirit of their respective neighbors. Parts of Poland and Hungary were closer to the backward East Russian and Balkan peoples than to the forward-looking, progressive West and are now far behind.

Under climatic and oceanic influences the western states have accomplished more in commerce and industry than has been possible in the more remote sections. The eastern states are still rural to a large degree; the western are no less rural but much more industrial and commercial. There should be extensive economic coöperation among the six states of this group.

Switzerland is by far the oldest state in the group; Poland, though having had different boundaries, saw a long independent history and then was partitioned among aggressive neighbors, to be reunited after the First World War. Germany, like Switzerland, is a federation, but of much more recent date; the other three are states that arose from the ruins of the dual Empire of Austria-Hungary and hence are called Succession States.

CHAPTER 30

Germany

Little things make Germany a lovely place;
Small square fields where cabbages grow red,
Fire glowing golden on blue tiles,
Flowered cloth around a feather bed.
—JOSEPHINE MILES

INTRODUCTION

General. In the postwar adjustments Germany and Poland have suffered greater changes of frontier than any other states. Their boundary lines are still unsettled, particularly the line between them. What is not in one, however, is in the other. No nation stands in any measure between them.

Situation. The German [1] nation occupies the largest area of any of the six Central Group, holding nearly one third of the total area, and Poland has more than any other three. In size it is the fifth state in Europe. The area is estimated at 143,200 square miles. Relief is not great. The Zugspitze, 9,850 feet, in the Fore-Alps is the only point higher than 6,500 feet. Germany possesses great plains, some plateaus, and several old mountain ranges. The increase in the relief from north to south nearly compensates climatically for the decrease in latitude.

Germany's remarkable industrial development, while initiated long after that of other western nations, has been favored by the mineral wealth of the old Hercynian (pertaining to the Harz) mountains that lie entirely across the country from Belgium to Bohemia and from Basel to the Brocken in the Harz. Saxony is enriched by buried ores and fuels in other parts of these old mountain structures. Tertiary seas and streams laid sediments that now constitute the Alpine Foreland, the plateaus that occupy the Danube Basin of Germany; glaciation of Scandinavian origin spread drift over nearly all the north German plains, modified the drainage, left a jumble of moraines, channels, lakes, and marshes, and deposited an intractable young

---

[1] It is not expected that Germany will need to continue its state of foreign occupation by the four victors for many years, hence our discussion here treats Germany as a whole, even though the map on p. 631 shows Germany still divided among the victors.

607

soil over most of the plains. Germany's central position, touching nine states and two seas, gives an illusory feeling of being crushed but offers splendid opportunities for trade and friendly relations.

Germany lies between the January isotherms of 28° and 34° F. and between the July isotherms of 62° and 69° F. Thus the mean winter temperature is close to freezing, and the mean summer temperature is close to the critical vegetation line of 68° for a growing season. West Germany is near enough to the sea to feel marine influences and much of the east is chilled in winter by continental cold winds.

Boundaries are somewhat diverse, two thirds being on the land; usually they are such lines as encourage rather than check friendly intercourse, commerce, and travel. The other third of the frontier line is water, favored with several small harbors along both Baltic and North seas. All the great harbors are short distances up the rivers, protected, and helpfully within the land.

History. For centuries the present German territory was occupied by Germanic tribes rising through stages of civilization and culture from nomads and primitive farmers to a group of petty nations, hostile, jealous, belligerent, but steadily evolving. Every niche of valley, plain, and basin sheltered a unit of this varied population, small ones in the mountains, large ones on the plains. In the fourteenth century hundreds of fragments were listed, some spiritual, some temporal. Fusions, fissions, and federations occurred as physical barriers became relatively less important or strong personalities arose, until in 1871 twenty-six sovereign states became the German Empire. How far the various cleavages and unions were related to the topography, resources, connections, and outlets would make a long and fascinating historico-geographic study, too long to be followed here.

People. In 1946 the census showed a population of about 67,032,000. The mean density is nearly 368 per square mile, five times that of European Russia. About 2 per cent are non-German; these include a small Slav group, the Wends on the Spree Wald, Danes and Frisians on the northwest, and even yet a number of Jews. Slavonic blood is common in the central and eastern plains and this may account for the stolidity, patience, industry, and lack of ingenuity of the inhabitants. The many Roman invasions and settlements along the Rhine and in Bavaria have left enough Mediterranean blood among the basic Alpine stock to help explain the vivacity, charm, and interest in art and education, as well as the physique of the Rhinelander. In general, the north German is Nordic and the south German is Alpine; the latter easily excels in music, literature, art, and science. The German language and many German people formerly spread into and through the mountains surrounding the western end of Czechoslovakia and formed a line of weakness in the Second World War. Most of these Germans have moved back into their homeland, i.e., from the borders of Czechoslovakia into Germany.

Languages are a group of Germanic Aryan tongues with many local dialects (Bavarian, Low German, Swabian) spoken throughout all the country. These dialectic differences of many sorts reflect long isolation of groups. Wendish still persists, though most of the other Slavic elements are absorbed. High German is the official, written language. In religion the people are Lutheran in central and northern sections but Roman Catholic in the Rhine states and in the Alpine Foreland, a distribution quite consonant with border contacts.

The people are capable, efficient, obedient, and hard-working; they love regimentation; as a nation they are arrogant, unsocial, and stubborn; possessed of little insight or tact when dealing with neighboring countries. These qualities seem to be responses to the political systems of administration under which they have lived rather than to geographic factors—perhaps inherited from too much and too long isolation. To make a living on German soils the farmer must be frugal, thrifty, and industrious. The people in general are less versatile and adaptable than residents of warmer latitudes. Harsh winters drive them to their cordial hearths, develop family sentiment, deep feeling, and a contemplative mind which finds its best expression in the details of science and philosophy.

Under the influence of western contacts, continuously multiplied in western Europe during the fifteenth century, and the urge of the individualism bred by the Swiss valleys, there arose in the early sixteenth century a growing freedom of thought which manifested itself in politics as opposition to the centralized control of the church by Rome; in religion as the rejection of Scholastic theology and a return to the Greek and Hebrew scriptures; in morality as an abhorrence of the whole system of indulgences and confessions, and the elevation of the right of private interpretation of the Scripture; and in learning as the freedom of the individual mind in science and in philosophy. Earlier reformers like Wycliffe in England, Huss in Bohemia, Lefèvre in France, and Erasmus, a Dutch scholar, had prepared the way for the immediate leaders, Luther in Germany, Cranmer in England, Calvin and Zwingli in Switzerland, and John Knox in Scotland; and so the Reformation was born of the times, the conditions, and the place as distinctly as was Christianity itself, and Judaism in the Levant centuries earlier. No one can fully reckon the total import of this movement for freedom, individualism, and nationalism which resulted in the formation of the older Protestant churches.

Unity. In spite of diverse topography and much variety in race, religion, language, and standards of living, there still is much unity in ideals and spirit. Political unity has been fostered since 1871, reinforced by the constitution of Weimar in 1919 and relentlessly intensified by the régime of the national socialists since 1933. The temporary occupation of Germany by four foreign powers since World War II may stimulate a tendency toward division but unity is made effective by the railroad net of nearly 35,000 miles of track, by an excellent system of stream and canal communications excelled only by those of Belgium and Netherlands, and by more air traffic in proportion to size than in any other country. No large town lacks an airport. Automobile roads are many and well kept. Electricity, generated from coal in the Ruhr, from lignite in many places, and from water power in Saxony, is transmitted from many great producing centers to every part of the land.

Regions. One may divide the territory of Germany into regions in many ways; he may make as many divisions as there were political entities in the times of difficult communication, or he may mark off a few regions on geologic lines. The regions suggested here are largely types of utilization, but utilization so intimately tied to resources and topography that most of the lines are physiographically or geologically determined as well. (1) The Northern Drift Plains extend in a belt of varying width from Denmark along the coast eastward through West Pomerania. (2) The Old Valley Zone reaches entirely across the country from Holland to Poland and with the former region occupies all the northern plains. (3) The Rhine Gorge Region is unified by its geology and the valleys of the Rhine, Moselle, and Lahn rivers. (4) The Central Highlands are mountains, valleys, and dissected plateaus drained by the Weser and Elbe rivers. (Regions 3 and 4 are as distinctively industrial as 1, 2, 5, and 6 are rural.) (5) The Southwest Highlands. (6) The Alpine Foreland. Each will be fully described, and the designations will form the headings for the remaining pages devoted to Germany.

THE NORTHERN DRIFT PLAINS

Topography. The hundreds of small outcrops of Tertiary rocks in little hills and along stream beds suggest that but for glaciation northern Germany would have been as characteristic a coastal plain as is much of New Jersey. The ice sheet from Scandinavia spread at least twice over these great plains, the second time not so widely as the first. In its last retreat it halted long enough to build two great recessional moraines and left innumerable kettles, marshes, eskers, drumlins, and boulders in a concentric zone 50 to 100 miles wide around the south end of the Baltic from Denmark eastward to patterns described in the Baltic states. Since the ice melted, streams have carved valleys in the drift; then a slight relative movement of the lands has drowned their mouths. Streams have made so little progress that much of the land is miserably drained. The relief of this region does not usually exceed 200 to 300 feet, but the drift is known to be over 300 feet thick in central and western parts. High hummocks are better drained and are tufted with forests, mixed in the west but mostly coniferous in the east. The lowest places are peat bogs, and the intermediate slopes are used for raising stock, flax, rye, and many less important crops. This topography isolates and re-

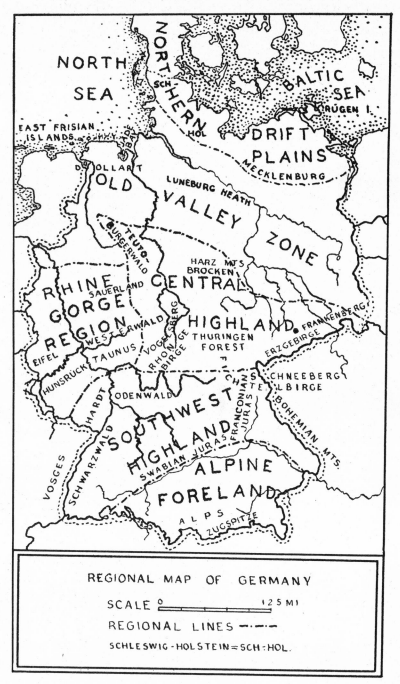

Geographic regions of Germany. Regions are shown by dot-dash lines, with names of physical features. (Based on geologic, topographic, resource, and land utilization maps)

stricts the inhabitants to such an extent that they are proverbially shy and backward, unsociable, individualistic, and independent.

Soils are young, acid, and unfriendly. They are yielding to scientific treatment but have yet far to go to be generally usable. Arability is determined by ice- and water-laid forms, moraines, outwash, lakes, and bogs.

Shorelines were originally established by a small submergence which created many small harbors between morainic hills and drumlins. Waves have cut into some of the headlands and built many miles of beach. Constructional wave work has built many small sandbars as seen round Barth

Plowing the fields, as it may be seen in the Drift Plains or Central Highlands. (U.S. Army photograph)

and Rügen. The Baltic was an inland sea from the glacial retreat until 5,000 to 6,000 years ago, when shiftings of level established the present meager connections with the Atlantic. Germany has about 400 miles of Baltic shoreline and 300 miles of North Sea coast but scarcely a harbor save in drowned river mouths. The harbor waters are shallow, brackish, and easily frozen. Fishing in the Baltic has never been important because fish do not like the conditions and because ice forbids the use of the dragnet. Fishing in the North Sea has engaged many more boats and men.

Divisions of the plains. Two sections of this region are Schleswig-Holstein and Mecklenburg. The first, an isthmus connecting Jutland with the mainland, is the most level and the best rural land in the whole coast zone. It produces hogs, cattle, beets, and cereals. The Kiel Canal was cut through this isthmus primarily for naval strategic reasons but is now used extensively for commerce. It was a reasonable development to connect two German seas. Over 50,000 boats a year, less than half of which are German and thousands of which do not even touch at Kiel, use the canal. Railroad trade is not checked by the canal, for the track is built across it high above stacks and masts of boats. Kiel (273,733) is an artificial, strategic, political town with no geographic reason for existence.

Harvesting turnips, which will be stored in pits for use in the winter and spring as food for both men and cattle. (U.S. Army photograph)

Mecklenburg. This section is much rougher with moraine than Schleswig-Holstein and hence has more pasture and fewer cultivated crops. It is a land of lakes and forests. Although the land is admirably adapted to dairying, not much has been so used. The subdivision of feudal estates into independent farms, a process going on for the last 60 years, has improved agriculture. Many farmers raise rye in a rye-oats-potatoes rotation which produces more oats and potatoes than formerly and still grows too much rye. There is an increasing number of hogs, dairy cattle, and sheep; hence farmers have more manure to spread, thus further improving the farms. The system of small farms and independent farmers is a much better rural adjustment to agricultural conditions than are the large estates.

The Mecklenburg coast was Hanseatic Germany. Lübeck (154,811), Wismar, Rostock, Stralsund, and Schwerin were all important in those days of small boats. The first three, by making ocean connections through Kiel and Hamburg, have improved their modern status, but none is of more than local importance. Most of the Hanseatic towns have declined, whether in Germany or elsewhere.

THE OLD VALLEY ZONE

Topography. Nearly one fourth of Germany is included in the Old Valley Zone, which comprises about two thirds of the northern plains. Three rivers flow entirely across the region; the Weser and Ems in the west, and the Elbe in the center. The Oder in the east also crosses the region but forms much of the eastern boundary of postwar Germany. The most characteristic physiographic features are the cross valleys, now mostly abandoned by streams, which connect the great river valleys. German geologists called them primitive valleys (*Urstrom-Täler*) because they antedate the present stream courses. The underlying geology is a continuation of that in the Drift Plains, but the drift in this region was mostly laid by the early ice sheets. The late sheet did not reach far into this region. When in the second or greatest advance the ice edge stood along the line from Magdeburg on the Elbe to Breslau in Silesian Poland, marginal waters ran westward across present waterways into the present course of the Black Elster to the Elbe and probably on west into the Aller, the Weser, and the sea. When the ice withdrew beyond Glogau on the Oder in Poland and Baruth, south of Berlin, a new lower channel was excavated past these towns, leading into the Elbe below Magdeburg. Again the ice halted on a line through Posen in Poland, Frankfort and Schwerin, and a third channel was formed where now flow the Spree and other small streams. When the latest ice sheet had advanced toward Thorn and the Netze in Poland, and nearly to Eberswalde north of Berlin, the Vistula turned west at Thorn, flowed down the Netze and on westward. Many streams flowed directly away from the ice-front to the Netze. When the ice withdrew completely from northern Germany, consequent streams flowed from the last moraine northward to the Baltic; by headward erosion they gnawed back through the moraine and captured waters still flowing in these cross channels, and so made elbows in the Vistula below Thorn and in the Oder where the Finow canal joins it. Most of the primitive abandoned valleys afford an unsurpassed opportunity to construct connecting canals that help provide the region with a network of commercial waterways.

Since the ice withdrew much longer ago from this region than from the Northern Drift Plains, this zone has a more efficient drainage pattern and more mature soils, which make the region better for agriculture. Because these plains are partly glacial, partly glacio-fluvial, and partly fluvial, they vary much in character from place to place. Level areas, till plains or lake-beds, are interspersed with moraines, kames, outwash plains, and abandoned alluvial plains.

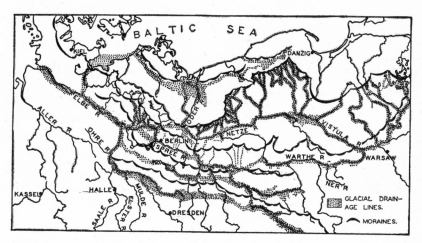

Glacial map of Germany and vicinity. Note the marginal east-to-west drainage lines, now among moraines, and drainage lines radially outward from the ice margins. The three older, more southern halts and the two later northern halts are marked by moraine symbols. (Adapted from Keilhack)

Western section. The western section may be considered to reach to Magdeburg. Its coast is nearly 200 miles long, deeply embayed at the Dollart and Ems estuary, at Jade Bay, and at the estuaries of the Weser and Elbe rivers, but aside from the estuaries very inhospitable to commerce. The East Frisian Islands, long sandbars, guard the coast, lagoons, and mud-flats behind them and furnish homes for many families of fishermen who through their remoteness and isolation have maintained their language, quaint customs, and independent ways of looking at life. In these they are distinct from the people on the mainland, whose contacts have promoted many changes.

Whereas the islands and parts of adjacent mainland are infertile or covered with heath, the muddy tidal flats are very rich, and men are struggling to redeem them. Polders are formed as in Holland, pumped out, washed free from salt by abundant rains, and planted to nutritious grasses; thus clam-fishing gives place to grazing. This shoreline and its lagoon, tidal flat accompaniments, are a strong stimulus to endeavor and ingenuity to hold and redeem, to use and not lose. For 700 years, or since the foundering of the Dollart and Jade Bay,[1] the struggle has been keen, but the gains have scarcely balanced the losses.

The estuaries were drowned by post-glacial submergence; thus they are recent and not yet critically silted. They, therefore, invite navigation and commerce and have become the sites of Emden, Bremen, Hamburg, and several auxiliary ports.

The geographic landscape in this western section includes great stretches of heath, lake, marsh, and peat moss areas; sandy or gravelly plains (in the main poor soils on cultivable parts); the great rivers, Elbe and Weser, upon which move many steamers, barges, and pleasure craft; the vigorous flourishing commercial cities, many villages, and occasional feudal castles with their girdle of humble peasant shelters; and thousands of independent small farms with crops of rye, oats, potatoes, and green pastures upon which feed cattle, sheep, and horses. Many patches of forest cap the hills or cover stony areas, and others are now being planted over cleared heaths. Man is doing much to change the aspect of the region, particularly in modifying the vegetation cover and adding buildings. Moors and peat bogs are yielding to peat harvesters, who use the peat both for fuel and to enrich infertile soils. For 75 years, draining and reclamation projects have been pushed to replace waste or bogs with meadows or arable lands. A marked trend toward stock-raising, especially dairying, has appeared in recent decades. While the contrast with Holland rural landscapes is impressive, so much has been done to improve these lands that one finds tobacco, sugar beets, and vegetables in the rotation, and many hogs now bred to feed upon the beet pulp. Honey, rabbits, and game birds are taken seriously as products of the plains. While the plains give in general unlimited freedom to roads and railroads, it is necessary in actual construction to adjust every mile to details of topography and water.

This region was originally all forest, bog, or heath. It was the cradle of the German race; political unity began here, and here the Germans met their severest challenge because the soils and topography were so difficult to develop. Inasmuch as knowledge concerning the natural landscape was necessary for Germany's evolution, this region has been mapped topographically, geologically, and pedologically; the soil has been studied, analyzed, and monographed; many types of soil conditions have been put through experiments with fertilizers, cultivation, and crops, to discover just what are the best adjustments possible. In spite of assiduous application of science to all phases of the problem, there still remain many acres that make little contribution to the economy of the region. Heaths, of which Lüneburg is the largest example, persist above the altitude of 100 to 150 feet as *Geest* or moors, not yet drained. The Lüneburg heath is 30 miles wide and 125

---

[1] Jade Bay was formed in the eleventh century; the Dollart dates from the fourteenth.

miles long but is interrupted by valleys with better drained, fertile, alluvial soils, and by marshes still undrained.

Two areas merit special consideration, the Hanover loess belt and the Münster plain. The loess belt is near the Harz Mountains. Winds from the great ice sheet picked up dust in drying mud and silt flats, drove it southward, and laid it as loess in the Hanover-Brunswick-Magdeburg belt. The land here is high enough and has been subjected to erosion long enough to be well drained. It bears heavy money-crops of sugar beets, tobacco, flax, and cereals. Vegetables find market in the Ruhr. Some areas raise asparagus, others peas and beans. Rural industries still flourish in village homes and in small towns, and coöperative selling aids many rural sections. Because of their situations the old market towns of Hanover (470,950) and Brunswick (201,300) have far outstripped scores of others in commerce. Local lignite beds near each have stimulated industry, which began by preparing agricultural products for use and has extended to iron, steel, and machine-making. Iron ore, brought from the Rhineland, is used, and its phosphate-bearing slag makes efficient fertilizers for pastures and cereals. Both towns were members of the Hanseatic League. Brunswick is a well-preserved economic center manufacturing machines of precision and mechanical inventions. Hanover was long an important political center in an independent prosperous state, furnishing the sovereigns who occupied the English throne from 1714 to 1837. Since railroads were invented, Hanover has become an important node in their connections. Each suburb has developed some specialized industry. One has dye-works and weaving factories; another wagon-works, chemicals, and sugar-mills; two have metallurgy and machine-shops; two others engage in rubber manufacturing. The old town of Brunswick preserves Hanseatic warehouses, even the gardens and residences of some of the commercial princes. The modern residential section has spread around the old town; the circuit of the old walls has become boulevards; and the city carries the aspect of a prosperous, gay town.

The Münster plain lies between the German west boundary, the Teutoburger Wald, and the highlands around the Ruhr Valley. It is a rich till plain, over Hercynian mountain structures, dotted with farmhouses and occasional large estates. The levelness lends itself to big Dutch windmills like those in adjacent Holland. Münster (over 100,000), the chief city, is becoming industrial as is the plain between it and the Ruhr, because the coal-beds, so well known in the Ruhr, descend beneath the plain in the buried mountain structures and can be reached in mines at Münster although here they are nearly 3,500 feet deep.

The two great waterways of this western section, Elbe and Weser rivers, have helped two important commercial centers, Hamburg and Bremen. Both were Hanse towns and became free and independent cities within the empire, a status still maintained in the republic. Each is situated about 50 miles from the sea on its respective river, at a place adapted for defense and for commerce. Medieval fortifications were of the severest, most effective type, but all walls are now replaced by streets, boulevards, or modern buildings.

Hamburg (1,711,900, including suburbs), with Altona (242,000) and other adjuncts of the commercial center, is easily the master port of Germany, both by virtue of its powerful economic highway to the sea and its $125 million harbor and because of its rich hinterland, which includes all

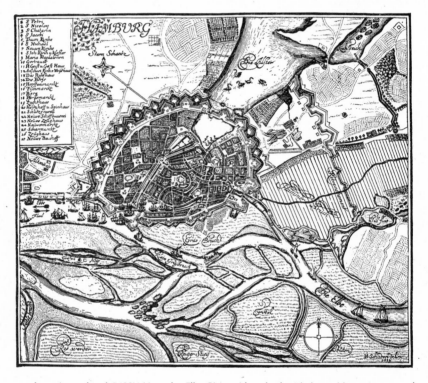

Hamburg (map dated 1689). Note the Elbe River, tides, the braided, troublesome stream, the heavy fortifications, the Alsters separated by the wall, and the harbor. Names in the upper left legend refer to numbers on the map, but most of them have become illegible. (Courtesy Historical Museum of Hamburg)

the Elbe Valley, Prague, Saxony, and even Berlin, Vienna, and Budapest. With its foreport, Cuxhaven, it can handle half of German maritime commerce. Hamburg is almost amphibious, for its waterways reach most parts of the city and its railways and roads reach all the docks. It has miles of docks and piers, acres of warehouses, rows of offices, scores of factories, and ships of every flag. There is no limit to possible harbor space, especially down the estuary, and water levels vary only 7 feet with floods and tides. Access to the interior is augmented by many canals and by a very efficient railroad net. It is first among continental ports, but has keen competition from Rotterdam, favored by the Rhine; from Antwerp, favored by preferential railroad tariffs; and from Havre, nearer Britain and America. A canal under construction west to the Rhine will reach coal-fields, mighty industrial centers, and the commercial cities of Bremen and Rotterdam. Hamburg builds many ships and by virtue of position contains the offices of several important freight and passenger steamship lines. It leads as an emigrant station, for which it has developed housing and every other facility. Specifically, Hamburg has a heavy trade with England, Scandinavian countries, France, and Mediterranean lands. Wines of Bordeaux and cognac sent in bottles through Hamburg reach many countries. Over 1,000 vessels, with an aggregate tonnage of 16,800,000, enter the port yearly under many foreign flags. With normal conditions Holland brings 2 million tons, Britain brings and carries away over twice as much. Cotton, wheat, hides, and petroleum arrive from the United States, coffee from Brazil, wool from Argentina, Cape Town, and Australia, jute from India. The exports of machinery and fabrics go to the whole world; salt and sugar floated down the river to Hamburg for distribution find a wide European market, and chemical products go to Japan. The harbor has every modern equipment, in crane, derrick, grain-suckers and floating elevators, lighters, powerful shovels, and trams. It unites every modern appliance with speed, safety, security, and continuity of process; its capacity is much larger than its business has actually needed.

Bremen (354,100), older than Hamburg, is as efficiently equipped in proportion to its size and has had a slow, substantial growth, but can never become as important because its river and its hinterland are smaller. It has much foreign commerce and is the first port on the continent in American cotton, rice, and tobacco. Many of its passengers take ship at Bremerhaven and avoid the hours of tedious river journey, four to six times as long by water as by rail. By building the Bremen harbor, at a cost of $25 million, the authorities sought to deflect Rotterdam wool, cotton, cereals, and Swedish iron ore. Bremen specializes in import of cotton, surpassing Liverpool by receiving 2,500,000 to 3,000,000 bales annually; and in import of cereals, surpassing Hamburg in floating sucker elevators. Bremerhaven has two thirds as much commerce as Berlin. Emden is a keen rival for foreign trade.

Eastern section. East of Magdeburg the Old Valley plains are less perfectly drained and are therefore strewn with many more lakes than in the west. The streams, in alluvial valleys 100 feet deep, are more completely connected by canals; soils are heavier in some places, sandier in others; pine timber is more abundant; and there is more livestock. The crops are rye, oats, and potatoes. Although settlement is not as old as in the west, Slavic and later German villages have been established over all of it. The early villagers built forts in the zone of combat between Slav and German, also markets at the easiest places to defend or hold for trade, at favorable stream crossings, and at suitable places to dig peat or to fish; but they overdid their building, for many abandoned ruins of ill-founded villages still remain. Surviving settlements have been extended, diversified in interest, and made trade centers, becoming the chief stimuli to rural activities. Agriculture is enriched by stock-raising and return of fertilizer to the lands in manure and in commercial fertilizers. Yet these advantages scarcely hold men on the farms, for many notable industrial cities have grown, drawing rural men 25 and 30 miles to urban life. These plains are inherently rural and forested lands, and their primitive aspect should never be disturbed. Much of the

Four new American fishing boats at the fish docks in Bremerhaven. (U.S. Army photograph)

land is ill adapted to agriculture, and cultivation has extended far enough but may yet be intensified. Systematic forestry should be continued and improved, and the cities maintained.

A map of rivers, lakes, and canals shows how completely man has taken advantage of present streams and abandoned valleys for his transportation. A map of railroads shows how completely Berlin is the master node in them, also how little in general the physiography influences them. But a detail map shows how every crook and turn is controlled by minor features.

Lobes of these plains reach out into bordering lands. One such embayment, into the hills, contains the notable cities of Halle and Leipzig as well as the river Elbe and its branches, the Saale and Mulde. The land of this

Rivers and canals of Germany. Note how much use is made of the glacial drainage lines.
(Compiled from Goode's *School Atlas* and *Oxford Advanced Atlas*)

section is rolling, well drained, and as valuable to the eastern part of the Old Valley Region as is the Hanover loess section to the west.

The Stassfurt-Halle-Merseburg area has the richest potassium resources in the world. Reserves within mining distance of the surface are estimated at 20 billions of tons of potash, sufficient to meet the world's needs at the present rate of consumption for 2,000 years. Germany produces three times as much potassium as France, her nearest competitor. Legal limits, however, are placed upon production in Alsace. German chemical industries are remarkably favored and stimulated by these subterranean deposits; and scientific research into the nature and needs of soils and the best methods of preparing potassium for fertilizers has been quickened for two generations. The fertilizer industry, in turn, is stimulated by the sugar beet culture and potato-growing of the Magdeburg, Mecklenburg, and other sections. Many chemicals, such as caustic soda, washing soda, dyestuffs, and nitrogen compounds, are now made. Halle (222,505) on the Saale is the most important town in this series. As a Hanse town it was more important than Leipzig. Years ago it lost prestige to the latter because of a great fire and domestic discord, but today its industry and research, encouraged by a strong university, are winning back its trade.

Magdeburg (236,326), a fortified crossing of the Elbe, has become the most notable beet-sugar center in the country. Farms, generally large on the rolling plains, specialize in the growing of beets. Production is organized with manufacturing. The section produces a third of all German sugar. No doubt the fertile nature of the soil, the gentleness of slopes, and the splendid supply of fertilizer close by have all contributed to the marked success of the industry. A six-year rotation has been found to be most favorable, two years of beets, two years of winter wheat, and two years of spring crops such as potatoes, peas, oats, or rye. Intensive, careful cultivation and weeding, done with extreme neatness, bring heavy crops. Horses for the farms are bought in Belgium, milch cows in Netherlands, and beef cattle in Bavaria. Laborers come from Silesia, in Poland, and work out from camps near the fields. Magdeburg feels the commercial competition of Berlin and Leipzig and probably will never quite measure up to its historic and economic importance. It has a commodious harbor to ship salts, sugar, and fertilizers, and to receive charcoal, coke, and ores for its metallurgical industries; and a great bridge that draws much traffic to the crossing.

Leipzig (701,606) is less satisfactorily located on the Elster River among marshes and forests. It was founded in the twelfth century, became a fur market because of its river and surrounding forests, then was favored by kings and emperors, and ultimately signed trade agreements with Breslau and Frankfort on the Oder. It became Protestant in the Reformation, allied its trade with France and Netherlands, and added to its rôle woolens, silks, and linens. Then came its fairs, specialized markets, and the commerce stimulated industry. Its wall was succeeded by a boulevard, and the railroad station was built beside the old town. Manufacturing has appropriated and built up many suburbs. Machines, optical instruments, pottery and china-ware, textiles, clothing, and electric devices have come one after another. Leipzig has the name of producing everything that appeals to the intelligence: paper, engraving, printing-presses, and books. Music, art, a great university, and a wonderful geographical museum are among its attractions.

This city was a famous book city before the rise of Hitler. It had two libraries of 3 million and 2,500,000 books and twelve lesser ones; 550 publishers, 320 booksellers, and 190 doing both publishing and selling. Each year an International Book Fair was held. Note the city's eight rail-roads, river, and its central position in Germany and among the nations.

German housewives shop in the open-air market. This Berlin market is on Unterden Eichen.
(U.S. Army photograph)

The lignite deposits recently discovered in the vicinity have added another interest to Leipzig and its suburbs. The fuel is mined by stripping clays and drift and shoveling the lignite on belt conveyors. It is burned for generating electric power, manufacturing sugar and beer, and tanning hides; briquetted to make it more usable in homes; roasted to make coke, tar, gas, ammonia, and sulphuric acid, and from these dyes, phosphate fertilizers, and many chemicals; and hydrogenated to prepare oils and greases. While lignite is fully as important in dollars as coal and its use conserves the latter or liberates it for export, not more than half the lignite mined is marketed raw. In some years Germany has produced three fourths of the world's lignite.

Berlin (3,169,689), the capital city, covers 348 square miles of miserable, abandoned-channel bottom, flood-plain, swamps, and till plain. While terribly cramped currently by foreign occupation, it was a pre-War II cosmopolitan administrative center; a center of commerce, industry, finance, and art; a railroad center for passenger and all kinds of freight traffic, having had seven adequate stations; a knot in a waterway net, better organized than is possible around any other great city. At one time more than 5 million inhabitants could be counted as belonging to the agglomeration which spread from the marshy valley lands to the uplands and into vicinal valleys, mowed down forests, remade swamps into beautiful lakes, scattered factories, palaces, gardens, and Sunday huts in scores of suburbs.

The Templehof airport in Berlin. In April, 1948, these planes were a part of the airlift flying from the Rhine main airfield with food and other freight. (U.S. Army photograph)

When the history of Berlin began on an island in the Spree, it was a squalid Slav village consisting of fishing Wends and their cabins. It stood where two wooden bridges permitted an easy crossing of the waterways around the island. When the Germans came they built a colony on the right bank, and the first German wall surrounded the two centers. More notable history began when the Electors of Brandenburg made this their residence. The canals of Brandenburg aided the Spree in completing the connections between Oder and Elbe, the great waterways of the German plains. Canals, constructed in most of the abandoned valleys, made east and west highways actual cross-roads, intersecting the Vistula, Oder, and Elbe, and facilitated

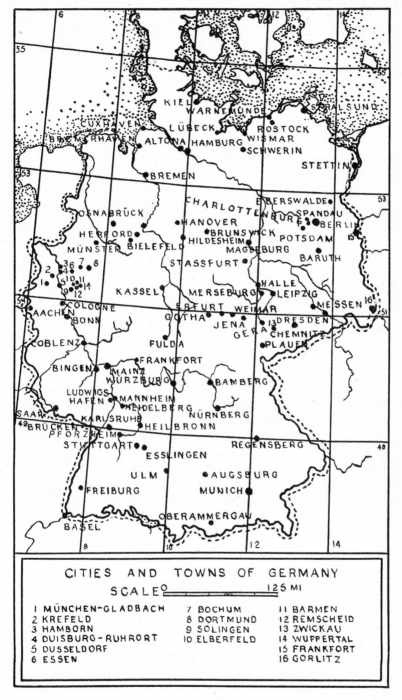

CITIES AND TOWNS OF GERMANY

SCALE 0 [========] 125 MI

1 MÜNCHEN-GLADBACH	7 BOCHUM	11 BARMEN
2 KREFELD	8 DORTMUND	12 REMSCHEID
3 HAMBORN	9 SOLINGEN	13 ZWICKAU
4 DUISBURG-RUHRORT	10 ELBERFELD	14 WUPPERTAL
5 DUSSELDORF		15 FRANKFORT
6 ESSEN		16 GORLITZ

German cities and towns. Several in the thickly settled industrial region are numbered in the legend. (Compiled from Goode's *School Atlas* and *Oxford Advanced Atlas*)

the movement of lumber, stone, ores, and foods from anywhere in the plains to the city and the transport of Berlin products out to Szczecin, the Polish for Stettin, Hamburg, the Baltic, and the North Sea. Berlin was also in touch with industry and materials from up these rivers in Bohemia, Silesia, the Carpathians, and even from beyond all three. Wealth poured in to develop the place, to build cathedrals, palaces, gardens, banks, factories, and warehouses. All that goes to make a commercial, industrial, militaristic city had to come to Berlin. It was then the capital of 50 million active, educated, ambitious people. The place was made as healthful and beautiful as possible. In the late nineteenth century it became more cosmopolitan and developed more world interests and ambitions. It drew the nations—students, artisans, and tourists—as surely as it attracted commerce and industry. It excelled in many lines of manufactures, in its superb railroad and air service, as well as in its water communications; it sent its electric supplies over all the world; it made machines, tools, pumps, turbines, compressors, motors, cables, drills, tractors, automobiles, agricultural machinery and tools, mining and railroad equipment, and airplanes. Textiles and fabrics of silk, cotton, wool, linen, and hemp were produced in Berlin; foods of every kind, builders' supplies, printing, engraving, and every type of scientific instrument were prepared.

Berlin was a religious center both for the 40 million Protestants and the 21 million Roman Catholics; a banking, insurance, educational, and social center with no rival in Germany. Potsdam, Spandau, and Charlottenburg, though miles away, were integral parts of this notable center.

Berlin has thus been not only the center for political activities but the center for scores of centralized, regimented institutions, occupations, and interests. Today it is a city of ruins with a feeble population struggling to recover under the handicaps of two city governments, in the east part of the city a Soviet-sponsored government and in the west a coöperative three-power-sponsored government. Its future is a subject for the crystal gazer. But its historical and sentimental value, quite apart from its industrial significance, appear to make its rebuilding essential to Germany's unity and morale.

RHINE GORGE REGION

Situation. The Rhine Gorge Region includes the gorge, 80 miles long from Bingen to Bonn, and the more open valley on down to Duisburg-Ruhrort. It also includes the hilly country west of the Rhine to the national boundary and east to the divide between Rhine and Weser rivers. The Rhine flows entirely across the region from the mouth of the Main to Coblenz, where it receives the Lahn and Moselle, and to the mouth of the Ruhr. Between Lahn and Ruhr are the tributaries Sieg and Wupper. The upland surface is a peneplain, 1,600 feet above the streams, in which the meandering rivers have carved winding valleys whose slopes have reached submaturity. The region is almost wholly in the old Hercynian mountains, so favorable for the development of mineral wealth. Six physical sections are recognized. On the west, south of the Moselle, is the Hunsrück; north of the Moselle, the Eifel; and beyond Bonn, the plains of Cologne. On the east, south of the Lahn, is Taunus; between the Lahn and Sieg rivers, Westerwald; and beyond the Sieg, part of the Sauerland and the Ruhr. Above the Hunsrück the Saar Basin, a rich mining region, is now functioning with France. Taunus and Hunsrück are forested. Eifel was largely cleared for agriculture, but large tracts have such poor soil that they have become

Man at lathes in German factory at Taunus. (U.S. Army photograph)

moors or are used now primarily for grazing. Volcanoes operated from Tertiary to Recent time and four beautiful crater lakes still persist. Quarrying of lavas in Eifel and of slate and other excellent rock in the other mountain sections is a common industry. Only Westerwald is of any considerable agricultural value. Its weathered volcanic rocks make rich soils, but its raw, inclement weather causes many a ruralist to turn to cattle-raising. The north lands east of the Rhine have large deciduous forests, home industries, many small, ancient iron mines, and scattered primitive agriculture. From the early furnaces in these hills arose the stimulus which fired the Ruhr people when their rich ores were found; and Ruhr coal has kept the furnaces of Siegerland in the steel business. Wuppertal will be described with the Ruhr. Population in this region is always sparse in the hills but concentrated along the narrow, winding valleys in almost continuous "string" town in form. The Cologne plains are largely rural. The first crops were wheat, rye, and oats; then, as the Ruhr industry developed, vegetables and market gardening followed; thousands of acres now are covered with sugar beets. Cologne (772,200) is the chief city and derives its name from its origin as a Roman colony. It has replaced its old wall by a beautiful boulevard; its cathedral is

General view of the mines 10-12 miles south of Cologne. Lignite is 25-30 feet in thickness, with half as much overburden which must be stripped. An endless chain hauls cars back and forth to the railroad. (Courtesy U.S. Geological Survey)

a Gothic treasure; its chocolate, chemicals, and drugs are important; commerce and industry measure its close geographic adjustments, but it is best known for its art and culture, expressed in the manufacture of glass, fancy textiles, perfumes which take the city name Cologne, and in the development of its modern university founded in 1920. Bonn (100,800), a few miles up the river from Cologne, is an equally classic and educational center though not as large, has a university dating from 1786, was the birthplace of Beethoven, 1770, and is the present capital of West Germany with its new constitution and its parliament.

Crops. The finest of wines in Germany, and more than two thirds of all produced, come from thousands of terraced vineyards along the incised meanders of the rivers, the steep slopes of which expose the ripening grapes to the best sunshine, and the waters of which reflect the light against the hills early and late in the day. Calcareous soils and limestone caverns for cellars aid the meticulous vineyardist. Farms are small; cultivation is intensive and manual; farmers live in villages and go out to their work. Vines, other fruits, and gardens occupy all available valley space and climb up to

Close-up of lignite mine shown in the previous illustration. This lignite deposit is of great value to German industry. (Courtesy U.S. Geological Survey)

the old castles along the crests of the bluffs. Where sufficiently sheltered, the valleys produce tobacco. The plateaus are forest and pasture, primitive and sparsely settled, with scattered little villages nestled in the lower patches; in some of the valleys quaint ancient customs still prevail, while others teem with life and modern rural, commercial, even industrial activities.

Commerce. As far back as the dawn of history and probably for millenniums before, the Rhine Valley has directed commerce between the North Sea borders and the Bavarian and Italian plains. Even the Main, Rhône, and Danube fed into the upper Rhine. Frankfort on the Main (553,650) has guarded the Rhine (gorge) gate from Roman times to the present. Commodities collected here, to go down the gorge, and those coming up are here repacked and shipped on toward the Rhône, Danube, and Main. Emperors were crowned in Frankfort; Goethe was born there, and other poets and artists lived there. In medieval times castles were constructed on the rugged heights of the bluffs, and through their halls passed lords and ladies, princes and kings, who lived by brigandage on the river commerce that passed below. Today cotton manufactures take advantage of the moist climate and prosper in Frankfort and vicinity.

The modern period of river commerce was ushered in as the modern industrial development came. Rhine waters had long been connected by canals with the Rhône, the Danube (through the Main), and the Seine. Plans are under way to connect the lower reaches with the Weser and Elbe. Canals now represent 1,500 miles of the 8,000 miles of German navigable inland waterways, but the present projects when complete will change the ratio. The Rhine is the most used waterway in the world, and its regulation by Lake Constance assures it a very constant flow. Ruhr, Rhine, and their branches floated rafts and logs, then boats; and river ports ever flourished with Cologne the leader. Before World War II barges numbered 7,000 with a tonnage of 6 million; 3,000 other boats, half using steam, plied the river. Barges in groups of five to ten are moved by one steamer. In a year the boats moved 100 million tons of freight, including ores, lumber, grain, building materials, and manufactures, but 46 per cent of all was coal. It still moves up the river from the Ruhr as well as down. Iron ore comes up from Rotterdam to Duisburg. Cereals from Rotterdam and Antwerp are absorbed little by little in many cities. Potash, building stones, and brick move down; but up-stream traffic is much heavier than down-stream. Ruhr interests are responsible for half of Rhine traffic; raw materials move to the furnaces, food to the workmen, and mine and mill products out in both directions. Fertilizers for the Rhine plains go up-stream. The Rhine was internationalized in 1918 with the Elbe and Oder, an item of much concern to the Low Countries. Forty-five per cent of the goods carried are German, 35 per cent Dutch, and 12 per cent Belgian.

Railroads have made a splendid development along the valleys and especially in and out of the Ruhr. They connect all mines and metallurgical plants and in 1940 comprised 70 miles of lines within the Krupp works at Essen. Stub lines connect the six great lines with every city in the industrial area. Railroads, canals, and rivers coöperate and supplement, instead of slashing, one another; Duisburg is the greatest river port in the world, the center of all this maze of transportation.

Coblenz (91,098), at the confluence of Rhine, Lahn, and Moselle, marked the boundary between Teutons and Latins and has often been a scene of military conflict. Since prehistoric days it has been a junction point on important commercial water routes; and railroads have contributed to its modern significance. Marvelous vineyards rise in repeated terraces from the flood-plain to the top of the bluff, with walks and walls and stone drainage troughs for every terrace. Many towns of 5,000 to 6,000 along each stream are centers for intensive gardening and horticulture. Treves, up the Moselle nearly to Luxembourg, was the birth-place of Karl Marx.

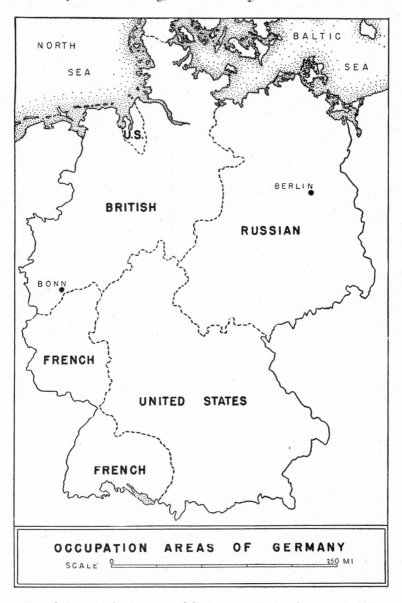

Map of Germany, showing areas of foreign occupation as they were in 1951.

Industry. Peasant and domestic industries have always held a prominent place in this Rhine Gorge Region. Vineyardists were manufacturers; grain-growers milled their rye and wheat; woodsmen sawed their logs, made staves, tubs, tools, and wagons; in many homes local wool was spun, and hides were tanned and made into boots and belts. Iron has been mined for many centuries in Westerwald and Siegerland and smelted with charcoal from the forests. Copper, manganese, zinc, and lead brought out a great number of little metallurgical centers, and the population has always ingeniously developed its resources. The Wupper River, a remarkably clear stream, determined the location of dye-works, washeries, textile mills, and recently of Wuppertal (401,672), which combines the great twin cotton textile cities of Barmen and Elberfeld, weaving imported cotton.

The discovery of coal in the Ruhr Valley marked the beginning of the concentration of heavy industry into the most powerful center in the world. Ninety-four coal-beds are now known with an aggregate thickness of 250 feet, and much of it is coking coal. One hundred seventy-five mines produce 100 million tons of coal annually, and Ruhr reserves are estimated at 54 billion tons. Coal is first in importance, then iron; but since there is not enough ore, some is purchased from Sweden, from Algeria, Tunis, Spain, and Luxembourg. Lorraine exchanges her iron ore for coal. In the Sieg and Lahn valleys there are extensive iron ore reserves which in recent years produced three fourths of Germany's domestic supply. Minette ores of Lorraine ceased to compete with these ores after World War II, but Swedish ores compete successfully and home production continues to decline. It will cease altogether when government bounty is withdrawn. Better ore deposits are sought in Germany.

The Ruhr furnaces have made 11 million tons of iron a year and 13 million tons of steel, 81 per cent of all Germany's iron and steel. Blast-furnaces and converters numbered more than 100 each. Rolling-mills, wire-mills, plate- and pipe-mills, foundries, and many other plants to use iron, glass works, brick-kilns, potteries, canning factories, factories making tools and machines of every sort, ship-building, chemical works—these are some of the items in the Ruhr landscape. Boats and barges, 1,000 smoking stacks, many of them 300 to 500 feet high, 10,000 cars on a maze of tracks, mine shafts, hoists, and piles of waste, coke-ovens, warehouses, and rows of workers' houses and apartments add to this marvelous industrial scene. While tremendously bombed out, this area is being rehabilitated very rapidly. The Ruhr Basin has fourteen cities with more than 100,000 people each, all so close together that they operate as one urban industrial unit. Many places have their specialties. Essen (666,740), Bochum, (305,500), and Dortmund (542,260) manufacture heavy steel; Düsseldorf (541,400) is commercial; Aachen (162,200) mines coal and lignite, and manufactures iron; Remscheid (103,900) and Solingen (140,460) make cutlery, tools, and hardware, because their metallurgy was for long a local charcoal industry; Duisburg (434,646, including several suburbs) and Hamborn (150,-000) manufacture chemicals, cotton, and wool textiles; Barmen and Elberfeld specialize in dyeing, washing, and cotton textiles; Krefeld (170,970) manufactures cotton, wool, and silk; München-Gladbach (128,400) is a leader in silk industry. These textile towns also tie in with similar towns in Netherlands.

Ruhr people need a large water supply both for domestic use of the millions of people and for their myriad industries. The river is wholly satisfactory, for its abundant, clear waters are conserved in the crystalline schists along the upper valley and come down constantly and steadily to meet the needs.

A shipping place from Roman time to the present. Duisburg handled 30 million tons of freight in 1928. Full modern equipment as a river harbor. (Courtesy German Railroads Information Office)

This little industrial area, 95 by 65 miles, with between 6 million and 7 million people, or over 1,100 per square mile, is the largest and most concentrated as well as the most diverse industrial district in Germany, probably in Europe. It has a prodigious array of natural resources, and has brought together workmen, engineers and merchants, capital, mills, transportation, administration, and withal a plenitude of political, social, and housing questions. In material ways the adjustments are much more satisfactory than in social, cultural, and spiritual ways. In spite of crises, growing-pains, and other ills the center still grows. New towns spring up among green fields to the north, coal-pits are dug, rows of workmen's houses arise, and industry overrides agriculture.

Food and clothes for these millions of people cannot come from so limited an area, especially when much of the land is utilized for other purposes than agriculture. Provision is made for the importation of cereals from Münster plains, meat and milk from Westerwald, vegetables from Rhine lands and Westphalia. Grains and wool come from Argentina through Rotterdam, legumes from France and Belgium, dairy products from Holland, Belgium, France, and Denmark; cotton comes from the United States.

CENTRAL HIGHLANDS

Situation. The Central Highlands, like the Rhine Gorge Region, are almost wholly in the old Hercynian mountains. In this region the mineral wealth is not so great as in the Rhine Gorge Region, but is more varied. Hydrographically, the Central Highlands Region is drained by the upper Weser and its tributaries with the assistance of the Saale and Mulde, tributaries of the Elbe. The Elbe emerges from Czechoslovakia through a castellated rocky gorge in the eastern portion of the Erzgebirge, crosses Saxony and passes Dresden before it comes down to the plains. This region differs from every other German region in having no canals. Topography and streams are much better for power than for commerce.

Physical character. Large areas of Mesozoic rocks lie nearly horizontally between exposed remnants and over concealed structures of the old baseleveled mountains. Many plateaus, dissected by the present streams, still maintain altitudes of 600 to 2,000 feet between valleys with floors 200 feet lower; above the plateaus rise several ranges or mountain masses. In the north are the Harz ranges with their culminating peak, the Brocken (3,800 feet); toward the south, the Thuringian Forests, which lead southeast through Frankenberg to the volcanic core, Fichtelgebirge, culminating in Schneeberg (3,500 feet). West of these forested mountains there are two volcanic masses, first Rhöngebirge (3,167 feet) and second the much larger Vogelsberg (2,600 feet). The latter stands in the eastern borders of a trough, which is considered to be a continuation of the Rhine Graben and furnishes an important highway from Frankfort on the Main northward a hundred miles through this mountainous region to Kassel and the Weser River and onward to the plains. German tribes expanded to the upper Rhine along this route. The Erzgebirge, Ore Mountains, mark the boundary between Czechoslovakia and Germany and descend from summits 3,000 feet high in a long, gentle slope northwestward across Saxony to the plains, which stand at about 1,300 feet. All these topographic forms are in maturity; all were in the early days heavily forested, as the frequent use of "Wald" (woods) signifies. Most of the mountains except the volcanoes had ore deposits, which have proven very interesting to geologists because of their complex and unusual rocks and minerals.

For centuries this region was a little-visited solitude; men seemed to fear it; beautiful folk stories arose in those early days during the working out of routes through the gloomy forests, and some were collected by Grimm. Today no more valuable or fascinating part of Europe exists than this confusion of mountain, plateau, and valley. Much of the Thuringian section of the region was first settled in the dawn of legendary times by Slavs. Later came the Germans, who gave many names (*Dorf, Hof, Leben, Hausen*) and, before the eighth century, made much progress in clearing and building. Villages first appeared about the end of the Middle Ages. People of today are as Germanic here as anywhere in the country.

Briquette factory 30 miles north of Dresden, making fuel briquettes of lignite. Tracks on posts guide the cars that move the briquettes from the presses to the railroad. (Courtesy U.S. Geological Survey)

Resources. The forests were the first recognized resource. They contained game, furs, and food, as well as lumber. Many thousands of acres of the gentler slopes have been cleared for farms, orchards, and villages, but the forests are still among the finest in Europe and are prized and cared for in an excellent system of forestry. Wild life is gone and one can use the forests for pleasure walks as freely as for lumber-cutting.

Minerals have been mined since the earliest Bronze Age. Copper, iron, lead, and silver were mined for centuries in the Harz, but many mines are now closed because their ores cannot compete with larger, richer deposits.

The Saxony slopes of the Ore Mountains reach 30 to 50 miles northward, and their streams furnish water power for lumbering and mining industries. Silver, nickel, iron, and tin were once mined in the upper slopes, but most of the ore bodies are now worked out. Metallurgical industries, however, became rooted, and many dependent metal-using factories were well established, before the ores were exhausted, and these have continued until the present. Coal which is present toward the base of the slope supplements wood for fuel. Several ceramic industries prosper on the clays, shales, and sands, both in Saxony and in Thuringia, where porcelain, glass, and cement are made. These mineral industries are the life of Freiburg, Chemnitz (250,000), Zwickau (123,000), and Plauen (85,000), although many other industries have followed in most of the towns. Clays at Meissen foster the government potteries there, but need to be amplified by importations. The iron industry in Thuringia began in the Middle Ages and then used only wood for fuel. In a century it became a fixed industry with furnaces and forges still consuming the forests. Metallurgists bought the forests to perpetuate their work, but because forests were failing they turned to water power, and the towns with their factories moved far back into the mountains. There they are today. One produced armor-plate and fire-arms, another specialized in cutlery, a third in hammers, spoons, and many small household articles. Copper manufacture concentrated in another center. Thus was trained up a great family of artisans, born of the rocks and ores.

Industries. Agriculture came as early as fixed habitations and has persisted to the present. It has become specialized and distributed in accord with the character of soils, slopes, and climate, perhaps in more close accord than anywhere else in Germany. The extreme diversity of physical elements has all but forced such adjustments. Forests have been left upon the Triassic sandstone plateaus, along limestone ridges, and on steep and stony slopes; pastures and grass have become fixed on the next better slopes; the more level and fertile soils support intensive cultivation. Density of population likewise follows soil, geologic, and topographic lines. Some strips and patches are so poor as to have only sixty persons per square mile, while others have ten times as many; towns and cities grow where resources can feed their industries. Commercial possibilities, even modern railroads, have stimulated later and modern development.

Thuringian forests, for centuries noted for their home and peasant industries, are now the domain of specialists in wood-carving, leather goods, lace and embroidery, and, where sands occur, in glass-making. Fertilizer works and farm-machinery plants are required by agriculture, and these in turn make possible better agriculture. Eastern Saxony, with good supplies of wool and with power and nearby markets, uses its climate, too dry for cotton manufactures, to good advantage in a wide range of woolen textiles. The large development of hydro-electric power among the hills has, instead of driving industry to cities and great factories, kept it in the homes. Here, then, is a difference between the industry of the Rhine-Ruhr district and that of the Central Highlands. Yet Saxony and Thuringia are very industrial. According to a pre-War II census, one third of the population were classified as workers; 28 per cent of the employed worked in textiles and clothing, 15 per cent in metallurgy, and 23 per cent in commerce. A further response to the mountainous, restricting topography is noted in the fact that 35 per cent of the textile workers are women, and 87 per cent of all workers are in home industries such as knitting, embroidering, making clothing, and lace-making.

Cities. Erfurt (174,000) as early as the thirteenth century was a center of foreign commerce and exported ingots of Thuringia iron. It now, like Gera, with busy railroads to assist, engages in metallurgy as of old, also in ceramics and chemical industries born of clays and Triassic salt-beds. Gotha and Weimar, each with about 50,000 inhabitants, are residence towns with parks. Gotha (58,000) is regularly and substantially built of stone and brick from its own quarries and ceramic plants. It is a printing center. Weimar (67,000) was the home of Herder, Goethe, and Schiller. Jena (83,000) has glass works and makes optical and precision instruments; and the chimneys of its chemical works outline the town. Its university is well known throughout the world. Sawing lumber and manufacturing wooden articles still continue in the forests throughout all this region. Some places specialize in paper; some in boxes, doll heads, or thermometers; others in toys of wood, or wood and metal, or in furniture; some prepare mine timbers or building materials such as sash, doors, floors, and roofing. Zwickau and Chemnitz with their moist climate are notable cotton-manufacturing centers, and to some extent, as the mines have been abandoned, textiles and automobile industries have replaced the metal industries.

Fulda (26,000) is a remarkable little relic town built around an old monastery near the source of Fulda River, with its clearings extended out over the gentle slopes of soft rocks. The monastery was set in the seclusion of the head of a valley in the dissected plateau. Scores of towns are as quaint in their setting, meaning, and architecture as Fulda, and as backward in their economic activities because of their age-long isolation.

Kassel (216,000) owed much in the early days to the extravagance of princes who established their royal residences here on the Frankfort-Kassel route for strategic, military, commercial, or political advantage.

Dresden (468,000), sometimes called the Florence of the Elbe, is noted for its art treasure, old palaces, museums of murals and minerals, its architecture, industry, and commerce. It early became the center of Saxony and the queen of a score of important places near at hand. Guard of the Elbe Gate into Bohemia, it has been more attached to Prague than to any place down-stream. River Elbe is a royal international highway; Dresden's quays are crowded with business and dominate the city. A river town, it is strung along the stream for 25 miles and in recent times has climbed the bluffs for residence. It reflects in commerce and industry the resources of Saxony and the manufactures of its neighbors.

The Central Highlands may be distinguished from the Rhine Gorge Region by the persistence of home industry, from the Plains Regions by its relief and geology, its resources, and its culture, but equally well by its lack of cosmopolitanism and broad outlook. As in other regions, poor soils drive ruralists to the beckoning urban industries.

SOUTHWESTERN HIGHLANDS

Situation and character. This region is as varied in topography and geology as the Central Highlands. Its geology is mostly Hercynian; where the old structures do not appear at the surface they are buried in their own waste of Mesozoic times. The Schwarzwald (Black Forest) and Odenwald, both east of the Rhine Graben or trough, are the largest remnants of the old crystalline rock structures and were left 2,000 feet above sea level. The Hardtwald, opposite Odenwald, is a Triassic area and covers Hercynian mountains. The Rhine trough, 180 by 15 to 20 miles, is half in Germany and is caused by the relative dropping-down of a block of old mountain structure between two blocks left high as the plateau. The Vosges Mountains, not in Germany, are a part of the western block. Swabian and Franconian Juras, cuesta areas east of the Black Forest and Odenwald, consist of Mesozoic beds useful sandstones, limestones and shales, still nearly horizontal, which dip beneath the Tertiary of the Alpine Foreland. The Neckar and the southern tributaries of the Main drain this Mesozoic area, flowing as obsequent streams, i.e., in the direction opposite to the dip of the strata. This region also includes the basin of the Naab, a tributary of the Danube, which receives its waters largely from the western slopes of the Böhmerwald or Bohemian Forest, the mountainous frontier between Czechoslovakia and Germany.

No part of this region was actually glaciated by the great ice sheets, though much outwash went down the Rhine trough and local glaciers formed in Bohemian Mountains and Black Forest. Owing to this fact, the soils except alluvium are residual and partake of the nature of the underlying rocks. They are everywhere mature and mostly podzols made beneath deciduous forests.

Resources. "Wald" indicates forests; most of the Southwestern Highlands belong to some wald. It seems probable that nearly all the land was forest when the present races of men came. Valleys and many gentle slopes have been cleared, but there still remain great stretches of heavy forest so carefully cared for that they resemble parks—indeed, are often so used. Splendid roads wind among the hills in and out of forests from town to town. The Bohemian forests, like those in Bavaria, are among the best in Germany. Local glaciers made cirques and moraines here as in the Black

Forest, produced bogs, charming lakes, and tumbling streams which encourage fishing, development of power, and touring. Tertiary clays, near the sources of the Naab River, give origin to porcelains of good grade. The uplands bordering the Rhine trough are 400 to 700 feet above the river, enough to make notable differences in temperature and exposure. Spring comes weeks earlier in the valley than aloft. The vine and peaches do well below, while rye, potatoes, wheat, and barley flourish above, and many flocks of sheep graze on the pastures. The altitudes are less toward the north, both in the valley and on the plateau, attracting a density of population three times as great there. But rich soils and moderate relief are not enough to explain population densities of 500 per square mile.

Aerial view of Heidelberg. The castle above the old part of the city shows at the right. (U.S. Army photograph)

Industries. Industry in these upland valleys dates from Roman times. It increased through the Middle Ages and still flourishes in the smiling Swabian hills. An efficient agricultural-economic system has been developed which resembles that in the hills of Switzerland. Fields with rotation of crops, fruit orchards, and a rationally adjusted forestry all fit together. Fruits are apples, pears, and cherries; chestnuts are abundant in the valleys and on sandy slopes. There is woodcutting, charcoal-burning, and even quarrying. Lumbering still takes a large place; scores of sawmills cut the splendid timber; gristmills along the streams mill the grain; glass works use wood and local sands; weaving mills in many valleys prepare cloth from local wool. Little family shops and peasant industries prevail. Ropes and cords of hemp and flax, linen cloth, copper and iron filigree, cooking utensils, and tools are common products. Wheelwrights, blacksmiths, printers, and shoemakers may be found at every turn. Clocks, matches, linen fabrics, and embroideries are produced in hundreds of little shops when weather is too severe for outside work. The workers draw most of their materials from local resources and persist in this domestic régime because they live in a hilly land where change is slow. With this system the population can

A German farmer near Bamberg is throwing scoops of liquid manure on his land. Before World War II he and many others sprayed this fertilizer by machinery not yet available. Note ox harness and muzzles. (U.S. Army photograph)

never become much denser. The southern part of the Black Forest comes under the industrial and intellectual influence of Basel, and consequently its domestic industries are more modern and include cotton textiles. The towns near the Rhine use much more coal than remote ones. All those along the Rhine Valley are continually stimulated by the ever-moving river commerce, and some influence of the Rhine industry and business reaches back into the uplands.

Commerce. The Rhine trough was a highway in prehistoric times, a line of march of Germanic tribes 2,000 years ago, and of Romans as they came

later to trade and Christianize the northern tribes; and ever since it has
been the most important inland waterway of Europe. The larger traffic
today is up-stream where the quiet waters mirror castles, terraced vineyards, and the ropes of ships, where valley walls echo the whistle of tow-
boats and the screech of trains hurrying along the valley railroads. Many
kinds of freight halt at Mainz and Frankfort, but fertilizers go on up to
bless the agricultural lands of valley and hill. Mannheim (285,000), with its
many basins entrenched in the alluvium at the confluence with the Neckar,
is the greatest port above Duisburg, but arrivals here are five times as great
as departures. They consist of coal for industries in every town up the
Neckar and Rhine, and raw iron and machines for mills. Boats also descend
loaded with salt from the Jagst Valley. The Main floats barges up to Bamberg whence the canal takes them on to Nuremberg and to the Danube. A
project is under way to connect the Neckar in the same way with the Danube. By these means and by the gates at the south end of the Rhine trough
through Basel into Switzerland and through the Belfort-Burgundian Gate
into France, the northern plains and mountain regions communicate with
the south of Europe. Canalization of the Rhine from Basel to Lake Constance is projected, and France may have a word to say upon it. Each of
these two valleys, Main and Neckar drain economically into the Rhine rift.

Cities. Freiburg (110,100), in the Rhine fringe of the fascinating Black
Forest, is a quiet university town. Heidelberg, heavily fortified, has guarded
the narrow granite entrance to the valley of the Neckar for many generations.
Its university dates from the fourteenth century; its chateaus and suburbs
among charming forests, its stretches of vineyards, and its great historic
interest grow out of its marvelous strategic situation. Industry is beginning
to disturb the classic old town and its population has reached 87,000.
Pforzheim (80,000), 30 miles west of Stuttgart, has 10,000 workmen and
300 shops making jewelry. Esslingen (49,370) is important for agricultural machinery, locomotives and rail cars, and shoe factories. Heilbronn
(77,500), 40 miles down the Neckar, is far-famed for its textiles and hot
springs; its chemical industries thrive on Jagst salt, local gypsum, and limestones. It is a very old city beautifully set in a great amphitheater of the
meandering river, the slopes of which are clothed with fruitful orchards and
vineyards. Stuttgart (458,500) is the commercial center for these industrial
neighbors and itself engages in printing and in the manufacture of cotton
and woolen textiles, chemicals, furniture, and machinery. It is also the
local capital. It stands beside the Neckar in the midst of the Triassic variegated sandstone plateau. The Hohenzollern castle crowns one of the cuestas
about 40 miles southwest of Stuttgart.

Nuremberg (423,400) has long been famous for its commercial history
and its medieval aspect. It has used its forests to make toys and now makes
cellulose and paper-pulp. Its rich agricultural lands make it an important
local market town. Hops and tobacco are the money crops. Grain and hops

make it a brewing center. It manufactures automobiles, bicycles, tile, and art glass and has book and art printing and electrical works. For centuries it has controlled routes to the Danube. Dürer lived here as a painter and engraver. Before and during World War II its medieval market place was the site for many harangues by Hitler to his storm troopers. Würzburg (107,500), also on the Main, relies mainly on agriculture and rural manufactures. It makes sparkling wines, liquors, and beer, grinds flour, makes brick and tile of local clays, and prints books on its own paper.

Residences on Schutzenstrasse in Bamberg used by personnel of the U.S. Constabulary of the army of occupation. These were not built by or for Americans. This city has long been famous for its printing of fine wall maps. (U.S. Army photograph)

Two growing industrial towns stand on opposite sides of the Rhine, Karlsruhe (190,000) and Ludwigshafen (144,500). The former is on the east side of the Rhine about midway of the trough. Specialized agriculture surrounds it and furnishes hops, tobacco, and beets for its industries. Fruits are abundant here also. Marble is quarried, chemicals are manufactured from local products, and books are printed. Ludwigshafen on the west side of the Rhine is called Mannheim's twin, a Rhine port and full of industry, a response to the opportunities at the mouth of the Neckar; hence first commercial, using the salt, coal, and forest products of the hills to the westward, then industrial, making chemicals, iron and steel machinery, and wooden articles such as boxes, barrels, and crates.

THE ALPINE FORELAND

The region. This region includes the southern part of Bavaria and portions of Württemberg. It is entirely within the drainage basin of the Danube. As its name suggests, the Alpine Foreland is a strip of land before or north of the Alps and consists largely of late Tertiary, Pleistocene, and Recent deposits brought from the Alps. After the Alpine uplift, streams built fans over this lowland, then the Alpine glaciers spreading in great lobes over a large portion of the Foreland built terminal moraines in festoons all the way from east side to west and scattered older drift even beyond the moraines. This interfered with drainage and left many lakes more or less shut in by moraines. Again, since the ice melted, streams have covered large areas with compound alluvial fans. The western end of the Foreland is in Switzerland and a smaller part at the east is in Austria. Because of the geologic nature of this region its minerals and rocks have meager values.

Germany and the Germans have always sought the Alps for their frontier and here the southern boundary lies far up in the mountains. Thus, much rough, rugged land on Alpine slopes is included in our Alpine Foreland. The influence of the Alps is felt in shadow, in rain shadow, in the clear, rapid, steady streams giving constant water supply, water power, and scenic charm; and even in the springs back among the foothills. Power plants on Alpine streams furnish 2 million horsepower of electric current, which makes possible the electrification of many railroads and the lighting even of small towns. Because of these influences and values, most of the Alps in Germany should be set apart as national park and forest reservation.

The northern boundary of the Foreland is placed north of, but very near, the Danube, which has been pushed far north by the stream-built fans made of Alpine waste and has been robbed of almost every tributary on the north side by the greedy Neckar and Main rivers. The Rhine has robbed the Danube on both sides in its upper reaches, where in low water all the Danube (and all year much of the Danube) is diverted in a subchannel to the Rhine.

Heavy rains fall in the mountains, and snow persists until May, but the plains have only a good agricultural rainfall and the snow disappears two months earlier. Most of the Foreland soils are immature; few are residual.

Resources. Forests now cover much of the Alpine slopes and did cover even more of the plains before man cleared them. Considerable areas in the east central parts are heaths. About 20 per cent is now in forest, regulated in a first-class forestry system. Lumbering attracts many men and is profitable. The wood leads to excellent wood-carving, frame buildings, wood-burning stoves of brick or porcelain, many shingle roofs, and a great fire hazard.

Clays and sands are abundant, though few are of high grade. Brick, tile, glass, and plain pottery are made. No coal is known. The greatest resource in the Foreland at present is agriculture. For its horses it is justly noted; plodding oxen do much of the farm work; cattle are raised everywhere for beef and on the Alpine slopes provide butter and cheese. Wheat, barley, oats—the first for food, second for beer, and third for stock—are grown everywhere up the slopes to the neat park-like forests with their boundary as "sharp as a barber's hair cut." The main interests are in the well-adapted stock, dairying, and hog combination, which has enriched the people and improved the agriculture. Many acres of hops, with their high frames, are grown to supply the beer industry at Munich.

The Walchensee hydro-electric power plant in southern Bavaria. (Courtesy German Railroads Information Office)

Commerce and industry. People of the Alpine race have occupied the Foreland ever since they reached the Alps. Other peoples and ideas have filtered in easily, for this open land was a highway from the Rhine trough to the Danube and down the latter to the Near East, as well as from Silesia and the Amber coasts to France and the Mediterranean. Alpine passes into Italy were far from impassable. Hence the Alpine Foreland has had more advantage in position than in mineral resources. It has always maintained a relatively cultured, joyous, sociable, yet serious people. Simple arts for centuries, the Passion Play at Oberammergau, and the music and science of Munich are witness to what these people can do. Railroads are frequent now, with nodes in the Foreland net at Munich, Augsburg, and Ulm. They bind the whole plain into an economic and social unit and have made possible its political unity.

Industries are closely linked with the forest and rural developments and with the two types of topography. Lace, embroidery, wood-carving, lumbering, and cheese-making, all peasant industries, flourish in the Alpine valleys. Ceramic industries, preparation of foods, and (in cities where electric power encourages) some textile industries have developed on the plains.

Cities. Towns and cities in the Foreland are essentially commercial. Augsburg (185,400), a Roman camp at the junction of the Lech and Wertach rivers, became an ecclesiastical center in the eleventh century and erected a fine cathedral. Italian commerce over the Alps started with Augsburg. The town grew both north and south along the flood-plains and became a typical, commercial "string" town. In the seventeenth century it was rebuilt in Italian style in response to its close Italian affiliations. When railroads came, it annexed villages and became an urban center for a large community.

Valley in the Bavarian Alps, Hindelang. Why is it more modern than Garmisch? (Courtesy German Railroads Information Office)

Ulm (74,400), at the head of navigation on the Danube opposite an important pass in the Swabian crests, easily became a commercial center and was heavily fortified in Carolingian time. Situated at the mouth of the Iller, it had an easy road up the stream to Lake Constance, to the Rhine, and to Alpine passes. Railroads now extend along all its old highways. Commerce is still its chief interest, but industries using hydro-electric power are beginning to develop on the raw materials that pass through. Regensburg (95,650), down the Danube at the mouth of the Naab, was a center of Roman trade and frontier interest. With the development of towns to the north and in Czechoslovakia, it began a larger commercial activity and in the last 30 years has prospered much.

Munich (829,500), like Augsburg, was a station on early highways and was given an early impetus by princes who saw its advantages, made it a capital, built palaces, and lavished much wealth upon it. It was a distributing center on the old salt route north from Salzburg, Austria. It has

City hall in Munich, Bavaria. Not damaged as severely as some buildings near it. (U.S. Army photograph)

become the third city in Germany and is still dominantly commercial. Occupying a tolerable site on the largest till and outwash plain in the region, it is surrounded by oak forests alternating with pastures and small cultivated patches. It makes use of the products of all in its industries but is much better known for its university, Academy of Science, its art, music, sculpture, painting, its museums, palaces, beautiful homes, and public buildings. Textile industries and related manufactures have stimulated technical education. Its influence reaches much farther than its commerce.

SUMMARY OBSERVATIONS

Agriculture. The use of the soil has always been of prime interest in Germany, but the acreage under cultivation and the percentage of the population engaged in agriculture have both declined for 50 years.

Germany had (census of 1935) 3,400,000 sheep, 19,100,000 cattle, 2,500,000 goats, and 22,000,000 swine; 47,000,000 meat animals for 67,000,000 people. There were reported also about 2,000,000 stands of bees, and 3,400,000 horses. In a few years these figures will be approximated again. The cities are demanding more meat and milk. The proportion of food animals is too small.

Feudal agriculture has been steadily passing since 1871, but there still are far too many landed estates for the best rural results. Horses fill a large place in the demand for farm power, but many farmers use electric motors for farm work, and many, new efficient farm machines are replacing primitive hand methods. In recent decades the use of fertilizers has increased, but the cost per acre has declined and production of crops has increased. A notable trend is recorded in the fact that in 1882 agriculture and industry engaged about equal numbers of men; in 1900 agriculture had but 36 per cent, and in 1934, 30 per cent, and in 1948 even less than 30 per cent. Germany is becoming over-industrialized and perhaps underfarmed.

According to Zon and Sparhawk, forests cover about one fourth of the country. One third of the forests are deciduous hardwood and two thirds are conifers. Imports of wood are very heavy, ten times as great as exports, and about one third of the total consumption. Production is about as high as it could be and still give place to other necessary interests; hence Germany will continue to be a good lumber market.

Industries. With the massing of industry in three or four localities there has been some decline in home industries, but Germany still clings to this method of production in all the hilly sections and too much even on the plains. Electric power is used more proportionally than in any country in Europe, except Switzerland, and more than half the available water power is developed. The use of wood for power has declined and is nearly disappearing with the tremendous production and use of coal. Iron and steel industries have been one bulwark of the nation, and the chemical industries, planted by careful scientific investigation upon coal, salts of both sodium and potassium, on limestones, gypsum, clays, and several vegetable materials, have become another. No nation has gone further in the iron and steel industry and none so far in chemicals. The list of the latter is formidable—fertilizers, dyes, stains, ceramic products, plastics, pharmaceuticals, beverages, alcohols, artificial fibers, oils, and greases. The Germans have gone far in the development and use of substitutes, such as paper for clothing, test-tube products for food, and cellulose for many wrappings.

Transportation is more highly developed than in many other countries. The waterways have been noted, region by region. Germany has 35,000 miles of railroads, and they are among the best built and equipped in the world. Highway mileage is 216,000. Railways, much more adjustable than rivers and canals, carry four times as much freight as waterways. No country had before World War II a more efficient air service than Germany. The civil air service is now handled by foreign lines. Germany was still, 1951, prohibited from having its own lines.

Foreign trade. The foreign trade amounted to $6,500,000,000 annually, and the exports tended to exceed imports. Of the exports, 75 per cent were finished goods; equally dominant among the imports were raw materials and foods. About 10 per cent of Germany's foreign trade was with the United States. Exports were iron and steel goods, chemicals and dyestuffs, textiles, coal, paper, copper goods, glass, and china; imports were cotton, rubber, iron ore, copper, wool, oil, coal, timber, coffee, tea, wheat, and butter. These statements are for pre-World War II, but current figures indicate a rapid return to similar levels. One can see geographic reasons for many items in these lists, but may well wonder at others.

When Germany abandoned all internal customs barriers, there followed its marvelous development and industrialization. The various sections of the country produce what each can best provide and then exchange. One wonders how this would work between all the nations of Europe. There is little more diversity in the whole continent than in Germany. Natural barriers are hindrances enough to trade without raising artificial barriers, such as customs, duties, imposts, tariffs, taxes, and tolls.

Future. Germany is still on the map, although many of her Junker, visionary, and ruthless leaders are displaced. New leadership is rising. Agriculture is nearly restored; industry has 80-85 per cent recovered; transportation is rapidly being put into shape, particularly in the western two thirds; and this rehabilitation seems to be for business, not for war, for domestic consumption, and for international trade.

German industry is essential for the good of Europe as well as for her own good. She has far too many people, 468 per square mile, to be decently fed without much importation of food which, in turn, must be paid for by manufactured goods. Germany stands between the industrial west and the rural east. Both need to buy what Germany can make. Germany must be commercial and industrial.

Plans have been made to improve more rivers and to extend canal connections so as to bring the Ruhr industry closer in time to the Plains north and to the Baltic Sea, to make direct routes to Bremen, Hamburg, the Ems, Weser, and Elbe rivers. Other canals to connect Ruhr and Antwerp, suggest an attempt to stimulate friendly relations and foreign trade on the west. If Germany could only see that friendly relations are more advantageous than a belligerent attitude, much more could be done. Emigration is still active. Germans say two great needs and aspirations lead her today; unity, and democracy in government.

What will be the future of Germany? In addition to purely economic, social, and political considerations, many geographic factors must be considered. Mineral resources are important, but Germany's nationalistic, commercial, and conservational attitude toward their development is significant. Soils and forests are valuable, and the people must continue to develop, conserve and improve them. Boundary lines and national contacts are vital, but more important is Germany's adjustment to them.

QUESTIONS

1. What has Germany's position, with reference to summer and winter isotherms, to do with Germany's agriculture?

2. Examine the industries and products of Leipzig and vicinity and see how many raw products are related to one another or have influenced the production of any other; how many manufactured products have stimulated or aided some other product; how many chains of dependent occupations can be constructed.

3. Against what disadvantages in lack of resources has Berlin struggled? How have these disadvantages forced Berlin to broader contacts?

4. What proportion of Berlin's significance can be traced directly and indirectly to the glacial marginal channels in the plains of Germany?

5. What advantages could the medieval princes have seen to lead them to build their palaces in Kassel? in Munich?

6. How integral a part of Germany was Silesia? Weigh the loss. How can it be compensated? What stake has Germany in European Peace? In World Peace?

7. Distinguish between the Rhine trough and the Rhine Gorge. Through which does the river pass first?

8. What elements of German foreign policy may be framed on geographic lines?

9. Why should Germany have a fringe of small buffer states?

10. How do the Northern Drift Plains and the Central Highlands supplement each other?

11. What effects on the industry and commerce of Germany may be expected to follow the political and trade cleavage cutting across Europe at present?

BIBLIOGRAPHY

BARRACLAUGH, Geoffry, *The Origins of Modern Germany* (Oxford, England, B. Blackwell, 1947), esp. last chapter.

BASCH, Antonin, *The Danube Basin and German Economic Sphere* (New York, Columbia University Press, 1943).

BAUER, H. A., "The Geographic Background of the Saar Problem," *Geographical Review*, Vol. 24 (October, 1934), pp. 555-565.

BECKETT, Sir W. Eric, *The North Atlantic Treaty, The Brussels Treaty, and The Charter of the United Nations* (London, Stevens, 1950).

BORKIN, Joseph, and WELSH, Charles A., *Germany's Master Plan* (New York, Duell, Sloan, and Pearce, 1943).

BOWMAN, Isaiah, *The New World* (Yonkers-on-Hudson, New York, World Book Company, 1928).

CAHNMAN, Werner J., "Frontiers Between East and West Europe," *Geographical Review*, Vol. 39 (October, 1949), pp. 605-624.

CAPOT-REY, Robert, "The Industrial Region of the Saar," *Geographical Review*, Vol. 25 (January, 1935), pp. 137-141.

CLAY, Lucius D., *Decision in Germany* (Garden City, Doubleday & Company, Inc., 1950).

COON, Carleton S., *The Races of Europe* (New York, The Macmillan Company, 1939).

CRIPPEN, Harlan R., *Germany: Self-portrait* (London and New York, Oxford University Press, 1944).

CROCE, Benedetto, *Germany and Europe*, trans. by V. Shean (New York, Random House, Inc., 1944).

DE MARTONNE, Emmanuel, "Germany," in Vidal de La Blache and Gallois, *Géographie Universelle* (Paris, Lib. Armand Colin, 1930).

DICKINSON, Robert E., *The Regions of Germany* (New York, Oxford University Press, 1945).

DOMINIAN, Leon, *Frontiers of Language and Nationality in Europe* (New York, Henry Holt & Company, Inc., 1928).

EBENSTEIN, William, *The German Record, A Political Portrait* (New York, Farrar and Rinehart, 1945).

EINZIG, Paul, *Bloodless Invasion*, German Economic Penetration into Danubian States and Balkans (London, Gerald Duckworth & Co., Ltd., 1938).

Europa, Encyclopedia of Europe (London, Europa Publications, Ltd.), annual.

FITZGERALD, Walter, *The New Europe* (New York, Harper and Brothers, 1946).

FLEURE, H. J., *Human Geography in Western Europe* (London, Williams & Norgate, Ltd., 1918).

———, *Peoples of Europe* (London, Oxford University Press, Humphrey Milford, 1922).

GEORGE, H. B., *Relation of Geography and History* (Oxford, Clarendon Press, 1924).

GLICKMAN, David L., *The Big 4 in Germany* (Washington, National Planning Assoc., 1947).

GOOCH, Geo. Peabody, *The German Mind and Outlook* (London, Chapman & Hall, Ltd., 1945), esp. Chapter 7.

KENDREW, W. G., *Climates of the Continents* (Oxford, Clarendon Press, 1942).

KISS, George, "A T.V.A. on the Danube," *Geographical Review*, Vol. 37 (1947), pp. 274-302.

KUSCH, Monica H., "Structure of Elbe River Traffic," *Economic Geography*, Vol. 13 (January, 1937), pp. 53-66.

LEHMANN, John, *Down River; A Danubian Study* (London, The Cresset Press, 1939).

LENGYEL, Emil, *The Danube* (New York, Random House, 1939).

LETELLIER, Albert, *Les causes des guerres avec l'Allemagne* (Paris, Charles La Vanzelle & Cie., 1945).

LEWIS, Cleona, *Nazi Europe and World Trade* (Washington, The Brookings Institution, 1941).

LOWIE, Robert H., *The German People* (New York, Farrar and Rinehart, 1945).

LYDE, L. W., *Continent of Europe* (New York, The Macmillan Company, 1924).

MACHRAY, Robert, *East Prussia a Menace to Poland* (Chicago, American Polish Council, 1943).

McCORMICK, Thomas C. T., ed., *Problems of a Post-War World* (New York and London, McGraw-Hill Book Company, Inc., 1945).

MOULTON, Harold G., and MORLIO, Louis, *The Control of Germany and Japan* (Washington, D. C., The Brookings Institution, 1944).

MUNK, Frank, *The Legacy of Nazism* (New York, The Macmillan Company, 1943).

NEWMAN, Bernard, *The New Europe* (New York, The Macmillan Company, 1943).

Occupied Europe (London, Royal Institute of International Affairs, 1944).

OVERBECK, A. O'R., "Freiburg—Gateway to the Black Forest," *National Geographic Magazine*, Vol. 64 (August, 1933), pp. 213-253.

PEARCY, G. Etzel, and FIFIELD, Russell H., *et. al., World Political Geography* (New York, Thomas Y. Crowell Company, 1948).

POLLOCK, James K., *et al., Germany Under Occupation* (Ann Arbor, Michigan, George Wahr Publishing Co., 1949).

RIPLEY, W. Z., *Races of Europe* (New York, D. Appleton and Co., 1899).

ROUCEK, Joseph S., *Contemporary Europe* (New York, D. Van Nostrand Company, Inc., 1941).

SCHEVILL, Ferdinand, *A History of Europe* (New York, Harcourt, Brace & Company, Inc., 1947).

SHACKLETON, Margaret R., *Europe, A Regional Geography* (London, Longmans, Green & Company, 1942).

Statesman's Yearbook (New York, The Macmillan Company), annual.

STODDARD, T. Lothrop, *Into Darkness, Nazi Germany* (New York, Duell, Sloan, and Pearce, 1940).

VAN VALKENBURG, Samuel, and HUNTINGTON, Ellsworth, *Europe* (New York, John Wiley & Sons, Inc., 1935).

VERMEIL, Edward, *Germany's Three Reichs,* trans. by E. W. Dickes (London, A. Dakars, Ltd., 1945), esp. Introduction and Conclusion.

WELLES, Sumner, ed., *An Intelligent American's Guide to the Peace* (New York, The Dryden Press, 1945).

WHITBECK, Ray H., and FINCH, Vernor C., *Economic Geography* (New York, McGraw-Hill Book Company, Inc., 1941).

WHITTLESEY, Derwent, *et al., German Strategy of World Conquest* (New York, Farrar and Rinehart, 1942).

CHAPTER 31

Poland

Visla our own Polish River shall be
She runs from Carpathians right down to the sea.
—Folk Song

INTRODUCTION

Position. Poland is roughly quadrilateral. The compactness of such a shape means an approximation to "the largest nation with the least periphery possible," in many respects an element of solidarity. The area is 121,131 square miles and population 24,500,000, or about the size of New Mexico, our fourth state, with more than forty-five times as many people. Poland is more comparable, in area and population, with our group of states, New York, Pennsylvania, and West Virginia. It is a little larger than the three but has a slightly smaller population.

Its most southern points are about the latitude of the northern tip of Maine, and its northern points are well within the latitude of Hudson Bay. It has a far better climate than the lands extending 350 miles north of Maine.

Geologic history. Ancient terranes and igneous rocks are almost unknown in Poland, but Mesozoic and Tertiary beds underlie almost all of the state, showing through the drift abundantly in the southern third, with hundreds of scattered small outcrops in the northern parts. Devonian and Silurian remnants of the old Variscan mid-European mountains are known in many small outcrops west and north of Kraków, and Pre-Cambrian on the Russian border south of the Pripet Marshes. Glaciation from the north spread drift over nearly all the country, and winds laid rich loess deposits over much of the southern plateaus and Carpathian slopes. Ancient bedrock has little to do with present topography but contributes much to the mineral resources. Northern slopes of the Carpathians give a fine tract of mature mountain topography and provide an elevated divide for a frontier line.

RACIAL AND NATIONAL HISTORY

Early stages. Lying on the Central European Plain, Poland was wide open to the Paleolithic and Neolithic hunters, roaming in scattered bands,

652

a fact occasionally witnessed by interesting finds of their implements and weapons. Neolithic commerce, like much later trade and travel, followed along the Vistula and Dniester as well as over the longer route, Vistula-Bug-Pripet-Dnieper, both routes connecting the Black and Baltic seas. Both commerce and route are attested by fragments of amber and of Near-East products scattered by the way and buried in the terminal countries. The hunt for edible game must have been remunerative in lands such as these plains then were.

But the present population owes much more to later occupants. Following the climatic changes incident to the melting of the great ice sheets 15,000 to 20,000 years ago and to the establishment of the zones of westerlies and trade winds approximately as today, there came large invasions of people from the east. Later, some 6,000 to 8,000 years ago, after the great inland seas of the Obi-Caspian Basin had given place to grasslands, another invasion spread across the plains from Asia to the mountains and hills of central Europe. Apparently there came wave on wave of nomadic farmers, many of them never reaching the mountains, who absorbed rather than exterminated their predecessors on the plains of Russia. These people, a part of the Alpine Race, are the Slavs of eastern Europe. Some of the choice vanguard, having spent generations in the European mountains apparently came down to the plains and became the ancestors of Poles and Czechs.

For Poland our "first glimmerings of light in these parts show us a number of kindred tribes holding the land between Oder and Vistula" [1] but wandering freely in small tribal groups.

Kingdom of Poland. The Slavs multiplied rapidly, and 2,000 years ago a group in Poland, more aggressive than others, gathered considerable power. As centuries passed this group became Christian, and Roman Catholic because the country lay west of the great church line. Thus a large beam was laid in Poland's west-facing national and social as well as religious structure. The Kingdom arose in an area with no natural frontiers. Migrations in and out were easy, and solidarity came reluctantly. These conditions fostered dissension. Although Poland once reached from Baltic to Black Sea, with much power over weaker peoples, the perpetual lack of boundaries, against which both expansion from within and repression from without could shove, brought discord among its rulers. National limits constantly fluctuated. By the latter part of the eighteenth century the weakness of Poland and the strength of three neighbors were such that Poland was dismembered, so to remain for over a 100 years.

The Republic. Attempts to Germanize on the west and south and to Russify on the east still left a burning nationalism which, when Russia collapsed in 1917, sprang up quickly for self-expression. With the help of the Versailles Treaty, the new Poland sponsored by the League of Na-

[1] Edward A. Freeman, *The Historical Geography of Europe* (1920), p. 482.

tions was established as a republic. It was, however, on the same topography as before and subject to similar weaknesses. It was essentially as always an interior nation with overgrown ambitions toward the sea. The facts of diverse government and ideals for more than a century have left their marks in language, religion, and economic efficiency; border zones contain a mixed population, and the eastern half is partially Eastern Slav. With strong aggressive powers both east and west, a buffer status is in-

Polish cities and rivers. (Adapted from *Oxford Advanced Atlas*)

evitable for Poland whether the state wills it or not. Present boundaries drawn and not yet recognized by the great powers place Poland farther west than for a generation. The eastern boundary is very nearly the Curzon line, suggested many years ago by Lord Curzon, an able British statesman. This places many Russian Slavs of the east in the U.S.S.R. where they should be, and many Poles on the west in Poland instead of Germany. Many Poles in the eastern excluded area migrated west and many Germans in the western included area moved west into Germany. With these adjustments the present post-World War II frontiers are much more acceptable than those set up in 1921. They include the southern half of East Prussia, most of Pomerania, a little of German Brandenburg, and all Silesia, all areas having a large number of Poles before War II.

While many Poles glow with an intense nationalism, many also are happily and brilliantly conscious that Poland cannot rise alone, that social, economic, and commercial federations and friendly relations are demanded by the geographic situation. Geographically and ethnically Poland is a better unit today than perhaps ever before.

In the early tribal days physical boundaries, such as recent nations have desired, were not significant. During the last 2,000 years, while the spirit of nationalism has been rampant, the Polish people have been under a real disadvantage as regards borders; but with the dawn of the idea of a friendly family of nations, such open highways between them and their neighbors are elements of great promise. The time must and will come when such a barrier as the Pyrenees will be looked upon as a positive disadvantage.

Unity—frontiers. The one unifying element in Poland is geographic— the Vistula River. It drains four fifths or more of the land. With its tributaries it furnishes navigation in several directions from Danzig and the Baltic back toward land borders. Canals connect across the borders with other streams to the north and west, and plans are developing to canalize the Vistula and to open a waterway to Odessa by connecting it with the Dnieper. Such a program would take advantage of the low grade, continuous flow, and easy divides of this great river. A common zeal for progress, education, and development of resources as nearly to self-sufficiency as possible dominates the people, but Soviet influence endeavors to direct education, development, and progress.

Poland is continental. The core is a solid block of prolific Roman Catholic, Polish-speaking, Western Slavs—Poles. The Poles are not naval, marine, seafaring, as are many coast Germans.

PHYSIOGRAPHIC REGIONS

Recently Glaciated Portion. This northern section of the country is rougher than the next described because it contains more moraines and has had less erosion to subdue them. It contains the Baltic Ridge of several authors. Some of the most beautiful rolling plains, dotted with lakes (i.e., Masurian Lakes), hold the purest rural population but the sparsest of all Poland. Root crops, notably sugar beets in the west, give employment to numerous laborers, and the beets are shipped by rail in hundreds of carloads to the vicinal sugar factories. In the more hilly parts oats and rye are the leading cereal crops. Rich pasture lands supply grass for many sheep and cattle. Flax covers large areas and does well in the northeast. Swampy still in scores of places, this glaciated portion once had many lakes and a network of waterways, the chief of which was marginal to the ice where the Vistula now flows from Warsaw to the elbow. From this point former melt-waters continued west as far as the Elbe and constructed a graded way which invites canal construction from the Vistula across the Oder, past Berlin, and on to the North Sea. When the ice disappeared, short Baltic streams began to lengthen their channels and, having captured sections of this waterway, diverted the Vistula and Oder to the Baltic.

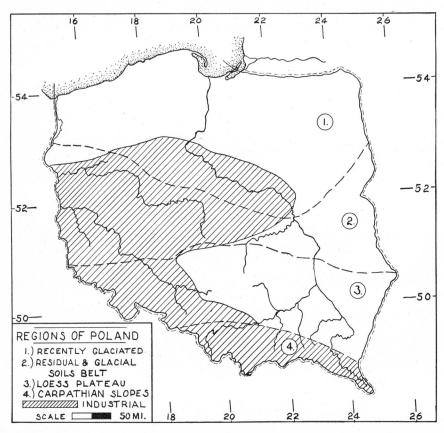

REGIONS OF POLAND
1.) RECENTLY GLACIATED
2.) RESIDUAL & GLACIAL
    SOILS BELT
3.) LOESS PLATEAU
4.) CARPATHIAN SLOPES
▨▨▨▨▨ INDUSTRIAL
SCALE ▭▬▭ 50 MI.

Geographic regions used in the discussion of Poland. Numbers one to four are largely physical. The industrial region cuts across the physical region lines. (Adapted from maps in *Atlas Republiky Ceskoslovenske*)

Residual and Glacial Soils Belt. South of the moraine region lies a strip more level but better drained because much longer exposed to stream work and never so rolling and hilly as the more recently glaciated northern section. Crossed by the Vistula and Bug, drained in the west by the Warthe into the Oder on the German border, it has most possibilities for commerce and yet fewest railroads of all regions. Since glaciation was so early here, rock and drift decay have proceeded further, and the soils have a larger proportion of residual material and are more mature but generally poorer than in the moraine belt. The wetter lands raise more buckwheat than other cereals. The western half has the most dense rural population. The two great potato-growing areas, around Lublin and Poznań and in the far west, share with the moraine belt in producing the most hogs, because of intensive agriculture and proximity to market. Cattle fit in with the crop régime of this belt both east and west, but sheep are scarce, being too hard on pasture. This is distinctly not a mineral belt but has considerable industrial development. Its people work in textiles and process farm crops. Coöperative societies are frequent and helpful in all the western and southern districts.

Workers in the salt mines at Wieliczka, a few miles south of Kraków. Salt is a Carpathian product and enters many industries of Poland. (Courtesy Polish Research and Information Service)

Loess Plateaus. The third physical unit, lying south of the last and reaching to the Carpathian slopes, attains an average altitude of about a thousand feet, and carries a rich veneer of loess and old drift over a wide variety of Paleozoic sedimentary rocks. Its population is more numerous per square mile, more progressive and literate than in any other region as a whole, facts related probably to the presence of mineral wealth and the accompanying industrial development. Rurally it is the wheat land, whereas rye, barley, and oats prevail in other regions. Soils are calcareous (favoring wheat), mature, and rich.

The minerals contributing most are potassium salts and petroleum in the east, with iron, coal, and salt in the west. These minerals, together with clays, sands, and limestones, form the bases for iron and steel manufacture, for fertilizer and chemical works, for cement and other ceramic industries, and for the making of machinery. Agricultural products are manufactured, notably wheat into flour, beets into sugar, hides into leather and leather goods. Where conditions are favorable, Poland has been very active in developing industry.

Carpathian Slopes. The bounding mountains on the south are reduced to maturity or beyond, and while rising to 5,000 feet in many rounded summits they range from 1,500 feet up and have thousands of acres of arable and pasture lands. Their roughness and altitude are sufficient to

Typical rural scene in southeastern Poland. Note styles of buildings, fences, and roofs in these old Carpathian hills. (Courtesy Consulate General of Poland)

reduce the density of population and check the growth of towns, except as minerals call for workers. Forests cover half the slopes, a proportion more than twice as great as the Polish average; and from 20 per cent to 50 per cent of the arable land is sown to oats, clover, and root crops. The rest is in pasture and hay and furnishes food for dairy and meat cattle. Although adopted as the frontier for Poland and Czechoslovakia, these mountains were not a prewar national boundary and have not been a great barrier to the movements of people. They were well occupied by the Alpine Race as it migrated into western Europe.

Across these physiographic regions sweeps the characteristically variable weather, or climate, of the cyclone-bearing westerlies. So transitional climatically is this Polish land that at times it has moist, cloudy, very moderate Atlantic winters, locally called "English," while at other times it has cold, clear, severe, continental winters called "Russian."

POPULATION DIFFERENCES

Whereas so much that is geologic and glacial in Poland is in east-to-west belts, a number of items are in approximate north-to-south belts. Roughly the Vistula River divides the rural interests into two parts. On the west over seven eighths of arable lands are sown; on the east usually much less is sown, because in general soils are poorer, more marshy, and suitable for little but pasture. Such a line divides the more densely from the more sparsely populated portions of the country. West of the line is no administrative division, except in the Carpathians, with less than 200 per square mile; some divisions run as high as 375; east of the line the density falls in places to less than 50 per square mile. The high yields per acre in wheat, barley, rye, oats, and potatoes are in divisions along the west side, where soils and methods of agriculture are the best. A part of this difference in aspect and production is related to Poland's neighbors. On the lands in Germany during Poland's partition, also on that derived from Germany after World War II, a higher response to the physical environments—civilization—developed and a higher culture than on the Russian holdings. In recent years a wave of rural population of a different ethnic quality and experience has been spreading eastward and is already changing the general aspect. West Poland is doing much to uplift and restore east Poland.

INDUSTRIAL REGIONS

Three industrial regions are recognized. The least occupies the lower Carpathian Slopes, from the Russian frontier westward in a belt some 30 miles wide to the neighborhood of Kraków. Petroleum and water furnish the power, and salts some of the raw materials. The second industrial area occupies much of Upper Silesia and some territory lying to the east of it. It contains many productive coal-mines and lead and zinc deposits. Iron ore, both from local mines and imported from Germany, and coking coal from Czechoslovakia help to make this area, Kraków to Tešín, the leading mineral-industries section of the country. This second industrial area has been the Silesian problem of three nations, Germany, Czechoslovakia, and Poland. The topography is old, no physical features furnish any suggestion of boundaries either for nation or industrial unit. Limits are set only by the distribution of iron ores and zinc-mines. Six towns of 50,000 people or over occur in the region, none of them dominant. Two of the six exceed 75,000. The whole industrial center is far inland but can serve the adjacent countries to which it belongs, even though the sea and foreign markets are far distant. The industries and towns have grown with little plan, simply following the mineral deposits.

In addition to an active metal industry in iron and zinc, sulphuric acid is made by oxidizing the sulphur of zinc ores. Glass is manufactured from sand layers, brick and tile from soft shales, and cement from limestones. Electric power for general consumption is derived from many perennial streams. Sand is poured into abandoned sections of mines to support the roof, while the last ore in supporting pillars and wall is being drawn out.

The third industrial region extends from Warsaw west through Lodz, Posen, and many lesser industrial towns. Here the handcrafts, textile and leather industries, and many subsidiary mills are operating. Some silk and flax are worked up, but wool and cotton, the former largely home-grown, the latter wholly imported, are the chief raw materials. This area was the great textile region of Russia before the First World War. Lodz is largely a woolen center and Posen (268,000) (Poznań) on the Warthe is a cotton

Barges carry coal on the Oder River from the Silesian mines to the port of Szczecin (Stettin). (Courtesy Polish Research and Information Service)

center. Several lesser industrial towns cluster along the Warthe to its mouth at the Oder. The capital, largest town, and most nearly central city, Warsaw, has the greatest diversity of industry and of product. To cotton and wool are added flax and jute spinning and weaving, brewing and distilling, flour-milling, lumber industries, machinery and leather works.

Breslau, Wroclaw (299,400), and Liegnitz (24,450) (Legnica) are the principal cities, but they are outside the mining area. Breslau, the capital of Silesia when it was a German province, will continue to be the capital and chief city of Silesia as a province of Poland. It is an old city appearing in the lists of Thietmer, Bishop of Merseburg in 1000 A.D. Silesia has given allegiance to Old Poland, to the Mongols, to Bohemia, Hungary, Prussia, Austria, then to the Hapsburgs until the break-up of the Austro-Hungarian Dual Monarchy, when it became a part of Germany. After World War II the whole province of Silesia came to Poland.

Breslau has an old university (1702), a cathedral, many churches, and fine public buildings. It is best known as a commercial and industrial center with a radial net of railroads, iron foundries, factories for machines, linen, clothing, furniture, paper, and railway cars. It holds two annual fairs, one each in the fall and spring. Proximity to the coal, iron, and other metal mines in Upper Silesia has greatly activated its industry and commerce.

Assembly line at the Ursus tractor factory in the Warsaw area. How does it compare with American assembly lines? (Courtesy Polish Research and Information Service)

Liegnitz is about as old as Breslau but has lacked much in location and connections. It is farther from the mineral wealth southeast of Breslau and has never had the political and religious attentions paid to the latter. Its factories work in linen, wool, cotton, leather, wood, steel, and rural products, making pianos, sugar, clothing, machinery, flour, and processed meats.

Kraków (299,396) has been the soul of the nation. Kings were crowned here for centuries, now industry and commerce make its history.

To be correlated with the growth of industry, wealth, and education have come two or three architectural and social responses. The proportion of stone buildings, both on the farms and in the villages, increases from about 5 per cent in the Pripet marshes and Wilno south and westward to over 80 per cent in the northwest. In like manner the frequency of fireproof roofs increases toward the west and northwest from less than 5 per cent to over 80 per cent. The number of persons per building increases sharply westward from six to ten, but the size of the house increases also. The number of persons per room, however, increases markedly eastward from two to four but, alas, the size of the room does not increase. Many a rural or village house in the eastern states has but one room and more have only two rooms, a response to poverty conditions elucidated above.

COMMERCE AND TRADE

Transportation systems. The rivers and canals have been mentioned. Railroads have an unfortunate inheritance from the divided Poland. The new nation has done much to improve their condition, unify the system, and extend the lines in many places. Poland plans railroad construction to adjust to the present frontier lines as soon as such work can be financed.

Exports and imports. In a land with so little for the visitor to see or purchase and with no history of foreign investments in its development, any balance of trade must be kept by actual sale and purchase of goods, or by the flow of gold and silver. Poland produces no gold and silver to export, or to buy with; hence there is a continuous effort to sell as much produce as must be purchased, or to purchase no more foreign goods than can be paid for in Polish goods. As a result of this careful watching, exports and imports frequently change rank.

Since World War II Russian influence has been strong in Poland, partly from Soviet pressure and partly from choice of those in power in Warsaw. Official trade figures published in the capital for 1946 show imports almost $140 million, about 70 per cent from U.S.S.R., and exports of nearly $133 million, about half to U.S.S.R. These values were nearly half the prewar level, but because prices were higher the bulk of goods was appreciably lower. Movement of persons and freight within the country was larger than in prewar years, and aviation was considerably expanded. Values of many products of the factories and mines were higher than in the late 1930's, others were lower. Index numbers for industrial and agricultural output were 12 to 18 per cent above those for 1938. Cost of living indices indicate enormous increases with less food to be had. Further recovery or changes will be watched with interest.

CITIES

Warsaw (594,000) (Warszawa). The immediate reason for a city on the great navigable Vistula here was the beautiful terrace high above flood level, suitable for a royal palace with terraced gardens, and for a fine residence and public building section. No tributary enters here, but four come in nearby. Somewhere on the great fertile plains a city must be built, and this specific place is central. Old trade routes converged on the site, from Russia on the east, and German states on the west, from Baltic to Black Sea and through the Moravian Gate to the Adriatic. When Poland was strong, Warsaw was one of the great European capitals. As modern railroad construction came, it grew to be even more a junction point, distributing center, and commercial, political headquarters for entrance to Old Russia. Warsaw had over a million people before War I, nearly 30 per cent of whom were Jews. Today there are about 630,000 inhabitants. A large stone bridge, destroyed in World War II, but now rebuilt, leading eastward to Praga, spans the yellow, creeping waters. The city has easy access to minerals on the southwest, to the potatoes of the surrounding plains, to hides from the

Reconstructed apartment houses in Warsaw. (Courtesy Polish Research and Information Service)

grazing lands and to forests on the hills; these resources help to explain its variety and abundance of manufactures—hardware, transport machinery, sugar, starch, and distillery products, boots, shoes, lace, and embroidery. River commerce could be much improved, but the stream is frozen about two months each year. Radial streets from the market on the south margin of the old city run out through the beautiful modern, spacious blocks to the south and into the quaint old city to the north. To walk these narrow, crooked lanes is to take a trip down the avenues of time, and catch glimpses of picturesque, medieval buildings rich in historical significance and suggestive of hidden deeds by long-forgotten people.

Lodz (497,000) (Lódź) is the textile center. It receives thousands of tons of foreign cotton, wool (both home-grown and foreign), and jute and

Ancient warehouse and gate on one of the canals of Danzig. Note the little roof over the pulleys used in hoisting goods from boats to different floors. How it savors of Hanseatic days! (Courtesy Walter Silber)

The great ship *Sobieski* in the Danzig harbor. What changes in harbor facilities since Hanseatic days! (Courtesy K. Komorowski and Polish Research and Information Service)

hemp for rope and coarser fabrics and sends out manufactures to Russia, Germany, and all neighboring states. Danzig (118,000) (Gdansk) is the natural clearing-house for the commerce of the Vistula. It should be as significant a river harbor as Gdynia (77,800) is a seaport; and both should give their fine facilities to systematic improvement and international trade. Danzig was a fortified city with a triple wall and moat; but moats are now duck-ponds, and walls shelter garage and blacksmith-shop equally well. About half the larger towns of Poland are on the Vistula and are thus in possible close communication with this river port. It has been famous for 2,000 years as an amber market. Water streets serve its warehouses and float boats from the Vistula to many parts of the city.

Cases of eggs to be loaded on the merchant vessel *Opole* in Gdynia port. Destination, Great Britain. (Courtesy K. Komorowski and Polish Research and Information Service)

Stettin (72,894) (Szczecin), on the drowned Oder above the bay or *Haffe* and the upper bay or *Damm,* is the port of the Oder River. It is one of the three German Hanseatic towns that has really survived. Most of them are drowsy, out-of-date, relic ports revealing a fascinating commercial history but scarcely sharing in the modern life of the nation. Stettin is a Baltic Sea port only and so far excels all other Baltic ports that it is the only one comparable with the busy North Sea ports. It stands far up the river between East and West Pomerania so as best to serve these rural regions: one in Poland, the other in Germany. It is connected with Berlin by canal. The Oder River connects Stettin with Breslau and with the mining and industrial activities in Silesia. The Oder is less perfect than the Elbe for commerce but stimulates trade on the Netze and Warthe and with the Vistula. Its canal connections are equal to those of the Ruhr. No port comparable with Stettin exists within a radius of 65 miles. Industries already established are cement works using local shales, petroleum refineries for imported crude, and shops for manufacturing lumber, machinery, wood articles, and furniture. Imports are timber and lumber from Baltic states and pyrite and iron ores from Scandinavia. Exports come from the interior for Baltic trade. In the present century as many ships, though of less draft, came and went as at Bremen.

The Jews. Cities were the home of Jews for centuries. They were invited to Poland to assist in trade and industry, but the recent German occupation liquidated them by millions.

PROBLEMS AND FUTURE

Poles long have been mediators between West and East, being one of the nations that have met the Eastern impact and have passed on to the East many Western ideas. For decades to come this process will be inevitable. It is one of Poland's missions.

Poland needs land reforms to outlaw large estates with serfs, a trend greatly promoted by the postwar exodus of millions of Germans to their homeland. More intensive, better organized and mechanized agriculture should mean better use of the land. Some good agricultural land was added to Poland in the division of East Prussia.

Poland's transitional nature, expressed in topography, climate, waters, race, culture, and religion, begets for the people a profound problem. There can be no isolation policy. There should be no tariff barriers. Strife with neighbors must be curbed. As a sixteenth-century Polish author has said, "While other nations are defended by water, have embattled gateways, impassable mountains, we have nothing of the kind. In our hands, our breasts, and throats is our armory: these are our mountains, waters, castles, walls, and the ramparts of Poland." Personalities are more powerful than powder. What he said in those contentious days to kindle the ardor of a warlike people must be translated today into terms of international friendly coöperation.

QUESTIONS

1. Is Warsaw now well situated to be Poland's capital? Better or worse than in the 1920's and 1930's? Discuss.

2. What reasons could be given for early commerce between Baltic and Black seas?

3. Some nations emphasize language as a means of expressing their nationalism. What methods could Poland use besides language?

4. What arguments can be presented for and against the internationalization of the Vistula?

5. What reasons appear for dividing Poland east and west into rural belts, and north and south into industrial belts?

6. How does the Silesian area fit in with the present Poland? Commercially? Industrially? What minority problems does it introduce?

7. How is the U.S.S.R. dominance of Poland liable to affect her outlook, which has been so long western? How serious to Poland may this U.S.S.R. relationship be?

8. Would it have been better for Poland to have proceeded to develop the commerce and the trade facilities of Danzig than to build a new harbor city at Gdynia? Discuss.

BIBLIOGRAPHY

ARMSTRONG, Hamilton F., *Tito and Goliath* (New York, The Macmillan Company, 1951).

BASCH, Antonin, *The Danube Basin and German Economic Sphere* (New York, Columbia University Press, 1943).

BOYD, Louise A., *Polish Countrysides* (New York, Amer. Geog. Soc., Paper 20, 1937).

BRANT, Irving, *New Life in Poland* (London, Dennis Dobson, 1946).

CAHNMAN, Werner J., "Frontiers between East and West Europe," *Geographical Review,* Vol. 39 (October, 1949), pp. 605-624.

COON, Carleton S., *The Races of Europe* (New York, The Macmillan Company, 1939).

DE MARTONNE, Emmanuel, "Poland," in Vidal de La Blache and Gallois, *Géographie Universelle* (Paris, Lib. Armand Colin, 1931).

DYBOWSKI, Roman, *et al.*, *Cambridge History of Poland* (Cambridge, England, Cambridge University Press, 1941).

EDWARDS, K. C., SCARFE, N. V., and MOODIE, A. E., "The Nowy Targ Basin of the Polish Tatra: Its Human Geography, with Special Reference to the Bukowina District," *Scottish Geographical Magazine,* Vol. 51 (July, 1935), pp. 215-227.

Europa, Encyclopedia of Europe (London, Europa Publications, Ltd.), annual.

European Conference on Rural Life, Poland (Geneva, National Monographs No. 29, 1940).

FITZGERALD, Walter, *The New Europe* (New York, Harper and Brothers, 1946).

GARDNER, Monica M., *Poland* (London, A. & C. Black, Ltd., 1942).

GARNETT, Alice, "The Nowy Targ Basin: the Morphological Background to Its Human Geography," *Scottish Geographical Magazine,* Vol. 51 (May, 1935), pp. 151-161.

HABETHA, E., "Die Karpathen und das galizische Erdöl," *Geol. Rundschau,* Bd. 32, Heft 1-2 (1941), pp. 137-177.

KISS, George, "A T.V.A. on the Danube," *Geographical Review,* Vol. 37 (1947), pp. 274-302.

KONOVALOV, Serge, ed., *Russo-Polish Relations* (Princeton, Princeton University Press, 1945).

KUBISCHER, Eugene M., *Europe on the Move* (New York, Columbia University Press, 1948).

LEHMANN, John, *Down River; A Danubian Study* (London, The Cresset Press, 1939).

MACHRAY, Robert, *East Prussia a Menace to Poland* (Chicago, American Polish Council, 1943).

McCORMICK, Thomas C. T., ed., *Problems of a Post-War World* (New York and London, McGraw-Hill Book Company, Inc., 1945).

MUNK, Frank, *The Legacy of Nazism* (New York, The Macmillan Company, 1943).

NEWMAN, Bernard, *The New Europe* (New York, The Macmillan Company, 1943).

PEARCY, G. Etzel, and FIFIELD, Russell H., *et al., World Political Geography* (New York, Thomas Y. Crowell Company, 1948).

PETRASCHECK, Walther E., "Gebirgsbildung, Vulcanismus und Metallogenese in den Karpathen und Balkaniden," *Deutsche Geol. Gesel. Zeitschr.,* Bd. 95, Heft 1-2, p. 70, 1943.

PRIBICEVIC, Stojan, *World Without End* (New York, Reynal & Hitchcock, 1939).

RETINGER, Joseph H., *All about Poland—Facts, Figures, Documents* (London, Minerva Publishing Co., Ltd., 1941).

ROUCEK, Joseph S., *Contemporary Europe* (New York, D. Van Nostrand Company, Inc., 1941).

———, *Central Eastern Europe* (New York, Prentice-Hall, Inc., 1946).

SCHMITT, Bernadotte Everly, *et al., Poland, Civilization* (Berkeley and Los Angeles, University of California Press, 1945).

SHACKLETON, Margaret R., *Europe, A Regional Geography* (London, Longmans, Green & Company, 1942).

SHOTWELL, James T., and LAZERON, Max M., *Poland and Russia 1919-1945* (New York, King's Crown Press, 1945).

SUPER, Margaret L., *Poland and U.S.S.R., Last Quarter Century* (New York, Sheed and Ward, 1944).

SUPER, Paul, *Polish Tradition* (London, George Allen & Unwin, Ltd., 1944).

THOMSON, Valentine, *Young Europe* (New York, Doubleday, Doran & Co., Inc., 1932).

VAN CLEEF, Eugene, "Danzig and Gdynia," *Geographical Review,* Vol. 23 (1933), pp. 101-107.

WELLES, Sumner, ed., *An Intelligent American's Guide to the Peace* (New York, The Dryden Press, 1945).

WOJCIECHOWSKI, Zygmunt, *et al., Poland's Place in Europe,* trans. by B.W.A. Massey (Poznan, Instytut Zachodni, 1947).

CHAPTER 32

Switzerland

A belated tourist at Zermatt says:
"First it rained and then it blew,
And then it friz and then it snew,
And then it fogged and then it thew;
And very shortly after then
It blew and friz and snew again."

The realism of Swiss writers is an effect
of Swiss democracy which is geographic.

GENERAL SURVEY

Introduction. If one would catch the real significance of topography and climate in the activities of a people, no better approach could be made than through a comparison of Switzerland and Netherlands. Switzerland is 100 miles from the sea; Netherlands is almost mixed with it. There are 3,000 square miles more of Switzerland than of Netherlands, yet the smaller land supports twice as many people. Contrariwise, compared with Maine, Switzerland contains half the area, 16,000 square miles, is two to three times as rough and high, and yet supports five times as many people. All activities as well as the density of the population are affected by the physical conditions. As important to the spirit of the people as relief and climate is the position. As this chapter proceeds, the reader may note elements of the temper of the people that are related to position, neighbors, relief, and climate.

Unity. Swiss physical unity is found in its mountains and valleys, but not half the Alpine region is within the one country. Italy, France, and Austria have territory just like that of Switzerland, and therefore have people, homes, and occupations not distinctly differentiated from those of Switzerland, but much more vitally interested outside Switzerland than within. Although more than three fourths of the boundaries are high mountain crests, they are not designed to protect, for they are too often breached by through-valleys, lakes and rivers. Yet the great war storms between 1600 and 1800 scarcely touched the youthful Swiss Confederation. Swiss defense as well as Swiss unity lay in the undesirableness of the Swiss country.

Relief and geology. Where the Alps now lift their rugged summits to altitudes of 12,000 to 15,000 feet, there rolled the waves of great mediterranean seas in the Mesozoic and early Tertiary periods. (See chapter on Mediterranean Sea.) Thousands of feet of sediments accumulated. During later Tertiary times repeated uplifts, folding, and thrust-faulting generated the complex structures of the Alps, and much simpler disturbances gave the elementary, long, parallel folds of the Jura. As the mountains were being elevated, streams carved their slopes and spread the waste between the Alps and the Jura. During the ice age gigantic Alpine glaciers carved the mountains, then transported and deposited the waste in the intermontane

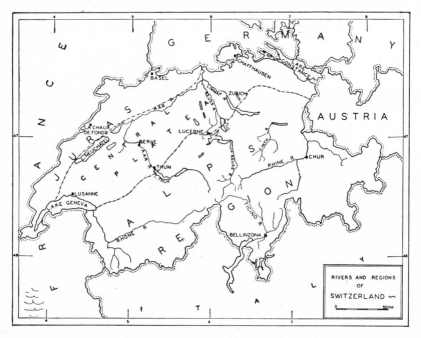

Geographic regions of Switzerland. Boundaries in dot-dash lines. (Based on topographic, geologic, population, and land utilization maps)

area. Streams and small glaciers are still at work at the same tasks. This complex mountain structure and the profound and intriguing ice erosion have furnished problems and inspiration for many an able native scientist; but mineralization in the Alps was so meager that very little mineral wealth occurs to stir industry; and erosion is still so young that transportation is woefully hampered, although the scenery is magnificent.

Rivers, usually steep-graded and burdened with waste, have little commercial importance, but in recent years men are making interesting use of them for power. Unusually long and deep lakes have been used for fishing and transportation since the homes of lake dwellers were built on poles and platforms over their shallow marginal waters. They are numerous and high enough to be effective regulators of floods and collectors of sediments. They also serve as reservoirs and thus help in the development of water power.

Regions. Three distinct types of region are found in Switzerland: (1) The simple Jura ridges and valleys, which support a population of 25 to 125 per square mile largely by dairying, supplemented by home and factory industries. (2) The Central Plateau between Alps and Jura, supporting 200 to 600 per square mile by general agriculture and industries. (3) The Alps Region of rugged, lofty mountains and glaciated valleys, which maintains a population of less than 25 per square mile by dairy agriculture, home industry, and caring for tourists. This third region is often divided geologically into a northern half, dominantly of sedimentary rocks and submature topography, and a southern half, with more youthful topography in which crystalline schists, gneisses, and granites predominate. While these two parts are obvious on any geologic map, and easily differentiated geologically in the field, they are too similar geographically to be separated here.

Boundaries. Central in position, the Swiss in centuries past have chosen to use the fortress character of their land to resist conquest, and have preferred independence to commerce gained only by affiliation with their peripheral neighbors.[1] Their scanty resources encouraged this independent segregation, but modern needs and communications are modifying their ideas.

Bulges and indentations in the Swiss frontier seem everywhere to be adjustments to topography. For example, both France and Switzerland need a water route on Lake Geneva, and consequently the lake is divided. Geneva is so significant that it has been called the western capital, and the boundary of necessity goes around it. The Rhône above the lake had no value worth controversy, hence the boundary was set along the lofty, uninhabitable, impassable crests of the Pennine Alps. Let the reader continue to trace, on good large-scale maps, the details of the Swiss frontier around the country, past Lake Constance, Schaffhausen, Basel, Porrentruy, and back to Geneva. In places it has been established during conflict between a mountain people, fired with a love of liberty, and the great tumultuous lowland states outside, whose histories had many varying motives. Some of the cantons were formed by blocks of people who seceded peaceably from their governments and joined the growing federation. The rough topography long checked the intercourse necessary for real uniformity in coinage, laws, and government. Not until 1848 did the cantons form a general constitution.

---

[1] E. C. Semple, *Influences of Geographic Environment* (1911), p. 141.

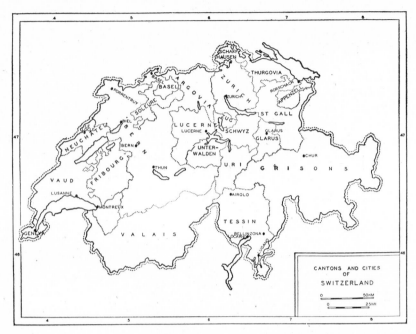

Swiss political units. Boundaries in dots; many lakes are shown. (Adapted from *Oxford Advanced Atlas*)

GEOGRAPHIC DIVISIONS

While the three regions were named and characterized physiographically, they may well be considered geographically, because human responses in each are as different as are the topography and the climate.

Central Plateau. About 30 per cent of Switzerland is included between the lofty Alps and the young Jura. The slight range in altitude from 1,200 to 3,500 feet gives to man a large proportion of land for agriculture and forest utilization and a minimum of waste land. The level lands are the lowest, formed as deltas and filled-valley plains, such as those at the heads of lakes Geneva and Constance, and along the Neuchâtel-Aar lowland from Lausanne or Geneva to the mouth of the Aar. Several subsidiary plains lead into the plateau as far as Berne and Thun on the upper Aar, to Lucerne on the Reuss, and to Zurich and Utznach on the Limmat, assuring easy drainage and communication from most parts of the plateau to the Rhine, Rhône, and industrial Germany. These are the areas of densest population, intense agriculture, large industry, and aggressive thought. Between the valley floors rise long, mature ridges and crooked spurs of the fore-Alps toward the Bernese and Glarus Alps. These ridges are still well timbered and furnish both abundant forest products and grass for grazing and hay.

With its moderate relief, this central region is favored by a more uniform climate than either mountain region possesses. Rainfall is ample; winter snow ensures sledding for logs in winter and flood waters to float them in spring; only toward the south on the highest parts of the plateau are the elements too severe for forest growth; there are ice and snow for winter sports, yet no permanent glaciers. Temperature range from warmest to coldest month is about 40° F. at Geneva, Montreux, Bern, and Zurich. Precipitation varies from 33 inches at Geneva to 46 at Lucerne, but is greater on the summits of the plateau. This range of the climatic elements is near the optimum for human activity and aids in explaining the industry, thrift, and progress of the plateau peoples.

Picturesque Rütli House on Lake Lucerne. Often called "cradle of Swiss liberty" because here, on November 7, 1307, 33 men from Uri, Schwyz, and Unter-walden assembled and swore to drive out their oppressors. These states have been free ever since and are the core of Switzerland. (Courtesy Wehrli)

Forests are not allowed in recent times on the plains and lower slopes, but they are well distributed over the hills and mountains, where they alternate with meadows and pasture. A federal conservation law ensures that the area utilized for forest shall never be reduced. The plateau is the stronghold of the broad-leaf species, oak, beech, maple, ash, linden, alder, poplar, and hornbeam, but during the last century spruce has increased by planting, urged by the building enterprise and the toy and paper industries.

Soils, recently derived from glacial drift and post-glacial weathering of bed-rock, are youthful with incompletely developed profiles. The altitude and latitude are high enough to check evaporation, and stream work has accomplished little since the ice melted; therefore, even with such rainfall as they have, the soils have developed under excessive moisture and are of the mountain meadow and swamp types. Upper horizons are rich in humus. When cleared they yield readily to tillage and with the frequent application of stable manure produce good crops and luxuriant grass.

Mineral resources are limited to salt, mined near Basel; asphalt near Neuchâtel; sand, gravel, and clays, generously distributed and freely used for building purposes, brick, and tile. Limestone is used in several places for cement and road-beds; sandstones are extensively quarried for building

One of the immaculate Lake Lucerne steamers. It makes the rounds of the resorts and scenery along the lake shores. (Courtesy Swiss National Tourist Office)

houses, walls, and bridges. Celebrated mineral springs occur in St. Gallen and Aarau. In the Alps region St. Moritz and Leuk are famous spas and winter resorts. Water power is developed on many streams, particularly on those that are subject to the regulating influence of a lake. In the absence of coal and peat, hydro-electric power has come to be the main reliance of industry. About 70 per cent of the railroads are electrified, and every town and many farm-houses have electric current for lighting and domestic power. Ninety-eight per cent of all industrial machinery uses hydro-electric power and still there is current for export. About 30 per cent (1 million horsepower) of this resource is now under control. It is therefore a most promising resource for Swiss future development.

Agriculture is limited by topography, altitude, and forest, but not by precipitation. Intensive use of the soil is common, and returns are often surprisingly abundant. The vine thrives on the sunny slopes of lakes Geneva and Neuchâtel, in the Ticino and lower Rhône valleys, and in sheltered places throughout much of the plateau. Jam fruits are extensively grown in northern valleys. Chestnuts are very prolific, entering into the local diet and even into the foreign trade. Wheat is produced in considerable quantities; rye, oats, and maize, in less amounts, and each less than needed; potatoes and a fine line of hardy vegetables are produced in every valley, nearly sufficient for the home market. Even before World War I the area under cultivation was decreasing in favor of grassland to meet the requirements for milk at home and for cheese and chocolate for export. Increasing demand for sugar encourages the culture of sugar beets. Meadows are brilliant with summer flowers, and gardens bring forth bountifully under the influence of ample rain, warm sun, and the deft care of faithful peasant women.

Dairying occupies many of the people in the plateau and constitutes the chief industry. By careful breeding and strict elimination of the less productive, cows now produce more and richer milk than those in any state in America. Some of the cattle are stall-fed all the year, but many of them feed in the pastures during the whole summer season.

Not only does the plateau have most of the lakes and the valleys to promote communications, but it has three fourths of the railroads and a larger proportion of the wagon roads. No long tunnels are necessary. A dozen excellent railroad lines connect cities west and north; three of the four reaching out southward have long tunnels and hairpin or spiral loops, and one has a long stretch of cog track. Five roads of the first group have over ten trains a day, while only one of the latter, the St. Gotthard, has as many. No rivers in Switzerland are navigable; but the Rhine floats boats to Basel, and its improvement to Schaffhausen is under consideration. The Aar has a precarious freight service. Lakes are frozen for some months every year.

Many towns of this plateau are strategically placed for defense, intercourse, or administration. At the lower ends of the lakes are Geneva, Thun, Lucerne, Zug, Zurich, Biel, and Neuchâtel. Bern (130,330), the capital called Federal City by the Swiss, is below Thun on the same plain; Konstanz [2] is the German city at the lower end (outlet) of Bodensee; Schaffhausen is at the Rhine Falls; Yverdon, Rorschach, Vevey, and Montreux are near the upper ends of their lakes; Lausanne is at the important junction of the Rhône and the Neuchâtel-Aar highways on Lake Geneva Of the twenty-seven Swiss towns having a population of 10,000 or more, twenty are in the Central Plateau; and of the 126 towns with the rank of *ville* or *commune*, sixty-nine are in the Plateau. Of the six towns having

---

[2] Konstanz—German spelling; Constance—English spelling.

50,000 or upward, five belong to the Plateau. Most of the Plateau towns are industrial centers, using water power, for coal is difficult and expensive to import. Cotton is spun at Winterthur and woven at Zurich, St. Gallen, and Aarau. Wald manufactures muslins and fine calicoes—cloth to be used in making embroidery at St. Gallen, Appenzell, and many vicinal villages. Much of this work is still done in the homes as women's "busy-work" during the winter. Zurich (390,000), the largest city, is famous for its silks, while Horgen and Rüti on opposite sides of Lake Zurich manufacture the machines for textile mills. Frauenfeld, within the best agricultural lands, makes farm machinery and tools. Geneva, conveniently situated to import copper and iron from France, makes dynamos and other electrical devices. Condensed milk, chocolate, cheese (Emmenthal in Emmen Valley, 10-12 miles east of Bern), and flour are typical rural manufactures.

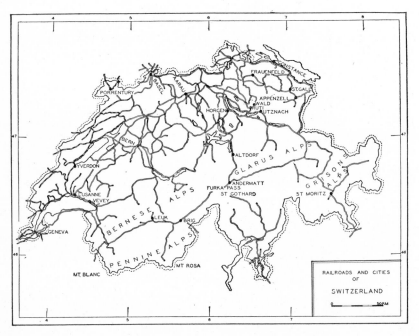

Railroads, cities, and large mountain units of Switzerland. (Adapted from Goode's *School Atlas* and *Oxford Advanced Atlas*)

As expressions of the buffer-state status, Geneva (124,430) was the seat of the League of Nations and is the headquarters of many international organizations. Lausanne (92,540) has entertained more than one great religious conference.

Industrial life began early here and started in the home because of winter spare time; the factory system followed, encouraged by need of a place to work, by abundant water power, and by physical handicaps placed on agriculture. No doubt the excellent markets, close at hand for exports, also stimulated industry. Easy transportation and the lack of fuel and raw materials led the people to develop skill and to produce high values by labor and art. Chemicals, textiles, watches, electric supplies, and fancy food preparations lend themselves to this type of production. Home industry has declined in recent years; there seems to be little pressure of

Lace weaving, another home industry. (Courtesy Swiss National Tourist Office)

population, although Switzerland has no colonies. Evidence of the healthy condition of the labor market is found in the immigration of Italians to work in cotton-mills.

Jura. Less than half the Jura Mountains lies within Switzerland, and that portion constitutes only one tenth of the country. A homogeneous, simple fold-structure pervades the whole Jura area; hence, there is no marked feature to distinguish French from Swiss Jura and, in consequence, no particular difference between French-speaking, Protestant Swiss and the neighboring French people in France in race, industry, or type of life, only in national allegiance. Therefore, with difficulty and not until recent time (1815) did this territory actually become cantons of the Swiss Confederation. It belonged loosely to older cantons for 300 years.

The geologic structure is expressed in youthful topography by long, parallel ridges of resistant limestone and sandstone alternating with structural or weak-rock valleys; this ridge-and-valley pattern controls a trellis drainage pattern and an approximate trellis arrangement of railroads. Long northeast-

Fashioning wooden shoes in which the natives of Lugano on the Italian border walk gracefully. These shoes are exclusively a home product. Richly embroidered straps furnish the desired diversity. (Courtesy E. Himmelsbach)

southwest sections of the railroads have many branching short spurs and are themselves connected by short cross-sections in water-gaps or tunnels. The pattern concentrates the forests in long strips on ridges and the people in the valleys.

Much of the Swiss Jura was once covered by the great Pleistocene Rhône glacier, the waste from which combines with that from the native rocks to furnish poor basis for soils. A severe climate with excess of rain and the short time available for making post-glacial soils have resulted in an unproductive, immature soil useful only for meadows and pastures; hence, the main rural occupation is grazing and the products are Gruyère and other cheeses, meats, and hides. Since in most of Switzerland the dominant natural resources are sands, clays, and common building stones together with forest products and water power, it is not surprising that the people are engaged in working up wood and imported metal into small but valuable articles, easy to export. Toys, jewelry, watches, and clocks all enter the export channels. In a single year more than 20 million complete timepieces are shipped away, besides thousands of cases and separate move-

Front of an arm of the Aletsch Glacier and a small iceberg floating in Marjelen Lake. This lake has no visible outlet but empties itself from time to time through a subglacial channel. (Courtesy Otto Furter, Davos-Platz)

ments to be mounted elsewhere. Watch-making began in the eighteenth century as a home industry, each man making the entire watch; but now it is concentrated, with much division of labor, in factories in Le Locle and La Chaux de Fonds. Aside from Basel these are the only towns of 10,000 people.

Basel (162,100) (Bâle), although included in the Jura Region of the map, is not a product of the region. It is strategically located at the Burgundian Gateway between Swiss Jura and the Black Forest of Germany at the head of the open Rhine Valley and river navigation, and at the convergence of the highways and railroads of northern Switzerland. It is more nearly a transition town than any other Swiss center, even surpassing Geneva at the Rhône Gate. Its people are actively engaged in commerce and in the maunfacture of chemicals, dyes, and silk ribbons, all for export and all based on imported raw materials.

The Alps. Three fifths of Switzerland is included in the region of the Alps, and to the great majority of the world this is Switzerland. Its complexity of geologic history and structure has been suggested. Its topography is wild, rugged, youthful, and almost useless because of the great altitude to which its rocks have been recently elevated, and because of the tremendous

Morteratsch glacier and Bernina Alps. Seracs of ice, moraine on the right of the ice tongue. Ice-gathering areas are above. (Commercial photograph, courtesy Alice Langelier)

activity of frost, stream, ice, and gravity to which they have been exposed. Hundreds of square miles unfit for human residence have not a single permanent inhabitant. Its valley floors are commonly less than 2,000 feet in altitude, whereas its crests, horns, *aiguilles, piz, dents, grats,* and stocks rise to 12,000 to 15,000 feet, in grandeur and glory rarely surpassed. Several lakes wholly or partly within this region lie in such valleys that they would readily be called fiords, were they salt water connected with the sea. A peculiarity of the Alps is the frequency of through-valleys, carved by glaciers, which permit passage over what would otherwise be almost insurmountable barriers. Most of the passes were found by the Romans twenty centuries ago, and many of them have been in constant use ever since; but for railroading they are generally too high and too liable to ice and snow obstruction; hence long tunnels pierce the mountains near or under them. The passes can be located and their connections worked out from good atlas maps or large-scale wall maps.

In addition to the passes, great stream-carved valleys offer means of communication far in excess of local needs, but as far inferior to the needs of subsistence and industry on opposite sides of the Alpine barrier. The Rhine and Rhône rivers have their sources near Furka Pass (8,120 feet), the former flowing east, the latter west; thus they open up a highway from Constance to Geneva directly through the massive core of the Alps. The Reuss rises 5 to 6 miles south of this through-valley, flows eastward in it 2 miles, then north to Lake Lucerne. A railroad, using only two or three short tunnels besides a 2-mile bore through Furka Pass, follows the entire longitudinal valley; but the higher reaches of the road are usually snow-bound until late in May. This same longitudinal valley serves as a cross-roads without grade crossing; for a double-track railroad climbs up from Italy past Bellinzona by four complete spiral tunnels to Airolo (4,500 feet), plunges into St. Gotthard tunnel (nearly 10 miles long), goes under Andermatt, and emerges at Göschenen to descend by spirals and tunnels and to lead through Altdorf (the home of William Tell) and Zurich or Lucerne to the fertile valleys and busy cities of Germany. How strong must be the commercial urge between Italy and Germany to demand effectively a railroad through such obstructions! At Brig by means of similar devices, and at Chur without much tunneling, this through-valley is crossed by north-south railroads.

The strong relief, varied exposure, and sunshine, the lakes, the foehn, and the condition of precipitation as rain or snow make striking local variations in climate. These, with the steepness of slope and the meager and patchy soils, combine to thwart all but the most precarious agriculture. Many vegetables and flowers are, however, grown in tiny gardens and in small quantities, never enough even for the natives. Grazing is the most important occupation and shows many interesting adjustments, among them the seasonal migration or transhumance. In the valley towns cattle and goats are fed in barns in the winter on forage gathered by strenuous work in summer from difficult rocky slopes and meadows. During the summer months the stock are driven up the slopes to graze higher and higher as the season advances from May to August. The herdsmen go with them to the meadows first, where a second village is built for summer occupance. Here the cattle feed a week or two, then go on up through the timber to slopes above the forest and just below permanent snow to graze until snow begins to fall, perhaps in August. Members of the family are left in the second village at the meadows to make hay by cutting two or three crops of grass. On the upper Alps [3] the men, living in crude shelters, make

[3] An Alp is a shoulder of gentle slope far up in the mountains, so common as to give a name to the whole mountain system.

Pasturing dairy cows in summertime on an alp in Bernese Oberland near Murren. Jungfrau is in the distant center. How does the place look in winter? Dairy industry is a characteristic as watch-making. (Courtesy Albert Steiner, through Swiss National Tourist Office)

Stock shelters, a water trough, and pasture on an alp. The Matterhorn is in the background.
(Courtesy A. Klopfenstein)

quantities of cheese from the rich milk of the goats and cattle, to be carried down and sold in foreign markets.

Forests in the Alps begin near the valley bottoms and extend up the slopes 5,000 to 5,500 feet, until the climate becomes too severe, windy, cold, and dry even for the spruce. Conifers make up 70 per cent of Swiss forests, and beech about 25 per cent. Fifty-five per cent of Swiss forests are

Lötschen Valley, carved by a glacier which may still be seen upvalley. Mail and freight meet on the bridge. (Courtesy E. Gyger)

in the Alps, and sawmills occupy the valleys at short intervals. With 23 per cent of all Switzerland under forest, one is surprised to find that lumber is an important import; but this is true because the people have long been schooled in the working of wood and find it profitable now to import raw material for the manufacture of wooden toys, tools, and spindles, and for building houses.

This region contains all the Swiss glaciers, most of the rugged, inspiring mountains, falls, and rapids, and many of the lakes; therefore, while it maintains the sparsest population, it entertains a large tourist trade. The income from guests is nearly enough to balance the great disparity between the national imports and exports. Villages are found in all the valleys. Davos-Plats (9,200) is an important railroad center. Chur (16,000) guards the Grisons. Lugano (17,000), Bellinzona (10,930), and Locarno (6,800) face south in quite another world, hidden among gardens and majestic mountains, the outlines of which are mirrored in limpid, warm lakes. These are the only towns in this whole mountainous region that have been able to pass the 6,000 mark. Glarus (5,000), situated on the Linth, manufactures cotton cloth and is the only industrial town in the Alps region. Here, industry has pushed up the stream from the east Plateau industrial section to make use of the water power.

INDUSTRY

A land poor in natural resources and cramped agriculturally must remain poor and live on a low level unless it can buy, improve, and sell foreign raw materials. It is strange to see a nation with such limited resources develop into an important industrial community. Forty-six per cent of the workers are in industry; 6 or 8 per cent more are caring for guests for wages; and nearly 20 per cent are in commerce. All the work is done with a characteristic niceness, whether it be cheese, lace, watch, or dinner. Not more than half enough foodstuffs for all can be grown at home; hence cattle, grain, fruits, oils, and even vegetables are imported. These raw foods, home- and foreign-grown, are processed ready to eat; this is an important phase of rural manufacture. Other raw materials—silk from Italy, cotton and wool from the general streams of trade, iron, copper, and aluminum ores from France and Germany—are refined and finished until most of the value is in work, skill, and patience, and then sent out in instruments, delicate machines, watches, and jewelry. Still, imports are nearly 50 per cent larger than exports. Mountains, glaciers, lakes, and climate are capitalized for inspiration and sport facilities, until tens of thousands of the people can collect the interest through service to the heartily welcome guest.

PEOPLE

Prehistory. The foundation stock of the Swiss people is the Alpine race. The Lake Dwellers who so admirably adapted their living to the conditions in the Swiss lakes were among the later Alpine tribes to occupy the country. Some of their villages are almost historic; a wealth of domestic material from them is now displayed in Swiss and other museums. Scores of village sites are known.

Steepest funicular in the world. Climbs 4,620 feet from the Ambripiolta power plant of the St. Gotthard railway to Riton's reservoir. Maximum gradient is 87.8 per cent. (Courtesy Swiss National Tourist Office)

Beginnings of the nation. While the people of the lakes and the mountains were called Helvetii and Swiss, the first confederation was a German League of the cantons of Uri, Schwyz, and Unterwalden, formed in the late years of the thirteenth century. These cantons lay at the mutual corner of the three great kingdoms whose languages still persist in Switzerland. Not only do the language and the commercial connections of the members of the first leagues confirm their Germanic origin, but a strong Nordic strain (complexion and head form) in the northern group of cantons shows the Teutonic mixture with the primitive Alpines. The sturdy inhabitants of the inaccessible valleys of the forest cantons around the picturesque Lucerne,

Haymaking in the Bernese Alps. Hay is bound in bundles and eased down the mountainside to feed cattle in the valley barns in winter. (Courtesy F. Hutzli Reichenbach)

clans living a long distance from centers of imperial power, loved freedom and formed a defensive alliance against feudal hosts who would subdue them. To their enemies they were frontier outlaws. Their remoteness in mountain fastnesses, together with their guerrilla tactics in familiar haunts, gave them victories, concerning which the stories have crystallized into many stirring legends. Love of liberty, independence from court and city were bred in all the surrounding valleys; and canton after canton pulled away from the German, Italian, and French empires to join the Confederation, until the latter included eight, then thirteen, and ultimately in 1815, twenty-two cantons. The spirit of mountain independence had spread outward until with the tension between it and surrounding imperial forces balanced, Switzerland assumed the most natural boundaries and limits possible.

The people today. To their love of physical and political freedom were joined religious and social ideals and a zeal for self-expression in education and art. Lyde (quoted by Dominian) tells us that Canon Taylor found thirty-five German dialects, sixteen French, eight Italian, and five Romansch in Switzerland, an eloquent confession of the power of such isolation to break up a language. It is only logical that Switzerland should have had much to do with the liberalizing of religion in and after the Reformation, until today Roman Catholics, Protestants, and Jews have equal and absolute freedom in this little state. Both religious and social tolerance and generous hospitality are a product of this spirit of liberty; exiles of many

Charming chalets near Aeschi above Lake Thun, Bernese Oberland. (Courtesy A. Baur Hiltenfingen)

nations find refuge here. Public education has almost banished illiteracy. The constitution gives to each canton special privileges, under which the local government works out legislation best adapted to the needs and conditions of its people. Art expresses itself in wood, the most abundant medium, and in imported metals, but rarely in stone.

The Swiss seem to feel that the traditional confederacy idea stands above everything else, but in the eyes of the world they exist as a host people to treaty-makers, to international organizations such as the late League of Nations, and to the tourist. Both points of view are strictly geographic. The people cultivate and extol freedom, liberty, and independence from external political power, and they have achieved it; but freedom within, giving personal liberty of mind and thought, was long unknown. They were a people of extreme narrowness in the inner sense which governs all values. The need to conserve every coin and blade of grass and the restrictions on intercourse have contributed much to this characteristic of the common people. Had not the republic become a buffer state, a host people, that narrowness of mind would still have ruled; but thousands of citizens, mingling freely with guests from every nation, bent on business, commerce, science, conference, and recreation, are losing their provincialism. If tourists penetrate the remotest valleys, break salt with the people, and buy their toys, embroideries, watches, and cheese, they may bring a blessing to many more.

QUESTIONS

1. Why are the Swiss lakes so beautiful? Note both the present qualities and past history.

2. What notable advantages have made the country of Switzerland so much more populous and important than Maine?

3. Which have been most important in fixing Swiss boundaries, pressure and other energies from within or ambitions and invasions from without?

4. Upon what countries does the Central Plateau border? Of what significance is this contact?

5. Where else is transhumance practised?

6. How has the physiography contributed to the provincialism of the people?

7. How has the geography been instrumental in breaking down provincialism?

8. Of what advantage to the Swiss is the manufacture of cheese, condensed milk, and wooden articles over the manufactures of iron and steel tools and machines?

9. Switzerland is called a neutral state. Discuss the geography of neutrality. In what respects has Switzerland maintained neutrality?

BIBLIOGRAPHY

BLANCHARD, W. O., "Switzerland-Austria," *Transactions Illinois Academy of Science,* Vol. 23 (March, 1931), pp. 461-464.

BLANCHARD, W. O., and VISHER, S. S., *Economic Geography of Europe* (New York, McGraw-Hill Book Company, Inc., 1931).

BONJOUR, Edgar, *Swiss Neutrality* (London, George Allen & Unwin, Ltd., 1946).

BOWMAN, Isaiah, *The New World,* 4th ed. (Yonkers-on-Hudson, New York, World Book Company, 1928).

CLARK, Sydney A., *All the Best in Switzerland* (New York, Dodd, Mead & Company, 1951).

COLBY, Charles C., *Geographic Aspects of International Relations* (Chicago, University of Chicago Press, 1938).

COON, Carleton S., *The Races of Europe* (New York, The Macmillan Company, 1939).

DOMINIAN, Leon, *Frontiers of Language and Nationality in Europe* (New York, Henry Holt & Company, Inc., 1928).

DE MARTONNE, Emmanuel, "Switzerland," in Vidal de La Blache and Gallois, *Géographie Universelle* (Paris, Lib. Armand Colin, 1931).

EAST, Wm. Gordon, *Historical Geography of Europe* (New York, E. P. Dutton & Co., Inc., 1936).

FITZGERALD, Walter, *The New Europe* (New York, Harper and Brothers, 1946).

Foreign Commerce Weekly (Washington, D. C., Government Printing Office).

Foreign Commerce Year Book (Washington, D. C., Government Printing Office).

FREEMAN, Edward A., *Historical Geography of Europe* (New York, Longmans, Green & Company, 1920).

GEORGE, H. B., *Relation of Geography and History* (Oxford, Clarendon Press, 1924).

International Year Book of Agricultural Statistics, annual.

LOBECK, Armin K., *Physiographic Diagram of Europe* (New York, Geographical Press).

LYDE, L. W., *Continent of Europe* (New York, The Macmillan Company, 1924).

MCCARTNEY, C. A., *National States and National Minorities,* (Oxford and New York, Oxford University Press, 1934).

MACFARLANE, John, *Economic Geography,* 3d ed. (New York, Sir Isaac Pitman & Sons, Ltd., 1930).

MACMUNN, N. E., and COSTER, G., *Europe, A Regional Geography* (Oxford Clarendon Press, 1930).

MARTIN, William, *A History of Switzerland* (London, Grant Richards, 1931).

Moody's Governments and Municipals (New York, Moody's Investor's Service, 1935 and later dates).

MUIRHEAD, Litellus R., ed., *The Blue Guides: Switzerland* (1948) (London, Macmillan & Co., Ltd.).

PARTSCH, Joseph, *Central Europe* (New York, D. Appleton and Co., 1903).

PEARCY, G. Etzel, and FIFIELD, R. H., *et al., World Political Geography* (New York, Thomas Y. Crowell Company, 1948).

RIPLEY, W. Z., *Races of Europe* (New York, D. Appleton and Co., 1899).

ROUGEMONT, Denis de, and MURTH, Charlotte, *Heart of Europe* (New York, Duell, Sloan, and Pearce, 1941).

SCHEVILL, Ferdinand, *A History of Europe* (New York, Harcourt, Brace & Company, Inc., 1947).

SHACKLETON, Margaret R., *Europe, A Regional Geography,* 3d ed. (New York, Longmans, Green & Company, 1942).

SIEGFRIED, André, *Switzerland: A Democratic Way of Life* (New York, Duell, Sloan, and Pearce, 1950).

Swiss Topographic Service, Bern, *Maps of Topography, Railroads, Forest and Culture.*

UNSTEAD, J. F., and TAYLOR, E. G. R., *General and Regional Geography* (London, G. Philip & Sons, Ltd., 1932).

VAN VALKENBURG, Samuel, *Elements of Political Geography* (New York, Prentice-Hall, Inc., 1939).

WHITBECK, R. H., and FINCH, V. C., *Economic Geography* (New York, McGraw-Hill Book Company, Inc., 1941).

WRIGHT, John K., *Geographic Basis of European History* (New York, Henry Holt & Company, Inc., 1928).

ZON, Raphael, and SPARHAWK, William N., *Forest Reserves of the World,* Vol. 1 (New York, McGraw-Hill Book Company, Inc., 1923).

CHAPTER 33

Austria

The Dolomites are the transcendentalists among the mountains.
—McCracken

INTRODUCTION

Structural relations. Modern Austria (32,388 square miles and 7 million people) is a very irregular block of mountains and hilly land related structurally to Switzerland, linguistically to Germany, religiously to Rome; located commercially athwart great international highways and bound economically not only to the states carved from the old Austria-Hungary, but also to all central European countries.

The Swiss Alps continue eastward, decreasing in height, increasing in width, until their structures pass beneath younger horizontal strata of the Hungarian plain. As in Switzerland, so in Austria, the central massif is of ancient crystalline gneisses and schists, with broadening flanks of limestones and other sediments. The southern boundary of Austria follows closely the crystalline limits, but not so the northern. The Inn-Salzach-Enns valley coincides closely with the north crystalline border and marks a great highway. Fortunately, more mineral wealth is known in the Austrian Alps than in the Swiss, and, owing to lower altitudes and more mature slopes, forests are more extensive and agriculture is more favored.

Historical relations. Austria emerged in 1918 as one of three succession states derived from the ruins of the decadent, collapsed, polyglot dual monarchy called Austria-Hungary. It was over-run by Nazi Germany in the late 1930's and remained under German authority until near the close of World War II. At that time Austria was restored to partial independence under the Allied Council and given its boundaries of 1937. By several steps it has set up its own constitutional government, a president, national assembly, and parliament, operating under the four occupying powers.

The new Austria is in language 96 per cent German, in religion 94 per cent Roman Catholic, in race an Alpine-Teutonic mixture with a few Germanized Slavs, Magyars, and Italians, and in topography possibly a better unit than Switzerland. A strong unity, a nationalistic spirit, and a determination to make good have grown up amid many difficulties.

691

Centuries ago the Teutonic language crept in from the north up the valleys over low divides and down valleys on the south side until it flooded essentially all parts of what is now Austria. The Nibelungenlied was probably Austrian. The religion from Rome dominated much more territory than the present Austria before the Holy Roman Empire came to power, and Vienna was even then an important Catholic center.

Arriving from the west (Munich), the border is crossed at this gate on the well-built auto road into Salzburg. (U.S. Army photograph)

REGIONS

General description. Eight political units (provinces), the principality of Liechtenstein in the extreme west, and the city of Vienna constitute the national domain of the republic. Each province has considerable physical unity. Vorarlberg lies next to Switzerland, Liechtenstein, and Germany and drains almost wholly into the Rhine. Tyrol with Innsbruck as its capital, Upper and Lower Austria, Salzburg with its capital Salzburg, Carinthia, governed from Klagenfurt, and Styria with its capital Graz are named from west to east. Burgenland consists of rolling hills and foothills of the mountains. It contains the German-speaking people of Old Hungary.

These political units are interpreted geographically much more satisfactorily if grouped into three regions, Eastern Alps, Plateaus and Old Mountains, and Vienna Plain.

Eastern Alps. In the Eastern Alps men have moved more freely east and west than north and south. A great valley lies along their northern part, drained by three streams, Inn, Salzach, Enns, which flow eastward many miles, then turn out to the north to reach the Danube. For centuries this valley has directed commerce and migration. Today a railroad through it serves the whole length of the Austrian Alps, connecting with Vienna over the Semmering Pass and with all the valleys northward where streams leave it. In a similar way the Drave Valley with its railroad serves the southern part of the Eastern Alps. North-south lines cross and connect these valleys. One through the Brenner Pass (4,500 feet) and Innsbruck was among the first trans-Alpine highways to be used; it is open all winter, and requires no tunnel. In comparison with this route, notice the difficulties that beset the Salzburg cross route, which completely traverses the country but has two long tunnels in Austria and one farther south through the Julian Alps.

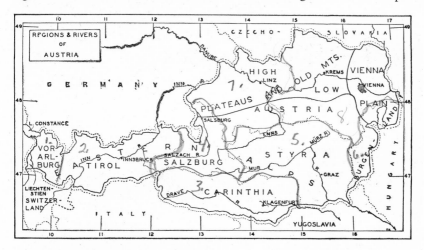

Geographic regions and political units of Austria. Solid lines indicate the former and dot lines the latter. (Adapted and constructed from *Atlas universel de geographie*)

As in Switzerland, climate and weather are intensely affected by altitude, air drainage, exposure, and foehn winds; hence weather changes are local and diverse from place to place, but in general more continental and severe to the eastward. More favorable climatic conditions lead to more and better forests than those in Switzerland; except in Burgenland, where mixed beech forests predominate, 60 per cent are coniferous. So important are forests in the Eastern Alps that the people have developed an excellent forestry system which covers government, commune, and private holdings alike.

Minerals. From very ancient times the Salzkammergut valleys have been famous for their salt production, such as that at Hallstatt; Salzburg, and Hall. Production is both from mines and from brines. Brines, formerly evaporated by wood fires near the springs, are now led down the valleys

Badgastein. The world's most radioactive springs and baths—commercialized. At Salzburg. (Courtesy O.V.W.)

Erzberg. Sorters, roasters, and waste dumps below the level of the mines. (Courtesy Erpho, Graz)

and boiled over lignite fires. Lead and tin are mined, but gold, copper, and silver, formerly important products of the crystalline areas, are now exhausted. Iron in fine carbonate ore, sulphur- and phosphorus-free, is the basis for important mining and metallurgical industries in Styria. At Eisenerz a whole mountain of ore is being quarried in sixty terrace levels of 40 feet each—a half-mile of open mountainside—systematically mined, electrically lighted, fully supplied with hoists, trams, and steam-shovels, and equipped for the comfort and health of the workmen. Since winter lasts longer on upper levels, lower levels tend to be worked back faster; hence work

Main Street, Innsbruck, during the American occupation. (U.S. Army photograph)

is concentrated on upper levels in summer. Magnesite and graphite near Leoben (33,500), Styria, lead and zinc ores at Bleiburg, Carinthia, and much lignite especially west of Graz (but with very little coking coal) occur in the Austrian Alps.

Agriculture. Valleys are lined with villages and hamlets, the sheltered inhabitants of which raise rye, wheat, barley, oats, sugar beets, and potatoes, but not enough for their sustenance; also cattle, sheep, swine, and poultry nearly sufficient for home needs. One fourth of the land is tillable, and more than half the workers are farmers.

Towns. Graz (207,747), favored by position in the open Mur Valley, by the iron and coal resources found less than 50 miles up the valley, and by proximity to generous water power, is the largest town and a prosperous distributing center. It manufactures iron, machines, and woolen goods and has an excellent university. Innsbruck (78,395), near the other end of the region, is strategically set in the valley of the Inn, which leads entirely across Austria and keeps the town in vital communication with Bavaria. West through the Arlberg tunnel, contact is had with Switzerland, and south over the Brenner Pass with Italy. No finer scenery is known than that about this Tyrolese town. Many citizens of the Tyrol as well as other Alpine provinces, often dressed in quaint and striking garb, are actively engaged in caring for guests. Others manufacture leather and furs, glass, and linen cloth or make choice embroidery. Innsbruck has a Catholic University. Salzburg (77,170), standing at the strategic doorway of the Tyrol, has made lavish use of local marble and profits not only by the salt industry but also by many visitors interested in its scenery. It is the birth-place of Mozart and a home of art and rich musical festivals. Klagenfurt (Glanford) (56,700) serves as the capital of Carinthia and has the advantages of position on one of the through routes, of an open agricultural valley, forest resources, and attractive stirring surroundings. Its woolen mills use local wool and water power. Excellent railroad connections north with Austrian valleys and over a route used for trade long before railroads came, have kept Carinthian interests with Austria rather than with Yugoslavia, even though anciently for centuries the people were largely Slovene Slavs. Bruck, at the angle in the Mur River where it joins the Mürz, has more economic and commercial opportunity than its narrow, terraced, restricting valley alone provides; and Leoben in the midst of the mining region has a strong mining school.

In the Arlberg and Liechtenstein homes and villages, close to Swiss influence, spinning and embroidery flourish, and in south Tyrol close to Italy the silk industry prospers.

Plateaus and Old Mountains. A continuation of the Central Plateau of Switzerland and southern Bavaria brings to Austria a small area of recent strata and topography, between the Alps and the ancient Boehmer Wald or Bohemian Forests (mountains). This area, more than 45 miles wide below Salzburg, narrows to 5, then widens to 25 miles north and west of Wiener Wald. North of this area lie the ancient mountain structures, now reduced to old age, which constitute the Plateau Region of Austria. Some parts were glaciated by ice flowing out from the Alps; others were covered by outwash from the glaciers or by alluvium laid by the Danube and smaller streams. Now all this combines to give an area 20 to 30 miles in width for agriculture, grazing, and forests, with a minimum of waste lands. Since there is little relief, climate is fairly uniform over all the region.

The Danube River generally keeps its course across the old crystalline rocks and repeatedly cuts into granite, making gorges and rapids—narrow, hurrying sections—which alternate with reaches of quiet waters, charming for scenic purposes but fraught with difficulties for commerce. Much work and money have been devoted to river improvement, but not much has been done for power development.

Although forests cover 30 per cent of the land and grazing and general farming are well favored, there have developed industries based on the forest products, on the dairy output including hides, and on the salt, coal, and iron from the foothills and mountains on the south. Krems (27,900) on the Danube makes chemicals and manufactures imported silk. Linz (128,195) also on the river, uses the salt for chemical industries, iron and

A high mountain lake with a quaint village on its shore. (Courtesy Alice Langelier)

wood for machines and tools, hides for leather goods, with coal from the south for power. Imported cotton feeds a growing cotton industry. Iron ore and coal are mined in many places south of the river, and on the north flax is grown. In several ways this region supplements the Alps Region south of it.

Vienna Plain. This plain, in considerable part alluvial, contains not more than 1,500 square miles but has an importance far beyond its size. It not only is rich agricultural land, but, traversed by the Danube and placed at the intersection of this river highway and the old, much used north-south amber route, it must possess commercial, military, and political centers. Not only does it now contain the great city of Vienna, combining all these interests, but dotted everywhere it has industrial plants, palaces, and gardens. It is much the smallest of the Danubian plains but has attained more urban significance than any other.

Before rivers were used as highways, an old amber route from Adriatic to Baltic passed through the Vienna Plain and the Moravian (March-Oder) Gate, between Alps, Boehmer Wald, and Sudetes on one side and Carpathians on the other. This was probably among the earliest commercial routes through the mountains and operated while the Massilia (Marseilles) route went around the mountains to the west and the Black Sea-Bessarabia route to the east. Romans kept watch here a few centuries and built Carnuntum east of the present city; but Vindobona on the Vienna site was the

Pouring steel into a large mold at Linz. (U.S. Army photograph)

military seat of Carnuntum. Then in early Middle Ages Germans made the plain their frontier against nomadic, mounted, Hungarian plains tribes and rugged mountaineers. Its later significance arose when the Hapsburgs made it the capital of their unfolding empire. In the middle part of the sixteenth century there were three large kingdoms, Austria, Bohemia, Hungary, in the basin of the middle Danube wholly or partly under the rule of Ferdinand I. Thus began the unity of the mid-Danubian empire.

From this beginning forward, Vienna was central to six great, rich, natural districts: the Eastern Alps with the forests, salt, and iron; the Upper Danube including Bavaria (more than present Upper and Lower Austria) then a home for colonists, as well as a source for wool and wheat; Bohemia, already industrial, skilful, and wealthy with coal, iron, silver, and prosperous agriculture; Moravia, the gate to Galicia and itself blessed with fertile soil covered with wheat-fields and vigorous vineyards; Upper Hungary (Slovakia, now a part of the Czech republic), a treasury of precious metals and copper; and last, the great, rich Hungarian Plain with its wheat, cattle, and luxuriant pastures. This central position was singularly adapted to make a wealthy capital and a commercial, industrial, financial metropolis. Transportation by river, road, and later by rail brought products from every direction and often from very far; and Viennese manufactures went out to many lands. This fortunate trade situation still exists, in spite of the fact that Austria touches no sea.

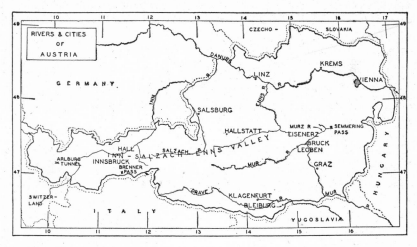

The country of Austria. The map shows its border countries, streams and valleys, many towns, and passes. (Adapted from *Atlas universel de geographie*)

Ruler after ruler built, with the result that Vienna has become a capital not only geographically and politically, but historically. The city had always labored against one great disadvantage until the Treaty of Versailles sorted the nationalities over which it ruled. Its surrounding dependent peoples spoke each a different tongue and came of three or four diverse races which cherished jealousies, grudges, and political and economic misunderstandings. These jealousies were geographic for centuries, but in recent years with rising education and outlook they became jealousies and differences of party, such as the clerical, Nazi, and Hapsburg parties.

Rulers and officers of the native and foreign governments gathered in Vienna, and, under the magnetism of the court and its patronage, came music, art, literature, theater—social, educational, and religious leadership. To meet the needs of the tens of thousands thus assembled came artisans, bankers, traders, industrialists, scientists, laborers, servants, and helpers, until court, society, industry, commerce, and finance were concentrated in a gay, prosperous fascinating city of more than 2 million people, befitting the capital of an empire of 261,000 square miles and 51 million people.

When the new Austria was defined, with one eighth of the former territory and about the same proportion of people, almost one third of whom lived in the city, Vienna was at once distressed. All lines of activity from government to labor were reduced, and there was insufficient work for the city's millions. Commerce was crippled, because surrounding states were effervescent with nationalism and determined to show the world that each could carry on independently; industries slumped because markets and sources of raw materials were denied them; food supplies became alarmingly short, because the great granaries and pastures of the former empire were now outside the new republic; purchasing power shrank, and financial concerns were weakened until disaster threatened a great and brilliant city which had lost its powers.

Vienna attempted adjustments until the political and economic disasters of the Nazi invasion and occupation. After the Nazis were expelled a new period of adaptation began. Probably 10 per cent of the Viennese migrated to villages and the country and 5 per cent to distant lands. Present population is estimated at 1,930,000.

Industries in silk, wool, cotton, linen, leather, hardware, in machine, vehicle, and locomotive construction, in chemicals and porcelain, in musical and technical instruments, are reviving, many of them built upon home resources. Several of the palaces have become museums or other public buildings, homes for the needy or afflicted. Commercial houses are trying to establish connection with old markets in foreign cities and thus restore geographic relations long recognized and used, but recently fettered by too much nationalism and foreign influence.

NATIONAL ACTIVITIES

Modern Austria is said to be rigidly handicapped by its lack of an outlet to the sea and by the loss of much agricultural and mineral territory, in addition to the concentration of nearly one fourth of its people in one great city. The city handicap is solving itself by emigration and many changes in occupation. Some comparisons with Switzerland are pertinent. Austria is twice as large as Switzerland, but has only 66 per cent more people. Austria has a little more arable land, equal grassland, 63 per cent more forest, and about one-third as much waste land. Both countries are well industrialized; Switzerland has 46 per cent and Austria 40 per cent of the people in industry; Switzerland has no coal, but 3,000,000 horsepower in its waters; Austria mined about 3,500,000 and imported over 5,000,000 tons of coal in 1948 and has nearly 6,000,000 horsepower available in its streams. Switzerland has no iron. Austria has much excellent iron ore, and produced

1,200,000 tons in 1948; also aluminum, lead, zinc, magnesite, copper, gypsum, salt, and graphite. Switzerland has the advantage in scenery but lacks a great historic, artistic city. Yet Switzerland's foreign trade was before the last world war perennially greater by 20 to 60 per cent.[1] Austria, when as old, may well be on as good terms with its neighbors and as peaceable within as is Switzerland. The complaint that Austria has no economic opportunity does not seem to be well founded.

In recent years, improvement in the economic conditions has been brought about by wise, often far-reaching, adjustments to the geographic conditions prevailing in the country. Since 1946 agriculture has shown steady gains in production per acre and in total production. Cereals and livestock show the largest gains, results of more intensive cultivation and more care in breeding. In neither case has production risen yet to domestic needs. If Switzerland after meeting its own and its visitors' needs for dairy and meat products can export tons of cheese, butter, chocolate, and condensed milk, Austria can do as well, for it has a larger percentage of farms and farmers and an equal percentage of grasslands. In the use of the forests, notable gains are reported. An excellent forestry system with wholesome conservation elements has been in operation so long that the people know the system and its advantages. Forest products are far in excess of home needs, and the making of paper, furniture, and woodwork for export has helped the internal condition. A larger effort than formerly is being made to sell the scenery and other guest-values of the country. Education, art, music, medicine, and science attract many to Vienna for temporary residence.

INTERNATIONAL RELATIONS

From a geographic point of view a profound mistake was made when, in the heat of rising nationalism, the succession states erected forbidding tariff barriers along their frontiers. No one of these states can succeed better without than with the others, any more than they could when all were under one government. Hungary can produce wheat and maize enough to supplement fully the meager crops of Austria and Czechoslovakia and can send meat, livestock, and eggs to both. Czechoslovakia can produce coal, sugar, and cotton and woolen goods enough to meet the needs of all three and can join with Austria in sending forest products and leather goods to Hungary. Austria has salt and many kinds of forest products for export to both of these other countries. Except in the matter of meat, dairy products, and eggs, each country can produce the items men-

[1] Foreign trade. Imports and Exports combined.

	1947	1948
Austria	$200,562,000	$300,138,000
Switzerland	$2,022,000,000	$2,200,000,000

Less than one eighth of Austria's foreign trade and about one eighth of Switzerland's were with the United States.

Michaeler Gate, Vienna. Note intricate fretwork over the open gates.

tioned for its export list better than can the country importing. Austria can raise plenty of these products for her own need by adopting a larger, more intensive dairy and grazing program. Here, then, in these ten leading articles of commerce is ample room for reciprocal trade relations.

Because of its almost universally spoken German language, Austria would naturally form alliances with Germany. Austria is German, as representative of German culture as Germany itself, and will some day again play a great rôle. The shortest route out to the world highway is southward through Italy. The easy geographic course for Austria's trade to follow, after satisfying contact neighbors, is southward to the Adriatic. Old Austria recognized this long ago. Since seacoast is denied, the logical next step is trade agreements with one or both of her southern neighbors; else the trade will trickle back to the Baltic through the common language area. Miss Semple well says, "Peripheral holdings are the lungs through which states breathe." Austria must have sea connections as free as those of Switzerland if it is to enjoy the prosperity Switzerland feels and avoid the benumbing influences of the continental interior. With such contrasts as grow between land-bound states and coast states, reactions are destined to come. Shall they be expressed in friendly treaties or in belligerency? Keyserling says, "International frontiers in Europe will mean less and less as time goes on."

QUESTIONS

1. What is meant by the conflict between "geographic relations and nationalism"?

2. What industries of Vienna use mostly imported raw materials?

3. Considering food supply, raw materials for industries, resources in and outside Austria, what contacts and connections should this mountainous nation make with her neighbors far and near? Discuss.

4. Which would be better for Austria, a treaty arrangement favoring trade through some bordering nation or a forced opening to the sea? Why?

5. In what ways does the Plateau Region supplement the Eastern Alps?

6. In what ways does the Vienna Plain supplement other parts of Austria?

7. What is meant by a forestry system?

8. Discuss advantages of trade barriers, such as tariffs, quotas, cartels, and duties vs. reciprocal trade agreements and open doors.

BIBLIOGRAPHY

BASCH, Antonin, *The Danube Basin and German Economic Sphere* (New York, Columbia University Press, 1943).

BOWMAN, Isaiah, *The New World,* 4th ed., (Yonkers-on-Hudson, New York, World Book Company, 1928).

BUSCHBECK, Ernest H., *Austria* (New York, Oxford University Press, 1949).

COLBY, Charles C., *et al., Geographic Aspects of International Relations* (Chicago, University of Chicago Press, 1938).

COON, Carleton S., *The Races of Europe* (New York, The Macmillan Company, 1939).

DOMINIAN, Leon, *Frontiers of Language and Nationality in Europe* (New York, Henry Holt & Company, Inc., 1928).

DE MARTONNE, Emmanuel, "Austria," in Vidal de La Blache and Gallois, *Géographie Universelle* (Paris, Lib. Armand Colin, 1931).

EAST, Wm. Gordon, *Historical Geography of Europe* (New York, E. P. Dutton & Co., Inc., 1936).

FITZGERALD, Walter, *The New Europe* (New York, Harper and Brothers, 1946).

Foreign Commerce Weekly (Washington, D. C., Government Printing Office).

Foreign Commerce Yearbook (Washington, D. C., Government Printing Office).

FOSTER, Carol H., *Austrian and Czechoslovak Lumber and Woodworking Industries* (Washington, D. C., Government Printing Office, 1924).

KENDREW, W. G., *Climates of the Continents* (Oxford, Clarendon Press, 1942).

KISS, George, "A T.V.A. on the Danube," *Geographical Review*, Vol. 37 (1947) pp. 274-302.

LENGYEL, Emil, *The Danube* (New York, Random House, Inc., 1939).

LEPRETTE, Jacques, *Le Statut International de Trieste* (Paris, Pedone, 1949).

LOBECK, Armin K., *Physiographic Diagram of Europe* (New York, Geographical Press, Columbia University).

Moody's Governments and Municipals (New York, Moody's Investor's Service), annual.

MUNK, Frank, *The Legacy of Nazism* (New York, The Macmillan Company, 1943).

NEWMAN, Bernard, *The New Europe* (New York, The Macmillan Company, 1943).

PASVOLSKY, Leo, *Economic Nationalism of the Danubian States* (New York, The Macmillan Company, 1928).

PEARCY, G. Etzel, and FIFIELD, Russell H., *et al.*, *World Political Geography* (New York, Thomas Y. Crowell Company, 1948).

ROTHSCHILD, K. W., *Austrian Economy since 1945* (London, Royal Institute of International Affairs, 1950).

ROUGEMONT, Denis de, and MURTH, Charlotte, *Heart of Europe* (New York, Duell, Sloan, and Pearce, 1941).

SHACKLETON, M. R., *Europe, A Regional Geography,* 3rd ed. (New York, Longmans, Green & Co., 1942).

Statistical Abstract of the United States (Washington, D. C., Government Printing Office), annual.

VAN VALKENBURG, Samuel, *Elements of Political Geography* (New York, Prentice-Hall, Inc., 1939).

WRIGHT, John K., *Geographic Basis of European History* (New York, Henry Holt & Company, Inc., 1928).

CHAPTER 34

Hungary

Were the earth God's hat, then Hungary would be the wreath
that decked it.—Sandor Petöfi, a patriotic Hungarian poet

Extent and general relief. Hungary is a land of agricultural plains
shielded somewhat by the Carpathians and other mountains. Half of it
does not exceed 300 feet in altitude, and very little of the whole country
attains heights over 600 feet. The boundaries, drawn by treaty in 1920-21
and slightly revised [1] at the close of the Second World War, give the nation
almost exactly the same lines as were set up for her in 1920-21. They enclose about 36,000 square miles and just over 9 million people. Some 85
to 90 per cent of these people are Magyars. There are Germans, Jews,
Czechs, Slovaks, and Russians in the land, and 2 million Magyars outside
with at least a half million Szeklers, a related group, in the heart of Rumania.

The land occupies a compact, bluntly crescentic area about 125 miles
broad and 280 miles long; 67 per cent is under cultivation, and three
fourths of the cultivated area produces cereals; about 16 per cent is meadow
and pasture, and 12 per cent timber; the 6 per cent classed as waste consists of sandy or swampy, in some places salty marsh, lands which for the
most part are capable of redemption as the pressure of population requires.
Three to 4 per cent of the area counted as under cultivation consists of
orchards and vineyards. Pasture and grazing are increasing at the expense
of cereal cultivation because of better adjustments to climatic and market
conditions.

In late Tertiary time considerable portions of the intermontane area
were flooded by a slight submergence and covered by thin deposits of clay,
sand, and calcareous material, which became rich in carbonaceous organic
remains as the basins were filled, covered with vegetation, and partly
drained. This accounts for the richness of much of the soil. Its origin and
subhumid climate account for its resemblance to the chernozems of Ukraine.
Such topography, geology, and climate hold little promise of water power
and mineral wealth. There is a rainfall of 16 to 30 inches, decreasing to-

---

[1] See Czechoslovakia for a small area ceded by Hungary near Bratislava.

ward the southeast, and in spring and early summer exceeding that of the rest of the year. It varies notably from year to year and often falls in heavy showers which produce floods. Atlantic and Continental types of climate meet in Hungary. Temperatures and winds are severe in winter, and heat and drought often blight in summer. Yet these plains have a good growing season, with three months as warm as 68° F. The extremes of heat and cold with capricious rainfall have kept them treeless and as ready for cultivation as western American prairies. Loess and lake deposits have provided excellent calcareous soils for grass and cereals, and the open country has invited nomadic invaders, first Huns and Avars, then in more recent centuries, Magyars, Tatars, Slavs, and Turks.

People. The ancestors of the Magyars are first found on the slopes of the central Urals, then between the Azov Sea and the Urals on the steppes of southern Russia. Their geographic adjustments involved nomadism, fishing, hunting, and a tribal organization, as they occupied the vast forests or spread over the arid plains. As their customs and many well-imbedded words of non-Magyar stock testify, they had come from near Turanian Asia and had neighbored with the Chazars and Bulgarians in southern Russia. Their language is one of the Finno-Ugrian group, and their race does not accord with either of the three primary races of present Europe.

After a halt for a few generations east of the Carpathians before Russians needed those plains, the Magyars, pushed by Patzinaks, filtered through the mountains and swung round them into the Danube plains in the last two decades of the ninth century, and there occupied their present lands. They even made excursions over all Europe and chose this Danube-Tisza plain as best adapted of all available lands to their type of life and domestic needs. They found France and Italy already settled, south Germany and Switzerland too mountainous and forested, north Germany mostly morass, and the Balkans mountainous, forested, and occupied. Thus they were all unfit for Magyar horse-breeders of the ninth century.

On the Danube plains, they absorbed the few dwindling groups of Huns and Avars, relics of whom are often found, along with scattered Slavs whom the Avars had vanquished. Building fortresses and great castles, they extended their warlike rule into the fringing mountains, where they subdued, but failed to Magyarize, the true mountain Alpine Slavs both north and south, Bulgarians in present Rumania, and later the Rumanians themselves. From a race of nomadic horsemen and shepherds there arose in 400 years a nation of farming peasants, a solid mass of Magyars with about 50 per cent Magyar blood. The approaching Turkish forces scattered many southern Slav and other refugees among them. Turkish occupation for two or three centuries left them with about one third Turkish blood. Germans, French, and Italians, at first garrisoned among them to oust the Turk, later became recognized, welcome citizens. During 400 years more the process of adjustment and fusion produced a new Magyar, about 30 per cent pure, and a people transplanted from a medium climatic-energy area to a climate of first class in point of energy. The people now living in Turania, whence they came, are today classed as low (fourth in a five-rank scale) in culture, whereas the Hungarians are ranked in the second class.

The Magyar today reflects his Turanian (Finno-Ugrian) origin in language, also probably in his vivacity and fiery temperament, in his fatalism and conservatism, and in his hospitality and good nature. In his new, stimulating climate he has preserved his speech but lost much of his former physical character and temperament, partly by infusion of new blood, partly in response to the new setting, with its westward outlook and aspiration. Although in many sections he still retains his semi-Tatar cheek-bone, he is

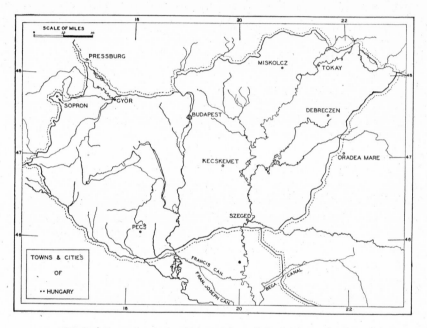

Principal Hungarian towns. (Adapted from *Oxford Advanced Atlas*)

often a strikingly fine-looking, well-developed man with regular features and with only slight suggestions of his Asiatic origin. He is a lover of the soil and until recently has had little instinct for business; this left abundant room for the Jew with his love of business and capacity for executive work. The partly Oriental language of the Magyar conceals much of his motives, ideals, and history from people speaking only Aryan tongues. His vitality is witnessed both by the fact that he has been the only Asiatic to "stick" in the Hungarian plain and by his hold on a fringe of subject peoples of diverse race and language, who have been unable to unite against their rulers. As rulers they are said to be "dictatorial and autocratic" over their alien districts but "mildly parental" over Magyar units. Many social institutions and services have been planned and maintained for Magyars and not for aliens; hence the usual unfriendly feeling of the surrounding neighbors. The suspicion on the part of neighbors has been increased in recent years by the grasping spirit of Hungary shown toward adjacent lands. Government-supported schools are largely in the non-Magyar areas because these had few private and religious schools.

The efforts of the state to aid and increase schools (illiteracy has been reduced to less than 9 per cent), to establish agricultural and other experiment stations, and to promote the redemption and colonization of new lands and the development of coöperative societies may well absorb the best minds and surplus labor.

Boundaries. The Danube-Tisza Basin, encircled by the heavily forested and sparsely settled Carpathians, is a physiographic unit. Its river system is markedly centripetal. Early coöperation and later governmental authority helped to bind the people together. Lumbermen in the hills, for example, built log rafts, loaded them with salt, floated them down to the plains, sold salt, logs and lumber, hired out until fall, and then returned to their hill homes. There were few forces of disunity in the plains, and no breaking-up into small units after the eight Magyar tribes federated. But the Magyars apparently never occupied more than their plains. They ruled aliens in bordering hills and developed resources in the hills but never gave even their speech to these minorities. These geographic relationships laid the foundations for the contraction of boundaries after World War I.

The present boundaries are in several places unfortunate. It was perfectly natural in the rising tide of nationalism following the centuries of Magyar oppression that Slavs on the north should unite in Czechoslovakia and on the south in Yugoslavia, and that the 3 million Rumanians in Transylvania should go to Rumania, just as a fringe of new states arose on Russian and Austrian borders. The trouble is not so much with these as it is with the nearly 2 million Magyars who are severed from Hungary on the borders. The Little Alföld north of the Danube, including Pressburg and Komarom, peopled mostly by Magyars, was shut out, placing an uncomfortable minority in Czechoslovakia. A portion of the Great Alföld on the northeast, north of Oradea Mare, is as Magyar as any part by race, but not by language. Between the Danube and Tisza on the south side and extending from the present national line to the Francis Canal there is an area, Magyar both in language and race, which was given to Yugoslavia. If these three areas could be restored to Hungary, they would add upwards of 2 million Magyars and very few aliens to the nation, would increase the topographic unity, and would remove minorities from three neighboring states. There is no good geographic reason for disturbing the treaty boundaries elsewhere.

Historians point out that the modern principle of nationalism carried to its logical conclusion will undermine every multinational state. Either Austria, Hungary, or their Dual (Hapsburg) Monarchy makes as good an example as European Russia. Boundaries should be racial, linguistic, and religious, as well as physical and economic, to avoid friction. The subjugated groups around the Magyar core long desired freedom and won it at considerable economic expense after World War I and again after World War II. Much time will be required for adjustment and for healing of animosities, but both can be accomplished. If language and race be given much significance in estimating unity of a country, Hungary is a good unit; and if the suggested boundary changes be made, both will be still further improved, and topography and drainage will be more appropriately considered than they have been thus far.

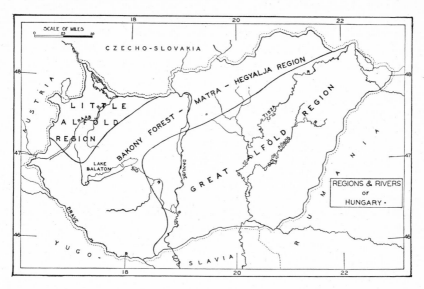

Geographic regions and physical features of Hungary. (Based on geologic and topographic maps and the uses men are making of the lands)

Little Alföld. In Hungarian speech "Alföld" means "Plain." Hungary has two plains with a small, old-mountain area between. The Little Alföld is about one sixth as large as the Great Alföld and nearly half of it lies in Czechoslovakia. Geologically, it consists of nearly horizontal Tertiary, Quaternary, and Recent alluvial deposits. It is a little higher than the Great Alföld, more rolling, and better drained with more rainfall. It has no sand dunes or long vistas but many small timber areas; it has no peasant cities as has the great plain. Because of these physical conditions it is a very attractive part of Hungary.

Little Alföld was well protected from the Turk, behind the Bakony Forest and Danube gorge, and in consequence it continued its development while the Turkish invader disorganized social, cultural, and economic life farther east. It was open to the influence of Czech and of Austrian Germans from whom it received many benefits in people, trade, and ideas that were denied the Great Alföld. Compared with any other part of Hungary, it pastures more horses and cattle per capita and as many sheep; it raises more wheat and barley; its people are happier, more open-minded, and more progressive. The adjacent plains north of the Danube are as rural, as forward-looking, and as dominantly Magyar in language if not in blood as those are on the south; yet recently, as stated in the chapter on Czechoslovakia, Hungary has generously ceded a little land near Pressburg (Bratislava) to that country. Pressburg is not Czech in its banking, education, language, or race. Hungarians have done much to improve this braided section of the river with its large islands and to correlate these improvements with those at and below Budapest. It would be better for Czechoslovakia, as well as for Hungary, if the treaty were opened and boundary adjustments made here. Sopron (28,200), in the foothills of the mountains, is an Austro-German city around which the Hungarian boundary was placed almost as completely as was the Swiss boundary around Schaffhausen. It serves a grain and grazing section. Györ (48,800), largely a Magyar town, stands among hills beautifully clad with vineyards and orchards and contains several factories for making machines, railway cars, vegetable oils, brushes, bricks, and matches. Its textile mills, as in the rest of Hungary, have trouble because the climate is too dry.

Bakony Forest, Matra, and Hegyalja. In Bakony Forest the summits of ancient, crystalline rock hills and the behavior of geophysical instruments testify to the fact that an old base-leveled, hard-rock area was depressed in Tertiary time, leaving many remnants protruding above the water as islands. Bakony consists mostly of Mesozoic folds with small areas of granite. Beyond the Danube gorge to the northeast the rocks are mostly igneous and give rougher topography. Near Pécs (69,000) both granite and old folded rocks protrude. This mountain structure from Miskolc (100,000) to the farther end of Balaton Lake has been an effective barrier during all historic time. Romans fortified the Danube gorge pass by building Acquincum; the Germans built Buda for a similar purpose on the heights of the right bank 3 or 4 miles below. Ferries avoid long river islands as much as bridges seek them; hence the specific location of Roman and German centers. No doubt the hot springs at the north end of Margaret Island and others on the mainland also attracted the Romans, while the narrow river channel tempted the Germans.

The altitude of these hills brings the greatest rainfall in Hungary, developing verdant pastures and the only forests of the country. Mountain structure preserves within reach hard coal (about one third of the Hungarian needs) and granite near Pécs; bauxite, marble, and granite throughout the hill belt; lignite at Salgótarjan and Esztergom on Czech frontiers, where half the country's fuel needs and some poor iron is mined, but only a small percentage of the metal needed. Miskolc has better iron mines.

The town of Eger as seen from the ancient fortress, now an outdoor cafe. (Courtesy Foto Kollectiva)

The Bakony Hills with their beech and oak nuts feed thousands of swine; their southern sunny slopes are terraced with Hungary's choicest vineyards; and on the volcanic ash slopes of Hegyalja and adjacent plains grow the grapes for the sweet, syrupy Tokaj wines. Some years Hungary produces 100 million gallons of wine, marketed in the town of Tokaj. Wheat is golden on hundreds of gentle slopes.

Balaton or Plattensee (10 by 50 miles) has been thoroughly studied. Although only 10 to 12 feet deep, it is much used for commerce, boating, fishing, and bathing, and has a very beneficial climatic influence on fruit culture above its northern shore. The southern shore is alternate marsh and sandbar with very shallow waters and is less frequented. Mineral springs make its waters brackish in spite of the outflowing Sio River.

Budapest (889,900), once two separate towns like several other pairs along the great river, has its administration, art, and intellectual life on the limited heights of the west side, while the industry, commerce, and teeming population spread over the ample plains on the east. Mills here manufacture more flour than in any other European city, make sugar and brew beer for home consumption, preserve meat (sausage for export), manufacture chemicals, glass, and leather from native resources, and make cloth from imported cotton. One paper-mill still operates here, the only one in the country. This capital city does over half the manufacturing of the whole state. Its river gives it extensive ship-building and water-borne commerce; its radiating railroads serve every city in the nation and reach far beyond, where, from a geographic point of view, trading and exchange of goods should be abundant and profitable.

Great Alföld. Fully half of Hungary is in this great plain, with a relief not exceeding 300 feet. Its soils, developed under grass with meager rainfall, are typical chernozems which make a rich steppe except where excessively wet with brackish lake or marsh, or where sandy enough to blow into great dunes under the fierce winds of the dry, late summers or of the cold winters. In many places locust trees have been successfully planted to fix the dunes. In some localities the sand has been so cemented that it holds water in brackish ponds among the sand hills. The largest area of dunes is between the great rivers which converge south of Budapest, and here most of them have ceased to move. Great fields have been planted to grapes over these dunes, where they are especially free from phylloxera.

The Tisza River formerly meandered excessively through its braided channels with a fall of only 100 feet in 200 miles, but has been straightened and canalized both to improve its navigability and to prevent floods. These improvements have redeemed many square miles of its rich flood-plain. Steamers now ascend it to Tokaj. Its valley, like many others, is very broad (20 to 60 miles) and only 30 feet below the uplands. Floods are characteristic; Szeged was almost wholly destroyed in 1879. Although floods are destructive, they irrigate thousands of farms, deposit fertile waste, and

Half of the city of Budapest. Looking over the Liberty Bridge, completely rebuilt since World War II. (Magyar Film Foto, courtesy Hungarian Legation)

National parliament building, as seen from the rebuilt Kossuth bridge across the Danube. The bridge was destroyed in World War II. (Magyar Film Foto)

build lands up above flood levels. The tributaries on the east descend more steeply than does the Tisza and move more freely, hence they overload the latter with waste. All are navigable up into Rumania. The Danube in this region, although flowing at a low grade, requires less care to make it equally serviceable. Over the Alföld, differences in soils and climate make differences in vegetation cover, both natural and cultivated. A desert area of moving dunes, 10 by 60 miles, still persists in the south.

Sunday strollers walking down a village street in native dress. (Courtesy P. Jonas, Budapest)

The uplands are dryer and more fertile between the Danube and Tisza rivers and east of the latter than are the alluvial plains of Netherlands and Germany, and the alluvial plains here are richer than the neighboring uplands. Between these rivers in the north the crops are barley, oats, and rye, but to the south, where the soil is less sandy, wheat and maize predominate. East of the Tisza, agriculture is least developed, but wheat, maize, and tobacco are grown. Great Alföld wheat is planted in the fall and its grain is especially hard. Other crops are beets for sugar, flax, hemp, hops, potatoes, melons, and forage crops. Cattle are no longer nomadic, although the silo stage has not arrived. Large areas are devoted to paprika, a red pepper now much used in America. Pigs, cattle, sheep, and horses are produced in increasing numbers; manure is hauled to the farms much as in our corn belt. Technique of farming is backward but is steadily improving. A system of crop rotations adapted to different soils is being worked out.

The peasant city or rural village is characteristic of the Great Alföld. Such a village is a double row of farm buildings, a group for each family, fringing a long street for several miles. This grouping of rural peasants is believed to have arisen for protection from Tatar and Turk. Between the rows of houses the road is broad, unpaved, and usually full of mud-holes or humps and holes of dry, hard earth. The broad road way is used to restrict the cattle, hogs, and poultry and to guard the wagons, tools, and fodder of the farmers on the street in a sort of community yard. Each family group of buildings has a compound wall, built usually of earth, farm waste, brush, or poles cut from the willows along the streams, rarely of stone or brick. For town and house sites high, dry hillocks are sought, and trees are planted around the houses.

Houses of the peasant city, sometimes called a garden city, are usually one-story, whitewashed, built of earth tramped between forms, such as we erect for pouring concrete walls; poplar poles stand at the corners and sometimes in the side walls to support the reed roof. Around the houses grow gardens of melons, plums, apples, and grapes, and around them a crop zone of all the cereals, fibers, and root crops. On the borders of the crop zone are little huts of reeds for shepherds, for even in summer cool nights demand protection. In winter the peasant sleeps near his great mud-brick stove, wrapped in his sheepskin coat. The farmer and family till the crops or work in the gardens from dawn to close of day with a persistence born of necessity and crude methods. There are hundreds of these villages, each containing 10,000 to 30,000 people and covering six to ten times as much ground as a town needs. Even the larger towns, such as Szeged (140,000), Debrecen (113,600 and 350 square miles), and Kecskemét (71,000), are really groups of such peasant villages sprawled over many thousands of acres. When a town or part of it becomes industrial, like the Szeged flour-milling section, it takes on a modern aspect, and some peasant towns have been rebuilt as real cities.

The *puszta* is a special type of agriculture, not a soil or climate type, and occurs on all kinds of soil. The word, probably from Slavic *pusty,* means "solitude" or "uninhabited." *Puszta* agriculture is a phase of the reclamation and rural expansion now taking place and is stimulated by a growing demand in West European states for rural products. Between the hundreds of village groups there are waste areas, left centuries ago when the villages grew up. Today, pressure of population and need of exports are driving the people to use these lands. In many places they had never been used at all, in other places only for grazing sheep and later long-horned cattle. Permanent farmers are now coming into the solitude and monotony, broken only by the well-sweep; here they build themselves simple shelters, level off the land to improve water conditions and facilitate culti-vation, then set grapes and plant and cultivate the fields. Whole new vil-lages of the usual type are growing in some *puszta* areas; in others the single-farmstead type of development is coming. Seasonal migration of har-vest labor is required in this expansion. It is estimated that 3 million acres await reclamation from *puszta* or marsh condition, and probably half of it is today in pasture.

Paprika market, Szeged. The greatest market for paprika in the world. (Courtesy of Magyar Consulate General)

Magyar landlords still hold 1,500 great estates where the laborer, little better than a serf, is held back in ignorance and poverty and without organi-zation. At the same time there are 750,000 small independent farms. The landed estate has been recognized as unfortunate, but so far no effective way has been found to break it up and distribute the land in small farms. The communist party prefers state or collective farms.

Commerce. The plains offer more barrier to travel and commerce than their relief would suggest, because many tracts are swampy, peaty, or too wet to support heavy traffic, some areas have moving sand, and other broad areas are still subject to river floods. The rivers were the great highways, a result of their low grades. Plains made connecting canals possible. The Francis, Francis Joseph, and Bega in the Banat, all outside of Hungary now, are valuable. Part of the Sio River, outlet of Lake Balaton to the Danube, has been canalized and then, where the river was too silted for use, it has been connected by canal with the Danube. This serves as a lumber route out of Bakony Forest. Most of the tributaries of the Danube and Tisza are used for small craft, and the great rivers are used throughout their entire length within the country. The Danube as far as navigable is or should be all internationalized. Thousands of steamers and motor vessels ply the waters from Belgrade to Vienna and Tokaj. Railroads, 80 per cent state-operated, have a mileage of over 5,000 and present a well-planned radial system from the capital to all parts of the land as well as to important cities and passes beyond. Built highways (38,000 miles) make possible the use of 16,000 automobiles. Compare this with a state of similar size in America such as Indiana with about 850,000 cars in 1935. One striking difference between Hungarian towns, as well as many others in Europe, and towns in America is their lack of light at night. Electric lighting is much restricted by lack of hydro-electric power.

Gipsy hovels in Hungary and a part of a family group. These shacks seem to be sheltered by low, overhanging bluffs. (Courtesy Mrs. Mary Jaszi)

While Hungary produces 2 million tons of wheat a year and nearly as much maize and potatoes and has actually over 4 million tillers of the soil, it seems clear that food enough to feed well all the people cannot be produced without much-improved agriculture and possibly the development of more industry. The latter is more difficult than improvement of the farming. People in many parts are underfed, and yet considerable food is exported under the artificial stimulus of taxation and tariff policies.

Land reform is still needed though well begun; industry, advanced during the Second World War, needs further expansion, especially in processing rural native products. The communist shadow covers all, politically, socially, and industrially. Industries have been extensively nationalized, and a system of collective farming is being established. The Roman Catholic church was nationalized in 1948.

Foreign relations. If, as Reclus wrote, Hungary was, when part of the Austro-Hungarian Kingdom, the most perfect national (political) geographic unit in Europe, it was far from the most perfect unit in many other ways. Geographic unity requires first of all that the trade relations formerly existing should be restored and improved. A clash of nationalities and a rise of nationalism may have checked the operation of geographic laws, but it does not nullify them. Reciprocal trade relations must be established in accord with natural highways and areas of production of fundamental resources in order to create prosperity and economic security. Small or limited states make a great mistake in hampering trade by erecting tariff barriers and trade restrictions. Political independence must not defy geography. Co-operation (exchange of products) should be as free by agreement as if the several small states were under one flag. Each nation should produce what it can produce best and exchange with others.

Rural Hungarian home interior. Plaster on dirt and stone walls; rack for pans and pots; vegetables and seeds drying; two adult beds and one for a child. (Courtesy Mrs. Recha Jaszi)

Hungary is rural; it has a notable granary; it can raise meat, make butter and cheese, grow poultry and eggs, all in excess of its needs. Iron must be purchased either as ore or metal. To conserve fuel it would seem better to buy iron and make machines and tools of it. Cotton must be imported raw or woven; as in the case of iron, it would seem better to import raw cotton and manufacture it. Flax, hemp, wool, and leather are natural products of the farms. These can be manufactured as flour and sugar are today and perhaps, like them, for export. Fruits, both fresh and preserved, can be raised in excess of local needs.

The exports and imports have been wisely kept nearly equal, and in recent years have totaled about $35.00 per capita. Meat and cattle now make half the exports. Half the imports are raw materials, half textiles and machinery.

With no seacoast, free trade should be maintained through other countries. Trieste is Hungary's free port. Trade with Yugoslavia in forest products and subtropical fruits is necessary. The Morava-Vardar would thus seem a logically important highway between Hungarian plains and the Mediterranean. In a similar way Italian silk and fruits are needed, and the Adriatic port at Trieste or even Spalato is a logical outlet. Hungary needs salt, iron, and petroleum from Rumania. Like the other railroad lines mentioned, one to Rumania was in fine working order before the Second World War. This may now serve not only for trade in these desired imports but as a way out to the Black Sea. Industrial products from Czechoslovakia and Germany are in demand. Hungary should be privileged to use the Oder and Hamburg, and thus a road to the ocean would lie where commerce dictates. To Hungary the Adriatic is more attractive than the Black Sea, and Hamburg much more so than the Adriatic. The route to Hamburg, 300 miles farther from Budapest than Trieste, has the easier grades. Trieste, internationalized, is beginning to help Hungary. As Cholnoky points out, railroads are all built far beyond the present national limits into valleys and mountains of other states, not as a conscious traffic policy but as a natural response to a physical condition of long standing. Hungary is sufficiently endowed to become a prosperous, stable country.

QUESTIONS

1. Why was the Hungarian plain so little disturbed by the battle lines of the World Wars, whereas the Turkish invasion 500 years earlier spread over all of it? (See the Morava-Vardar trench.)

2. Why did the mass of the Magyars come to the Hungarian plain over the Carpathians and not up the Danube?

3. Name and discuss relative values of the various elements of unity of present Hungary.

4. Discuss relative values of the several routes to the sea that are mentioned in the text.

5. Why not grant Hungary all the requested areas and people?

6. Why would it be better for Hungary to buy iron and cotton than to buy the steel tools and machines and the cotton cloth?

BIBLIOGRAPHY

ARMSTRONG, Hamilton F., *Tito and Goliath* (New York, The Macmillan Company, 1951).

——, "Danubia: Relief or Ruin," *Foreign Affairs,* Vol. 10 (July, 1932), pp. 600-616.

Atlas: *Das Neue Mitteleuropa in Wirtschaftlichen Karten,* ed. Albert Halász (Berlin, Verlag von Reimar Hobbing, 1928).

Atlas: *Hungary before and after the War in Economic-Statistical Maps,* eds. Aladar Edvi Illés and Albert Halász (Budapest, Institute of Pol. Sci. of the Hung. Statist. Soc., 1926).

Atlas: *Statistical Data of the Homogeneous Hungarian and German Enclaves in the Succession States* (Budapest, 1929).

BASCH, Antonin, *The Danube Basin and German Economic Sphere* (New York, Columbia University Press, 1943).

BOWMAN, Isaiah, *The New World* (Yonkers-on-Hudson, New York, World Book Company, 1928).

COON, Carleton S., *The Races of Europe* (New York, The Macmillan Company, 1939).

CUNNINGHAM, Charles, *What I Saw in Hungary* (London, Jarrolds, Publishers, Ltd., 1931).

DE MARTONNE, Emmanuel, "Hungary," in Vidal de La Blache and Gallois *Géographie Universelle* (Paris, Lib. Armand Colin, 1931).

DOMINIAN, Leon, *Frontiers of Language and Nationality* (New York, Henry Holt & Company, Inc., 1921).

Europa, Encyclopedia of Europe (London, Europa Publications Ltd.), annual.

European Conference on Rural Life, Hungary, No. 27 (Geneva, League of Nations Publications, 1940).

FITZGERALD, Walter, *New Europe* (New York, Harper and Brothers, 1946).

GEORGE, H. B., *Relations of Geography and History* (Oxford, Clarendon Press, 1924).

GRATZ, Gustav, *et al., Hungarian Economic Yearbook,* up to 1940, probably later (New York, Columbia University Press; also Grill's Bookshop, Budapest).

HILDEBRAND, J. R., "Budapest, Twin City of the Danube," *National Geographic Magazine,* Vol. 61 (June, 1932), pp. 729-742.

International Reference Service, U. S. Dept. of Commerce (Washington, D. C., Government Printing Office), many numbers per year.

KAROLYI, Alexander F., *Hungarian Pageant; Life, Customs, and Art of Hungarian Peasantry* (Budapest, G. Vajna & Co., 1939).

KISS, George, "A T.V.A. on the Danube," *Geographical Review,* Vol. 37 (1947), pp. 274-302.

KOSARY, Domonkas G., *A History of Hungary* (New York, The Benjamin Franklin Bibliophile Society, 1941).

LEHMANN, John, *Down River; A Danubian Study* (London, The Cresset Press, 1939).

LENGYEL, Emil, *The Danube* (New York, Random House, Inc., 1939).

MCCORMICK, Thomas C. T., ed., *Problems for the Post-War World* (New York, London, McGraw-Hill Book Company, Inc., 1945).

MENDE, Tibor, *Hungary* (London, McDonald & Co., Ltd., 1944).

MONTCHILIFF, Nicolas, *Ten Years of Controlled Trade in S. E. Europe* (Cambridge, England, Cambridge University Press, 1944).

MONTGOMERY, John F., *Hungary, the Unwilling Satellite* (New York, Devin-Adair Co., 1947).

Moody's Public Utilities (New York, Moody's Investor's Service), annual.

Moody's Governments and Municipals (New York, Moody's Investor's Service), annual.

NAGY, Ferenc, *The Struggle Behind the Iron Curtain,* trans. by Stephen K. Swift (New York, The Macmillan Company, 1948).

NEWMAN, Bernard, *The New Europe* (New York, The Macmillan Company, 1943).

PASVOLSKY, Leo, *Economic Nationalism of the Danubian States* (New York, The Macmillan Company, 1928).

PEARCY, G. Etzel, and FIFIELD, Russell H., *et al., World Political Geography* (New York, Thomas Y. Crowell Company, 1948).

PRIBICEVIC, Stojan, *World Without End* (New York, Reynal & Hitchcock, 1939).

RIPLEY, W. Z., *Races of Europe* (New York, D. Appleton and Co., 1899).

ROUCEK, Joseph S., "Economic Aspects of the Danubian Plain," *Economic Geography,* Vol. 8 (October, 1932), pp. 400-408.

———, *Central Eastern Europe* (New York, Prentice-Hall, Inc., 1946).

———, *Contemporary Europe* (New York, D. Van Nostrand Company, Inc., 1941).

SHACKLETON, Margaret R., *Europe, A Regional Geography* (New York, Longmans, Green & Company, 1942).

Statesman's Yearbook, Steinberg, S. H., ed., (New York, The Macmillan Company).

TELEKI, Count Paul, *Evolution of Hungary and its Place in European History* (New York, The Macmillan Company, 1923).

United States Statistical Abstract (Washington, D. C., Government Printing Office), annual.

WELLES, Sumner, ed., *An Intelligent American's Guide to the Peace* (New York, The Dryden Press, 1945).

CHAPTER 35

Czechoslovakia

I, too, believe before God that when the storms of wrath have passed,
to thee shall return the rule over thine own things, O Czech people.
—COMENIUS

GENERAL SURVEY

Position. Czechoslovakia, farthest from the sea of all European countries and one of the smaller continental nations, has problems of international relations similar to those of Austria. However, its language and race, both largely Slavic, and its territory, a Slavic peninsula lying athwart Central Europe between important German states, give it a set of problems that Austria does not know. Its large east-west length and scanty breadth among its five alert neighbors introduce national problems of administration and defense without supplying advantageous latitudinal and climatic diversities. But this position has advantages in variety of resource, topography, and foundation rocks which may outweigh the disadvantages.

Until recently the frontiers of central Europe concealed previous history, national tendencies of small peoples, and the long historic processes by which these peoples many generations ago rose to a national consciousness —a carry-over from dark days of earlier centuries. The many racial groups had been under the domination of the Hapsburgs—German, German-Austrian, or Magyar governments, all "democratic" but impossible—long after such control had been completely outmoded. From this subject position with its conditions of servitude and the experiences which it supplied, these people at last arose and did just what they, through the centuries, had been made ready to do. The succession states, Czechoslovakia, Yugoslavia, Austria, and Hungary, were established.

The Czechoslovakia of today is built on border lands, between Alpines of the plains and Alpines of the mountains, between Slavs and Nordics, between the fringe of the Eastern Church and that of the Roman Catholic Church. In many respects this is a fortunate situation for the development of a people because it has been a place of varied conflicts, sometimes military, sometimes economic and commercial, often religious and racial.

All frontiers of Czechoslovakia are land lines with the exception of 100 miles of Danube River; but mountain passes, both broad and narrow, and valley gateways are so numerous that railways cross the national boundary at nearly sixty places and locate as many national passport offices. These railroads were constructed when the country was part of the great Dual Monarchy, and the passport offices are a response to the present situation. The Elbe or Saxon Gate accommodates probably the largest amount of commerce. The Moravian Gate, with the Oder, Vistula, and Morava valleys, all heading in it at low altitude, has had probably the greatest prehistoric and historic importance. On the south the valleys of the March (Morava), Váh, and Tisza, the latter in four source streams, all make passage of the frontier easy. Many low passes in the Beskides of the Carpathians, Sudetes, Ore Mountains, and Bohemian Forest (Boehmer Wald) invite wagons and railroads to cross.

Political units. Bohemia and Slovakia are closely related in race and language, but in culture and standards of living they are far apart. For centuries the people of the former have been called Czechs, and long ago they ruled the Moravians, who occupied, in general, lowlands between the two more powerful ancient states. The Moravians had also ruled both Czechs and Slovaks. In 1918, these three very naturally united as the body of the new state. A Czech-Moravian part of Silesia fell by plebiscite to the government at Prague. Silesia's interest in Czechoslovakia was economic and grew out of the easy passage of these western Slavs through the gate to work the coal and iron deposits of Upper Silesia. After World War I a small area occupied by Ruthenian Ukrainians was tacked on the eastern end of this state; but after World War II, when Russia was much stronger, this area became a part of U.S.S.R. where it really belongs.

People. In part the present people have descended from prehistoric inhabitants of the land. Paleolithic remains are known in thirty-five widely scattered localities, but their connection with the Neolithic inhabitants is not known. There were continuous encampments of Neolithic men in the Bohemian Lowland and in the Morava-Váh plains, but not many in the higher or mountainous regions. Pottery-makers came in from the south about 3,000 B.C., and occupied the Moravian plains. Bronze-workers occupied the same areas as Neolithic men and also parts of the southwestern crystalline region. In the Iron Age four colonies of people are recognized: in the crystalline region, in the Bohemian Lowland, in the vicinity of Brno, particularly on the crystallines west of the city, and in a large area in the lowlands and valleys of Slovakia. They apparently obtained all their iron from small deposits and never found the Silesian ores. Workers of iron, crude tillers of the soil, and tenders of cattle and sheep in tribal units were found in these regions when discovered by the Romans and other early southern European explorers and traders. They may hail in an unbroken line from the pottery-makers, but more likely several later intrusions of migrants pushed the earlier peoples on or assimilated them so that when history opens a people at least half-Alpine were here.

Germans strove long to Germanize the people of these western sections, and many Germans, lured by the mining and industrial opportunities, migrated over the mountains which surround the Bohemian Plateau. Others filtered through the northern gates, and still others, working east along the Bavarian uplands, crept into Moravia. Germans were welcome to come and build cities, but in the ninth century pagan states would not have German Christian teachers and therefore sent to the Byzantine Emperor for Slavic teachers. In spite of this Eastern church influence, however, in the thirteenth century German colonists entered, finding untouched forests in

Tepla River, running through Karlovy Vary. Not a traffic artery, but an interesting beauty spot. (U.S. Army photograph)

Bohemia and southern Moravia. As a result of World War II all this German infiltration was reversed, and 2 to 3 million Germans migrated to Germany. Migration of Magyars at the same time left the population of 14 million divided about as follows: Czechoslovaks over 90 per cent, 1 to 3 per cent of Poles, Jews, Hungarians; and several other small groups.

Czechoslovaks are mostly Roman Catholics who broke off from Rome 30 years ago. There are many Protestants and a few Orthodox as well as a number of Jews, and not a few today who are without confession. The Czechoslovak language is used by nearly all.

Diversity and unity. It is indeed a heterogeneous mixture in a country where conditions have brought together under one government Jew, Protestant, and Eastern and Roman Catholic; where Czech-Moravian, and Slovak, and a very small Magyar unit, occupy a land of mountains, plains, hills, and great valleys, with nowhere a definite physical boundary around a people, some of whom are educated, capable, and progressive, while others are backward peasants.

Benés, the Czech Premier, once said, "Individual states . . . are not self-sufficing and in Europe of the future they cannot be." Czechoslovakia seems to have recognized this truth and has proceeded to use such resources as it possesses, to maintain such industries as its skills can best handle even if it needs to buy raw materials, and to feed its people well even if the land does not produce enough food.

Opportunity for unity in Czechoslovakia inheres further in the variety of supplementing resources: agriculture, possible in every state; forestry in the east; manufactures in the west; coal in the north and in many places in Těšín (Teschen), Bohemia, and Slovakia; and iron, though insufficient for the country's industries. Although in the country as used at present there is not enough agricultural land to grow food for all, there are resources which, if developed by labor and skill, can be sold for enough to buy needed food. Also, while there are notable shortages in petroleum, fibers, and iron, there is the skilled labor and power necessary for the manufacture of imported raw materials into useful or artistic saleable articles. In this sense Czechoslovakia is a unified nation, a working unit, self-sufficient in the sense that it has skill, labor, art, and science, sufficient with its resources to balance its export-import trade sheet. There are no doubts in the geographer's and economist's minds that Czechoslovakia is and can be a successful industrial nation in Central Europe. Other factors working toward this end will be examined in the study of the several regions.

Geologic and physiographic regions. Czechoslovakia has more variety in its geology than many larger countries. The old Variscan Mountains are present in Bohemia; very recent mountains consisting of strata laid in recent periods are in Slovakia; young strata, still horizontal, cover the Bohemian Lowland north of Prague; still younger beds, also horizontal, occupy southern Moravia. Topographically, the mountains on Bohemia's border are advanced mature; the Tatras are younger and have been retouched by many glaciers. In the Variscan Mountains there are ancient crystalline schists, gneisses, marbles, and granites, much used for construction work. West of Prague there are Silurian and Carboniferous rocks, and north are Cretaceous and Recent ones.

It is possible to treat the human activities by geographic units based on both physical and utilization characters. Six regions are suggested: (1) the Southwestern Bohemian Plateau, occupying all of old Bohemia south of Prague, except the Prague-Pilsen Area; (2) Prague-Pilsen Area of

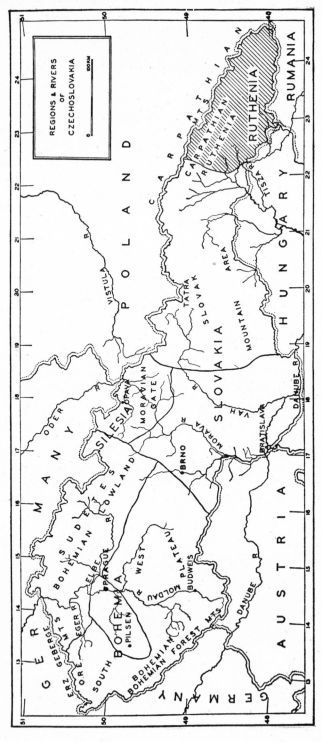

Geographic regions of Czechoslovakia. Regions are outlined in solid lines; the national boundary is solid lines accompanied by short dashes. Mountains, rivers, old states composing the new country, and some cities are shown. Shaded area represents part lost to U.S.S.R. after World War II. (Adapted from Atlas Republiky Ceskoslovenske)

Paleozoic rocks; (3) Bohemian Lowland, north of (1) and (2), under-lain by Recent alluvium and Cretaceous limestones and sandstones, and extending into the Sudetes foothills; (4) Broad Moravian Gate; (5) Morava-Váh Valleys; (6) Slovak Mountain Area.

ᵣGIONAL STUDIES

Southwestern Bohemian Plateau Region. Soils are deep and well-matured podzols, formed partly under deciduous forests, but they lack the fertility of those on younger rocks. Everywhere in the region they partake seriously of the nature of the underlying crystalline rock because glaciers have done very little. The lack of fertility seems to make but little difference in cereal production; wheat, rye, and oats yield as well on the old rock areas as anywhere. Barley is not as successful; maize and sugar beets are not grown at all. One of the three honey-producing areas is on this plateau. Potatoes flourish in the sandy soils and increase in acreage and productivity toward the mountains to the south, where cooler, moister conditions favor them. Flax flourishes here also. Bog soils cover many square miles in the Boehmer Wald. Prague has 50 per cent more rainfall in summer than in any other season, and all western parts of the land have summer precipitation in excess of that of winter. Forests are carefully protected and become better and more prevalent as the mountains on the south and west are entered, because here the rainfall is twice as great as around Prague. Wood is made into pulp and cellulose in the mountains above the deciduous line or floated down the Moldau to be manufactured into barrels, furniture, building stock, and agricultural implements in the towns and cities. Practically all manufacture of vehicles and of agricultural machinery is in the first and second regions. Cattle and hogs do well in this region, but sheep are scarce. Mineral springs attract guests to Karlovy Vary (German Karlsbad), Lázně Marianske (German Marienbad), and Lázně Frantiskovy (German Franzensbad). Mineral resources other than the building stones and residual clays and sands contribute little or nothing. Excellent hard glass and china are made. Notable marbles, however, are worked south, east, and west of Prague.

Budweis, using the grains, hops, and potatoes for brewing and dis-tilling, is the largest city in the region and a world-famous beer center. Few and small are other towns in the area.

Prague-Pilsen Area. This small unit, nearly surrounded by the crystal-line plateau, has soils richer and just as mature as in the previous unit. Crops are similar, but production is better. Hops are grown extensively to enter the beer manufacture at Budweis and Pilsen (106,914) (Plzeň, na-tive). Clean glass sand contributes to Pilsen's reputation for plate and cut glass. Both coal and iron stimulate many manufactures at Pilsen and the capital. Kladno has large steel furnaces. Prague (934,933) is the chief city not only of the region but of the nation. Its greatness is not all derived from this region. In the midst of the old Bohemian unit, it at once became the capital, the chief commercial center, and the most advantageously situated industrial city. Located on the navigable Moldau above its debouchment into the Elbe, where rapids over porphyry dikes made a halt necessary in river commerce, it had for centuries all the prestige of the best river navigation. An island aided crossing by ferry and later helped bridge construction. It is at the threshold of the upper, higher, southern Bohemia, which supplements the lower, richer lands to the north. The ancient highways in several valleys converged here, and a great east-west route intersected the Moldau, hence Prague became a significant commercial, political, and defense center. History has been built into its very texture, and scores of castles, palaces, and monuments stand to record its glories. Being a center of such note, it acquired a canal to connect the upper Moldau with the Danube, and when railroads came it was further favored by becoming a junction point on six lines.

Masaryk social homes. Modern provision for old age in Prague. (Courtesy Consulate General of Czechoslovakia)

When the new Czechoslovakia was set up and delimited, Prague became as eccentric for a capital as Vienna in Austria was ponderous. Railroads converged at the city, but in the eastern districts they converged equally on Budapest and Vienna, and their prewar business led them across the new country. No roads ran lengthwise of the land, for Prague had always meant little to Slovaks.

Modern Prague is not only the largest but also the most highly industrialized city of the country. Iron, steel, machines, sugar from beets, glass of many sorts, soaps, chemicals, fertilizers, paints and varnishes, lead-pencils, leather from native tanbark and some native hides (80 per cent imported), gloves, shoes, textiles both in cotton and in wool, clothing, carpets, blankets, underwear, hats, fancy goods, characteristic laces and embroideries, furniture (often of bent wood), toys, musical instruments, and scores of lesser items appropriate to a city of nearly a million people are made here. The city is a notable aviation center and builder of railroad engines and cars. More, it is a publisher of books, and a center of learning, culture, science, art, and music.

Bohemian Lowland. The Bohemian Lowlands have strongly rolling, mature topography with a relief of 500 to 2,000 feet. They consist of Cretaceous sediments and alluvium, fringed on the north and northwest by ancient crystallines with Paleozoic rocks in the Sudetes slopes. The Elbe drains the eastern part, the Eger the western, and lower Moldau the central. The lower altitude neutralized by higher latitude results in a climate similar to that of the Plateau. Rainfall in places, and everywhere in some years, is precarious, requiring irrigation. Soils are brown, well-matured, fertile forest-made coverings for the rocks, but in the northeast the rocks break up into slabs over the hillside, much to the detriment of the soil and its cultivation. Wheat is an excellent crop and provides grist for many water-power flour-mills. The other cereals, beets, and potatoes do well and furnish the basis for flour-mills, for the sugar industry with its widely scattered refineries, and for the industrial alcohol factories and distilleries. Hops, far beyond the generous needs of Bohemia, provide abundant exports to Germany. Apples and plums are a large crop. This abundance of fruit and cereal crops favors bee-culture and makes these Lowlands the second center of apiculture. Ninety per cent of the region is agriculturally productive.

Glass, made from the Cretaceous quartz sands with fuel from northern forests, shows the skill of the Czechs and makes a large item in the national export column. Porcelain, resembling faïence of Italy and long famous from Karlsbad and other cities, is made of clays weathered from the granite hills of the plateau and burned by means of the local coals and lignite. In the homes of the people at Jablonec, a town among the hills east of the Elbe Gate, the hundreds of kinds of showy ornamental beads so characteristic of Czechoslovakia are made. Paper-mills dot the mountain valleys, where forests and water power combine to favor both the lumber and paper industries. But the finest products are the textiles of the upper Elbe Valley, where mills use local hydro-electric power, cotton from the United States, flax from Poland, and wool both from the native sheep and the flocks of the valleys to the southeast. Metal industries use local coal, lignite from Teplitz, iron, nickel, cobalt, and copper. Silver and leather artistic industries have here had a long and successful history. All these opportunities and activities bring to this Lowland the densest population of any part of the country. Towns of 10,000 and upward are numerous and busy.

Broad Moravian Gate. If this were a narrow gateway as is the Elbe gorge route, it would not be selected as a region. The Oder, Vistula, and March or Morava all have sources in this wide, low pass between the ranges of the Sudetes on the west and the Carpathians on the east. They could be connected by canals with a summit altitude of less than 1,000 feet. Moravia on the south and Silesia on the north have had long, active economic histories following longer political and tribal annals running back to times when the northern branch of the Alpine Race migration, rounding the Carpathians, made this gate its entrance into Bohemia. Silesia is rich in minerals, coal, and iron; Moravia is rural. When men passed out of the Stone Age and began to work iron, these deposits became more important than the previously worked Silesian gold-mines. And ever since the working of iron began in southern Silesia there has been free movement of people

Women at work in the fields, a common sight. (Courtesy U.S. Dept. of Agriculture)

through the Broad Moravian Gate. As the forests yielded to local coking coal, larger mines and smelters were made, and the great iron and steel industry was assured. Ore is now so nearly exhausted that Swedish, Hungarian, and even Spanish ore is imported.

Excellent agricultural land occurs on either flank of the highway, so that an industrial population can be well fed. About 200 coöperative dairies have developed on the grazing lands of the west side. Ostrava (107,084), Těšín (11,000), Opava (32,000), and Vitkovice are the great industrial cities of the gate today. Opava has less of iron and more of forest interests than have the others.

Morava-Váh Valleys. These two valleys are separated by the ridge called Little and White Carpathians, which reaches the Danube at Bratislava.[1] The valleys contain most of the Old Moravia, a rich rural land with brown forest soils or alluvium, whose plentiful crops are barley, wheat, sugar beets, maize, and the vine. Other fruits are cultivated in the south. These crops cater to the third honey-producing region of the country. The grazing lands have promoted dairying until they sustain the second largest group of co-operative dairies, a promising industry of the future. Linens are made in several small towns. Two cities belong in large part to these valleys. Brno (258,333) (Brünn) on the western border, with coal-mines west and marble-quarries north, highly industrial, leads in the manufacture of woolen goods. Once a German strategic center, it has become the present Slovakian capital. Bratislava (138,000) on the Danube is commercial. A parcel of land

The High Tatras, seen across a well-cultivated rural valley. These mountains are partly in the National Park, and partly over the boundary in Poland. (Courtesy Consulate General of Czechoslovakia)

near Bratislava gained by a recent treaty with Hungary allows the enlargement of this Danubian port. So important is the Danube to the country that the International Danube Commission was seated at Bratislava. Many Magyar citizens farm in the lower plains, but their grains do not go into breweries in Czechoslovakia. There are only fifteen brewing plants east of Bratislava-Těšín, but hundreds west. In the east some of the grain is made into whisky which is used locally.

Slovak Mountain Area. A complex mountainous jumble of high peaks and valleys culminating in the beautiful High Tatras occupies so much of Slovakia that it characterizes all. High and Low Tatras are parts of the Beskide Mountains. Tarns, here called "sea eyes," dot the higher slopes. The grandeur of these once-glaciated, granite-ribbed mountains is not surpassed in Europe save in southern Spain. Such topography suggests mineral

[1] Pressburg in German; Pozsony in Hungarian.

wealth, but unless this area is richer in minerals than it has yet proven to be, its chief interests will long be in grazing and lumbering. Choice southern slopes produce grapes. Barley is sufficiently hardy to be the surest cereal crop. The Váh heads far east in the mountains, and its valley, strewn with charming watering places and mineral springs, is an attractive agricultural belt entirely across the region. Travertine deposits of commercial value have been made by some of the hot springs. Many slopes yield flax for the linen industry and forests for a large paper industry. This region leads in the breeding of sheep and lambs. Enough iron and coal are found near

Girls of Váh country in native dress. (Courtesy Consulate General of Czechoslovakia)

Svolen to make a large steel furnace profitable. The old town of Kosice [2] (70,230) is the market for the opals found at Dubnik, 18 to 20 miles northeast, where ground-water has deposited opal, amethyst, agate, carnelian, and other varieties of quartz in a porous lava. From these sources were gathered a large part of the showy gems adorning the walls of a local chapel and those of the cathedral at Prague. This region is a land of rough people, dreamy with beautiful folk songs and lore. They are farmers, shepherds, and lumbermen, of rural interests, living in small towns nestled in valleys between forested ridges. They are not concerned with mills, shops, and railroad cities.

THE NEW NATION

The Czech is more materialistic and practical, less romantic and imaginative, than the Pole. The Slovak is romantic and as musical as the Pole. The new nation takes its national problems very seriously. One of the dangers long feared has come. Communism has been forced upon it from the east. Intolerance and characteristic Communistic purges are now tearing apart the political life.

Although careful consideration has had to be given to the problems

[2] Kassa in Hungarian; Kaschau in German.

of the minorities and diversities within the nation, they are not considered as insurmountable. Minorities have been well treated. The larger ones have representation in the government, education in their native tongues, theatres, clubs, and other privileges. Work for all, generous treatment, and religious liberty have helped to subdue these internal asperities.

Czechoslovakian claims for independence are historic and geographic. Slovaks reached Europe in the sixth century B.C. Bohemians have been in the same area 1,000 years, beginning their national history 700 years ago; although under foreign rule the last 400 years, they have successfully resisted Germanizing and Magyarizing influences in spite of considerable physical encroachment. They have produced characteristic writers, scholars, and musicians and manifest increasing intellectual, artistic, scientific, and industrial strength.

The Czechoslovakian must have commerce with his neighbors, far and near; hence treaties must be negotiated. These are commercial and economic, not political. By initial treaties the Danube was internationalized and the country was given special Elbe privileges with free port at Hamburg. The Elbe has been and will be improved, canalized, and provided with docks as has been the Moldau in Bohemia. A recent decline in water transportation is accompanied by increasing rail transportation. The original treaty said, "goods, persons, and means of transport" shall have free passage to natural (geographic) outlets. This gave Czechs not only the use of the Danube, the Elbe, and Hamburg, but entry to Danzig, to Stettin on the Oder, to Trieste, and to Fiume. Austro-Hungarian trade was much heavier down the Elbe than overland to Trieste, and Czech trade recognizes the same geographic advantages.

It is hoped that the privileges in the treaties now being outlined between this country and her neighbors will be as specific and generous, as realistic and geographic as were those after World War I.

It has been predicted that "Czech trade will be with agricultural Rumania, Hungary, and Yugoslavia in cereals and meats; with industrial Germany in machinery, tools and equipment; with Balkan states for wool; United States for cotton and Sweden for iron ore," an excellent geographic prophecy and one that can hardly fail. The present foreign trade includes not only these items, but forest products to Hungary to pay for cereals and meat; textiles, cotton cloth and thread to the Balkans to compensate for wool; coal to Germany; porcelain, glass, shoes, and fancy goods to the United States. From Rumania are purchased maize, oats, and hogs; from Australia and Argentina, wool, because the Balkans do not furnish nearly enough; cotton comes from Egypt and India because they are nearer and more easily reached than is the United States.

After World War I, Czechoslovakia was given from the supplies and mills of prewar Austria-Hungary, 83 per cent of the coal, 60 per cent of the iron-mills, 75 per cent of the cotton-mills, 85 per cent of the hemp- and

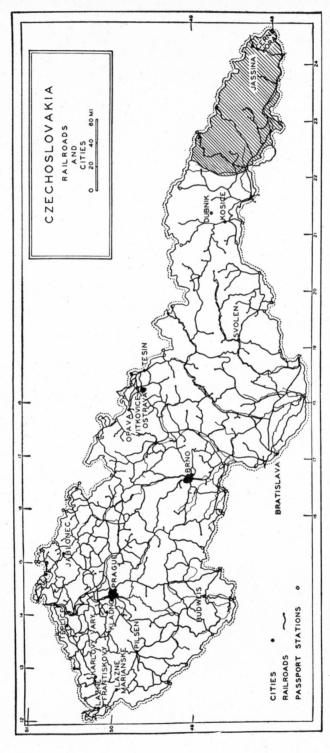

CZECHOSLOVAKIA

RAILROADS
AND
CITIES

0   20   40   60 MI

CITIES   •
RAILROADS   〜
PASSPORT STATIONS   ○

Railroads were constructed to unify the Dual Monarchy, and Czechoslovakia is endeavoring to connect them so that no one will need a passport to reach his capital city. Shaded area as in last map. (Adapted from *Atlas Republiky Československé*)

glass-mills, 44 per cent of the paper-mills, 80 per cent of the woolen-mills, and 95 per cent of the sugar-mills. Yet the Czech government controls much less than one fourth of the lands of the Dual Monarchy. To market the manufactures and make possible the imports of raw stuffs for food and manufactures, Czechoslovakia has had to adjust a rail transportation system from one that crossed the country to one that converged upon Czech cities. Connecting lines within the country have been built, gathering up all cross lines, from Kosice to Těšín coal-fields, thence to Bratislava, Brno, and Prague—a splendid element of unity. Foreign trade is back to prewar levels, but it is larger with countries east and smaller with those west. Nationalization of many activities has already come, so that aside from farming only 5 per cent of the nation's work is left as private enterprise.

Agricultural schools, experiment stations and other professional and technical schools have been organized in all parts of the country and aligned with the national educational system—evidences of the practicality of the people and a stroke of genius to bind them together.

QUESTIONS

1. List the disadvantages of position and shape. List the advantages of lying across diverse geology, topography, and resources. Then weigh the advantages against the disadvantages.

2. Why are the Slovakian mountains so much less commercialized than are the Alps?

3. What are the opportunities for the future development of some sort of dairy industry in this country? Where?

4. Why have these western Slavs so far outstripped eastern and southern Slavs?

5. What reasons can be suggested for the differences in personal qualities existing between Poles and Czechs?

6. Why were not the Alpine peoples of Czechoslovakia as easily and completely Germanized as were those of Austria?

7. Why do we have minorities in these central European states?

8. What difference does the loss of Ruthenia, a part of its country for 25 years, make to Czechoslovakia?

BIBLIOGRAPHY

Atlas: Republiky Ceskoslovenske (Prague, l'Académie Tchèque, Ministère des Affaires Étrangères, 1930-1935).

BASCH, Antonin, *The Danube Basin and German Economic Sphere* (New York, Columbia University Press, 1943).

BAUDIS, Josef, *Czech Folktales* (London, George Allen & Unwin, Ltd., 1937).

BENEŠ, Edward, *Czech Policy for Victory and Peace* (London, Czechoslovak Ministry for Foreign Affairs Information Service, 1944).

BOWMAN, Isaiah, *The New World* (Yonkers-on-Hudson, New York, World Book Company, 1928).

BRUEMMER-BOZEMAN, Adda von, *Czechoslovakia, Its Rise and Fall* (Dallas, Texas, Southern Methodist University, 1939) Publications of Arnold Foundation.

CAPEK, Thomas, *Origins of the Czechoslovak State* (New York, Fleming H. Revell Co., 1926).

"Czechoslovakia's First Ten Years," *Review of Reviews,* Vol. 78 (August, 1928), pp. 202-204.

DE MARTONNE, Emmanuel, "Czechoslovakia," in Vidal de La Blache and Gallois, *Géographie Universelle* (Paris, Lib. Armand Colin, 1931).

DOMINIAN, Leon, *Frontiers of Language and Nationality* (New York, Henry Holt & Company, Inc., 1921).

Encyclopédie tchécoslovaque: Industry and Commerce (Budapest, 1923); *Agriculture* (Budapest, 1928).

Europa, Encyclopedia of Europe (London, Europa Publications, Ltd.), annual.

FITZGERALD, Walter, *New Europe* (New York, Harper and Brothers, 1946).

FLEURE, H. J., *The Peoples of Europe* (London, Oxford University Press, Humphrey Milford, 1922).

FODOR, Frank, *The Geographic Impossibility of the Czech. State* (London, Low, W. Damson and Sons, 1920).

GEORGE, H. B., *Relations of Geography and History* (Oxford, Clarendon Press, 1924).

GERINGER, V. A., and GERINGER, Herman, *Commerce Reports: Commerce and Finances in Czechoslovakia* (Washington, D.C., Government Printing Office).

HEISLER, J. B., and MELLON, J. E., *Czechoslovakia, Land of Dreams and Enterprise* (London, Czechoslovakian Ministry of Foreign Affairs, 1945).

HINDUS, Maurice G., *We Shall Live Again* (New York, Doubleday, Doran & Co., Inc., 1939).

International Reference Service, U. S. Dept. of Commerce (Washington, D. C., Government Printing Office), many numbers per year.

KENDREW, W. G., *Climates of the Continents* (Oxford, Clarendon Press, 1942).

KERNER, Robert J., *et al., Czechoslovakia, Twenty years of Independence* (Berkeley and Los Angeles, University of California Press, 1940).

KISS, Geo., "A T.V.A. on the Danube," *Geographical Review,* Vol. 37 (1947), pp. 274-302.

KUNOSI, Alexandre, *Basis of Czechoslovak Unity* (London, A. Dakers, Ltd., 1944).

LEHMANN, John, *Down River; A Danubian Study* (London, The Cresset Press, 1939).

LENGYEL, Emil, *The Danube* (New York, Random House, Inc., 1939).

McCORMICK, Thomas C. T., ed., *Problems of a Post-War World* (New York and London, McGraw-Hill Book Company, Inc., 1945).

NEWMAN, Bernard, *The New Europe* (New York, The Macmillan Company, 1943).

PACKARD, L. O., and SINNOTT, C. P., *Nations as Neighbors* (New York, The Macmillan Company, 1930).

PAPANEK, Jan, *Czechoslovakia* (New York, International Universities Press, Inc., 1945).

"Prehistoric Man in Czechoslovakia," *Science,* n.s. 70: supplement, 14 (November, 15, 1929).

PRIBICEVIC, Stojan, *World Without End* (New York, Reynal & Hitchcock, 1939).

RISTOW, Walter W., "Influence of Geography on History of Bohemia," *Bulletin Geographical Society of Philadelphia,* Vol. 3 (1933), pp. 73-86.

SETON-WATSON, Robert Wm., *A History of the Czechs and Slovaks* (London, Hutchinson & Co., Ltd., 1943).

Statesman's Yearbook, STEINBERG, S. H., ed., (New York, The Macmillan Company).

THOMSON, Samuel H., *Czechoslovakia in European History* (Princeton, Princeton University Press, 1943).

WHITBECK, R. H., and FINCH, V. C., *Economic Geography,* 4th ed. (New York, McGraw-Hill Book Company, Inc., 1941).

Part VII

LOWER DANUBE STATES

THE LOWER DANUBE REGION

Rumania north, Bulgaria south, and Yugoslavia on both sides of the Danube constitute the states of the Lower Danube group. The similarity of their climate has been noted in Chapter 3. Topographically, they are occupied largely by mountains but include also the Danube plains below the Iron Gate. No great wealth of minerals is known within this area, but the soils and climate combine to promote a rich and varied agriculture. The Danube does for these states what the Rhine does for Germany, Netherlands, and Belgium, but the Black and Adriatic seas cannot possibly serve them as effectively as the Atlantic Ocean and North Sea serve the Rhineland.

The great river has for ages been a strong unifying influence, because it was the only transportation system. Now, modern railroads aid the river traffic and make it even more obvious that these three states should form an economic union. They supplement one another to some extent for Yugoslavia has no oil, while Rumania has a surplus for export. Yugoslavia has forests to supply the plains of Bulgaria and Rumania, and the latter can furnish wheat in return.

Two states are South Slavic in language and race; Rumania is Mediterranean in both to a notable degree. Rumania, Hungary, and Austria, all non-Slav states, separate South from North Slavs. All three of the Lower Danube states are dominantly Eastern Catholic in religion but are sprinkled with Mohammedanism and Protestantism. In education all are backward but awakening.

Boundaries of these states have shifted much in recent centuries, one country wresting from the others all the territory it could take. Since World War II there have been controversy, claims, and counter claims but no warfare or change of boundaries. The United Nations on one hand and the Kremlin on the other help to steady them. Yugoslavia had a vigorous civil war and revolution in 1941, resulting in the rise of Tito. Friendly coöperation across such frontiers as are now established would seem to be the wisest method of trade and intercourse.

CHAPTER 36

Yugoslavia

Oh, we're back to the Balkans again,
Back to the joy and the pain—
What if it burns or it blows or it snows?
We're back in the Balkans again.
Back, where to-morrow the quick may be dead,
With a hole in his heart or a ball in his head—
Back, where the passions are rapid and red—
Oh, we're back to the Balkans again!
—Song of the Balkan Peninsula

General considerations. Yugoslavia, one of the Succession States, occupies about 95,558 square miles in the northwestern part of the Balkan Peninsula. The population in 1949 was estimated at 16,040,000. It is Balkan in its associations and problems, and Mediterranean as well as continental in its climate. Although 75 per cent of the country is mountainous, no mountain barrier separates it from northern lands. Forest covers over 30 per cent, and considerable portions in the south are dry enough to check tree growth and to call for special agriculture. For these reasons Yugoslavia is not densely populated and engages chiefly in agriculture, grazing, and lumbering. The eastern part, near the Eastern Church centers, and the western, near Rome, respectively reflect these contacts in their religions. All religions are recognized. Mohammedanism and Protestantism have a considerable following. Over 89 per cent speak Slavic tongues. Upwards of a half-million or 3 per cent belong to each of two races, Magyar and Albanian. Many of these nationalities have recently migrated to their respective states.

The name *Yugoslavia* means "Southern Slav," often supplanted by "Serb" (= "kinsman") and "Serbia" or "Servia." Racially the people differ but little from Russian Slavs, all being of Alpine stock. They came from beyond the Carpathians about the sixth century in tribes and patriarchal families. The first moved far west into Slovenia, Croatia, and Carniola and have always had valuable western contacts. Later tribes, like true Alpines, halted in the mountains and along the hills bordering the Morava River. So rough was the topography that groups became separated and proceeded to develop differences in interests, in language, and in philoso-

741

phies. Most of the Yugoslavs are western enough to be joyous, even exuberant, until their mountains reëcho with folk songs of genuine Slavic type and the people have the mobile, restless spirit of the west. In course of time numbers of them came to occupy the cleared valley floors and little plains.

There is nothing equal to isolation to develop independence and conservatism. The Serbs, like ancient Swiss, clung to everything—customs, costumes, creeds, songs, standards—that could remind them of past glories and status. They were mountaineers with the virtues and faults appertaining thereto; their social groupings were mostly patriarchal; the people were individualistic, patriotic, counting bravery and hospitality chief among virtues, and cowardice the greatest of crimes.

National consciousness first appeared 600 years ago, among rulers only, when the Serbs pulled themselves together under Dushan in a nation that stretched from Save and Danube to Ægean and from Adriatic to Euxine. The Turk came late in the fourteenth century and drove many from their plains and valleys, scattering and oppressing them for 400 years, but, as the nations to the north repelled the Turks and started them back, the Serbs with rising spirits took up the fight and group after group asserted its independence. As they slipped from under the Sultan, the little units were absorbed by Austrian Germans or by Russians as naturally and inevitably as they had fallen under Turkish power, for they were athwart a great intercontinental highway which was becoming more important every century. No wonder Turk, Magyar, German, and Russian aspirations included it; for the good not only of Southern Slavs but of Europe and Asia this highway must be cleared of all four and made free. The Turks were never more than a minority, but their blight checked political, social, economic, commercial, and religious development, and set southeastern Europe back a thousand years.

Nationalism has been a strong postwar trend. Freer communications, freer economic intercourse, and much wider knowledge of other nations, their doings and ideals, methods and philosophies, have so quickened Yugoslavs that they are fast outliving their extreme isolationist programs and are coming to realize their own unity. They could not exist under Turk, German, or Russian, although their position invited the foreigner. They could not prosper divided, though separation has been imposed upon them for centuries. Their unity and independence are essential, and all must come into the new nation. To unite all Southern Slav territory now is to fall in with a geographic opportunity. So the nation has grown, snow-ball like, from two states: Montenegro, a wild, reckless, belligerent people on a rugged, forested, most detached mountain mass, independent since 1456 because it was not worth as much as it would cost to subdue; and Serbia, independent since 1821, occupying an area valuable by virtue of position, soils, topography, and resources. The accretion culminated after World War I by treaty and agreements laying down the present inclusive limits.

Boundaries. Yugoslavia presents a formidable mountain barrier and a difficult coast to Italy and the southwest, but descends graciously and gracefully to the lands north and east, and opens a tempting avenue to southlands. It is a physiographic unit, albeit a variegated one. It is a South Slav racial and linguistic unit. Its commercial connections, when viewed in the light of modern engineering skill, are quite satisfactory. Its resources are diverse, but sufficient to support a prosperous nation. The day has come when rough topography and physical barriers, tremendously hampering in centuries past, are powerless before the onslaught of telegraph, cable, telephone, post, planes, and radio. Education can be stimulated by radio broadcasts; and coöperative societies, experiment stations, and adult education

National Croatian costumes. Note iron filigree fence. (Courtesy Consulate General of Yugoslavia)

all may assist to bind together a scattered populace. A five-year plan effective in 1947 called for agrarian reform, expanded the railroad and truck system, provided for universal education, reorganized and unified diverse tax and land-tenure systems, and spread their best types of culture, ideals, and standards of living.

Physical foundations. As delimited by the boundaries described above, Yugoslavia has about as much diversity of topography and climate and as intricate a geologic pattern as any equal area possesses. A great triangular area of ancient crystalline schists and igneous intrusions, with its apex toward Belgrade, its western side running south toward Monastir, and its eastern side trending southeastward toward Drama in Greece, makes roughly the geographic region called the Great Valley, which corresponds also with old Serbia. The combined valleys of Save, Drave, Danube, and lower Tisza, so far as they lie within the country, constitute the Great Plains. A small area in the northwest, drained largely by the heads of the Save, is called the Slovene Alps. Extensive folds, uplifts, faults, and occasional intrusions have given rise to the Dinaric-Pindus range extending from the Slovene Alps far into Albania and Greece. Such part of this range as lies in Yugoslavia is called the Dinaric or Western Mountain Region. The western half consists largely of limestones and is typical karst topography,

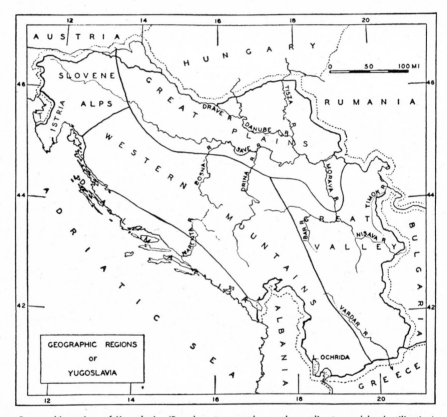

Geographic regions of Yugoslavia. (Based on topography, geology, climate, and land utilization)

while the eastern half, made of late Paleozoic and early Mesozoic rocks, has mature stream-carved mountain forms with rich podzolic soils. Along the Adriatic, multitudes of islands and channels, peninsulas and bays, make a very ragged coast. These elements and a strip of mainland 15 to 25 miles wide constitute the fifth region—Dalmatia. Climatically, the last region and the southern part of the first are somewhat under the influence of Mediterranean factors. The Great Plains and Slovene Alps are rural; the Dinarics are grazing and forest lands; the Great Valley is devoted to general farming of many types, to grazing, and to mining, but its distinctive characteristic is its commercial value.

Great Valley. This region is nearly coextensive with the combined Morava-Vardar valleys. On the east the folded Balkan mountains extend far south from the Iron Gate, but the national frontier, as well as the regional boundary, finally draws away from the mountains as they turn eastward. The unity of the region is not only topographic but also historic and commercial. Morava Valley is an ancient center of Serb culture. It has furnished soil for grazing and agriculture, minerals, and forests for exploitation by Romans and Turks and has always been an inviting passageway between central Europe and the Near East. It suggested two Roman roads through the region, and in modern times the German Berlin-to-Bagdad project, and promoted the Orient express from London to Istanbul and Athens. One Roman road came up from the Adriatic, across the Dinaric Mountains to the Ibar Valley at Novibazar, and on eastward across the Morava. The other, Via Egnatia, came up from Albania, through Monastir, and on east to Salonika.

The Diagonal Furrow, a branch valley, leaves the Morava-Vardar Valley at Nish, follows the Nisava Valley toward Sofia, and then runs east to Istanbul. The Rumanian branch leads from Nish down the Timok to the Danube; and the branch to Dalmatian ports follows up the Serbian Morava, across the Drina to Sarajevo, and down a difficult route to Ragusa and to Cattaro Gulf. The Great Valley route connects with two other routes from Skoplje, one north through the Ibar Valley, the other southwest to Lake Ochrida. Many of the railroads using these routes should be double-track, and all the same gauge. The international character of travel in the valley is shown by the use of five languages on the signs in the railroad cars which caution passengers not to smoke or lean out of the window. The commercial significance of this depression is enhanced by the distance around, via Danube River, Black and Ægean seas, and by the Dinaric barrier toward the Adriatic. This highway reaches the sea in Greece at Salonika. The port has been free and probably will be so again when friction with Greece is eliminated.

Rocks of the Great Valley region were folded and later faulted so as to make many tectonic valleys, into which quantities of waste were washed as the mountains were eroded to maturity. A broad submergence allowed the sea to spread in shallow, many-branched, fresh lakes, whose deposits together with those of the tectonic basins provide splendid agricultural lands. Many of these neat plains have their own chief cities, such as Kosovo, Skoplje, and Shtip. Maize is the most frequent crop in the north; wheat leads in the drier south. Irrigation, practised for 1,000 years at the foot of alluvial cones south of Skoplje, promotes nowadays the cultivation of tobacco and rice, cotton, pepper and sesame, chestnuts, mulberries and silkworms. Vineyards grow everywhere on terraces; apples, pears, and peaches, and the ubiquitous plum abound. Beets, and hemp for rope are grown in the northern section. Transhumance for sheep and cattle between the plains and the Dinaric Mountains was long practised but is now being crowded out by expanding cultivation. The many bordering hills are forest-covered in the north but very bare in the south.

Regions of Yugoslavia with political connotation, towns, and canals. Trieste area shown. Adapted from *Oxford Advanced Atlas*)

Towns along the valley have small industries in thread, cloth, rope, flour, footwear, silver filigree work, and the preparation of tobacco. Several coal deposits are worked; the finest with the largest reserves is mined in the Timok Valley. Lead, zinc, copper, aluminum, antimony, chromium, and iron are mined in the region, the first two since Roman times and the third since the time of stone sledges. Yugoslavia is now the greatest copper-producing state in Europe. Glass is one of the products of Skoplje (91,557) (Uskub), the south nodal city and the birthplace of Emperor Justinian. Nish (60,690) (Niš) at the northern node, the birthplace of Constantine the Great, has an indestructible natural site and a long, turbulent, fascinating history from the days of chariots and horsemen to the Orient express, *wagon-lit,* and *Speisewagen.*

Great Plains. If Yugoslavia's basic industry is agriculture, these plains are typically Yugoslavian. They are the granary of the state, a continuation of the Great Alföld of Hungary and the Banat of Temesvar, a very valuable gift to the country. They are formed of Tertiary deposits and recent alluvium spread over older topography, the schists, granites, and limestones of which show through here and there in old hill forms decked with mixed timber. The Plains have extremely varied agriculture in spite of severe winters and hot summers; since they are low, rainfall is merely enough to prevent their becoming a desert. The level stretches invite intensive agriculture and are covered with extensive fields of corn and wheat, whence emerge numerous villages marked by orchards and well-sweeps. Chernozem loessal soils are especially devoted to corn, whereas the sand dunes and calcareous hills support extensive vineyards, the fruits of which are highly esteemed for table use, raisins, and wine. Corn, wheat, and barley, the leading cereals; plums for prunes, jam, and brandy; grapes, tobacco, beets for sugar—all these are grown and manufactured here. Wheat, tobacco, and wine are the money crops. Cattle, mainly for meat, black, curly-haired pigs, horses, and bees are abundant, subsisting on the prolific grains, grass, and forage crops. Rivers yield quantities of fish.

Low, marshy, riverine plains capable of great production are subject to disastrous floods. Some attempts have been made to control the rivers, in the interests of flood prevention, navigation, and agriculture. No solution of the problem can be satisfactory that is not international, taking into account forests and reservoirs on the headwaters, channel improvement in the Hungarian plains, and sedimentation along the river below the Iron Gate, as well as the local interests. Three canals for boats have been built, the Francis, Francis Joseph, and Bega. Easy grades permit the railroads and rivers to furnish hundreds of miles of cheap transportation.

The Plains are, for obvious reasons, the most densely peopled region of the country, growing some commercial crops (one third of all national export), and favored by educational and coöperative organization. The population of the Plains is only 8 per cent industrial. Too many aliens for easy assimilation abide in the Plains, but their competition gives a stimulus to agriculture. The Plains are deficient in fuels and minerals, as well as in lumber, but timber for fuel and building can be had easily from hills to the south.

Subotica (112,550), lying far north on the Plains, engages in the manufacture of rural products, but is essentially a peasant town. Zagreb (290,400), on the Save at the western edge of the Plains and near the foot of an old granite mountain, gathers roads and railroad lines from several directions. Its main street parallels the river for 5 or 6 miles. It has served as a Croat culture center and is now both a university city and a rallying point for separatists and Yugoslav aspirations. Urbanization here as well as around several other centers has been rapid during the last thirty years. Zagreb has commerce, industry, and large banking interests. Oil refineries, flour-mills, and other food-preparing industries, paper-mills, and breweries supply local markets. Churches, palaces, and parks testify to the cultured life of the present population.

Belgrade (288,486), whose Slavic name, Beograd, means "White Castle," has an excellent situation at the junction of the Danube with the Save, wholly a Yugoslav river, on a subdued promontory of Cretaceous and igneous rocks. The promontory so stands that the rivers flow on three sides of the city and leave almost no flood-plains, marshes, or abandoned channels on the city side. Rather, for miles back from the river the land consists

Modern street and the Institute of Technology (engineering college), Belgrade. (Courtesy Consulate General of Yugoslavia)

of beautiful rolling hills rising with easy grades 100 to 300 feet above the stream bed. Many roads converge on the city, and the master railroad from central Europe to Athens and Istanbul passes through its western part, whence another good railroad connects with Fiume. Its river traffic involves 6,000 boats of 560,000 tons capacity, a testimony to its commercial significance. These go down to the Black Sea and up to Vienna. Belgrade is a worthy successor to the old fortified Roman military station, Semendria, which stood near the mouth of the Morava and guarded the same valley, but was not so well situated for trade. Later another Roman fortress, Kalemegdan, was built on the site of the present castle at Belgrade. That is now in a part overlooking the junction of the rivers. The fortress was destroyed and rebuilt by Huns, by Avars, and by Byzantines and was besieged by Greek, Bulgar, Serb, Turk, Hungarian, and Austrian—events which well attest the importance of the site for military purposes. It was not well situated for a capital when the national boundary followed the Danube and Save, but now there is more buffer land beyond the rivers than is necessary. To make any other city the capital would weaken the position of the Serbs and possibly the nation. Belgrade, in spite of its long, eventful history, has the appearance of a modern metropolis. The beautiful, graceful bronze figure on a park pedestal overlooking the rivers symbolizes well the strategy, trade, and political outlook of the growing city.

Slovene Alps. This little region is given separate treatment because its people have become clearly differentiated from other southern Slavs. Although they are Roman Catholics and active particularists, the smallness of the territory renders inadvisable the status of a separate state.

The region is Alpine in its structure, molded by glacier as well as by stream, western in its connections; the people, by virtue of their long-continued western contacts, are the most advanced in culture and economic life of all Yugoslavians. The topography is that of old, subdued mountains with a relief of 2,000 feet. A part consists of limestones and partakes of karst pattern. Climatic conditions, the severity of which is surpassed only in the Dinaric Mountains, stimulate and challenge the people without oppressing them.

Forests of oak, beech, chestnut, and conifers growing over the hills furnish logs which are floated down the rivers for active fuel-wood, lumber, and charcoal industries. The lumber is shipped to Sušak, Trieste, and Fiume for export. The broad, pleasing valleys and many cleared slopes smile with remunerative agriculture and grazing; many hills are pierced with mines for coal, iron, lead, zinc, and antimony, and frequent villages support metallurgical industries. Chestnut trees furnish thousands of bushels of nuts for the street vender operating his roaster in every central European city. The rural village strings along one wide street; every family yard abounds in forage, fowls, cattle, hogs, and goats for milk; a corn-crib flanks each farmhouse; hops, legumes, potatoes, vines, and orchards of hardy fruits surround the village and add to the range of crops.

Ljubljana (121,000), Laibach in German, on a vanishing branch of the Save as well as on the Trieste-Vienna railroad and highway, has cotton textiles and glass works in addition to its metallurgy.

Dinaric Mountain Region. Genetically and structurally the Dinaric Mountains are a continuation of the Alps as much as are the Carpathians. As yet, however, erosion has uncovered no crystalline core in them as it has in the Alps. These mountains consist of large folds, which, as shown by the shoulder-like changes in slope, the high-level terraces, and the plateaus, have been base-leveled and twice reëlevated. The region is one of the roughest sections of Europe and becomes wilder toward the south. Altitudes of 8,000 feet are reached, and local Pleistocene glaciation added rugged details. The mountains comprise most of Bosnia, Herzegovina, and Monte-negro and constitute a real barrier between Dalmatia and the Adriatic on one side and the Morava and Danube on the other. It is not so much the altitude that prevents passage as it is the dense forests, wild life, and lack of cultivable land, and the steep slopes of the nearly waterless karst strips. Inhabitants in these limestone lands store rain-water for every purpose in great cisterns in spite of a rainfall of 60 to 180 inches. History shows the mountains have been approachable from the east, yet parts of them never were taken by the Turks. The rise of the land toward the south has more effect upon the actual temperature than has the decrease in latitude.

Rugged mountain valley, sheep yards, and barn in the Western Mountains. (Courtesy Consulate General of Yugoslavia)

Upper levels furnish grass to the transhumant shepherds who with their sheep and goats come in spring from deep valleys among the mountains as well as from plains and valleys to the eastward. Heavy forests of deciduous and coniferous trees clothe the slopes and lower summits and feed enormous herds of swine, who love to crack the acorns and nuts of oak and beech. These forests are a rich reserve for Europe, inaccessible as yet in large areas for lack of roads of any sort. Beautiful valleys open out among the mountains and where cleared support subsistence agriculture and scores of villages. Many of the villagers specialize in some kind of domestic industry, such as tanning and leather-work, fur-curing, wool-weaving, woodwork, copper-smithing, silver filigreeing, poultry-raising, and collection and pack-ing of herbs such as gentian, belladonna, lavender, and thyme. Tan bark and extracts therefrom are also sent out. These products are carried down to Split and shipped to Italy or France. Other towns depend upon some mineral deposit, as the salt of Tuzla, iron in several Bosnian valleys, copper, gold, silver, lead, and zinc in other valleys, some mines of which were worked by Romans, suppressed by Turks, and now are being revived by Serbian enterprise. Water power and fish abound in the permanent streams.

Old walled town of Pettau on the upper Drave. There is a long line of docks and piers for commerce. (Courtesy U.S. Geological Survey)

Far up the Sava River within the limits of the town of Trifail. Railroad cars along the right; wagon road in center. (Courtesy U.S. Geological Survey)

In the larger valleys of the long northern slopes the growing of plums for jam, prunes, and brandy is a flourishing rural industry, and the raising of geese and turkeys is widespread. Agriculture in the karst section is limited to the *poljes* (large solution depressions), which are moist enough for wheat

Modern prune-processing plant in Bosnia. Prunes arrive by horse- or cattle-drawn wagons. (Courtesy U.S. Dept. of Agriculture)

Prunes, in bags, are hauled in any kind of wagon to the packing houses. Notice the wagon and the horses; the latter are common here in Bosnia. (Courtesy U.S. Dept. of Agriculture)

and even corn, and to the little *dolinas* (sink-holes), with gardens and to-bacco on the floors and grapes on the craggy walls. The home of the farmer is put on the crest of the depression to avoid floods which frequently cover the floors of the basins. It has been suggested that this section would be an admirable place for the development of the theory of a spiritual nether world.

A detail map of railroads or even of cart roads shows the intimate and complete control of transportation by tortuous valleys or gorges. Railroads usually reach just into this region and scarcely make expenses. One wonders if they will be more profitable when they are extended across or through the Dinaric Mountains and connect with other lines and cities with Adriatic ports.

Monastir (31,131) (Bitola) is a declining town, off the present highways, in the southern part of the mountains. Possibly the opening-up of the railroad from Durazzo and Tirana in Albania to Salonika will revive it. Sarajevo (118,000) is now reached by railroads from three directions. It is centrally located in a broad, open valley of the mountains, the only place in them where a large town could well be established; hence it has become their commercial center. It is 38 per cent Moslem and shows the Turkish influence as well as the persuasion of local environment in its industries—swords, cutlery, tobacco, leather, woolen goods, and woodworking. It has a formidable citadel on a crag above the city and a row of handsome modern buildings. Mostar (= "old bridge") (23,240), marked by a fif-teenth-century stone structure across the Narenta River, shows the same influence in its manufacture of weapons, tobacco, and leather articles. It is favored with beds of lignite and bauxite.

Dalmatia. The rocky strip of coastland, elongate islands, bays, and straits, included in the Dalmatian region, owes its origin to the folding of Mesozoic and Tertiary strata into long wrinkles parallel with the coast, their elevation and erosion until the soft clastics were etched out and the limestones remained as ridges, then their submergence to make islands and peninsulas of the ridges and waterways of the valleys. Subsequent changes of level are witnessed by elevated beaches at several heights above the sea. The present shoreline was established so recently that little wave-work has been done. Since rivers are small and few, cliffs are more common than deltas; fans, talus, and screes conceal the base of many rocky slopes; and most of the houses, towns, and cultivation are on these slopes and tiny deltas. Culture rarely goes above the talus. In general the climate is Mediterranean, warm and dry in summer with beautiful blue skies reflected in deep, clear water and cool in winter with much rain and cloudiness. Precipitation ranges from 40 to 60 inches near sea level; up the mountains it exceeds 100 inches. Natural vegetation, responding to these conditions, presents but little forest, which is further depleted by fires and by cutting for winter fuel, charcoal, and building material, and gives a bare

Characteristic Yugoslav village on the Dalmatian coast.

Mediterranean aspect. Grass, fruit, flowers, pistachio nuts, carobs, and aloes grow luxuriantly. Adriatic drainage is very limited except for the Narenta (Neretva) River; and the Herzegovinians, whose homes spread over its valley, are therefore more Mediterranean in outlook than any other group of Yugoslavians. Of all the 600 islands and islets only sixty-two are inhabited. The complex relief and diversified climate tend to perpetuate economic, political, linguistic, and cultural differences and general backwardness.

Both Romans and Greeks planted colonies on this coast by ships 2,000 or 3,000 years ago, but the territory was never really occupied until the Slavs, coming by land, built typical city-states on suitable harbor sites. Venice was to them an inspiring city model, and Italy offered well-adapted architecture and modes of living. The Slavs who settled here lost much contact with their mountain brethren. With meager agricultural opportunity and great marine possibilities, many became sailors and fishermen, possibly pirates, for no finer coast was ever constructed to lead men into such lives. The Austrian navy recruited for years from Dalmatia. Venetians took possession of much of the coast to eradicate the pirates, who preyed upon their commerce. Zara (Zadar) is the only remnant of Italian colonization, and it is now unimportant because, like all other ports along the coast, it has little hinterland. Dalmatian people are 97 per cent Slavs.

While rural opportunities are slim, intensive Mediterranean agriculture is profitable on this sheltered riviera. Grapes, figs, olives, pomegranates, and vegetables are planted on the scattered patches of terraced soil. Grapes and wines are of first importance; fisheries—coral, tunny, sardines, and sponges—are second. Olive oil is a substitute for milk in the diet and is used to preserve fish at least half as much as is salt. Lack of forage crowds out cattle, even sheep and goats.

Cattaro (Kotor) has a large harbor, narrow at the throat, twice widened into a lower and an upper bay as it extends beyond the first and second ridges, but with no Hudson River leading far inland. Walls extend up the hills to the castle and surround the town. Cattaro has been selected and developed as the national naval base. A railroad starts on the outer bay, follows the coast some miles to Dubrovnik (Ragusa), then turns into the Narenta Valley and climbs up to Sarajevo. Ragusa has fine stone buildings with red tile roofs, street-cars, buses, a lumber market, a fine, deep harbor, and well-equipped piers. It once had a Venetian route up the mountains to Nish. Split or Spalato [1] (49,885) is a little farther north, surrounded by more mature topography, and has been chosen for the chief Yugoslav harbor. It is a railroad terminal, has well-equipped docks and piers, transfers coal, marble, bauxite, fats, and cattle for export market, and is undergoing rapid growth. Besides Diocletian's palace seven other castles and the

[1] The name comes from *palace,* the palace of Diocletian erected here for his declining years.

ruins of Roman Savona still stand. There is a valley route from the interior, and down it the Turkish hosts once came, but failed to take the castles. The best route from Split inward leads northward into Una Valley. Sušak and Fiume (72,130), Rijeka in Serbian, now both in Yugoslavia, help export the lumber and other products. Trieste, a free port, will share the trade. Sebenico (16,015), Sibenik in Serbian, has a short railroad and manufactures cement and electro-chemical products including calcium carbide, thus putting the limestone wastes to a profitable use. It exports bauxite, cellulose, wood, and lignite.

The grape harvest festival in Venezia usually begins with a joyous parade of floats and banners.
(U.S. Army photograph)

So beautiful is all this Dalmatian coast that it attracts artists from many European countries, and a few tourists, as in times past it attracted kings and nobles with their palaces and fortresses. Most of these towns have hillside houses one or two stories lower on one side than on the other. So steep are the mountain spurs that wonderful auto roads zigzag across them often to make their ascent at easy grades. Steamboats keep all the coast towns connected.

Future and foreign relations. Yugoslavia responds to geographic differences between itself and its neighbors by commercial treaties. Under trade agreements, Poland sends petroleum, salt, sugar, and manufactures and in return receives meat, lard, tobacco, and prunes. Austria receives grain and cattle and sells sugar. The trade can reach through to Germany, which needs tobacco, meat, and lard and has machinery and textiles to sell. Yugoslavia is poor in coal, and immediate neighbors have no surplus. Coal or wood must be had for warmth as well as for commerce and industry. In this situation it is difficult to develop the metal ores in Yugoslavia and several of them are exported raw, while the manufactured metals are purchased. Metallurgical industries are beginning, but textile mills are still most important. Railroads are not sufficient to haul coal, for they can scarcely distribute the farm products.

Yugoslavia exports corn, forest products, and minerals; aluminum, copper, antimony, and chromium ores. Much export goes over the sea to Italy and over the mountains to Central Europe. Textiles and machinery come from Czechoslovakia, making a three-cornered trade. Cotton is imported from the United States and is also raised in the Vardar Valley, for the rising textile industries. Relief and rivers favor trade with north and northeast as well as south, but in the first direction economic status is much the same; hence trade goes a more difficult way. Of the foreign trade about 60 per cent is with Italy, and England sends 35 per cent of the imports. About 4 million tons of bauxite are annually shipped away from the Dalmatian coast. The backwardness of the land is reflected in its export and import lists, while both backwardness and resources are displayed in native art. Perhaps wool may be said to be first in art in hand-made carpets, rugs, and tapestries. Flax is much used in linen with threads of gold and silver. Some work is done in bronze, silver, and leather. Stone, oils, and paints are almost lacking, although plain stones, clay, and sand (in brick) are much used in architecture. Although wood is much used in construction it is not so common in art. The dainty art of distilling aromatic plants for oils and perfumes is practised in several coast places on plants shipped down from the mountains as well as on supplies collected locally.

Nature has put upon man here a constant struggle for existence, yet not so severe that he has not risen to independence, albeit very late compared with many neighbors. As a forest producer and a raiser of meat, eggs, fruits, and nuts, the future is open to him. A prosperous, well-governed, independent nation over these hills and mountains is a geographic necessity for the peace and intercourse of two continents.

QUESTIONS

1. Why is the foreign trade primarily with Italy, Austria, and Czechoslovakia?

2. Would adjusting the Hungarian boundary so as to let most of the Magyars return to Hungary make any difference with the course of foreign trade of Yugoslavia? Explain your answer.

3. Why was it "natural and inevitable" that Turk, Russian, and German should be invaders of the Balkans?

4. Why does Yugoslavia start off with several economic, political, tax, and land-tenure systems? Does this historic background affect other phases of the present solidarity of the nation? Discuss.

5. What do you suppose has made the Yugoslav slow to appreciate the wealth of unity he already possesses?

6. Discuss the last sentence in the chapter. Why would not Austrian control be better? Or Russian control of the trade routes?

7. What geographic factors have influenced the recent history, and the economic and political relationships of Yugoslavia?

BIBLIOGRAPHY

ADAMIC, Louis, *The Native's Return* (New York and London, Harper and Brothers, 1934).

——, *My Native Land* (New York and London, Harper and Brothers, 1943).

ARMSTRONG, Hamilton F., *Tito and Goliath* (New York, The Macmillan Company, 1951).

BAERLIN, Henry, *The Birth of Yugoslavia*, 2 vols. (London, L. Parsons, 1922).

BASCH, Antonin, *The Danube Basin and German Economic Sphere* (New York, Columbia University Press, 1943).

BEARD, Charles, and RADIN, George, *The Balkan Pivot* (New York, The Macmillan Company, 1929).

CHATAIGNEAU, Y., and SION, J., "Yugoslavia," in Vidal de La Blache and Gallois, *Géographie Universelle* (Paris, Lib. Armand Colin, 1934).

CVIJIC, Jovan, "Geographic Distribution of Balkan Peoples," *Geographical Review*, Vol. 5 (1918), pp. 345-361.

——, "Zones of Civilization in the Balkan Peninsula," *Geographical Review*, Vol. 5 (1918), pp. 470-482.

——, "Das Karstphaenomen, Versuch einer morphologischen Geographie," Geog. Abhand., Penck, Vol. 3 (1893).

——, *Hydrographie souterraine et evolution morphologique du Karst* (Grenoble, France, Institut de Géographie Alpine, 1918).

DOMINIAN, Leon, *Frontiers of Language and Nationality in Europe* (New York, Henry Holt & Company, Inc., 1928).

European Conference on Rural Life, Yugoslavia, No. 23 (Geneva, League of Nations Publication, 1939).

FITZGERALD, Walter, *New Europe* (New York, Harper and Brothers, 1946).

Foreign Commerce Year Book (Washington, D. C., Government Printing Office).

HOGG, Robert D., *Yugoslavia* (Toronto, McDonald & Co., 1944).

International Year Book of Agricultural Statistics (Rome, Printing Office, International Institute of Agriculture).

KENDREW, W. G., *Climates of the Continents* (Oxford, Clarendon Press, 1942).

KERNER, Robert J., *Yugoslavia* (Berkeley and Los Angeles, University of California Press, 1949).

LEHMANN, John, *Down River; A Danubian Study* (London, The Cresset Press, 1939).

LENGYEL, Emil, *The Danube* (New York, Random House, Inc., 1939).

LEPRETTE, Jacques, *Le Statut International de Trieste* (Paris, Pedone, 1949).

LONG, George W., "Yugoslavia, between East and West," *National Geographic Magazine*, Vol. 99 (1951), pp. 141-172.

McCormick, Thomas C. T., ed., *Problems of a Post-War World* (New York and London, McGraw-Hill Book Company, Inc., 1945).

Markham, Reuben H., *Tito's Imperial Communism* (Chapel Hill, University of North Carolina Press, 1947).

Moody's Governments and Municipals (New York, Moody's Investor's Service), annual.

Newman, Bernard, *The New Europe* (New York, The Macmillan Company, 1943).

———, *Mediterranean Background* (London, Robert Hale, 1949; also New York, British Book Center, 1949).

Obradovic, S. D., *La Politique Commerciale de la Yougoslavie* (Belgrade, 1939).

Pasvolsky, Leo, *The Economic Nationalism of the Danubian States* (London, Macmillan & Co., Ltd., 1928).

Patton, Kenneth S., *Kingdom of the Serbs, Croats, and Slovenes,* Department of Commerce Trade Promotion Series, No. 61 (Washington, D. C., Government Printing Office).

Petrovitch, W. M., *Serbia—Her People, History and Aspirations* (London, George G. Harrap & Co., Ltd., 1915).

Pribicevic, Stojan, *World Without End* (New York, Reynal & Hitchcock, 1939).

Ristelhueber, René, *Histoire des Peuples Balkaniques* (Paris, Fayard, 1950).

Roucek, Joseph S., "Resources of Yugoslavia," *Economic Geography,* Vol. 9 (1933), pp. 413-425.

———, *Central Eastern Europe* (New York, Prentice-Hall, Inc., 1946).

St. John, Robert, *The Silent People Speak* (Garden City, New York, Doubleday & Company, Inc., 1948).

Schevill, Ferdinand, *The History of the Balkan Peninsula* (New York, Harcourt, Brace and Company, Inc., 1933).

Shackleton, Margaret R., "Economic Resources of Yugoslavia," *Scottish Geographical Magazine* (Edinburgh, 1925).

———, *Europe, A Regional Geography* (London, Longmans, Green & Company, 1942).

Stanoyevich, M. S., ed., *Slavonic Nations of Yesterday and Today* (New York, H. W. Wilson Company, 1925).

Stavrianos, Leften Stavros, *The Balkan Federation; History of the Movement toward Balkan Unity in Modern Times* (Northampton, Mass., Smith College, 1944).

Stoddard, T. L., *Racial Realities in Europe* (New York, Charles Scribner's Sons, 1927).

United States Commercial and Industrial Handbook of Yugoslavia (Washington, D. C., Government Printing Office).

Welles, Sumner, ed., *An Intelligent American's Guide to the Peace* (New York, The Dryden Press, 1945).

West, Rebecca, *Black Lamb and Gray Falcon* (New York, Viking Press, 1941).

Whitbeck, Ray H., and Finch, Vernor C., *Economic Geography,* 4th ed. (New York, McGraw-Hill Book Company, Inc., 1941).

CHAPTER 37

Bulgaria

The houses lay behind fences of wattles of mud—
corncribs, stacks, buffaloes, pigs, carts, faggots.
—FARSON

People. About 7 million people occupy Bulgaria, a rather rectangular area of 42,808 square miles in the eastern lobe of the Balkan Peninsula, the smallest state in area, population, and prestige, except Albania, in all the Peninsula. Recent treaties transferred about 3,000 square miles of the South Dobruja area with about 350,000 people, predominantly Bulgars, from Rumania to Bulgaria. Bulgaria has considerable unity in race, in religion, and in its natural boundaries.

In the seventh century a horde of Mongoloid nomadic horsemen migrated from a temporary home near the Volga River and Ural Mountains to the lands between the Pruth and Dniester rivers, through the Dobruja, across the Danube, and into the Plateaus north of Balkan Mountains. Occupying this Northern Plateau Region, they soon spread around and through the Balkans into the Rumelian basins. In these more favorable conditions they abandoned their nomadic habits and began to practise fixed agriculture. They mingled with a Slavic rural people who were scattered very sparsely over these desirable plains and adopted much of their language and many rural customs. Interbreeding and new conditions changed their appearance. Their name *Bolgaria* is a Finno-Ugrian word and like many others in the present language suggests the racial connection ascribed to them. Living on land so near Constantinople, they easily passed under the influence of the Eastern Church when embracing Christianity. Four fifths of the present population affiliate with the Eastern Orthodox Church.

The untanned leather boot, the sheepskin coat, and an appetite for cheese curds (called yourt) and meat are reminders of the treeless steppes; stolidity, independence, virility, patience, and reticence are inherited from steppe ancestors. They possess a strong attachment for the soil, which they cultivate, albeit crudely, with the passion of a gardener. The Bulgars are now an energetic, persistent, hard, resilient peasant people, enthusiastically following high national ideals. Although many leaders have had a western

760

outlook, the government since World War II has become actively communistic.

Among them there are many Turks, left from days of Turkish rule; about 15 per cent of the population are Moslems, and 11 per cent speak Turkish. The Turks are segregated in two compact groups, one northwest of Adrianople, the other in the approaches to the Dobruja, in Deli Orman. A few reside in the villages along the Danube and practise handicrafts.

Probably 1 million Bulgars are outside the present frontiers—a solid wedge toward Monastir and a thick sprinkling around Seres and Drama, as far east as the Mesta River. Some students call these people Macedonian Slavs and not Bulgars at all. They are Bulgarized so thoroughly that they, like Bulgaria itself, want their territory annexed to Bulgaria.

In former centuries ambitions have visualized a Bulgarian instead of a Balkan Peninsula. In the ninth and tenth centuries, and again in the twelfth, the Bulgarians actually extended their rule over much of it; but the usurping residence of the Turk in their lands ground them down for 400 to 500 years. The modern nation became an entity in 1885 when it banished Turkish authority, yet the Bulgars have fought not alone against the Turk. Their feeling for expansion is against Greek, Yugoslav, and Albanian alike. They never have realized their great opportunity astride the Diagonal Furrow, an intercontinental highway.

Physical conditions. Geologically the country embraces a belt of nearly horizontal later strata 25 to 50 miles wide south of the Danube and a broader belt of complexly folded and faulted crystalline and sedimentary rocks of many ages from the very old to the most recent. The general trend of these rocks and structures swings in great curves from the west, sprawling toward the east. After the folding, stream erosion continued until it reduced the topography to old-age forms, a peneplain with rare monadnocks. Uplifts followed, and new valleys were etched out and widened to maturity; then the work was interrupted by another recent uplift, and young, rugged, gorge-like valleys have been developed below the shoulders of the last interrupted cycle. During the later uplift and erosion, faulting occurred so frequently that a block-mountain structure was developed; some blocks were elevated more than others, some were so depressed that lakes filled basins and sediments accumulated upon them. These are especially common in the borders of the Balkan Mountains and across the territory between the latter and the Rhodopes. These structures and processes have given rise to the four clearly marked geographic regions into which the country is divided. Between the Danube and the Balkans is the Northern Plateau, sometimes called the Balkan Foreland or the Northern Bulgarian Platform. The Balkan Mountains form its southern limit almost entirely across the country, and constitute the second region. The Central Basins Region includes more than the Maritza Valley of some authors, and is quite different from Rumelia or East Rumelia, a political unit of Turkish times that included many of the Central Basins. The fourth region may best be called the Rhodopes, though it is neither all mountains nor all of the mountains.

Across these four regions the climate varies notably with relief and exposure. North of the Balkans the temperatures and rainfall seasons are distinctly continental; south of them the climate partakes more and more of Mediterranean characteristics.

Boundaries of Bulgaria have shifted much. The adjustments due to the Balkan and World wars have given a more unified people than ever before because drawn with ethnic interests in mind. There are no hostile minorities within, and the remnants without are becoming consoled and somewhat comfortable. Any of the desired boundary adjustments outward would enclose more Greeks, Turks, or Yugoslavs than Bulgarians, and therefore the

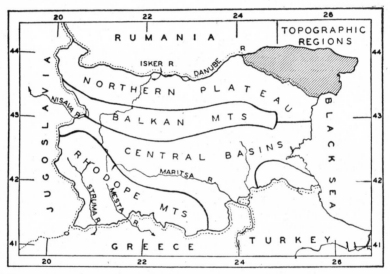

Bulgaria divided into its geographic regions. Shaded area won from Rumania. (Based on topographic and land utilization data drawn from many sources)

best methods of meeting the geographic conditions are by transfers of people who so elect and by trade treaties and agreements. Danube and Black Sea are good trade boundaries. Outlets from the capital by rail west and south are simple, and the great route east leads entirely across the productive valleys to Istanbul.

Northern Plateau. Across this otherwise level plain a score of streams and their branches flow out from the Balkan Mountains and have carved deep, narrow, meandering valleys to the Danube. Between the streams long strips of treeless plain terminate north at the Danube in bluffs 400 to 600 feet high, admirable sites for towns and for defense and control of the river. The uplands of loess or porous calcareous rocks, with a rainfall of 20 to 30 inches, must needs be treeless and grass-covered with mature cher-

nozem soils. In winter they have cold, sweeping winds, driving snows that
block railroads and isolate peasants for weeks at a time; but summers are
bright, warm, and showery. Native grasses have given place to wheat and
some corn and recently to thousands of acres of sunflowers introduced from
Rumania. The upland is dotted by rural villages around deep wells from
which farmers daily go out 1 to 3 or even 4 miles with tools, often a cart
and horse, to tend the wheat and other crops. How many miles of weary
travel does rural village life impose upon a peasant year after year!

The valleys contain many villages and towns, great orchards of plums,
apples, and cherries, and walnut and chestnut trees, as well as vegetables,
corn, and oats that require more moisture than is found in the uplands.
Roads rarely follow the valleys because the uplands furnish direct routes
with gentle grades and easy construction. Valleys are often infested with
mosquitoes and malaria. They are of no commercial value, present little
opportunity for the development of water power, and constitute a continual
hindrance to east-and-west travel. Sheep and cattle which pasture on the
uplands are fattened in the valleys. Surplus farm produce consists of wool,
hides, eggs, chickens, cheese, pigs, and some corn. The people eat wheat.

One sees many water-lifting devices to aid irrigation but no windmills;
houses are of blue, sun-dried brick or red, burned brick; tile roofs are
very frequent yet floors are as often of packed dirt. Think of the simplicity
of sweeping, scrubbing, or mopping! All wagon roads reach the towns, but
railroads rarely do because of anti-railroad prejudice when they were built.
Some towns are now reached by stub roads; others are being rebuilt near
the railroads. Few villages have any lights save the oil house-lights and the
lanterns carried by belated pedestrians. Modern conveniences are coming in
rapidly.

Rain in the west means corn and wheat; in the east mild climate induced
by the sea favors fruit, grapes, and tobacco. In several sections the farmers
are instituting a three-year rotation of five crops, wheat, lucerne, corn, sunflowers, and rape. The corn and sunflowers are sometimes planted together
for forage as in Canada, and the lucerne like the wheat is on the ground
over winter. The land added to this region from the Dobruja is rather dry,
semi-karst, dusty sheep pasture with a transhumance to the mountains in
summer.

Six old fortresses overlook the Danube, and six commercial towns, their
successors, now invite trade. All have a 7-foot river channel. Ruse (Ruschuk) (53,420), the most important, has a mile of docks and warehouses,
an active ferry, and a good railroad that starts near the river and climbs a
lateral valley to the upland. This town receives about one third of the nation's imports and sends away most of the export wheat. Beet sugar is
manufactured here, hides are tanned, and great quantities of fish are
handled.

The principal town on the plateau is Tirnovo (15,000) (Tŭrnovo), the

Bulgarian capital from 1186 to 1393. Ruins of its old granary and its watch-tower still remain, and fragments of wall, pavements, and palace testify to its ancient significance. It is singularly built on the flood-plain and steep slopes of the Yantra Valley, through which the railroad goes; it also spreads on the upland remnants among the deeply incised meanders of the river. It guarded a Balkan pass, and now has an important railroad, a motor-road intersection, a weaving and a clothing factory, and a cotton thread mill. Shumen (31,169) (Kolarovgrad) guards another Balkan pass, stands at a point of ancient strategic value, is still surrounded by a ring of forts, and is near an important railroad junction with modern commercial importance. Pleven (39,000) (Plevna) has long been a trade node and was bitterly contested in 1877. It controlled an ancient route over the

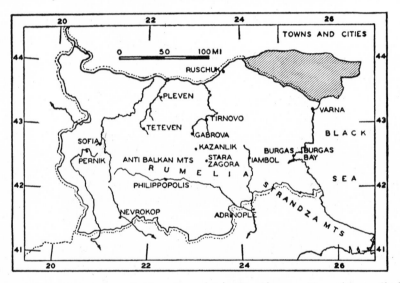

Some of the mountain areas and old provinces of Bulgaria, with many cities and towns. Shaded area won from Rumania. Adapted from *Oxford Advanced Atlas*)

Balkans and today controls a modern one, occupying a strong position on the Varna-Sofia (Sofiya) and Ruschuk-Sofia railroads. Gabrovo and Teteven, situated well up in the Balkan foothills, occupy excellent hydroelectric sites, manufacture woolen textiles, and use forest products. The former guards Shipka Pass and has a stub railroad from Tirnovo. Varna (72,000) (Stalin), an old Greek military and trading point, has maintained its commercial importance because the shelter from winds is good and the stream widens here in two long lakes. The sea freezes occasionally in January, but the climate gives a Mediterranean aspect to the region by permitting almonds, prunes, mulberries, and an abundance of vines. Since Varna is commercial, it has become industrial, manufacturing cotton and woolen goods, tanning skins, and grinding flour by local water power. Thirty miles west of the coast there are extensive salt-mines which contribute to Varna's chemical industries.

Balkan Mountains. This region is separated for treatment because it is a sparsely populated belt, an ethnic line though not a serious commercial barrier, and because it is sharply distinguished from its neighbors by its deciduous forests. They are valuable in the west but until recently have been wasted in the east. Three erosion levels are recognized, and on many of the more level shoulders and terraces there is more primitive agriculture

Street scene in a mountain village, showing one-story stone-roofed houses. The extended roof on the house at the left covers the cellar for the storage of root crops. (Courtesy Library of Congress)

than on either bordering region. Transhumance is common between the Northern Plateau and the Balkans, for pastures top most of the rounded summits. Six routes, two of which now have railroads, have crossed the mountains since antiquity. The Isker (Iskŭr) gorge is by far the best known, for its railroad leads to the capital, whereas the other railroad connects Ruschuk and Philippopolis through Stara Zagora. Many quarries in the limestone ridges, and brick-kilns near shale and clay beds furnish great quantities of building material, cement and other road-making stock. These are most abundant along the Isker but are frequent on the Yantra River line. Both railroads have spiral tunnels and steep grades to make their way through the Balkans. Copper is mined and smelted on the Isker, and coal and lead are worked in a small way. Sawmills, often with water power, and fuel-wood yards utilize the mouths of valleys leading out of the Balkans.

Central Basins. The Central Basins consist of two rows of basins, some many times as large as others, occupying a wedge-shaped area between the Balkans and the Rhodopes. The northern row includes the Sofia Basin at the west end, Kazanlik (Kazanlŭk) central, and Burgas partly submerged at the eastern end. The southern row comprises the great plain round Philippopolis (Plovdiv) at the west, Stara Zagora central, and Iambol in the east.

Street in Sofia, the capital city. Note the trolley tracks, the horses and wagons, the Moslem mosque, with its lone minaret. (Courtesy Library of Congress)

In each row there are also several lesser basins. The Anti-Balkans lie between the Kazanlik and Philippopolis basins. Some of these numerous basins are the result of down-warping or down-faulting associated with the vulcanism which was responsible for the syenite near Sofia and in Philippopolis. All have been aggraded with recent alluvium: the great Maritza plain was partly occupied by a lake, the sediments of which form a featureless plain, swampy enough for many rice-paddies and a fine crop of mosquitoes and malaria.

The Sofia Basin has four ready outlets down four streams: (1) the Nisava, toward Nish and Central Europe; (2) the Isker, toward the

Northern Plateau, the Danube, and Rumania; (3) the Maritza (Trajan's Gate), to its fertile plains and to Burgas, Istanbul, and the east; and (4) the Struma to coal-fields, rich Mediterranean rural lands, the Ægean, and southern Europe. Thus it is a most favored place for the metropolis Sofia (434,888), the commercial, industrial, and educational center and national capital.

Although in the midst of lofty, rugged mountains, the Sofia plain is only about 2,000 feet high. Streams coming into the plain furnish hydro-electric energy for power and city lights. Air drainage from the high valleys often brings chill and fogs to the city, but rarely fills the valley deeply enough to affect the former American University campus, seven miles out and 200 to 300 feet higher. Abundant fruit orchards and many field crops furnish thousands of bee-stands with honey. Sugar beets, potatoes, peas, and beans are notable crops. The factories make sugar, rugs, carpets, brick, and tile and spin and weave both cotton and wool.

Kazanlik Basin, long and narrow, with mountain shelter, rolling topography, sufficient, timely rainfall, and fertile soil, long ago tempted an observing man to cultivate the Damascus roses running wild in the hills. Today many thousands of acres and eighty villages are devoted to rose-culture. One ounce of aromatic oil is distilled from 3,000 to 5,000 ounces of rose-petals. About 2,000 ounces of attar of roses is thus produced and sold annually to France for $1 million. Another rose center flourishes in the southeast near the Turkish frontier.

Philippopolis (Plovdiv) plain contains the famous old city of the same name, built there in 350 B.C. by Philip of Macedon, because of its prospect and the building stone of the seven syenite hills in the midst of the plain. Springs emerge at the foot of some of the hills, but the present city service comes from Rhodopian waters, seven miles across the plains. The city now has over 125,000 people; a score of great tobacco sheds and several silk-mills care for two leading products of the plains. The fertile soils and sub-Mediterranean climate favor many fruits, especially grapes, almonds, and plums, besides cherries, apples, pears, peaches, and apricots. Other farm crops are wheat, corn, anise, sesame, melons, squash, pumpkins, peanuts, English walnuts, hazlenuts, kanob for cordage, and millet for poultry food. A millet drink is made by grinding the grain and fermenting the flour in water. The thin gruel-like drink is non-alcoholic, refreshing, and snappy, like lemonade, but with a large food value. Sheep and goats are always present; many herds and flocks go to the mountains for summer grass. Although nearly all the land is cultivated, the methods are crude and the results are poor compared with those in Finland or Estonia.

Around the syenite hills in the city and in places in mountains bordering the plains, weathered rock furnishes sand for roads, sidewalks, and park areas; red tile roofs adorn most of the houses. Villages dot the plain as far as one can see. The seasonal change in geographic landscape is well worth studying. Household industries are diminishing on the plains, not because of industrialization but because of inflow of cheap foreign manufactures.

Burgas (43,684), the second important Black Sea port, has a brisk salt industry from sea brines. It exports copper ores from near the town to Belgian furnaces; wheat to Finland; tobacco and cocoons, corn and lentils to Spain and Marseilles. It imports oil from Ceylon and Algeria; cotton and coffee from Holland (East Indies); pelts and raffia from Madagascar; chemicals from Germany; and machinery from the United States. Its industrial establishments include beet-sugar factories, oil refineries, textile mills,

Poultry raising is a common branch of farm activity. Here is a poultry house improved, plastered, painted, and equipped with glass windows. (Courtesy U.S. Dept. of Agriculture)

soap factories, and even a copper reduction plant. Burgas is in the midst of interesting shoreline features. Streams bring waste and drop it in three lakes, each of which is a drowned, isolated river mouth; waves and currents cut waste from cliffs and silt the harbor, build bars across river mouths, and tie islands to the shore.

In the past the East Rumelian plains have always been tributary to Istanbul. They were Hellenized in Byzantine days, then garrisoned by Turks and dominated by Islamism, as attested by Turkish names and residues of Turks in Stara Zagora and other places, Turks who should have gone home to Asia Minor when their authority was overthrown. Now since all pressure from Istanbul is toward Ankara, the new capital, the Bulgar has full authority save for Communist interference, and, with his agricultural instincts, is making these plains the rural backbone of the country.

The Rhodopes. A high, rugged mountain mass, not quite all in Bulgaria, bears the name Rhodopes. The region includes the rich Struma Valley with its choice porcelain clays, its tobacco and Mediterranean fruits, its important lignite at Pernik, and its metallurgical plants in the south. It includes the Mesta Valley, with its acres of tobacco and its metallurgy at Nevrokop. It includes the north slopes of the Strandza on the frontier between Turkey and Bulgaria, with their timber, shepherds, and charcoal-burners. It is made also to include, because structurally related, the valley of the Arda, very old topography on ancient crystalline rocks, the corn belt of Bulgaria and a rich tobacco region.

The Rhodopes proper are alpine in character with cirques, tarns, and moraines, alpine flowers and grasses. Cols and passes are rare; profound gorges, waterfalls, steep scarps, lofty peaks, and heavy winter snows excel all others in their respective lines in southeastern Europe. Lumbermen cut the magnificent pines and oaks and float the logs down to the sawmills and lumber markets at the foot of the mountains. Shepherds and cattle herdsmen move large herds in and out of the mountains with the change of season; many make cheese for market. Tillage crowds far up in the mountain valleys, using terraces, fans, and talus with diligence farther west where there is lacking the competition of the Maritza plains.

Population is sparse in the Rhodopes; the isolation of small groups is keen and effective. The seclusive mountaineer is hardy, self-sufficient, ignorant, poor—qualities which breed suspicion, backwardness, and jealousy. Agriculture is little more than subsistence work. No towns of note have arisen, nor can they unless some mineral wealth is uncovered. Rather one finds acres of goats and patches of cabbages. Four groups of restless people are Pomaks, Islamized Rumanians, Islamized Slavs, and nomadic Greek herdsmen. Pomaks are typical; they are defined as Bulgars converted to Islam, resident in the mountains; they are charcoal-burners, lumbermen, and growers of cereals and potatoes. In fineness of facial features, jealous exclusiveness, and tendency to diminish they have three leading characteristics of a very old race. Some say they are of Greek origin, but they surely have no signs of having been Hellenized; others think they are an indigenous survival of the peninsula.

Foreign relations and future. Since agriculture is the mainstay of over 80 per cent of the people, exports must be rural and forest products, and imports mostly manufactured articles. Backwardness and low standards of living are reflected in commerce, which is the lowest per capita of any European nation. Bulgaria has sufficient physical variety and resources to be a stable nation. The industry of the people and the soil fertility are the best material out of which to build the nation. Its national entity should be maintained, because, though the people scarcely know it, Bulgaria occupies the much coveted intercontinental highway.

QUESTIONS

1. What geographic reasons may be advanced for a Bulgarian corridor to the Ægean Sea? What objections are there to such a commercial outlet? If one were opened, where should it be? Why?

2. Present reasons why Bulgaria should continue a national entity and be encouraged to develop.

3. What possibilities are there that Bulgaria will become notably industrial?

4. Compare Tirnovo, Sofia, and Philippopolis as possible federal capitals. (Each has had its turn.)

5. Would it be better if Bulgaria were divided into two states? Discuss.

6. What advantages and disadvantages might come to Bulgaria because of her position on the Diagonal Furrow? What should be her policy in view of her position?

BIBLIOGRAPHY

ARMSTRONG, Hamilton F., *Tito and Goliath* (New York, The Macmillan Company, 1951).

BASCH, Antonin, *The Danube Basin and German Economic Sphere* (New York, Columbia University Press, 1943).

BLANCHARD, W. O., and VISHER, S. S., *Economic Geography of Europe* (New York, McGraw-Hill Book Company, Inc., 1931).

BOWMAN, Isaiah, *The New World* (Yonkers-on-Hudson, New York, World Book Company, 1928).

CHATAIGNEAU, Y., and SION, J., "Bulgaria," in Vidal de La Blache and Gallois, *Géographie Universelle* (Paris Lib. Armand Colin, 1934).

COON, Carleton S., *The Races of Europe* (New York, The Macmillan Company, 1939).

DOMINIAN, Leon, *Frontiers of Language and Nationality in Europe* (New York, Henry Holt & Company, Inc., 1921).

Europa, Encyclopedia of Europe (London, Europa Publications, Ltd.), annual.

FITZGERALD, Walter, *New Europe* (New York, Harper and Brothers, 1946).

Foreign Commerce Year Book (Washington, D. C., Government Printing Office).

GEORGE, H. B., *Relations of Geography and History* (Oxford, Clarendon Press, 1924).

HUBBARD, George D., "The Turning of Tirnovo," *Economic Geography,* Vol. 22 (1946), pp. 109-115.

International Reference Service, U. S. Dept. of Commerce (Washington, D. C., Government Printing Office), many numbers per year.

KENDREW, W. G., *Climates of the Continents* (New York, The Macmillan Company, 1942).

KISS, George, "A T.V.A. on the Danube," *Geographical Review,* Vol. 37 (1947), pp. 274-302.

KOSACK, Dr. Hans, "Bulgaria, Petermann's Nationalitätenkarte von Bulgarien," *Zeitschrift Gesell. für Erdkunde* (1937), pp. 348-372.

LEHMANN, John, *Down River; A Danubian Study* (London, The Cresset Press, 1939).

LENGYEL, Emil, *The Danube* (New York, Random House, Inc., 1939).

MCCORMICK, Thomas C. T., ed., *Problems of the Post-War World* (New York and London, McGraw-Hill Book Company, Inc., 1945).

MICHAEL, L. G., *Agricultural Survey of Europe: The Danube Basin, Part 2, Rumania, Bulgaria, Yugoslavia;* United States Department of Agriculture, Technical Bulletin No. 126 (Washington, D. C., Government Printing Office, 1929).

Moody's Governments and Municipals (New York, Moody's Investor's Service), annual.

NEWBIGIN, Marion I., *Geographic Aspects of Balkan Problems* (New York, G. P. Putnam's Sons, 1915).

————, "The Human Geography of the Balkans," *Journal of Geography*, Vol. 53 (1919), pp. 112-113.

NEWMAN, Bernard, *The New Europe* (New York, The Macmillan Company, 1943).

PASVOLSKY, Leo, *Bulgaria's Economic Position* (Washington, D. C., The Brookings Institution, 1930).

PEARCY, G. Etzel, and FIFIELD, Russell H., *et al., World Political Geography* (New York, Thomas Y. Crowell Company, 1948).

PRIBICEVIC, Stojan, *World Without End* (New York, Reynal & Hitchcock, 1939).

RIPLEY, W. Z., *Races of Europe* (New York, D. Appleton and Co., 1899).

RISTELHUEBER, René, *Histoire des Peuples Balkaniques* (Paris, Fayard, 1950).

ROUCEK, Joseph S., "Economic Geography of Bulgaria," *Economic Geography*, Vol. 11 (July, 1935), pp. 307-323.

————, *Central Eastern Europe* (New York, Prentice-Hall, Inc., 1946).

————, *Contemporary Europe* (New York, D. Van Nostrand Company, Inc., 1941).

SCHEVILL, Ferdinand, *History of the Balkan Peninsula* (New York, Harcourt, Brace & Company, Inc., 1922).

SHACKLETON, Margaret R., *Europe, A Regional Geography* (London, Longmans, Green & Company, 1942).

Statesman's Yearbook, STEINBERG, S. H., ed. (New York, The Macmillan Company).

Statistical Year Book of League of Nations.

WELLES, Sumner, ed., *An Intelligent American's Guide to the Peace* (New York, The Dryden Press, 1945).

CHAPTER 38

Rumania

Blessed be our land and kin,
And filled with flour our every bin.
—FOLK SONG

Extent and general relief. Rumania [1] is one of the new states of Europe, not even a resurrected state like Poland or Lithuania, but a state set up 1859-1877, augmented greatly at the end of World War I, and trimmed at the end of World War II by transfer of Bessarabia to Russia and a small area in southern Dobruja to Bulgaria. These two parcels have been transferred back and forth in former treaties.

It is Balkan in many characters, Mediterranean in language and water connections, yet distinctly Austrian-Succession in that it benefited territorially by the Austro-Hungarian collapse and has persistently developed since. Its boundaries surround a broadly oval area of diversified topography, mountain, plain, plateau, and shoreline, bordering for about 400 miles the largest river in Europe. It may be described as the Carpathian Mountains with their valleys and bordering plains. It is a rare nation that occupies so completely both sides of a mountain range and its bordering plains, a status possible here because of the maturity of the mountains. Rumania is strongly controlled by both the Carpathian Mountains and the Danube River. It may be called European west of the mountains, but Oriental east of them. The people number about 17 million scattered over 91,584 square miles with a density of 185 to each square mile, a density exceeded by only six states in our country, and over three and one half times as great as our average.

In general the soils are fertile, and in spite of mountains and marsh about 60 per cent of the country is in crops and pasture, three fourths of which latter is actually arable. Over 25 per cent of the land carries forest, about two thirds of which is hardwoods, and the same proportion is under state or other public ownership. Livestock is more abundant per capita than in Italy, but less so than in the United States. The abundance of sheep gives the land a Mediterranean aspect.

Rumanian climate is predominantly continental with a touch of Medi-

[1] Roumania is preferred by some; Romania, by others.

terranean characteristics. Usually winters are cold, snowy, and windy. Springs are short and rainy and pass quickly to summer, which becomes dry, particularly in the eastern sections. The great winter Asiatic high spreads to Rumania, bringing crisp, dry cold with frozen streams; but when the high weakens, Mediterranean cyclones drift eastward, bringing winter fog, rain, and cold weather. Dobruja is the most Mediterranean region in its vegetation. Climate presents a great range in temperature and precipitation because of differences of relief and exposure. Mountain rainfall amounts to 60 inches in places and exceeds 40 inches in almost a complete girdle around the Transylvanian Basin, while in some years it is actually less than 10 inches on eastern plains. Whirlwinds here sport with snow in winter and dust in summer when the tail of the northeast trades out of the Asiatic hot interior blows toward hot Africa deserts.

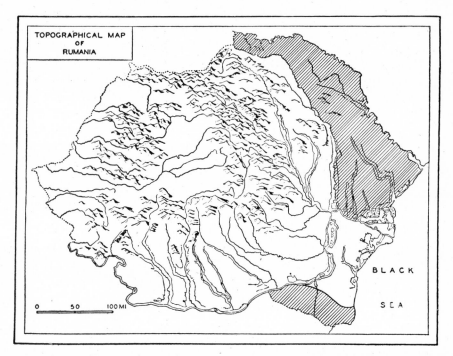

TOPOGRAPHICAL MAP OF RUMANIA

BLACK SEA

0   50   100 MI

Hachure map of Rumanian relief. Shaded portions represent land lost to U.S.S.R. and Bulgaria. (Constructed from Goode's *School Atlas* and *Oxford Advanced Atlas*)

People. About the beginning of the second century, Roman colonies were planted in parts of Rumania. They persisted for 150 years; then the colonists either returned or were absorbed by the barbarian natives. Again, about 1,000 years later, new Latin colonists came who Romanized Gothic, Hun, and Slavic remnants and later absorbed Turkish, Tatar, and Bulgar blood; there still remains a strong Latin pride, an Aryan language closely akin to Latin, and because for centuries under Byzantine rule, an Eastern Church. The frequency of Slavic words for rural terms indicates the strength of Slavic blood in peasants, and similarly Latin words are very common in cultural, governmental, and religious fields.

The modern Rumania began when for political reasons neighboring nations saw fit in 1859-1861 to set up a buffer state consisting of the old Walachia and Moldavia, provinces which had been under Byzantine, Turkish, and Russian rule successively and hence were backward. Boundaries were indefinite, but the new state included about all of the present domain except Dobruja and the Transylvanian Region, which came to Rumania after the Bulgarian and World wars respectively.

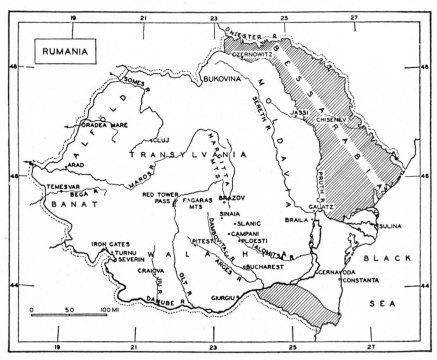

Places in Rumania: rivers, passes, towns, mountains, and old political units. Shaded areas lost to U.S.S.R. and Bulgaria. (Adapted from *Oxford Advanced Atlas*)

The present population consists of about 14,700,000 Rumanians, less than 350,000 Germans, 150,000 Jews, 200,000 Gipsies, 200,000 Turks, Bulgarians, and Tatars, and 700,000 Szeklers, most of whom are sympathetic with the Rumanian government, but not so happy at the tightening of the communistic grip on the nation. In addition there are 500,000 Magyars, who are restive and could be made much happier by adjusting boundaries on the west. A treaty granted equality of privilege to minorities, but it is not liberally interpreted for the Jew, who is restricted as to business, trade, lands, education, and professions. Religious restrictions are not serious for any group.

This semi-Oriental mixture of peoples has a literacy of but 43 per cent, still uses poor agricultural methods and obtains small yields, lives in poverty and dirt; and all these characteristics become more pronounced from west to east. The people are 80 per cent rural; inclined toward neither industry nor commerce, a fact which leaves room for the German and Jew among them. Although rural, the peasant even yet does not know how to make the most of his land. He sows broadcast·by hand, reaps with a sickle or crude cradle, threshes by the treading of oxen, and winnows by tossing grain into the wind. His output is about one third as much as his land should· yield. Improvement in agricultural methods has been moving very slowly for seventy years. At present 92 per cent of the land is in small farms, a change which cut down yields at first but gave increased independence and responsibility and increased the food supply. Mechanization is increasing under the Russian influence and other gains are being made. Probably collectives and state farms are increasing.

Only 7 or 8 per cent of the people live by industry, 1 per cent by mining, 4 per cent each by lumbering and commerce, and about 2 per cent by administration and the professions. No such educated surplus exists here as in Austria and Hungary.

Boundaries and unity. Most of the Black Sea boundary consists of unapproachable delta margin and shifting shoreline, with sandbars, lagoons, and marshes. Sulina harbor is an improved river mouth, and Constanta is an improved shelter behind a sandbar. The Danube River, with its Rumanian flood-plain, marshes, and lagoons, makes a good barrier boundary, but it is difficult to cross; hence it is not favorable to trade. Two bridges cross the river, one near the Iron Gate at Turnu Severin (31,259), the other at Cernavodă between Bucharest and its seaport Constanta. Northward from the Danube River across the Great Alföld the frontier runs through thickly populated plains in a very arbitrary, unsatisfactory course, which might be revised to advantage. Through the Banat of Temesvar,[2] Timişoara in Rumanian, it seems to be as ethnic as possible, but it vexatiously crosses railroads, streams, and irrigation canals. Farther north it was drawn ostensibly to help trade by putting it west of some towns and their connecting railroads, but it has deranged Hungarian commercial life and brought an unhappy minority into Rumania. A line drawn from an ethnic, religious, linguistic, and physiographic standpoint would make it easier for the people to become friendly and to restore trade relations. Perhaps personal adjustments of neighbor to neighbor along the boundary will help, but that too will require time and patience. The northern frontier crosses the Carpathians

[2] Probably the only Banat now existing. It is the territory ruled by a Ban or military chief formerly appointed by the king to keep order on a certain frontier. An office discontinued for some time.

among lofty peaks and ridges and comes down across the southern Bukovina ("Beech-land") plateau to the Pruth, which it follows nearly to its
mouth, then cuts across the plains to the Black Sea near the mouth of the
northern Danube distributary. This throws much of Bukovina with its
capital Chernovitsy (Cernăuti) to the U.S.S.R.

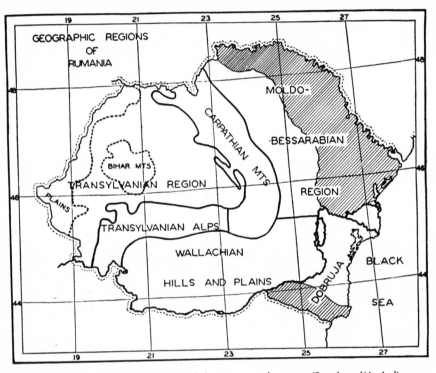

Rumania divided on geographic lines. Shaded areas as on last map. (Based on *L'Agriculture en Roumanie, Album statistique 1929,* and *Oxford Advanced Atlas*)

The state is delimited as satisfactorily, from an international point of
view, as any unit in Europe. If a nation's motives can be judged by the
nature of the boundaries it selects, Rumania would seem to be friendly,
for none of the frontiers is well chosen for defense and all are suitable for
exchange of goods and ideas. The Eastern Church, a gift of Byzantine
control, is numerically the strongest religious group. The country is favorably situated and in many respects happily constituted. Russian size and
policy present a problem, and the proximity of the turbulent Balkans
another.

Rumania's diversity of topography and resource makes apt a regional
treatment. The mountains are divided into two regions called the Carpathians and the Transylvanian Alps. East of the mountains is the Moldavian Region. Toward the south the Walachian Hills and Plains similarly

are known by an ancient name. Between the Black Sea and the lower Danube is Dobruja, trimmed a little for Bulgaria's benefit; and west of the mountains is the Transylvanian Region.

Carpathians. The Carpathians are a continuation of the Alps, but they are lower, narrower, and simpler in structure, possess more minerals, were glaciated less, and retain no glaciers; hence they are of much less interest to the tourist and the seeker for scenic thrills, but of more value to miner, forester, and agriculturist. The upland topography consists of mature stream-made forms, a peneplain with monadnocks occasionally rising above it; the plain bevels folded structures in which subsequent erosion has carved cuestas with trellis drainage lines. On the east no sharp boundary exists, but foothills grade into the plateau. On the western flank the Braşov plain, a subsidence area of 10 by 50 miles, and two valleys clogged by late Tertiary vulcanism provide splendid farmlands in the mountains. The Hargita (Hărghita), the great volcanic mass that closed the valleys, lies between them and the Transylvanian Region. Below the old upland, glacial streams have carved more youthful valleys, often gorges, and the valley tops are fretted with glacial cirques and narrow aretes. Three railroads cross the mountains.

Alpine vegetation and extensive sheep and goat pastures cover the mountain uplands; conifers clothe the upper slopes, deciduous trees the lower slopes and foothills; valleys are generally treeless but nourish many villages on their rich, warm soils. Sunny slopes carry terraced vineyards, the grapes from which are made to yield many gallons of wine; quantities of plums are used for Damson brandy. The inhabitants of the mountains engage in coal- and salt-mining, quarrying, and lumbering, floating their logs down to the Danube or to sawmills on the local streams to be sawed before continuing their journey. Probably the purest type of Rumanian is found in the seclusion of the Carpathian valleys.

Braşov (82,984), the only town in the Carpathians, recently given a new Russian name, Oraşul Stalin, was founded centuries ago by Germans for trade purposes. A citadel on a hill dominated the beautiful plains of the depression, and a trading center at the foot of the hill accommodated caravans from Ukraine, Asia, and the cities up the Danube. Wool, skins and furs seem then to have been the most important local products. Two routes lead southward. To the Bran Pass and the southwest goes a wagon road, and through the Predeal Pass an important railroad leads to Bucharest (Bucureşti). The road south traverses the charming valley and town of Sinaia with its ancient castle and monastery, royal palace, and modern summer homes. A railroad to the west connects Braşov with Transylvania and central Europe. Another railroad leads north and across the mountains to Moldavia. The stimulus of these modern means of travel and commerce has brought many industries, such as tanning, weaving and knitting of wool, making of machinery, paper, furniture, and chemicals, and refining of oil.

Recently an aviation field and a factory for airplanes have been established here. Braşov has grown rapidly and has been considered as a possible site for the national capital on account of its central location, security, and climatic advantages.

Transylvanian Alps. These mountains are still a part of the great arc of Tertiary structures but contain a much larger exposed core of crystallines and smaller zones of sedimentaries than the Carpathians; they are equally mature but have the three erosion terraces better preserved than the Carpathians. Summits reach 8,000 feet; sheep are pastured in summer above 6,000; and forests clothe the steeper, occasionally inaccessible, slopes below and spread out over the foothills until agriculture claims the land. Maize is the chief crop in the valleys; wheat, flax, and sugar beets alternate with the corn. Rows of glacial cirques have been nibbled in the edges of the valley walls of the Fagaras (Făgăras) Mountains, east of the Red Tower Pass of the Olt River. The antecedent Danube breaks through the range in a gorge, the Iron Gate, which in spite of canalization and much clearing is still an obstruction to navigation; and the Olt, also antecedent, with its sources in two of the basins of the Carpathians parallels the Fagaras for 40 miles, then opens up a route for a road and railroad across the central part of the region. In the western part of the mountains coal, iron, and copper are mined, supporting a little metal industry, and in the eastern part salt is produced in abundance at Slanic, north of Ploeşti.

Moldavian Region. Much of this region is a dissected plateau of horizontal late Tertiary and Quaternary sediments. The drainage reaches the Danube by the Pruth and Sereth rivers, two streams flowing nearly parallel from the Russian border, southeastward and south to Galatz (Galati). The whole structure descends toward the Black Sea, and large areas between the Sereth (Siret) and Pruth (Prut) rivers have an altitude of only 300 to 600 feet. The surface is hilly to rolling almost everywhere except on the upland remnants. Valleys contain broad flood-plains with marshes, bayous, and meandering streams.

Because of altitude, in the northwest, heavier rainfall, and western contacts, this section possesses the densest population and the most advanced people. The people are busy raising oats and rye and working in the beech and oak lumber camps. At many places in the foothills, petroleum has begun to attract attention.

Rather pure Rumanian stock may be found in Moldavia, whence colonists have gone out to the steppes on the east and south. Greek and Armenian traders continue to occupy the coasts, and Jews are numerous in all the towns. Aliens constitute about one third of the population. The steppes offer a singular ethnic mosaic. Rumanians are rarely in the majority in the villages but easily predominate in rural parts.

Since so much of this region is hilly, black-earth steppe, grazing becomes the chief occupation. Horses are characteristic in the south, and cattle farther north. Large villages of sheep-herders with their deep wells and high well platforms are found in all parts. Farther north where rainfall is more satisfactory the cereals are cultivated, and grasslands give place to corn and beans rather than to potatoes. Grapes do well if the trunks are buried in winter under mounds of earth, and other fruits flourish. Roads are miserable; loess does not make good roads and hides the rocks that might make better highways. The country is so trenched by the great valleys that travel is seriously handicapped.

Several noteworthy towns mark the contact of the foothills and the plateaus. Jassi (94,075) (Jasi), a Jewish town, occupies a point of convergence of trade routes on a branch of the Pruth. Its picturesque site, clear streams, historic interest, and trade with Odessa, Galatz, and central Europe make it an important, thriving city. Galatz (80,411), between two great feeders of the Danube, partly on the bluffs of the great river, partly below on the alluvial plain, is the market town for the region. Its elevators, docks, and railroad connections rival those of Braila. Its citizens manufacture glass, build ships, saw and export lumber, and export corn; still it is not keeping pace with Constanta on the sea, although its river channel is dredged to 18 feet. Urban life does not develop in the east of Europe as it does in the west.

Walachian Hills and Plains. Great alluvial slopes, compound fans rising 600 feet between the Danube and the mountains, have pushed the river southward since Tertiary time and spread a very useful plain below the sunny slope of the Transylvanian Alps. The streams are bent eastward by their own deposits; all are so steep-graded and loaded with waste that they have little economic value. Some that do not reach back to the mountains become dry early in the summer. The master river, Danube, decreases in volume from the Iron Gate to the mouths of the Sereth and Pruth, which restore some of its lost power. Marshes, the rule of the day as on the Danube plain, also interfere with the use and the crossing of most of the streams. Willows and reeds mark the stream courses, which are frequented by wild ducks, geese, pelicans, coots, herons, storks, and plover. Sturgeon, sarda, salmon, and pike are abundant in season in the streams.

Walachia is too dry for trees; its chernozem soil has developed under grasses and is excellent for cereals. Corn in the moister parts, and wheat elsewhere, furnish 90 per cent of the exports. The former is the chief local food. In still drier parts, sheep swarm over the fields and add a Mediterranean aspect to the landscape and wool to the export list. With all these activities rainfall is the critical factor. Its vagaries are reflected in the annual statistics. Dry-farming would pay generously with a more literate, enlightened, industrious people. In spite of all difficulties, Walachia and Moldavia constitute the greatest corn belt in Europe.

Even home and town sites are water-determined. Springs along valley walls attract multitudes of farmers' homes. Villages have one great well drilled to perennial waters. The towns are mostly where the streams come out from the hills—Pitești, Ploești, Craiova. The map of population density shows how the people concentrate along streams, both for the water and for the rich alluvial soils.

North of Bucharest near the mountains is the Campani (Câmpina) oil field, so prolific that Rumania produces more petroleum than all the rest of Europe outside of U.S.S.R. With the decline of wheat exports, Rumania has found oil export most valuable, and it has saved the balance of trade. Gas provides more power than all the coal in Rumania. In the vicinity of the oil fields salt is extensively mined.

Public well with wheel and bucket. (Courtesy Library of Congress)

Braila (95,514) (Brăila), the rival of Galatz, serves similarly another region. It handles more grain but less lumber than Galatz. Its real competitor is Constanta, actually on the coast and 12 miles nearer Bucharest. Braila's exact location is at the head of the 18-foot river channel on a great turn where the river leaves the marshy plain and crowds a firm bluff. It manufactures cement from local materials and oil products for fuel; it has sawmills, textile and flour mills, and makes beet sugar, beer, and chemicals.

Eastern church built of stone in Bucharest. (Courtesy Library of Congress)

Craiova (85,574) is a grain market, manufacturing foodstuffs and shipping to Bucharest and Braila or Constanta for export. Giurgiu (30,200), St. George in English, an old Genoese fort and river port, has an active ferry across the placid Danube and with Ruschuk forms another pair of Danubian towns.

Bucharest (1,041,800) has a long history in an important central position where it commands routes across the Walachian Plains into the mountain passes to Russia, Hungary, and Bulgaria. Invader and merchant from east and south have been drawn to it. Its trade easily reaches the Black Sea and through it the Mediterranean. It has been a center for Turkish wars, earthquakes, fires, floods, and pestilence; but the modern city is clean, substantial, above flood-level, and built largely in stone and brick. It is larger than any other five cities in Rumania, and has a population as cosmopolitan as any inland city in the east. Besides being a commercial city and the capital, Bucharest is becoming industrial. Aided by petroleum and salt from the foothills it manufactures chemicals. It is abundantly supplied with perennial water; hence its inhabitants work in foodstuffs and textiles and can manufacture sugar, pack meat, and develop metallurgical works. They manufacture beer and furniture, refine oil, make bricks, work in the railroad repair shops, and maintain splendid retail stores. In Bucharest as the capital city many institutions are centralized for the nation, such as banks, the telegraph system, the post-office, commercial companies, and education. The university has 20,000 students. In the sixteenth century Bucharest was a walled city, all on one side of the Dâmbovita River. Thrice a new, larger wall was built, until in 1853 a considerable area on each side of the river was included. In 1910 the city had expanded beyond the wall, and a score of suburbs were growing up. The wall has now been demolished, and eight railroads communicate with the city, although none actually reaches into it.

The city is in a favored part of the plain, in the midst of an area already as densely populated as any, and, now that oil and gas are produced abundantly, it will surely be a leader of a developing nation.

Dobruja. In relation to the rest of Rumania this region may be called Trans-Danubia. It is very diversified in its geology, and cosmopolitan in race and language. The north section is a growing delta, mostly subject to inundations when the Pruth and Sereth rise, but having two or three sand dune areas. It is known to hunter and fisherman for its fish and waterfowl. Over $100 million worth of fish are caught each year. Beyond the delta toward the south there are the highest topography and, outside the crystalline areas in the mountains, by far the oldest structures, where the rocks yield copper to the miner. Altitude here is sufficient to bring rainfall adequate for deciduous forests. In 1940, 3,000 square miles of hilly south Dobruja went by treaty to Bulgaria. The people of the Dobruja have been, successively, Greeks, Armenians, Turks, Tatars, Russians, Germans, and Bulgars; but in the north Rumanians now replace or outnumber all others.

In the middle and northern sections moisture sufficient for cultivation results in fine corn crops around Constanta.

Sulina is the delta port on the only distributary kept navigable. It reloads and exports wheat. Constanta (78,586) is on a small bar bay of the Black Sea which is never frozen, and by artificial deepening its waters accommodate ocean vessels, which here load wheat brought by train from the wheat plains across the great Danube bridge at Cernavoda. Tank steamers take on petroleum, conducted in pipe lines from the wells across the same bridge to modern, marine loading racks at the docks. Whereas Braila is closed during two or three winter months, this port is always open, hence is capturing Braila trade. It is far enough from delta mouths to avoid silting.

The royal palace in Bucharest. Is it any farther from the rural peasant home to the ruler's palace in Rumania than from the farmhouse to the White House in America? (Courtesy Library of Congress)

Transylvanian Region. In this region are included not only the Transylvanian Basin but also the Bihar Mountains, little strips of the Great Alföld, and as much of the Banat as lies in Rumania—all of Rumania west of the Carpathian arc. The basin received Tertiary sediments, as did the Great Alföld, but was lifted higher and never had a Quaternary deposit. Instead it has been maturely dissected by many streams, so it now comprises a maze of old hills very suitable for agriculture. The Bihar Mountains consist of a core of ancient crystallines, surrounded by Paleozoic and Mesozoic sediments, extensively intruded and complexly disturbed and left at such altitudes that soft layers have been etched out and hard ones stand as rugged mountain forms, somewhat forbidding to agriculture but high enough to catch sufficient rainfall for better forest growth than anywhere else in Transylvania. Streams furnish power to work up the lumber and mine the ores of gold, silver, copper, and lead. Only 2 per cent of the water power is at present developed. Wide-open, rural valleys lead out of the mountains to the Alföld. Villages occupy many flood-proof sites along these cultivated valleys, and grazing flourishes on the slopes.

Rural home, with a garden fence of poles. Pumpkins lie beside the fence. (Courtesy Library of Congress)

The Transylvanian Basin is still contributing enormous quantities of sediment to the Alföld. The Olt River drains large valleys in the southeast section, where the Carpathians cast a rain shadow and produce the driest place in Transylvania. Other streams, emerging from the basin each side of the Bihar, float lumber down to sawmills and pulpmills and direct traffic, roads, and railroads to the towns at the foot of the hills and to the Alföld. It was this topographic situation that helped lead the treaty-makers to draw the west boundary of Rumania with more reference to economic conditions than to ethnic factors.

A little oil, believed to be an earnest of more, is known in northern

Transylvania. Coal and iron in the southwest and in the Banat foster a metallurgical industry which has somewhat declined since World War I. Seventy per cent of Rumanian coal is in this region.

Transylvanian agriculture is for subsistence and not for export. Grazing predominates over the hills, but cultivation in the valleys. Sheep are the most important stock; cattle, horses, and camels are raised, and all are used for draft animals. The country is admirable for a lively dairy industry, but it has only begun. Hogs feed upon the corn and mast. Corn and wheat lead among cereals; other crops are oats, barley, hops for grain beer, beets

Mill and old overshot water wheel beside a country road; two residences beyond. (Courtesy Library of Congress)

for sugar, tobacco, and potatoes. In many places the cultivated fields spread entirely over the old hilltops. The vine is cultivated amid tree orchards in almost every valley, and in the Banat rice and beans have become important. Transylvania has 16,000 square miles of forest, much of it dense; some fine stands are valuable virgin hardwoods. Forest laws and a system of forestry have been inaugurated. This region has a remarkable forest opportunity.

In Transylvania some peasants live in villages and go out to their farms; but here much more than elsewhere they live on the farms, because the Carpathians protected these sections from Tatar and Turk invasion and

village life was never necessary. There has resulted a rural independence
rare in Rumania. This spirit of freedom spread in the past century to the
old states and led to the movement for national unity and independence.
The peasant home is often of stone, perhaps as frequently of wood, roofed
with slate or even with great shale and sandstone slabs piled on the roof.
A characteristic long, simple porch, from which a door leads to each room,
runs the whole length of one side of the house. The two gable ends are cut
off, leaving a triangular piece of shingled roof. Many houses are painted
blue. The most progressive, forward-looking population in the region is
in the Banat, where Germans, Serbs, and Magyars mingle with Rumanians
and where westward contacts have been more frequent and intensive.
Higher forms of social life and of agriculture, among which sericulture and
fruit-preserving may be mentioned, prevail here.

Leading towns are all "Saxon" because the Germans are commercial
and industrial and while not numerous give a stamp to the town. Oradea
Mare (82,282) in the western foothills is a sample, though a little more
Magyar than some. It manufactures farm machinery and food products and
trades in lumber and wool. Few streets are paved. It looks like an overgrown, rambling country town. Cluj (117,915), on the Szamos (Somesu)
River, much farther within the country, hence more rural and Rumanian,
has a university and a museum striving to preserve the records and instruments of native life. In the university the professor of English literature
described himself thus, "My father was a German, my mother was French,
I was born in Rumania, educated in England, teach English in a Rumanian
University and look like a Bolshevik." The town is a railroad junction point
and more commercial than industrial. Temesvar (111,987), is far south
in the Banat near the hills, in which are ores of iron, copper, and lead, with
various grades of fuel; hence it engages in metallurgical industries and
possesses a very mixed population. Arad (87,290), on the great Maros
(Mures) River just where it comes out of the hills, shares in the life and
products of both the hills and the Alföld. Like all towns, it is rural with
rambling streets, largely unpaved, and centers round a big, dirty market for
stock, vegetables, fruit, garments, textiles, and tools.

Foreign relations. Commerce in a land so wholly in the extractive
stage must move raw products out and bring in manufactured goods; nor
can there be any large trade. Only Russia and Bulgaria rank lower per
capita in foreign trade than Rumania; of all European states it has been
least touched by western influences. Commerce trends toward central
Europe, partly because of physical connections along the Danube and its
plains and along railroads around the Carpathians, and is stimulated by
the difference in industrial development existing between Rumania and
central Europe. Exports and imports are nearly equal, for there are few
other items to assist in maintaining a balance.

Wheat has long been the chief of the exports, but it is giving place to corn. Cereals constitute in value nearly 60 per cent of all exports; forest products and petroleum each about 16 to 18 per cent. Textiles and metal goods, such as tools and machinery, make up half of the imports. Neighboring nations are in much the same stage of production and use as Rumania; hence trade with them is small. Hungary, however, buys about half the exported lumber.

Transportation is yet insufficient. In spite of the handicaps of shoals, Iron Gate, a great mud delta, ice, and inland mouth, 37,000 boats with 10 million tons displacement navigate the Danube. Railroads are not yet reoriented for best internal service, and there are only about 7,000 miles of them.

Burnt wood work and worker, a home industry. (Courtesy Library of Congress)

Rumania needs to increase its commercial and industrial facilities, use more than 5 per cent of the 1,600,000 horsepower of available hydroelectric energy, develop forestry and mineral production, promote the education of the peasantry, increase livestock production, and modernize its agricultural equipment.

Rumania is a rich land, but poorly developed. It is backward socially, politically, economically, educationally, religiously. It is off the great world-travel routes, but foreign contacts are bringing vision and aspiration.

The government is developing industrial and agricultural technical schools, experiment stations, coöperative societies, a rural credit system, and a public school system. Industrialization far ahead of the present is possible and practical under enlightened, honest leadership. A large proportion of the country's industry has been nationalized. The state is young, vigorous, and alert. Leadership, mostly communistic and Moscow-directed, in government, science, and finance is leavening the people from the top down.

QUESTIONS

1. How can political independence of small nationalities be made compatible with the economic law of trade and exchange which grows so definitely out of geographic circumstances?

2. Why is Rumania said to have a remarkable forest opportunity?

3. What has Rumania's position to do with its backwardness? Test out your answer in the several listed phases of backwardness.

4. How can conditions of modern communication help Rumania forward? Show how this is a geographic question.

5. Compare Rumania with Czechoslovakia as to advantages and disadvantages of geographic setting.

6. Would Rumania be damaged by adjusting the Hungarian boundary so as to place the Hungarian minority on the other side of the boundary?

7. How seriously did the loss of Bessarabia affect Rumania?

BIBLIOGRAPHY

ARMSTRONG, Hamilton F., *Tito and Goliath* (New York, The Macmillan Company, 1951).

BASCH, Antonin, *The Danube Basin and German Economic Sphere* (New York, Columbia University Press, 1943).

BIGELOW, Donald F., *Rumanian Petroleum Industry in 1921* (Washington, D. C., Government Printing Office, 1922).

BLANCHARD, W. O., and VISHER, S. S., *Economic Geography of Europe* (New York, McGraw-Hill Book Company, Inc., 1931).

BOWMAN, Isaiah, The New World (Yonkers-on-Hudson, New York, World Book Company, 1928).

British Survey Handbooks, Vol. 2, *Rumania* (Cambridge, England, Cambridge University Press, 1944). C. Kormos, compiler.

CLARK, Charles Upson, *Bessarabia, Russia and Roumania on the Black Sea* (New York, Dodd, Mead & Company, Inc., 1927).

DE MARTONNE, Emmanuel, "Rumania," in Vidal de La Blache and Gallois, *Géographie Universelle* (Paris, Lib. Armand Colin, 1931).

DOMINIAN, Leon, *Frontiers of Language and Nationality in Europe* (New York, Henry Holt & Company, Inc., 1921).

Europa, Encyclopedia of Europe (London, Europa Publications, Ltd.), annual.

FITZGERALD, Walter, *New Europe* (New York, Harper and Brothers, 1946).

Foreign Commerce Year Book (Washington, D. C., Government Printing Office).

HALASZ, Albert, *New Central Europe in Economic Maps* (Berlin, Verlag von Reimar Hobbing, 1928), in German and English.

International Reference Service, U. S. Dept. of Commerce (Washington, D. C., Government Printing Office), many numbers per year.

KENDREW, W. G., *Climates of Continents* (Oxford, Clarendon Press, 1942).

KISS, George, "A T.V.A. on the Danube," *Geographical Review,* Vol. 37 (1947), pp. 274-302.

LEHMANN, John, *Down River; A Danubian Study* (London, The Cresset Press, 1939).

MCCORMICK, Thomas C. T., ed., *Problems of the Post-War World* (New York and London, McGraw-Hill Book Company, Inc., 1945).

DE MARTONNE, Emmanuel, "Transylvanian Alps," *Geographical Review,* Vol. 3 (1917).

MILLER, William, *The Balkans, Roumania, Bulgaria, Serbia, Montenegro* (New York, G. P. Putnam's Sons, 1926).

MITRANY, David, *Land and Peasant in Rumania* (New Haven, Yale University Press, 1930).

Moody's Governments and Municipals (New York, Moody's Investor's Service), nearly an annual.

Moody's Railroads, American and Foreign (New York, Moody's Investor's Service), annual.

NEWMAN, Bernard, *The New Europe* (New York, The Macmillan Company, 1943).

PASVOLSKY, Leo, *Economic Nationalism of Danubian States* (New York, The Macmillan Company, 1928).

PEARCY, G. Etzel, and FIFIELD, Russell H., *et al., World Political Geography* (New York, Thomas Y. Crowell Company, 1948).

PRIBICEVIC, Stojan, *World Without End* (New York, Reynal & Hitchcock, 1939).

RIPLEY, W. Z., *Races of Europe* (New York, D. Appleton and Co., 1899).

RISTELHUEBER, René, *Histoire des Peuples Balkaniques* (Paris, Fayard, 1950).

ROBERTS, Henry L., *Rumania: Political Problems of an Agrarian State* (New Haven, Yale University Press, 1951).

ROBERTS, M. C., "Rumania Today," *Economic Geography,* Vol. 9 (July, 1933), pp. 230-244.

ROUCEK, J. S., "Economic Geography of Rumania," *Economic Geography,* Vol. 7 (October, 1931), pp. 390-399.

———, "Roumanian Manufacturing Interests," *Bulletin Geographical Society of Philadelphia,* Vol. 30 (1932), pp. 200-206.

———, *Central Eastern Europe* (New York, Prentice-Hall, Inc., 1946).

———, *Contemporary Europe* (New York, D. Van Nostrand Company, Inc., 1941).

Rumania, an Economic Handbook, United States Department of Agriculture (Washington, D. C., Government Printing Office).

SHACKLETON, Margaret R., *Europe, A Regional Geography* (London, Longmans, Green & Company, 1942).

Statesman's Yearbook, STEINBERG, S. H., ed., (New York, The Macmillan Company).

WELLES, Sumner, ed., *An Intelligent American's Guide to the Peace* (New York, The Dryden Press, 1945).

WHITBECK, R. H., and FINCH, V. C., *Economic Geography* (New York, McGraw-Hill Book Company, Inc., 1941).

Part VIII

CONCLUSION

GEOGRAPHY IN THE FOURTH DIMENSION

In previous chapters we have looked at the countries in their length and breadth, in their height and depth, and in their relations with each other. In the chapters that follow, attention will be centered on the historical aspect of some of the geographic relationships. As in the chapter on geology and physiography it was necessary to carry the mind back to the beginnings of the history of the earth and come forward through eons of time and periods of geologic labors to find the explanations of the present topographic forms, distributions of land, sea, soils, and life, so here in agriculture, commerce, and even in civilization and culture, the foundations were laid millenniums ago and there has been slow progress by adjustment, response, even by halts at times, until the present status has been attained. Nor does any one feel confident that these processes of attainment are going to stop soon. We point the camera, click the shutter, take the picture, and on they go. One can but wonder, when he looks back 2,000 or 5,000 years, where our agriculture, commerce, and industry, yes, and our civilization and our culture, will be in as many more thousands of years.

CHAPTER 39

The Geography of Agriculture

When tillage begins, other arts follow; the farmers
therefore are the founders of human civilization.
—DANIEL WEBSTER

Early stages. The chapter on prehistoric men made it apparent that
in the earliest stages of human occupation of Europe food and safety
were the greatest of human needs, and beside them little else mattered.
The choice of food depended upon the physical environment. Forest hunting engaged men in the more open forest areas, whether plains or mountains,
and fishing in the north and middle parts, especially on the coasts of the
sea and great lakes. Just as plants and animals adjust to conditions in which
they find themselves, so men, often just as unconsciously as a vine or a
deer, become adapted or adjusted to elements of environment. Men everywhere seem to have supplemented the diet of meat with fruits, leaves, buds,
stems, nuts, seeds, and possibly roots. What more do we eat now? Early
man may have begun by eating his meat and plant parts raw, but with the
discovery of fire many items became available that were indigestible before.
These early adaptations to the environment and modifications of the
environment to suit the people, were both simple and local. No large environment was laid under tribute, no strong bonds were made between man
and his surroundings.

Combinations of activities occurred in places among early people, i.e.,
occupations were influenced by two or more geographic elements or resources. In some places only one occupation seems to have flourished.
Hunting was practised over the ranges of edible birds, deer, bears, or boars;
fishing, in lakes, sea borders, and streams. The taking of fish was so easy
that very little hunting was practised by those who could rely upon fishing,
and fishing became so satisfactory an occupation that the great fishing
peoples did not start agriculture and rarely mingled in their shell-heaps any
refuse of hunting or rural foraging. The best hunting also checked the
beginning of agriculture in north central Europe. Usually hunting seems to
have associated itself with both agriculture and grazing because the hunter
was continually roaming through the forests or plains, where wild plant
life could be used to supplement his meat foods and where a more con-

tinuous meat supply could be had by keeping alive some specimens taken. A wild boar and sow, a wild mountain sheep or goat, or even a beef animal could be arrested and tethered or yarded and fed until needed. Thus feeding began; and breeding must have been a simple next step. The care of stock thus became an occupation, and at the same time it strengthened the bonds between the man and his environment. Hunting and grazing, and hunting and farming, became supplementary occupations.

The hunter or the grazer could have, must have, a more permanent abode, and even a better living, if he made bold to plant a few seeds of wheat, lettuce, asparagus, or cabbage or transplant to his door a grapevine, a gooseberry bush or a strawberry plant; so native plants, adopted into a domestic environment, constituted the beginnings of agriculture. Hunting and agriculture were made to supplement each other, and even more did grazing and agriculture interplay in the moister parts of Europe.

Grazing and forestry have often been associated. Aside from the occasional felling of a tree for a dugout, trees were rarely cut in Europe until men, perceiving that grass did not prosper beneath thick tree growths, began to cut trees to give grass a better chance.

Reasons for agriculture. Primary causes for planting were more than curiosity or accident, though these played their part. Man wanted the advantage gained in the results of his planting, a crop beyond simply harvesting what had grown wild. He wanted more permanent or continuous supplies than he could get by simply gathering leaves, grass, seeds, fruits, or vegetables. He may in some instances have wanted some plant to grow nearer than it did naturally, or wanted a cache and less necessity for roaming. To make a success of his planting he must not have too rigorous a climate or extended droughts.

While limited planting and transplanting occurred very early in many parts of Europe, no part of the continent was particularly favorable to agriculture except the southeastern regions, adjacent to the great river valleys and the "fertile crescent" of Breasted.[1] The world's successful agriculture sprang up more or less simultaneously in three regions: in China and the lands southward from China, scattered in scores of separated localities; in the Levant, or as we say now in the Near East, including southwest Asia, southeast Europe and the flood-plain of the Nile of Africa; and in the Highlands of Mexico and the Andes, where altitude contravenes the normal temperature effects of low latitude. In these favored places intensive agriculture developed, plants were improved, new varieties were bred, and other species were introduced from surrounding lands. The Near East center, at the meeting of three continents, was very favorably situated and became important in dispersions of plants. Europe had a goodly number of native plant species which have been put under cultivation and in most

---

[1] James H. Breasted, *Ancient Times, a History of the Early World* (1935).

cases much improved; and it has profited by introductions from all three centers, more abundantly from the Near East and more recently from the American center.

Native plants in Europe. More than a dozen plants of wide variety now cultivated in Europe were found native in the continent. Of cereals, oats were wild in East European Russia and south to the Danube. They preferred a moist, cool climate, and spreading westward and northward they passed under cultivation from Switzerland to Finland and Sweden. Swiss Lake Dwellers gathered them, as their presence in the refuse shows; German tribes and Celts of England raised them 2,000 years ago; but they did not become common until A.D. 1500.

Cabbage grew wild along coasts of the British Isles and western Europe. It was a long, loose-leafed, sprawling plant and by selection has produced kale, collards, kohlrabi, broccoli, cauliflower, and brussels sprouts; its cultivation has spread over European gardens everywhere. Its relative, the turnip, is a native of temperate Europe. By cultivation and selection many varieties adapted to different soils and climate have arisen.

Celery was native from moist, cool Sweden to the Caucasus, was enjoyed by ancient nations, and has been cultivated more than 2,000 years. Lettuce has had a similar history. Carrots and parsnips are natives of Europe, Germany to Caucasus; being used as food through the early centuries, they were cultivated in Italy and elsewhere more than 2,000 years ago. Horse-radish was native from Finland to eastern Europe, and Romans used it in the early days of the republic. Beets, which grew wild near the Mediterranean coasts, were probably the parents of our table beets, sugar beets, and chards or leaf beets. Chards and beets were used in the classical period and probably long before. Sugar was discovered to be abundantly present in certain varieties of beet in 1590, and the sugar-beet industry was established in the early nineteenth century. These root crops are wonderfully adapted to the moist, cool weather, with warm summers, of central and northern Europe.

Asparagus is a native of salt marshes in temperate Europe, especially in France, Poland, and southern Russia. It was cultivated by the Romans more than 200 years B.C. Chestnuts are natives of Europe, and have been used from man's first records in caves, and later in lake dwellings. They constitute a large item in human diet of central Europe today. Roasted nuts are munched on street-cars; baked or boiled, they are used as a vegetable; and dainty, tasty desserts can be concocted from them.

Europe had a number of substantial though wild fruits. Apples, native in open woods of central Europe, were gathered and used by lake dwellers 6,000 years ago. They were cultivated 3,000 years ago. Some varieties may have grown wild in the Near East, for Phœnicians raised them and they were well known in southeastern Europe in 400 B.C. Pears were used by the Swiss Lake Dwellers and others 4,000 years ago. Several varieties of currants and gooseberries are native in northern Europe and were used from Sweden to Greece. They spread then as now by cuttings. Strawberries were wild in western Europe from Lapland to Spain and were taken to Greece. They were cultivated early and improved as agriculture rose.

Species of blueberries and cranberries were native in sour, moist soils in many parts of Europe. These belong to the families known as heaths, which include similar plants from high altitudes in southern Europe to tundra plains in the far north. In Sweden, Finland, and Russia is the prized golden berry, much like the blueberry, only yellow. These lands are also blessed with blue, red, and black berries closely resembling our huckleberry except in color. No doubt most of these fruits were eaten long before they were cultivated and improved. Poppies were native in southern Europe and were cultivated as flowers but not for a narcotic, though that property was known to the Greeks over 2,000 years ago. Swiss Lake Dwellers also cultivated the poppy. The above plants, being native to Europe, were adapted to the climates and soils; man's adjustments included his adoption of them.

Agriculture was more ancient in temperate Europe than classical Greek writers knew; yet only the crudest breeding and selection processes came into action anywhere until about 200 years ago, and scientific experiments in plant improvement did not begin earlier than about the year 1800. Before that date many plants were transplanted from place to place, where they became adapted and acclimatized if the new seasons permitted bloom and seed-bearing, and if the plant had sufficient resistance to cold and drought.

Plant introductions from the Near East center. Only southeastern Europe was favorable to agriculture. It was a part of the Near East center and imported freely from other parts of the Near East, then extended the range and use of many plants to other parts of Europe. Men seem to have early sensed the possibility of importing plants to please their palates, and Europeans have been no exception.

Aryan-speaking people, migrating from northern Mesopotamia to Europe between 2000 and 2500 B.C., brought several species of plants. While these are the first of record, Near East plants are known to have been cultivated and harvested in Europe centuries before. When the Lake Dwellers in Switzerland were still in the late Stone Age and used no metals, they raised wheat derived from the Near East. In fact, the earliest Lake Dwellers left grains in their refuse, possibly 6,000 to 8,000 years ago. In their Bronze Age their agriculture was more varied, and was more advanced than Bronze-Age agriculture in Italy.

Phœnician voyagers, Persian warriors, Alexander in India, and travelers with Greek and Roman armies carried plants and seeds to Europe with the expressed purpose of introducing them to European cultivators. The Punic Wars brought much farming knowledge, for Carthaginian agriculture was more scientific and susceptible of higher profits than Roman. The Crusaders later made other introductions. From early prehistoric days on through the centuries of war and migration, European agriculture has been tremendously enriched by all these additions and improvements.

Not only wheat came this way, but barley from Asia Minor was cultivated widely more than 4,000 years ago; rye came over 2,000 years ago into latitudes more suitable for it than the south, and was unknown to ancient Greece and Rome. Millet was a common forage crop in Europe at the dawn of South European history; and Stone Age Lake Dwellers in both Italy and Switzerland used it. Millet as a grain, not as forage, probably was brought from Egypt and southwestern Asia. Other crops that were used more for stock food, such as the clovers, came later. Alfalfa and lucerne were cut for hay by Greeks and Romans, who received their seed from Media, the latter in 470 B.C. Sweet clover spread over Europe at an early date.

Among vegetables, spinach was brought to central Europe from the Near East before any written history, but was not used by early Greeks and Romans. Onions, garlic, and leeks were cultivated from the wild forms in the Near East. Onions were known 4,000 years ago in Persia and Palestine and spread over Europe with early peoples. Garlic and leeks came later. Rhubarb came into cultivation in southeastern Europe in prehistoric times and has now spread over all the cool, moist part of the continent, even into the far north, where it makes a splendid growth and supplies a needed spring food. The bean of history, or broad bean, originated, like the pea, in western Asia. Both were used by the Lake Dwellers in their Bronze Age and by the Greeks in their golden age, and now both are used in every country of Europe. Parsley came from the Lebanons and was prized by Greeks and Romans as a garnish 2,000 years ago; and the artichoke, whose buds are considered a delicacy, arrived by a similar route but centuries earlier. Salsify came from the Near East, but is not ancient. Muskmelons also were brought from western Asia about the time of Christ but were not common nor liked until the seventeenth century.

Many important fruits were also brought from the Near East. Pomegranates came from Persia through Armenia and Asia Minor, where their cultivation is known to have occurred 4,000 years ago, and from whence they were introduced through the Mediterranean lands to Iberia. Plums originated in the Caucasus, and the stones of their fruits are found in the refuse of Bronze-Age Lake Dwellers. Plums are so hardy and adjustable, resistant and attractive, that they are now grown in all countries. Apricots are Armenian, cherries are Persian, and both were cultivated in Europe in earliest Greek times. The quince was naturalized from Armenia and Persia into Europe 4,000 years ago and became well known in Greece and Rome in their heyday. The almond is a native of the Near East, was brought to Palestine in pre-Biblical times, and has been cultivated in Europe for more than 4,000 years. Grapes seem to be natives of Caucasus and Black Sea lands. They were cultivated in Armenia, used by Lake Dwellers in their Bronze Age, cultivated in Egypt 5,000 to 6,000 years ago, and have spread as far over Europe as climate permits. A thousand varieties have been bred from the old stocks. The olive grows wild in Mediterranean regions and in southern Russia. Palestinians were familiar with its peculiarities long ago, and it has probably been under cultivation for at least 4,000 years. Figs are native in southern Arabia, where they passed into cultivation; they occupied southern Europe as far west as Spain in prehistoric time. The black mulberry for fruit came from Persia at an early date, and the white mulberry, excellent for its leaves, originated in China, was introduced into Persia, and then entered Europe. The latter has been cultivated for more than 4,000 years.

Two fiber plants, well adapted to European conditions, have been introduced and extensively used. Hemp, native to western and central Asia, was cultivated in the Levant, then imported into central Europe, where its soft fiber is used for cloth, cords, carpets, sacking, upholstering, and belt webs; frayed, it is used for calking seams and pipes and for packing pumps and engines. Its seed makes poultry and bird food and, when pressed, oil for soaps, paints, and some varnishes. Scythians cultivated it more than 4,000 years ago, and it has been in Europe for at least 2,000 years. Flax makes an even softer, finer thread and cloth. It was known by the Lake Dwellers in their Stone Age about 6,000 years ago. An abundance of linen cloth, of superior weave and greater durability than cotton, has been found around their platforms. Egyptians and Mesopotamians cultivated the annual flax 4,000 to 5,000 years ago. Finns picked up the perennial sort en route and took it to northern Europe before Aryan languages arrived. The bearers of Aryan tongues brought the annual varieties later to southern Europe. Today flax is hardy in the moist lands from Ireland to the heart of Russia. Its seed has been used for food throughout 2,500 years and is now used for oil and oilcake, for fertilizer and stock food. The fiber finds large use in cloth, thread, tapestries, and paper.

Hops are native in the Near East, came to Europe more than 2,000 years ago, rose to their present malt-flavoring uses in the eighth century, and still maintain their prestige. Roses are likewise natives of the Near East; they were brought to Europe at least 2,000 years ago, but were not much appreciated until the Middle Ages.

Plants from the Far East center. A few plants have come to Europe from India and the Far East center, some directly, some after a halt in the Near East. The citrus fruits are far the most important to Europe and to the world. No other fruit has ever been introduced into Europe that has taken so large a place in the food and drink of the people. Sweet oranges were native in southeastern Asia, were moved to India and to China 3,000 years ago, and then were carried by Moors and by Portuguese navigators from China to Iberia and Italy in the time of the Crusades. Sour oranges arose in the same place and stepped along to India, Persia, Syria, Sicily, and Spain during the ninth and tenth centuries. Lemons may have originated in southeast Asia, but they came with limes and citrons to southern Europe, first as potted ornamental plants, then as orchard fruits in the second century A.D. Peaches were cultivated in China 4,000 years ago, came as peach-stones to Persia "before the beginning of the Christian Era," and reached Europe about 400 B.C. They have spread as far as climate will permit.

One cereal came from southern Asia. Rice, cultivated from wild seed 4,000 to 5,000 years ago in India, was introduced at once into China but did not come to Europe until Portuguese and Moors brought it to Spain and Italy a few centuries ago. So little of southern Europe has the necessary water and the summer temperature of 77° F. that rice has not become an important crop. Another grass, the sugar-cane, was a native of southern Asia. In India it was cultivated for forage and after about A.D. 600 for sugar. During the Crusades it was planted along the southern patches of coastal and delta plains in Europe and became a source of sugar there in the twelfth century, and thus began to supplement honey, the only sweet in European diet to this date. Very little cultivation of sugar-cane has survived outside of Spain. The egg-plant is a native of India and came to Europe in the ninth century. The radish was domesticated in China from the wild, then was introduced into Egypt, where it was common 4,000 years ago. It spread in later centuries into the Near East and possibly varieties were domesticated there. Its introduction into Greece and from there throughout Europe and America shows its importance. Ginger root is a native of India and the East; it came to Arabia next, then, in classical times, to Europe. The soy bean, a native of southeastern Asia, was brought to Europe three or four centuries ago as a forage crop, a rotation crop, and a green manure. It was an important introduction.

Plants from the American center and scattered places. The third or American center of primitive agriculture has made several very notable contributions to European agriculture, all since the famous voyage of Columbus. Potatoes, tomatoes, red peppers, mangoes, tobacco, kidney and lima beans, maize, peanuts, sunflowers, sweet potatoes, squash, and the black walnut are the most valuable. Blackberries, dewberries, and raspberries have added much to the small fruits of temperate Europe.

Several scattered introductions round out the plant list for Europe and make it varied and attractive. Watermelons and the sorghums were added from tropical Africa; paprika was brought from Jamaica in tropical America; buckwheat came from its native habitat in north central Asia, where it had been domesticated. Tatars brought it to Russia during several invasions in the Middle Ages, and it proved to be well suited to temperate Europe and later to similar conditions in America. Cotton, a wild herbaceous plant of tropical Asia and America, was domesticated independently in each place. Although placed under cultivation in India 5,000 years ago, it did not reach Europe until about the opening of the Christian Era. It needs so long a growing season that not all the Mediterranean Region can raise it. It did not supplant linen in Rome until the Dark Ages and never reached its supremacy until heavy imports of the fiber from America and India could be made in the nineteenth century.

Since the rapid scientific experimental work to improve seeds and plants has begun, scientists have explored the world for new plants and new varieties of plants to supplement the present cultivated floras of Europe and America. The result has been a rapid exchange of plants and hundreds of introductions of new varieties into both continents. This is a closer utilization and adaptation of geographic conditions than the production of the plant in its former habitat, followed by the importation of its useful parts—seeds, fruit, juice, or fiber.

The great transhumance. Transhumance means "across the humus" or soils and is derived from the French. When hunting was being replaced by grazing in the more open plains or old topography of southern Russia, Poland, and Spain, the wanderlust was met by long treks twice a year with sheep or cattle. The mesta described in the chapter on Spain is a recent continuation of such a migration system. Transhumance of as much as 500 miles was in some places necessary twice a year to give the stock adequate pasture without encroaching upon the hay and haymaking of one locality. Thus, sheep wintered in the south in Spain and summered in the north, permitting the farmers to cut and store hay in the south to supplement the fresh grass that might be available for the stock in the next winter. In the plains of Poland and Russia the journeys and their purpose were similar. In parts of France, Italy, Yugoslavia, and Rumania, similar transhumance continued from prehistoric to recent and, locally, to modern times. This is a more systematic migration than that of nomadism, but is a seasonal adjustment of true nomadism. Examine the environment and see if general farming, or any special type of farming would be a better adjustment in some country than is nomadism or transhumance. The latter now exists in Italy as in old Roman days, in Spain, in Provence of France, and in the Balkans, as well as in open plains farther northeast under a drier climate. Russia has made a vigorous effort to replace much of both customs by fixed stock farms and state wheat fields.

The lesser transhumance. Not only did men adopt the long-journey seasonal transhumance but they found a great advantage in a short journey, a seasonal migration. The latter developed in the hills and mountains, where a journey of a very few miles and 5,000 to 8,000 feet vertically gave as much difference, often more, in climate and grass as 500 miles in Spain or southern Russia. Such migration of cattle and sheep was common thousands of years ago in the Balkans, in Crete, in nearly all parts of the Ægean Sea lands, and in Asia Minor. It developed in the Pyrenees, in the Central

Plateau of France, in the Alps, and in Italy before Rome began. Well-established transhumance is described fully 300 years before our era. The Alban Hills and passage for stock through the *salinas* (salt marshes of the plains) are mentioned. Rugged, remote lands, called state pastures, are described in the Apennines. Patricians and plebeians had equal legal rights and privileges, but the former carried larger flocks and, by bribery, drove plebeians out. The transhumance system provided extraordinary self-sufficiency, but it involved economic, social, and, at times, political problems.

Alpine grasses were nutritive, often aromatic, because they grew in clear, dust-free, rich light of greater altitudes. The nutty taste of Gruyère cheese, an Alpine product of long standing made originally at Gruyère, Switzerland, is said to be due to the musteline lovage, a plant of the celery family, of which cattle are very fond. Men discovered long ago that the grasses on Alpine limestone soils "gave fineness to the wool."

Although the earliest mountain migrations consisted simply of a journey to the Alps pastures in the spring and a return in the fall to the permanent valley homes, the pressure of cattle population called for widening pastures and a closer utilization, which was achieved by a spring and autumn halt at intermediate heights. Temporary shelters were built, not only on the Alps but on these intermediate levels, and later some members of the family abode weeks in them, making hay during the summer to be carried down to the barns for forage the next winter. Some of these midway homes had gardens, but they were small and not comparable with those around the valley homes.

The journey twice a year, between the plains and the mountains of Abruzzi, Umbria, and Calabria, "involved migration of sheep, fattening oxen, and baggage horses, mules, and asses, in bands of 500 to 1,000 along recognized cattle or 'green' roads with a shepherd for each 100 to 200 sheep." In 1800 one wrote, "1,000,000 head with 5,000 shepherds, in sheepskin jackets and heavy leather shoes, make the journey which occupies a month." In Abruzzi the sheep ate and climbed higher and higher, reaching greatest heights when days were hottest at these altitudes and grass was best. Similar migrations occurred from the Tuscan maremma to the hills eastward. Shepherds, finding the life hard and the many months of separation from their families trying, wore a look of sadness and rarely sang or yodeled, but became wild and gloomy in disposition. Gathered around their hut fires at night they told, over and over, the legends of their surroundings. They have been described as frugal, honest, sober, and content with their simple living and diet of polenta,[2] cheese, skimmed milk, and water. The winter confinement in valley homes with little to do gave the men a sluggish life and left them anemic and debilitated in the spring. There was little reading, discussion, or culture anywhere. Women were

[2] Polenta is a gruel or porridge of chestnut meal.

more active and came out of the winter in better condition. In many places transhumance encouraged smuggling, first of sheep and cattle down unfrequented valleys, then of merchandise up a valley, over a divide, and down on the opposite side in the course of the season. Isolation for centuries in these transhumant valleys limited the people to the science, lore, and arts of centuries before and fostered conservatism and backwardness. Only in recent years, when modern communication and transportation have connected them with the outside world, are influences of the progressiveness of the plains reaching them. Great changes are imminent.

As the migrations and numbers of stock increased, forests were cut back in places to increase the grass areas. The great products of this type of life were two, an annual crop of wool and a continuous stream of cheeses, much of which found its way to towns in the plains. Subsistence was always the main issue with all the shepherds.

This lesser transhumance is very old. Some consider it an outgrowth of the great, but its age suggests that it is rather an adjustment of a once nomadic people who moved into much restricted mountainous topography and, as their flocks increased, needed to expand and conserve pasture and so developed transhumance. The great transhumance also arose directly from nomadism as a distinctly seasonal migration and was found to meet the exigencies of the case. The people participating in the lesser transhumance are largely of the Alpine Race; Mediterraneans and Slavic Alpines engage in the great transhumance, and Nordics have little to do with either type.[3] Both types of transhumance admit of agriculture to supplement grazing, but as recently as the fifteenth century the pastoral type of life got the favors, and cultivation was legally restricted even in Italy. The mesta in Spain, whose codes gave the sheep-raiser many privileges, was anti-agricultural in spirit and hence anti-Moorish.

Irrigation. Irrigation is an ancient practice in Europe. It belonged with early nomadism before the nomads came to Europe and was an important accessory of the lesser transhumance thousands of years ago. Mountain alps were irrigated to increase the amount of grass by little streams of water led across them from melting snows and glaciers. Lower pastures around the winter, or permanent, homes were irrigated in the drier summer for the same reason. The use of water arose to increase the growth of grass long before it was devoted to fruit and vegetables, but as the advantages for grass became manifest irrigation was adapted to the garden, then taken down the slopes to larger gardens, and recently to the general crops on plains.

Irrigation almost universally lifts the social order. It involves several families, frequently living at different levels in the hills, and requires acquaintance and coöperation, mutual dependence, and responsibility. It gen-

[3] See Sater life in Norway.

erally leads to codes, legal regulations, and treaties, and therefore involves governments. Thus it affects not only the grazing, agriculture, and more recently horticulture (in Spain, floriculture), but the social and political institutions.

Tools and power on farms. When one speaks of cultivation of certain plants 4,000 years ago, he must think of such cultivation and cultivators as then existed. Primitive agriculture could not have had better methods and tools than has the worst today. Wooden plows, crooked sticks with men to pull, spades of wood, hoes of stone on a stick—these are still in use, and no doubt are better today than were the best when cultivation began. Hoe culture has prevailed in Africa, but spade culture is European. A smooth, shaped steel spade, however, is a modern tool. Spades, like plows, were of wood. Some were of stone before the age of iron. A plow or cart presupposes a draft animal, horse, camel, ass, or ox. Imagine the surprise of the natives when the first ingenious farmer hitched a donkey to a plow to dig his field. It was in the early part of the first century A.D. that northern Gaul sported the first wheeled plows, but agriculture, like industry and commerce, made little gain until the Industrial Revolution and the rise of the age and spirit of invention.

From reaping with a hooked sickle or a straight scythe, plowing with crooked sticks or wooden plows with metal points, and threshing by beating with a flail or driving cattle over the straw, to plowing with steel mouldboards, harvesting with machines pulled by horses, and threshing with a machine that could stand near the barn or granary and separate the wheat from the straw, then from the chaff, and pour out straw, chaff, and wheat in three different places: these were changes that took ages. Some countries in Europe still use the primitive tools. As the changes have arrived, man has come into more vital and useful relation with the soil, the climate, the plants, and the crops.

The invention of motors and tractors and the preparation of gasoline inaugurated a rapid evolution in tools and in rural velocities. Mechanization is extremely modern. In the last 10 to 15 years tractors and power seeders, harvesters, and threshers in many plain areas of Europe are displacing the horse, ox, or cow, even the camel, in their respective kinds of farm work. Trucks are common in parts of Europe. The size and number of agricultural power machines in any country today are conditional upon its topography and the nature of its soils—a modern geographic response. Russia probably leads in mechanization, but France, England, and Germany follow; and Sweden, Italy, and Poland are now using trucks and power machines. All these improvements help man to take advantage of his soils more effectively, put a wider market into his hands, extend his purchasing power to other towns, and increase his rural service.

The new tools in the rural evolution of 200 years ago came to France and England first, instead of to the old-time cultured lands of Greece and

Italy. Then they spread to Belgium, Netherlands, Denmark, Germany, Sweden, and Italy. The modern tractor came into France and Germany, then Poland and Russia, and all since World War I.

Mediterranean agriculture. Cultivation and crops are so different in Mediterranean lands and climates that they merit a special discussion, but only mention can be made here. The winter rainfall involves fall planting and spring harvesting of many crops, and almost as much retirement and withdrawal from activities in summer as northern agriculture imposes in winter. Many of the local peculiarities of Mediterranean agriculture have been noticed in the chapters on individual countries.

Agriculture in central and northern Europe. Early agriculture in these lands was of the crudest and simplest sorts, as in much of Rumania today, until about the opening of the Christian Era. Dry uplands and ridges, where least labor told most, were first put under cultivation. Prehistoric hillside terraces tell of very ancient farming. Great improvements came when the Romans spread their roads, law, and order over most of the lands. Roman cultivation followed, but with many adjustments to the different climate and soils. Roman tools did not come north and west, and Roman crops usually could not be introduced, but methods and ideas that the local people would not have devised or used for centuries were passed on. The invaders took back and used many central European plants.

In all the older grazing industry, wool, manure for agriculture, and hides had been the products sought; but with the improvement of agriculture under Roman stimulus, there were many changes; cheese, butter, and milk became important; draft animals and crops such as wheat, rye, and fruits became specific ends. Large-scale wheat farming began in many places. Sicily became well known for its wheat. France likewise raised wheat, and Germany rye. The Visigoths in the fifth century ravaged agriculture until sheep-raising nearly replaced it and then was given a broad pastoral code. But they could not stand before the Saracen in the eighth century. Moors overran Spain and other lands, restoring and improving agriculture, expanding irrigation, and introducing many fruits and plants. Since they did not reach central Europe, it was left to recover along from Visigoth ravages, and the process was slow, long, and trying. Thus central European agriculture was far behind Mediterranean status at the close of the Middle Ages and the beginning of the Columbian influences.

The Industrial Revolution stimulated all farming, and four or five countries studied the problems of soils, rotations, fertilizers, suitable crops, and the improvement of seed and output. Britain worked on all five problems. France worked on soils, rotations, improvement of seed, and nitrogen fertilizers; Germany, on fertilizers, soils, and improvement of seed; Belgium and Netherlands attempted intensification of agriculture, and later Denmark led in coöperative work. In the last twenty-five to thirty years many nations have vigorously attacked their rural problems; their status has been described in the preceding chapters. The United Nations, by means of its Food and Agricultural Organization (F.A.O.), has taken an active part in assisting the nations in Europe as well as in other continents as they proceed to solve their rural problems.

In many cases European agriculture has felt the keen competitions of bonanza agriculture in new countries or in colonial lands. Examples are wheat in Argentina, America, Australia; wool and later meat in Argentina and Australia; sugar in India and Java; fibers (American cotton) supplanting flax. Scarcely an element of rural life now escapes the influence of similar life in other parts of the continent, and many crops in all leading countries are affected by intercontinental influences.

QUESTIONS

1. Why was agriculture less popular than war as an occupation? Give geographic reasons if possible.

2. What changes in agricultural adjustment helped men to pass from self-supporting to profit-making agriculture? from subsistence crops to money crops?

3. What is the evidence for and against the theory that transhumance is a transitional form of living?

4. What types of agriculture should be looked upon as primitive? as transitional? as permanent? List reasons for your classification.

5. To what extent is it wise for nations to tamper with the free movement of rural products from land to land? To what extent is it possible to regulate their movement?

6. How is the social status of men related to their agricultural status and success?

7. What has refrigeration during shipping done for agriculture?

8. How far is it possible, by diversifying and adjusting agriculture, to provide a satisfying level of living for the respective types of rural life of the world?

BIBLIOGRAPHY

BAKER, Oliver E., *Atlas of World Agriculture,* United States Department of Agriculture (Washington, D. C., Government Printing Office, 1917). A new edition was in preparation in 1949.

BOWMAN, Isaiah, *Limits of Land Settlement* (New York, Council of Foreign Relations, 1937).

———, *Pioneer Fringe* (New York, American Geog. Soc., 1931).

CAMPBELL, D. H., *Outlines of Plant Geography* (New York, The Macmillan Company, 1926).

CARRIER, E. H., *Water and Grass* (London, Christophers, 1932).

COLEMAN, Henry, *European Agriculture,* 2 vols. (Boston, Philips and Sampson Company, 1846-1848).

DE CANDOLLE, Alphonse, *Origin of Cultivated Plants* (New York, D. Appleton and Co., 1885).

ERNLE, Rowland E., and PROTHERO, Baron, *English Farming, Past and Present* (New York, Longmans, Green & Company, 1912).

HALL, William H., *Irrigation Development* (Washington, D. C., Government Printing Office, 1886).

MARBUT, Curtis, F., Translation of Glinka under title *The Great Soil Types of the World and Their Development* (Ann Arbor, Michigan, Edwards Brothers, 1927).

MORGAN, O. S., *Agricultural Systems of Middle Europe* (New York, The Macmillan Co., 1933).

ROBBINS, Wilfred Wm., and RAMALEY, Francis, *Plants Useful to Man* (Philadelphia, P. Blakiston's Sons and Co., 1933).

STURTEVANT, Edward Lewis, *Notes on Edible Plants* (Albany, New York, J. B. Lyon Company, 1919).

VIDAL DE LA BLACHE, Paul M. J., *Principles of Human Geography* (New York, Henry Holt & Company, Inc., 1926).

CHAPTER 40

The Growth of Commerce

The craft of the merchant is this bringing a thing
from where it abounds to where it is costly.
—EMERSON

INTRODUCTION

Definition. Commerce, in a broad sense, is the exchange of goods by barter, money, or credits. It is not simply the buying and selling over a counter or in a stall at a fair or market; it involves both the transfer of commodities from one place to another and a change in ownership of them.

Commerce is discussed here because it has passed through a long series of developmental stages that are related to each other as intimately as the commercial transactions of neighboring regions in any given year are related to each other. Commerce cannot be carried on without involving two or more places, nor can it occur as a modern institution without having evolved from simple to complex forms.

Reasons for commerce. Commerce is a geographic phenomenon. It arises in response to two groups of factors: differences in the products of place and place, and differences in the needs of men. The products of regions differ because of variations in climate, in topography, in distribution of land and water, in soils, forests, metals, and other resources. Much has been said in previous chapters of these differences in the several regions and states. But commerce is equally evoked by differences in the needs and desires of men. The physical needs, such as clothing, shelter, food, tools, and weapons, vary as do the climate and weather, resources and topography. Still more subtly, men are stimulated or repressed by environmental circumstances. As suggested in the chapter on climate, men's ambitions and ingenuities rise in some types of climate, and their enthusiasms, vigor, and health decline in other surroundings. With a rise in ambition and vigor man's desires increase. He can achieve more and use a larger amount of commodities; he can find new sources of materials and develop new technics. He widens his reach. Thus these differences in men, augmented by race variation, itself partly an adaptation to geographic conditions, constitute another type of factors animating commerce.

Optima of temperature, humidity, and general atmospheric condition for high efficiency and energetic performance are now recognized. Tests of accuracy and endurance and tests of efficiency in piecework have been made in several types of weather and climate, and the best results were obtained in such climatic conditions as are found in the western temperate part of Europe. Also a map of health in Europe shows this portion more highly favored than all others. Response to these favorable conditions is shown in the distribution of literacy, income per capita, and several other items of calculable data already mapped by geographers.

In the favored parts of Europe men have developed the higher skills, finer arts, and greater efficiency; here they live on a higher economic and social plane. Men's personalities are more creative, energetic, inventive, and ingenious here than elsewhere. It follows that here they want the greater quantity and variety of goods.

Furthermore, in the favored environments the people continually develop their resources. Even a sparse population, when in unfavorable conditions, may make such limited use of its resources that the home space will not support any increase of inhabitants without lowering the living or economic standards. Other people, more densely settled but climatically stimulated, will increase production by adding labor value to their output or by importing and manufacturing raw materials for resale. Thus they draw their subsistence in part from other lands. Through commerce, aided by industry, their subsistence space becomes broader than their home space.

In recent centuries men have devised a number of schemes to influence commerce, to force goods to move to the trader's seeming advantage. By imposing tariffs, taxes, tolls, customs, or duties, men seek to overcome geographic conditions, reverse geographic advantages or nullify geographic influences. Thus they construct barriers against the natural flow of goods from places of easy production to places of difficult production.

The beginnings of commerce. When prehistoric men in France made arrowheads of flint taken from the chalk beds, and men in Greece and on the isles of the Ægean Sea made tools of obsidian, men in Germany and in Asia Minor with neither flint nor obsidian must buy or go without stone tools. When men on the south coasts of the Baltic or on the Frisian Islands found beautiful, light, attractive amber, they soon learned that with it they could buy flint or obsidian. When the hunters in the German forests and in the hills of Asia Minor had gathered furs and skins, they were ready to trade for amber or flint in the north, or for obsidian in the east. Hinterlands became markets for coast products; flints and obsidians were enticed out of their respective lands to purchase amber for ornaments or skins for coats.

Industry, a promoter of commerce, began in Europe with the making of the first weapons and tools of stone, bone, and wood for the hunt. Commerce began from the need of the necessary materials for the tools or possibly from the desire for ornaments of coral, shells, gold, or amber. These beginnings occurred, so far as is known today, about the time of the Günz or first glaciation.

Down through the time of the several ice advances and retreats and the intervening interglacial stages, little improvement or increase in either industry or commerce appears, but after the last ice retreat both showed marked progress in southeastern Europe. Several of the Ægean Islands had unique resources: obsidian in Santorin (Thera), emery in Náxos, red pigments for paint in Keos (Zéa), and copper in faraway Cyprus. Commerce among these islands and with the surrounding mainlands included many materials and articles. Obsidian, raw and in manufactured flakes, was traded from island to island 7,000 to 8,000 years ago. Pottery, metal articles made by pouring copper and bronze, and woven threads in cloth followed. The exchange of commodities proceeded from fixed points of production on bay heads, headlands, river junctions, and other strategic places, through definite topographic lines of easy communication.

Progress in the Bronze Age. That men did not reach the same stage in commerce and industry over wide and separate areas at the same time is not strange. The Bronze Age and even the Iron Age began in some places before Neolithic events closed in others. Even today the range of culture and civilization on the earth is wider than ever before. People already advanced make progress faster than those more backward. In speaking of culture ages we date only their beginnings, for we are still in the Bronze Age in the sense that we still use bronze tools and ornaments. Bronze was in the commercial stream of the Ægean Sea region very early because materials for making bronze (copper and tin) were found approximately together there. Five thousand years ago the emery, marble, and obsidian of this region were exported to Crete and to Egypt. Cyprus exported its copper to the Sumerians in the Euphrates Valley fully as early, and Crete imported bowls of syenite, porphyry, and diorite from Egypt 5,800 years ago. These rocks are not found in the Ægean region, and the skill to work them had not at the time been developed in that region.

The Morava-Vardar route from Ægean Sea to Hungarian Plains was recognized as a highway in 3000 B.C. and possibly was used in Neolithic times. The Danube Valley served as a highway before the river did, but it did not become important in Neolithic time. Other routes into these plains were used in the Bronze Age. Lower passes of the eastern Alps and Carpathian passes at the heads of the Tisza and Maros rivers were traversed southward to Italy and northeastward to Russia. A route through the Slovene Alps was also used. The plains of Hungary seem to have interested the people of the Bronze Age.

From earliest times salt, frequently made naturally in lagoons on the coasts, was an article of barter from seacoasts to hinterlands. It may have been carried inland before there was any effort to make it artificially from sea-water. Via Salaria, the oldest Roman road, was used to carry salt from the evaporating ponds near Ostia into the Apennines. Another route led into the mountains from Herculaneum. In later times Mediterranean coasts of France exported salt to the Auvergne plateau and imported cheese from its valleys. Amber went south from Samland up the Vistula River over low divides near Lemberg and down the Dniester; and Frisian amber traveled the Rhine-Rhône route to the Mediterranean, possibly in exchange for salt evaporated in lower latitudes or in higher temperatures and drier air.

Obstacles to commerce. Commerce had to develop against many obstacles, the chief being costs. Goods carried even short distances increased in value rapidly; hence only small articles of considerable value could meet the charges. Destruction by storms and loss by robbery in border lands or in inhospitable places, far from administrative centers, interfered perhaps as much as did prejudice and suspicion arising from ignorance and isolation. Risk of deterioration in transit prohibited many things from travel, and as governments arose tolls were barriers. Difficulties encountered on land drove men to sea trade, but marine commerce hugged the shores while navigators peopled the depths and distances with impossible monsters and unknown terrors until historic times. The compass was not known in Europe until well into the Middle Ages.

In the light of these introductory remarks setting forth some of the fundamental principles of intercourse and the beginnings of trade in Europe, we can now turn to certain of the regions of Europe and trace their expanding commerce.

IN THE EASTERN MEDITERRANEAN REGION

Before the Christian Era. It is somewhat of a venture to ascribe commerce to tribes and peoples before recorded history begins, but it is not difficult to establish the fact of the movement of goods in the eastern Mediterranean Region before any people purposely told its story.

In the Near East powerful nations arose and built cities thousands of years before the Christian Era, and before the Iron Age began anywhere. Some such cities, buried in sand and their own waste, covered by later cities and forgotten by following generations, have but recently been excavated. The Mesopotamian Valley was the seat of several such ancient empires that arose in their Stone and Bronze Ages. By 3000 B.C. they engaged in trade westward in metals, wool, grain, and building materials, some of which probably reached Europe. This trade served mainly luxury needs, scarcely touching the masses, and was carried on by land.

Cretan commerce dates back at least to 2000 B.C. and involved pottery, bronze, building materials, wheat, and many luxuries. Phœnicians engaged in sea trade as early as 1500 B.C. They carried linen and wool fabrics, dyed with Tyrian purple, a red color, made from the fluids of the tropical shellfish *Murex*. They exported glass which they made from sand; imported tin from England, copper from Spain and Cyprus, iron and silver from Spain, gold and ivory from Africa; and carried spices westward from the tropical spice islands in the Indian Ocean. This was sea trade.

The commerce of the Greeks grew with their colonizing policy, urged forward as much by the desire for wealth as by any geographic factor; yet this desire for wealth was an outgrowth of the ambition and brilliant genius of the people, stimulated, scholars now suggest, by the characteristic climatic conditions of their land. Their poor agricultural possibilities, thin soil, hilly topography, and dry climate, assisted commerce by driving men out to sea. Greek colonizing wove a border of race and culture around the Black Sea as early as 800 B.C. There were Greek trading centers at Malaga

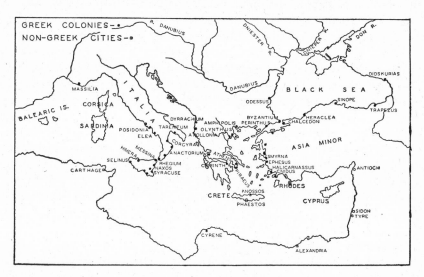

Greek colonies and non-Greek cities figuring in Mediterranean commerce before and near the time of Christ. (Adapted from Gibbins's *History of Commerce in Europe* and from historical atlases)

in Spain, Marseilles in France, Syracuse in Sicily, and in many places on the shores of the eastern Mediterranean. Greeks manufactured olive oil, wine, and clay and bronze objects, raised honey and figs, and wove wool for export. Athens exported silver from its Laurium mines, and imported wheat from the plains of Russia north of the Black Sea, and from Sicily, Egypt, and Syria. Athens also imported ship-building materials, salt fish, and slaves from the Black Sea borders and brought in delicacies from Sicily, lower Italy, Cyprus, Egypt, Lydia, and Pontus. Cities were built under the stimulus of commerce; in fact, populations of 100,000 and even 200,000 assembled in cities but only when foreign commerce had developed to help sustain and feed their people.

Roman commerce began about 200 B.C. and rose as that of Greece declined. Rome brought home products as tribute and taxes and sent out service in government, roads, and administration, a legitimate exchange but not trade in any such sense as that the Phœnicians and Greeks. The trade of Rome with India and the Far East was more important commercially than all its trade north and west. Routes by sea led to Alexandria in Egypt, then overland to the Red Sea, and by water to India. Other routes by sea met the Syrian coast and converged on ancient Petra, and eastward to the Persian Gulf, then by sea or by land to India. Other routes led by land across the Balkan Peninsula to Istanbul [1] and thence by land to India and to China.

Trade developed between ancient industrial cities, such as those in Phœnicia, Syria, Egypt, and on the Grecian shores of Asia Minor on the one hand, and backward regions producing only extractive products on the other: for example, the shores of the Euxine and Adriatic and those of the western Mediterranean. It was also active between Mediterranean cities and temperate regions of Central Europe as well as subtropical regions in Africa.

The early Christian centuries. During the early centuries of our era the Romans completed their net of hard, straight, unyielding stone roads over southern Europe and as far north as Roman authority went. They reached Spain, France, Germany, and the Near East, alike topping mountain passes or traversing plains. A road led from the Mont Cenis Pass down to Châlon-sur-Saône, over Côte-d'Or to Rheims, down the Seine to Paris, and north-westward to Calais. Boats took the freight across the channel to Dover, and the road led on to London. A map of the Roman roads resembles a modern railroad map with nodes or centers and radial or connecting patterns. Nodes occurred at Merida in Spain, others at Rheims and Marseilles in France, and at London. One road followed the Riviera, and three or four made their way over Alpine passes.

The great barbarian invasions, incited by Turanian thrusts from the East, where there may have been drought sufficient to start migrations, occurred mostly during these centuries. They disturbed trade routes, brought information, and left Europe to arrange new commercial patterns. Belligerent occupancy by the barbarians of the Danube Valley checked its use for commerce and aided in setting trade routes across the river. But soon the resulting disorganization gave place to more effective and far-reaching organization.

Great changes came over all of southern Europe as the organizing and administrative strength of Rome waned, but there was no sudden break between the old and the new. The changes and adjustments occupied more than a century, as long as American history since the beginning of our republic.

[1] This city has had its name changed several times; today it has gone back from "Constantine's city" to the old name Istanbul. It was first called Byzantium by its Greek founders in the seventh century B.C.

During the Middle Ages. As the commerce of the Bronze Age grew from that of the Neolithic, and the early historic developed out of that of the prehistoric, so medieval commerce and industry found their roots and trends in what had gone before.

Trade in the Levant and with the East was less disturbed by medieval changes than that in the middle and western parts of the Mediterranean Basin because the Eastern Roman Empire endured longer. An ever-increasing stream of spices, drugs, dyestuffs, and other luxuries came from the East to be distributed through Europe. Pepper from India, and cinnamon, nutmegs, mace, ginger, and cloves from the Molucca Islands and hence

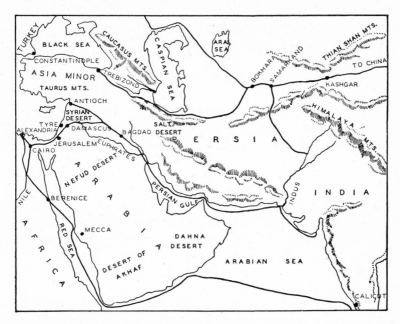

Principal routes from the East toward Europe in the Middle Ages. The route through Bagdad seems to be the oldest and was in operation about A.D. 750. The route through Berenice was most used at the close of the period. The western termini of these routes are the beginnings of the European routes. (Adapted from Day, *History of Commerce*)

three times as costly as pepper, were much appreciated among the people in Europe who could afford them. Alum from salt marshes came with several dyes and was used to help set their colors. Among drugs were aloes, balsam, borax, camphor, and other gums and resins that brought large prices for small packages; they were therefore worth the long, precarious journey. In the later Middle Ages sugar began to come from India to supplement the honey of Europe, which until then had been the only table sweet known. Gem stones were always articles of commerce as well as of wealth and continued to move in these east-west streams. Cotton fabrics also came from the East, because Europe grew no cotton and had little skill in manufacturing it. The Mediterranean Region exported linen and woolen fabrics to the East and probably furnished as many slaves to the East as it received from the Orient.

The routes from the East were three. One from India reached the Persian Gulf and Mesopotamia, then divided to Antioch, Damascus, Tyre, and Alexandria. This was essentially a land route. Another was by sea to the Gulf of Aden and through the Red Sea to Alexandria. This prospered when the Mesopotamian route was later closed. The northern route out of India reached to Samarkand and Bokhara and there divided, one branch leading north of the Caspian Sea and up the Volga, the other south of the Caspian to Trebizond and Istanbul. The several termini of these three routes were the beginnings of European routes.

Venice arose because of the arrival of the commerce-devastating Huns in the fifth century, when their invasion blocked the routes through the Danube Valley. The first exports from Venice were salt and salted fish. Venetians became very notable traders in Oriental and Near East imports, which they often increased in value by manufacturing processes. They brought wool and amber from the Baltic regions when peace made this possible, and, as the Hanseatic League developed in the north, Venetian galleys, passing through the Strait of Gibraltar, met Hanse boats and traders at Bruges. Venice must trade, must live by trading, because it had no lands to cultivate. It captured trade privileges at Constantinople and contested with Genoa for trade in the Black Sea, where were found hides, fish, timber, and slaves, and the Ukrainian wheat which was more essential to Venice than to Genoa. Lumber from the slopes of the Caucasus Mountains was used for ships, gondolas, and houses; hides and furs were dressed and manufactured into garments and ornaments. Traders came to Venice from Germany, Bavaria, France, Hungary, Tuscany, and Lombardy. Venetian trade was aided by the Crusades, though the latter were not commercial in spirit; Venice became a synonym for commercial power and luxury as the Crusaders returned to their homes in western and central Europe.

The merchants of Pisa and Genoa developed Mediterranean commerce as did the Venetians and often came into keen competition with the latter. Carrara marble and Elba iron helped to weight the scale in favor of Genoa and Pisa. Since the only strategic position on the whole Adriatic belonged to Venice and position on the west side of Italy had to be shared by several cities, Venice became as powerful as all on the west side combined and ruled the commerce of the eastern Mediterranean as Britain later controlled the Atlantic. Brenner Pass, opened long before Venice was founded, was the chief outlet northward, but other pass routes converged on the lower Po and Venice. With all this advantage Venice remained supreme until the Atlantic highway was opened by Columbus, a Genoese; then Venice slowly yielded as the West in general came into power.

After the Middle Ages. The entry of the Americas into commerce and
the extension of trade with the Orient induced slow but important changes
in the Mediterranean commercial outlook. From the East still came dates,
alums, and sugar; from Africa skins, and from the Near East scarlet and

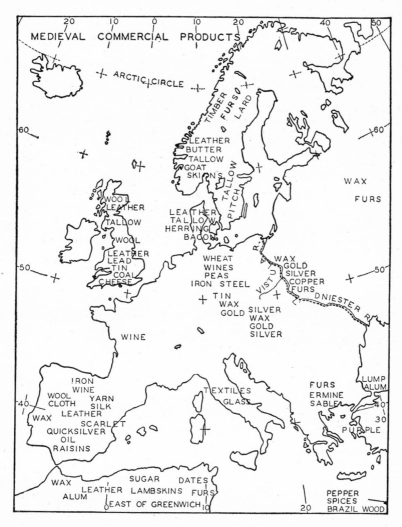

Commercial products listed on the books of the merchants of medieval times, with their
usual sources. The Vistula-Dniester route is shown. (Adapted from Day, *History of Commerce*,
and from historical atlases)

purple dyes, coral, sponges, and salt. The Iberian Peninsula furnished raisins, figs, olive oil, wine, quicksilver, and wool. The Mediterranean became
an increasingly important purchaser of fish from the northern countries
and America. Probably no less business was done in the Mediterranean

Region, but more was done in northwestern Europe, and trade with the East continued to gain in significance. The improvements of harbors, ships, and systems of credit and of exchange helped to lift both northwest Europe and the Orient to new importance.

IN NORTHWESTERN EUROPE

Another commercial center developed in northwestern Europe around the North and Baltic seas. Until it held intercourse by sea with the Mediterranean cities this center was not important, but it possessed commercial possibilities of consequence.

Before the Christian Era. No such powerful and cultured nations arose in Northwestern Europe as developed in the Near East, and the beginnings of commerce lay in local differences in products and needs. Strabo points out that local trade in Helvetia (Switzerland) had excellent opportunities in his day because the hills and mountains furnished resin, gum, pitch, torch pines, honey, beeswax, and cheese, while glen farming was good, producing vegetables, grains, and fruits that the hill tribes needed.

Similarly, exchanges were made between the coast and interior tribes. Fish and other sea products were bartered for grains and animal and forest products; and the commodities were moved in boats along the streams.

As pointed out in describing the commerce of the Mediterranean Basin, Baltic amber was probably the first export from northwestern Europe. It was carried up the Vistula and Oder and down the Tisza and March to the Danube, then across the river below Belgrade, up the Morava and down the Vardar to the Ægean. Amber also traveled other routes as shown by the discovery of fragments along several of them.

Alpine passes were used for commerce and the movements of people before Roman roads sought them. Celts filtered through them in 350 B.C., and Hannibal struggled through one in 220 B.C. One of the amber routes also crossed the Alps, and the Mont Cenis Pass was used between France and Italy at the same time. Traders, migrants, armies, and pilgrims crossed the Brenner Pass in early days. Its favorable altitude of only 4,495 feet served several routes from the north and from the south, and it was used in 1500 to 1800 B.C. or in the Bronze Age of Central Europe.

Both the lower and middle Danube were on routes from northwest Europe and the Near East. The two sections of the river and valley were quite distinct because of the gorges and rocks at the Iron Gate, and separate routes from each part reached out both north and south. The Greeks who traded on all shores of the Black Sea drew resources from the plains of the lower Danube but did not work above the Iron Gate. They brought into the plains wines and olive oil from Mediterranean lands and took away wheat, honey, and slaves.

As the Christian Era approached, trade between the northwestern parts of Europe and the Mediterranean Region increased, always fostered by Roman military roads and Roman stability of government.

The British Isles were more remote from the continent, and their people remained backward, even compared with those of Flanders and Central Europe, until the Romans came in and brought refinements in living. There was little commerce to mention.

Christian centuries before the Middle Ages. The decline of Roman authority and the invasion of the barbarians disturbed the beginnings of commerce around the North and Baltic seas relatively more than in the Mediterranean Region. There was less to lose, and the losses were serious. Local trade suffered least. Everywhere the peasant brought his produce to the village and exchanged it for needed manufactures from the local village supplies. Traveling traders were less common than in previous periods. There were peddlers, shopkeepers, merchants (partly wholesale traders), associations, and partnerships. All these decreased in importance and numbers in northwestern Europe as the Dark Ages advanced, and commerce was nearly paralyzed until, about A.D. 1000, reorganization began to be necessary.

Hanseatic League. Just as commercial unit areas developed in the Mediterranean, a strong one in the east and a weak one in the west, so also unit

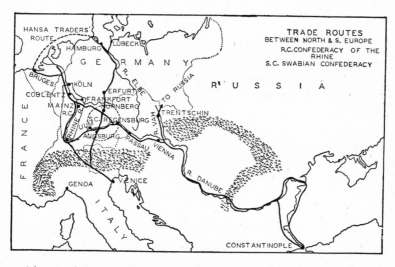

Commercial routes between north and south Europe in the days of the Hanseatic League. (Adapted from Gibbins's *History of Commerce in Europe* and from atlases)

areas developed in the northwest of Europe. The Baltic area was one, the North Sea unit another; but in neither case was there the urban unity of Venice. About A.D. 1000 German cities began to sense possibilities and Scandinavian towns to feel their importance. The merchants in each of several towns united for safety in travel and in business at home. Then large federations were needed, and the German merchants in four groups of cities united. A Rhine group came first with its head at Cologne; soon after the North German and Baltic groups were set up with their heads at Lübeck and Visby; the Saxony group rallied to Brunswick; all four united under the name Hanseatic League (*Hanse* means a band or society) and Lübeck became the capital of the League. The first treaty looking toward the organization of the League bears the date 1157; a hundred years later the organization was very strong. In the thirteenth and fourteenth centuries it controlled essentially all the commerce of the Baltic and North seas, and while mercenary and selfish it did much to build up commerce and free it from the shackles of pirates, robbers, taxes, governmental interference, and fear. It greatly encouraged the awakening of industry in its cities from London to Koenigsberg, a revival of industry less affected by any physical change in the environment of the cities than by the maturing of men under the stimulus of the energizing climate. It hurried the march of northern civilization and brought transcontinental contacts of inestimable value to both north and south. Merchants of thirty countries met amid aggressive people at Bruges, "the Venice of the North," intermediate between Mediterranean and Baltic seas. The League made and enforced vigorous laws, improved harbors, studied, mapped, and planned trade routes, and swept into its schemes the business of all northern lands from Russia to France and England, and from the Scandinavian states to the Rhine trough and Leipzig.

It greatly increased the range of commercial items because it was systematic, banished many tolls and taxes, used larger ships, and handled vastly more goods. Flemish and German industrial cities sent woolen and linen cloth and many metal articles to Russia. The Rhineland sent wines, beer, and rock-salt. Russia returned hides, furs, honey, beeswax, pitch, and other forest products. Scandinavia furnished iron and copper ores, leather, butter, tallow, lard, and skins. England furnished wool, leather, lead, cheese, and tin. Both seas furnished herring and other fish, and most border nations salted the fish for export to inland towns and to the Mediterrean. Metals, furs, lumber, and animal products came from the continental interior, and the Mediterranean furnished quantities of its characteristic commodities.

The League took a long time to develop, and its disintegration was slow and long, related to many detrimental factors. A fundamental influence in its decline was the discovery and development of America, which placed England, France, Holland, and even Spain and Portugal in the front row with reference to commercial enterprise and turned great trade routes away from the German cities. Commercially, the Mediterranean and Baltic lost heavily to the North Sea and the Atlantic. The rise of English commerce and independence was as phenomenal under this new ægis as was the growth of the League 300 or 400 years before. With these developments in non-League territory, boycott came to mean nothing, for a boycotted city could still trade with thriving commercial and industrial cities outside the League. The rise of democratic ideals in central western Europe and the failure of Hanseatic autocracy to adjust to changing conditions and rising competition further helped to weaken the League. The great migration of herring from the Baltic to the North Sea that began about 1425 gave its impetus in the same direction. Internal jealousies and bitter discussions over disaffections and concerning ways and means of saving the League also tore it apart, so that it ceased to function in the eighteenth century, and final legal actions closed its affairs in the early and middle nineteenth century.

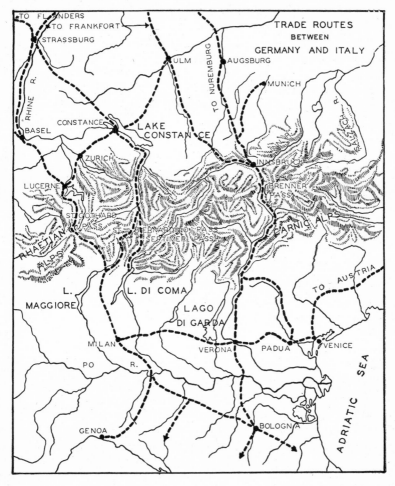

Trade routes through the Alps connecting the Hanse towns and towns of Italy. The Brenner Pass route was probably most important, but the various routes changed in importance as used. St. Gotthard Pass was the last one opened. (Adapted from Day, *History of Commerce*)

Every European country shared in the trade engendered in the Levant and by the Hanseatic League; and not only commerce, but industry, democracy, and the general level of living and of culture improved.

Markets and fairs. During the early Middle Ages many traveling merchants were so nearly robbers in spirit that laws were made requiring all major trading to be done in the presence of village or town authorities. This move gave standing to local markets, and their convenience to producer, consumer, and salesman alike became very obvious. They were established in most towns in northern Europe and in many in the south and persist today in some form, often specialized as flower or cattle markets.

It was a natural step from the local market to the fair of wider scope; many cities, at least one in every country, organized and provided place and shelter for fairs. Here people brought every conceivable kind of merchandise and exposed it for barter or sale, and here people from hundreds of miles gathered to see and be seen, to hear and to tell, to buy and sell. Many merchants went from one fair to another throughout the year. Each fair operated for a number of days, sometimes weeks. The first one was at St. Denis in Paris in the seventh century; later there came to be a hundred or more scattered from Nizhni Novgorod, east of Moscow, through Germany as at Leipzig, on to France, Spain, Italy, and even to Constantinople. A few still continue, and others have become permanent bazaars, such as the old bazaar in Istanbul. The social aspects of a fair included the gathering and dissemination of news, the display of side-shows, dancing, dramatics, the performances of clowns, poets, musicians, and gamblers. Strategic trade situations were usually selected for fairs, and, in addition, shrines, holy places, and historic objects for pilgrimages were often used to help draw the business. Such fairs were necessary, because Europe had only a small shopkeeper class, and even merchants in cities kept limited stocks. Transport of goods was slow and perilous and needed just such an urge as the fair supplied.

Guilds. In England about the time of the Norman Conquest, A.D. 1066, when industry and trade were just beginning, merchants saw the advantage of organization and formed guilds for fellowship as well as for business. The idea spread to artisans in England and to many types of workers in other lands, so that the guild in business and industry and in religion and art became a common thing in most countries. While it was constituted locally for protection and coöperation, it acquired broad social aspects because of the federation of like guilds over a whole country.

EUROPE FACES AMERICA

Transitions. The entry of the New World into commerce and the extension of trade with the Orient have made slow but mighty changes in the commercial and industrial outlook of Europe, particularly of western states. Nations have come naturally to specialize in occupation or kinds of production. Norway, Denmark, Netherlands, and England have become carriers; Belgium, Netherlands, Germany, and England have become manufacturers. Poland, Germany, and France produce sugar beets; Netherlands, Denmark, Switzerland, and France, dairy cattle and products; and Hungary, Rumania, Russia, Bulgaria, and Yugoslavia, agricultural products in general.

The acquisition of colonial possessions which followed the period of discovery and exploration, 1492 to 1700, added to the long list of human migrations yet another chapter, and this, by shifting the relative values of commercial routes and commodities, gave more business to western Europe than to the classic Mediterranean lands that for 3,000 years had held chief place. Great trading companies were organized in several of these west European states to develop trade and production in Canada, in India, in various parts of Africa, in the West Indies and the East Indies. These, while in themselves causes for trade growth and expansion culminating in the imperialism of the nineteenth century, were prompted by the same geographic and climatic forces that had been operating down through the ages.

The Industrial Revolution which began in the late eighteenth century and is still in rapid progress speeded up many manufacturing processes, particularly in England; the invention and use of machinery spread to France and the Low Countries, thence over western Europe and America. In speeding industry, often a hundredfold, the revolution hastened commerce. The spirit of invention came rapidly to pervade commerce and communications and almost to eliminate time in commercial transactions. Such increase in the power and celerity of production and communication was one of the causes underlying the social and political revolutions that followed and that have, in recent decades, nearly remade Europe. Its influence is now penetrating remote parts of the continent.

The Industrial Revolution, though it worked hardships, was unavoidable, a necessary development for the growing and awakening populations of the earth. It could not have been prevented if men were to live and develop in the stimulating conditions of western Europe; the new technology cannot now be dispensed with if men are to make the best uses of their new and widening horizons. Present improvements in commerce and communication are bringing even greater social and economic revolution than did the introduction of machinery 150 to 200 years ago. From the dugout to the super-liner, from the plodding oxen to the streamlined automobile and train, from the earth-bound caravan to the winging plane, man has moved forward, sometimes steadily, sometimes by leaps and bounds, until today commerce and travel link the world, with its industry and agriculture, in a speed and exactness only dreamed of in the tales of the magic carpet and Aladdin's lamp.

Another transition. For several decades the open-door policy partially and intermittently applied in the Orient has promoted a growing trade between many oriental lands and the nations of Europe and America. The Orient has raw materials to sell, silk and other fibers, fruits, nuts, eggs, selected minerals, and in the warmer, subtropical stretches lumber and forest products, rubber, tanning extracts and medicinal products. It manufactures artistic textiles, embroideries, bronzes, and chinaware by which the people can sell their skill, art, patience, and labor without sapping heavily their natural resources.

As the Orient finds market for its products it becomes a market for Western manufacture, tools, machines, gadgets, books, roads, and means of communication.

This transition might be expressed as a change from the medieval luxury pattern for the few to a mass market for necessities, conveniences, and utilities for the millions.

QUESTIONS

1. Why did commerce in the Mediterranean Region so far exceed that in other parts of Europe in the pre-Christian eras?

2. Compare the Rhine and the Danube as commercial highways. Will their importance become more nearly equal? Why?

3. Examine the changes and progress in commerce and communication that have occurred in the last 2,000 years and try to think what may be their status and nature 2,000 years hence.

4. As the history of commerce is surveyed, note any changes in the relative value of the several causes for commerce; in the nature and significance of the obstacles to commerce.

5. We have seen that the Eastern Mediterranean, Western Mediterranean, and Baltic Sea regions have been at times distinct commercial units. What are some of the more or less definite units today? What areas seem to be tending toward definite units? Will there, should there, be such units?

BIBLIOGRAPHY

ABBOTT, W. C., *Expansion of Europe* (New York, Henry Holt & Company, Inc., 1924).

ALLEN, Nellie B., *Europe, Geographical and Industrial Studies* (Boston, Ginn and Company, 1928).

BASTABLE, Charles F., *The Commerce of Nations,* 9th ed. revised by T. E. Gregory (London, Methuen & Co., Ltd., 1923).

BLANCHARD, W. O., and VISHER, S. S., *Economic Geography of Europe* (New York, McGraw-Hill Book Company, Inc., 1931).

BOWMAN, Isaiah, *The New World* (Yonkers-on-Hudson, New York, World Book Company, 1928).

———, *Limits of Land Settlement* (New York, Council of Foreign Relations, 1937).

———, *Pioneer Fringe* (New York, American Geog. Soc., 1931).

BROWN, Harry G., *International Trade* (New York, The Macmillan Company, 1927).

CHATER, Melville, "The Danube, Highway of Races," *National Geographic Magazine,* Vol. 56 (December, 1929), pp. 643-697.

CHISHOLM, G. G., *Handbook of Commercial Geography* (New York, Longmans, Green & Company, 1922).

DAY, Clive, *Economic Development in Modern Europe* (New York, The Macmillan Company, 1933).

———, *History of Commerce* (New York, Longmans, Green & Company, 1922).

DELL, Burnham N., and LUTHRINGER, George F., *Population, Resources, and Trade* (Boston, Little, Brown & Company, 1938).

DIETRICH, Bruno, and LEITER, Hermann, *Produktion Verkehr und Handel in der Weltwirtschaft* (Vienna, L. W. Seidel and Son, 1930).

DIETRICH, Ethel B., *World Trade* (New York, Henry Holt & Co., Inc., 1939).

EAST, W. Gordon, *Historical Geography of Europe* (New York, E. P. Dutton & Co., Inc., 1935).

ELLSWORTH, Paul T., *International Economics* (New York, The Macmillan Company, 1938).

ENKE, Stephen, and SALERA, Virgil, *International Economics* (New York, Prentice-Hall, Inc., 1947).

FEIS, Herbert, *The Changing Pattern of Economic Affairs* (New York, Harper and Brothers, 1940).

FREDERICK, John H., *Commercial Air Transportation* (Chicago, R. D. Irwin, Inc., 1947).

HIRSCHMAN, Albert O., *National Power and the Structure of Foreign Trade* (Berkeley and Los Angeles, University of California Press, 1945).

HEYD, Wilhelm Von, *Histoire du commerce du Levant au Moyen-Age* (Leipzig, O. Harrassowitz, 1936).

HODGES, Charles, *Background of International Relations* (New York, John Wiley & Sons, Inc., 1931).

HUNTINGTON, Ellsworth, and CUSHING, Sumner W., *Principles of Human Geography* (New York, John Wiley & Sons, Inc., 1934), and later editions.

HUNTINGTON, Ellsworth, *World Power and Evolution* (New Haven, Yale University Press, 1919).

LEHMANN, John, *Down River; A Danubian Study* (London, The Cresset Press, 1939).

LENGYEL, Emil, *The Danube* (New York, Random House, Inc., 1939).

LYDE, L. W., *Some Frontiers of Tomorrow* (London, A. & C. Black, Ltd., 1915).

MATTHEWS, W. H., Jr., "Norse and Hanseatic Trade Routes and Commodities," *Bulletin Geographic Society of Philadelphia,* Vol. 29 (1931), pp. 35-46.

MENDELSSOHN-BARTHOLDY, Albrecht, *The European Situation* (New Haven, Yale University Press, 1927), Esp. first and last chapters.

NASH, E. Gee, *The Hansa* (New York, Dodd, Mead & Company, Inc., 1929).

NEWBIGIN, Marion I., *The Mediterranean Lands* (New York, Alfred A. Knopf, Inc., 1924).

OGG, Frederic A., *Economic Development of Modern Europe* (New York, The Macmillan Company, 1917).

PEAKE, Harold, and FLEURE, H. J., *Corridors of Time,* 8 vols. (Oxford, Oxford University Press, 1927).

POLANYI, Karl, *The Great Transformation* (New York, Farrar and Rinehart, 1944).

SALISBURY, Ethel Imogene, and STEDMAN, Lulu M., *Our Ancestors in the Ancient World* (Boston, Little, Brown & Company, 1936).

SEMPLE, Ellen C., "Development of Hanse Towns in Relation to Their Geographic Environment," *Journal of American Geographical Society,* Vol. 31 1899), pp. 236-255.

———, *Geography of the Mediterranean Region* (New York, Henry Holt & Company, Inc., 1931).

STRABO, *The Geography of Strabo,* trans. by Horace L. Jones (London, William Heinemann, 1917-1928).

TAYLOR, T. Griffith, *Environment and Nation* (Chicago, University of Chicago Press, 1936).

THOMPSON, J. W., *An Economic and Social History of the Middle Ages* (New York, The Century Co., 1928).

TOZER, Henry F., *A History of Ancient Geography* (Cambridge, England, Cambridge University Press, 1935).

TREVER, Albert A., *History of Ancient Civilization* (New York, Harcourt, Brace & Company, Inc., 1936).

TYLER, John Ecclesfield, *The Alpine Passes: The Middle Ages* (Oxford, B. Blackwell, 1930).

VAN VALKENBERG, Samuel, and HUNTINGTON, Ellsworth, *Europe* (New York, John Wiley & Sons, Inc., 1935).

WHITBECK, R. H., and FINCH, V. C., *Economic Geography* (New York, McGraw-Hill Book Company, Inc., 1941).

CHAPTER 41

The Geography of Civilization and Culture

Civilization is simply a series of victories over nature.—WILLIAM HARVEY

Culture is the habit of being well pleased with
the best and knowing why.—HENRY VAN DYKE

GENERAL STATEMENT

Introduction. A chapter upon civilization and culture in America would be a set of disjointed notes dealing with separate races and transplanted cultures. In Europe it is a tale of long evolutionary struggle from the brutish biped with flint-tipped arrow and scratches upon the cave walls above his open fire to the modern man peering through spectacles at the newest machine whose measure is gaged to the exactitude of a millionth of an inch, or listening to a symphony brought halfway around the globe by harnessed invisible waves.

Civilization, or material civilization as it is sometimes called, has to do with the material well-being of men. It is the sum of the physical responses to the physical part of the environment.

Culture, or spiritual culture if one includes both physical and spiritual aspects under the general name, emphasizes the intellectual aspects of well-being and of life. It is the sum total of spiritual responses to environment. For this group of responses the environment consists much more largely of spiritual or at least of non-material circumstances.

Civilization works with tools, weapons, clothing, shelter, machines, and whole systems of industry and trade. Culture is non-material and invisible; it is the form of human behavior; it includes methods and patterns of thought, it progresses from folklore and superstition to language and literature, to art, science, religion, and philosophy; it leads toward the full appreciation of spiritual values.

Civilization as mentioned in previous chapters. Many references to specific civilizations and to civilization in the abstract have been made in the chapters that describe the various countries. Ancient and modern civilizations are recognized; rural and urban civilizations have been noted; simple and complex, elementary and mature, nomadic, agricultural, and industrial civilizations have been discussed.

Several of the nations in central and eastern Europe—Hungary, Rumania, Bulgaria, Yugoslavia, and most of Russia—are devoted essentially to rural pursuits and enjoy a rural civilization. Their livestock, their methods of cultivating and harvesting crops, and their rural and village life are adjustments to soils, slopes, and climatic conditions. All European nations have agriculture. In most of them at least half the people live in close contact with the soil, and in all of them the people have been more fully occupied with rural problems in earlier centuries than they are today. Rural economy has now gone so far that there are many subdivisions of agriculture, or kinds of specialization. Dairying in Denmark and Netherlands, poultry-raising, floriculture in parts of southeastern Spain and Netherlands, horticulture in Italy and France, and bee-raising in Czechoslovakia are some of the types of specialized adjustments to particular conditions.

Industry—manufacturing—follows agriculture and manifests quite another type of geographic adjustment to conditions. A nation is not considered to have entered an industrial civilization until 10 to 15 per cent of its people are engaged in the nation's industries. Every nation manufactures some products, and a few nations have become so actively industrial that 25 to 30 per cent of their people give their attention to manufactures. France, Belgium, England, Austria, and Germany are the leading industrial nations. They have taken advantage of minerals, fuel, and other resources; their citizens have built factories, installed power plants, and crowded themselves into cities so that many operations can be carried on in close proximity. A rural civilization tends to keep people scattered over the land, but an industrial civilization tends to bring people together into great agglomerations. People in the former way of life have many common interests in rural affairs, much freedom, and great individuality; people in industrial centers have fewer interests in their work, are restricted to routines and to specialization in performance, and tend to herd together in mass reactions and movements. Social unrest flourishes; people are more susceptible to excitement and turn more quickly from one idea to another in industrial environments than do farmers in rural communities. Although individuals in industry may be as short-sighted and backward as in a rural community, large coöperative and social organizations are more likely to develop where so many more people occupy a limited area.

As industry develops, commerce becomes necessary in order to amass raw materials near the factories and to distribute manufactured articles to a wide range of purchasers and users. In pursuit of commerce there become necessary many items of response or adjustment to geographic conditions that are unknown in the rural or industrial civilizations. Cities are needed, and in addition roads and waterways; all kinds of communication are established; interest in far-off places grows; forms of transportation multiply; methods of business contact between strangers are elaborated. These developments are unnecessary in a rural civilization. England, Norway, and Netherlands have a larger proportion of their people engaged in commerce than any other nations in Europe, and they are said to have a commercial civilization. While a city can become largely commercial, it is hardly possible that a whole nation shall become so, because commerce requires commodities and a commercial nation's responses must include some extractive occupations, such as quarrying, lumbering, mining, or else manufacturing to provide the goods to be transported. For those groups of people engaged in commerce a more far-reaching geographic relationship exists than for those in a rural or industrial civilization. They care for another category of environmental elements and respond in a different way to weather, topography, water, and land.

A civilization is described as high, advanced, or mature when it includes many and often intricate adjustments and responses to the physical environment; a civilization is spoken of as low when it makes only simple and few alignments with the physical surroundings. When a nation uses its territory extensively and intensively for the various rural pursuits, uses its agricultural products, its mineral and forest products, and its power to maintain industry, and makes an active, intelligent business of transporting, buying, and selling its products, it is classed as a highly civilized nation. This means that it uses its environment not only in one way but in two or more ways and in an intelligent, systematic manner, profitable for the growth of its own people and for that of the people of other nations. It is therefore appropriate that civilizations should be classified and graded with reference to the number, complexity, and completeness of their correlations or connections with, or responses to, the physical conditions that surround man.

It is recognized that some types of civilization are developed later than others in the history of a people, but that fact does not mean that one type is necessarily a better civilization than another. Consider a region like southeastern Russia, capable of nomadic civilization and nothing else; then, when that adjustment has been made, any other civilization that might be tried, no matter what, would be a lower, a less satisfactory, use of the region. If, however, a region like central Belgium devotes itself wholly to agriculture or wholly to industry, its adjustment is less complete and its civilization is lower than if it made both uses of the region. If nomadism and a sparse population remain the only type of utilization when a region is capable of intensive agriculture, heavy industry, extensive commerce, and the sustenance of a dense population, that region must be classed as one in a low stage of civilization.

Many occupations besides those already mentioned are involved in varying degrees in the evolution of civilization. Mining, lumbering, and quarrying enter in important ways into the round of activities of a maturely civilized people. The various phases of conservation are also factors. Education, both cultural and technical, building and construction, finance and government must be coördinated as parts of the adaptation of a highly civilized people.

The impact of geographic factors upon civilization is illustrated simply and concretely by the type of architecture employed and by the materials used for building roads and houses. In Norway, Sweden, Switzerland, Finland, and northern Russia, lands of forest, most houses are built of wood. In France, with open fields and chert in the chalk beds, many houses are made of cobblestones or of oölitic chalk trimmed at the corners with chert. Beyond timber line in Lapland and along the arctic coast of Russia there are houses of ice and snow. Open houses, scarcely shelters from our point of view, and yet often built of the ever-present stone, are common in Greece. In mountainous countries where winds are high, the roofs are weighted down with slabs of stone. Porches and even rooms are roofed with glass in those parts of France where gloomy, cloudy weather is common. Roads were built of fluvio-glacial gravels in England and other glaciated countries, and when the speeding automobile was invented roads of gravel were bound with tar, or made secure with cement.

CULTURE AND CIVILIZATION

Culture as defined at the opening of this chapter has gone, in some places, hand in hand with civilization and in others has lagged far behind. Culture may become nobler among one people than among another even though they are in similar types of civilization. Usually there is interplay between culture and civilization. They demand much of each other. The intimacy of relation between them and the possibility of the development of the one without the other constitute an interesting study.

The use of fire and the methods of building fire are elements of civilization; the choice of uses to which fire shall be put—warming, cooking, worship, or power—and the interpretation of what fire really is are elements of culture. Material used for fuel varies much with geographic circumstance. Wood, in northern, timbered countries, is used on trains and steamboats as well as in houses. Peat is a common fuel in many glaciated countries, for example, Ireland, eastern Netherlands, northern Germany, and much of central western Russia. Charcoal is a common house fuel in the southern peninsulas, where wood is scarce and only small fires are needed or where a single room or less is to be warmed at one time. With the rise of transportation, concentrated fuels are shipped hundreds of miles on cars and boats or in pipe-lines, broadening the use of the fuel and the reach of the user. All this is civilization, and perhaps the processing of fuels to increase their usefulness should be so classified, but the skill in research to develop the processes is culture called forth by resources and the needs of men.

The use of fish by the builders of the kitchen middens and the methods of fishing are matters of civilization; the recognition of property rights, etiquette, and pertinent ritual observances, the development of prohibitions and taboos, are items of culture.

Flint was used for ornaments, tools, and weapons; quarries were opened to provide flint; shells, bones, corals, and amber were collected and manufactured into necklaces and anklets. All this is civilization. But these items bespeak a cluster of ideas about dress, about work, intertribal relations, and art; this is culture. Inventions of processes, technique, and skill in flint-working are expressions of the mind, are culture, and the same aspirations can be expressed in flint-chipping skill as well as in song and epic.

Now translate these terms of primitive civilization and culture into terms of modern civilization until chipping flint becomes a manufacturing industry, quarrying includes mining and, combined, they build the metal industries of England, France, and Germany. Stringing of beads becomes the clothing industry of Warsaw and Manchester; the arrow and spear become machine-guns, tanks, and atom bombs. Shall we call them civilization? On the other hand, invention grows into research, skill into technical education, and the pictures on rock walls of caves become a symphony, a drama, or a painting.

The machine for harvesting, quarrying, dressing hides, or propelling a boat is an element of civilization; it has been made as a response to geographic conditions and is a part of man's conquest of his physical environment. The feelings which its presence and operation arouse, the method and philosophy of life it engenders are parts of the culture of the machine age. When the neighboring peoples with all their talents are included in the environment, both civilization and culture are often urged forward. Interesting examples of the interplay of environments, resources, and neighboring peoples are found in the growth and decline of Mediterranean nations, whether one is studying civilization or culture.

Culture is an accretion of traits, some handed down from generation to generation, some borrowed and some invented. Cultural decay stems from a state of mind hostile to change. Nations have feared a static population, but a failure of population to increase does not mean static minds. A growth of population beyond the means of subsistence is much more serious. When population ceases to increase, invention should continue and the level of subsistence rise as man makes his living more easily. Then comes more time to think and to devote to creative activities. In man's power and freedom to think are the springs of culture. These flourished in Greece and more recently again in France as opportunity came; they expressed themselves in myth, religion, art, science, social forms, government, education, and the whole round of cultural elements.

The culture of the individual, the group, or the nation has rights to be observed by other individuals of the family, by the community, or by other nations. Here is one of the sources of friction in the Danubian states.

No one has the right to infringe upon another's culture rights, any more than upon his railroad, harbor, fishing, and mining rights.

How environment works. Environment in soils, resources, vegetation, and position offers opportunities and obstacles to man. Opportunities may be utilized or neglected; obstacles may be overcome or passively accepted. Thus one part played by geographical environment in the development of civilization or culture consists in promoting decisions as to what may or may not become part of the human experience. A wide range of experience becomes possible. The most important part of environment is probably not the material but the ethnic factor, formed by the surrounding civilizations, cultures, and personalities.

Physical barriers restrict the spread of culture when they limit contacts. Man now has discovered and built up in Europe means of transportation and communication over ancient barriers, and he listens, speaks, and even sees through former walls. Thus much more is now at his disposal than was a thousand years ago. Isolation restricted civilization and culture, and no doubt does yet, but culture in its eternal progress has steadily struggled to annihilate isolation. The distance from a Roman road was very important; towns and cities took a more liberal attitude toward learning if on a road, and when at a junction point or node of Roman roads they surpassed those on one road only. Cities on the coast became seats of learning of more note than those in the interior. Today towns some distance from a railroad are backward compared with those on leading railroads. Lack of language must have been a tremendous barrier; lack of a universal language is a significant barrier in Europe today. Besides language, man has thought out many social amenities and commercial methods which remove barriers and help him meet his fellows.

Environment sets few real barriers but many opportunities and challenges. Man may meet them in any one of several ways. The Dutch have met their delta situation in one way, the Venetians theirs in another, the modern Greeks at the mouth of the Vardar in a third, and the Rumanians the Danube delta problems in a fourth. Responses to transportational problems have been quite different in different ages. Some generations have walked; others have built roads and driven animals so they might ride; others have built ships and steamboats and dug canals; some have built railroads and automobile roads, while some are already flying.

Small mountain valleys in Switzerland have promoted little groups of *communes* of tightly organized individual workers; the wide-open plains of Russia have led to loosely organized broad estates with the village *mir* and later the collective farm, the state farm, and the coöperative farm with the several institutions that minister to them. Each geographic form has promoted its own peculiar design of government. Many other illustrations can be found of the influence of geographic factors upon the direction of civilization or the tone of culture.

Some elements of culture are closely related to definite factors in the physical environment. For example, art is limited by the media available. The Greeks and Italians of old found a different, possibly a more beautiful and a truer expression of form in marble than the Hittites found in their black, porous basalt. Soft, melodious accents arose in the languages of the mild southern European climate, and the harsh aspirate tones are more prevalent in higher latitudes with severe climates.

Literature is colored in many ways by the locality in which it is written and by the experiences of the author. Sagas of the north countries, folk stories of the middle countries, and the folk songs in any country are full of response to local influences. A generation ago, Geikie called attention in his *Scenery of Scotland* to the weird music of the peoples of the west coast under the influence of wind and sea, cloudiness, storm, and fog. Dostoievsky's novels and philosophy grew on the Russian plains, Grimm's *Fairy Tales* in the mountains and forests of central Germany, and the Robin Hood legends in the Lincoln woods in the Jurassic belt and the Chalk areas north of the Fens of eastern England. A poet of the Lake District cannot have the mind of a son of London, nor a peasant of the heart of Ireland one like that of a resident of sunny Sicily.

A climate that stimulates inventive genius and makes generous provision, albeit with hard work, for subsistence will permit a higher and more universal development of education and will invite more creative thinking and expression of such thinking than an isolated, austere, or penurious environment that gives no leisure and intercourse between groups.

A high culture was worked out by the Greeks and later by the west European nations. Grecian climate was salubrious and stimulating but probably not more so than that of western Europe. The climate and country in eastern Mediterranean lands were never more productive than those of western Europe, but Greece had in addition a well-developed institution, slavery, that gave to a small class leisure as valuable as any leisure western Europe ever had. The institution of slavery was disturbed by the spread of Christianity, and Grecian culture declined. Many believe that the development of malaria in the Greek and Roman lands assisted in the decline of education and other forms of culture. Whatever the cause was, there is no question but that culture declined in the Near East and rose in western Europe. Another factor to urge western peoples forward was no doubt the growing knowledge of subsistence methods in the cooler and more stimulating western climate. There is scarcely evidence enough to predicate sufficient change of climate in both Near East and western Europe to completely shift the position of the leading culture center. But it is true that the Near East yielded to the West.

Roman influence followed Grecian and brought ideas of marine safety and of the Roman city social order. The town was superseded by the city, worship of the fatherland displaced the sanctuary of the home, public allegiance transcended private relations, and the Roman road became the vehicle for the promulgation of the new spirit.

A similar, though less complete, spread of learning, ideas, and ideals prevailed through the coastal belt of the Hanseatic League. Here the result was a blending of civilizations and cultures of the several peoples until the general level of living was raised and men knew and tolerated one another through the whole zone. Through commercial intercourse the Renaissance and Reformation, 1525 and following, spread, and there came centuries of rapid intellectual expansion and geographic exploration followed by colonization to promote commerce.[1]

When America was discovered and its settlement had begun, culture in Europe spurted forward in the countries most concerned. More liberal views of trade and religion began to emerge; even governments had to adjust to the new relations. Education became more liberal and more widespread. A broader civilization was attained by many people because they traveled, adventured in strange surroundings, took a strong hold on new resources, and undertook more commerce. With all this came a fresh outlook and an opportunity to evade or change old customs. During this period many material conquests were made. The compass, gunpowder, and printing were discovered or invented; machines multiplied, and man's physical contacts broadened with every move. His dominion expanded over sea and land, and his education, with the press to help, had possibilities of becoming universal. The whole sweep of physical advance, civilization, liberated men's minds, opened new vistas, and placed new opportunities before men and new responsibilities upon them; this is the geography of culture. Eliot says "true culture is not exclusive, sectarian, partisan, but the very opposite and is not obtainable in solitude." The broadening horizons of world knowledge broke old intellectual barriers and let men go.

The spread of civilization and culture through Europe can be observed in the development and present distribution of education, language, religion, and government, as well as in the movement of agriculture and commerce described in the two preceding chapters.

Education. Literacy and education are hardly synonymous, but education proceeds much more readily when illiteracy has disappeared. A map of literacy showing the number of persons who can read and write in percentages of all people, nation by nation, indicates that the highest literacy

[1] *Renaissance* = rebirth, between Middle Ages and Modern Period, especially, in learning, science, art, literature, and architecture. *Reformation* = reshaping, especially in religion, philosophy of Church and State, and in leadership. The following events and dates helped to usher in these great periods of change; Invention of the printing press, 1440; Fall of Constantinople to the Turks in 1453; Luther's nailing of his 95 theses to the Wittenberg church door, 1517; Zwingli's revolt and publication of his 57 theses in Switzerland, 1523; Luther's protests against many customs of Roman Church, 1529; Calvin's "Institutes" published in Basel, 1536; Separation of Anglican Church in England from Roman Catholic church during 1558 to 1603. The Crusades, 1096-1222, did much to prepare people in western Europe for rebirth and reshaping.

is at present in nations living in the stimulating climate of temperate western Europe and that, in general, illiteracy increases outward from this irregular central area. Under the spur of the success of nations in this favored area, less favored nations are now enforcing elementary education, an illustration of the influence of neighbors. One cannot map education as easily as literacy, but one can arrive at approximate measures of education by ascertaining the percentages of the people who have gone through recognized stages of formal education such as the eighth grade, the high school, the university, and the technical schools. Such data are obtainable for the countries in temperate western Europe, but not for most of the other countries for the simple reason that here less interest is taken in higher education. Even such measures of education as are here suggested would not wholly reveal the constructive educational activities, or the discipline of the mind, feelings, and manners carried on in any nation. A survey of the intellectual output in literature, science, music, and education per thousand people, the quality and permanent value of such output, and the relative appeal that the output makes to other nations would help to measure the educational status of a people.

It does not seem possible to make the computations suggested above; hence conclusions must be left to each one's own reading and imagination. The writer shares the impression with many that there is considerable correspondence between the lines of equal climatic energy and the lines of equal education. It is probably quite unfair to judge a people's backward position in education or in other fields of endeavor without considering its environment.

As was mentioned above, the position of a people with reference to commercial routes and contacts with other peoples is a factor of much significance in the development of culture. A map of classical Greek commercial routes and the "universities" of the times reveals that most of the schools were on trade routes and frequently at junction joints— Athens, Massilia, Corinth, Rhodes, Miletus, Tarsus, and Alexandria. In these cities lived the philosophers, poets, and artists, as well as the geographers. Here was so much of thought and progress, so much of news and information that thoughtful, scholarly men flourished. There was much in such cities to digest intellectually. Semple wrote in 1931, "Traders were the apostles of civilization in the Mediterranean basin," and "poets, artists, and philosophers were found in commercial cities, for here the currents of thought flowed full and fast." Further, commercial centers were disseminators of the elements of culture. Not only seamanship and politics were products of Greek colonization and commerce, but a lifting of the standards of living and a spreading of Grecian ideas. The colonies knit a fringe of Mediterranean culture around the Black Sea, while the hinterland where Greeks never penetrated remained destitute of their culture. Religious tolerance entirely around the Mediterranean Sea is a result of this same Greek influence and represents the emancipation of intellect here in centuries before the Christian Era.

Commerce, so important an aid to civilization and culture, arises not primarily for their sakes but from sources fundamentally physical on one hand, and selfishly personal on the other. Yet the resulting educational progress may well be sufficient reason for any city or nation to desire and encourage commerce.

Language. The languages of Europe belong almost wholly to the Aryan group of tongues. It is obvious that these languages have spread from some center in the Near East, perhaps Iran, to the southeastern part of Europe and then northward and westward across the continent, carried by men as they were learning to live in the cooler, wetter climates. They are closely related to Sanskrit and the modern Aryan tongues of India and are believed to have a common origin with that group.

This family of Indo-European languages in Europe embraces the Teutonic group, English, German, Dutch, and the four Scandinavian branches, Danish, Swedish, Norwegian, and Icelandic; the Romance group, Portuguese, Spanish, French, Italian, and Rumanian; the Hellenic of the Greeks; the Slavic group, White, Great, and Little Russian branches, the Polish, Wendish, Czechish, Slovakian, Slovenian, Serbian, Croatian, and Bulgarian; the Lettic-Lithuanian group; the Celtic group, which includes Bretons in France, Welsh, Irish, and Scottish; and the Iranic group, three branches of which, Kurdish, Armenian, and Persian, are spoken in the Caucasus and Transcaucasian lands. These seven groups of tongues serve more than 95 per cent of the people of Europe or over 500 million persons. About 140 million speak Romance languages; over 150 million Teutonic; and over 200 million Slavic. The Greek language is used by over 6 million; Lettic languages by over 4 million, and Celtic and Iranic by nearly as many each.

Non-Aryan languages are spoken by many small groups: the Basque by about 500,000 people, the Albanian by about 1,000,000, the Magyar by about 8,600,000, the Finnish and Estonian by nearly 5,000,000, Turkish by nearly 1,000,000 in Europe, and Mongoloid tongues by several groups of Asiatic origin, mostly in eastern Russia and in Bulgaria, whose numbers are estimated at about 5,000,000.

The Basque language is called Pre-Indo-European, and the Albanian tongue Pro-Indo-European. Both languages seem to be relic tongues almost crowded out by the westward march of the Aryan language. The people speaking these relic tongues are interpreted as relic peoples very much diluted by intermarriage. In each bit of country the people with their ancient language are shut away in young mountains from most of the great streams of travel and trade. Similar races, possibly with similar languages, occupied great areas of Europe in the early ages, but they have been completely absorbed by invaders, and their languages have been displaced by the sweep of the Aryan languages over all the continent. These relics, then, are the least diluted peoples with least disturbed languages. Similarly Irish, Welsh, Scots, and Bretons speak relic Aryan tongues almost displaced by later variants. The displacing languages have spread through many types of people, some differing more than do their languages. Furthermore, language lines, kinship lines, and national lines do not usually coincide. Isolated languages differ from each other more than do those near together; and languages close together but isolated as a group resemble each other. Portuguese and Spanish are more nearly alike than either is like any third language. Spanish, French, and Italian differ more than Dutch, English, and German. The three Scandinavian tongues also have much more in common than do the south European tongues. Yugoslavic differs more from East Slavic than either does from West Slavic. In many places, more or less isolated, dialectic differences have developed.

The modern facilities for communication and intercourse are breaking down most language lines, and if it were not for the unfortunate expression of nationalism through language the natural response to the geographic conditions would continue to melt the languages into one.

From prehistoric times Mongoloid languages called Finno-Tataric or Finno-Ugrian have spread into eastern Europe, in part with Mongoloid peoples. In the far north where the population was sparse, these peoples and their languages pushed farthest and placed Lapps and Finns with their non-Aryan tongues in their present situations. Relic groups of both types, left stranded in northeastern Russia when Slavs spread northward, have been absorbed in large part, and their languages are much colored by Slavic influences.

The Magyar people were Mongoloid both in blood and in language. Their migration is well understood because, so far as Europe is concerned, it is wholly historic. Not only are the Magyar people blended with neighboring peoples at least up to 50 per cent, but the language has been diluted on every side. Pure Magyar does not exist. Some students feel that the people have become mixed more than the languages and assert that there is now no Magyar race distinction aside from language.

Tatar-Turkish people also spread over southeastern Europe and when they departed left relic centers of language which are continually fading out under the influence of the surrounding languages.

It is thus clear that languages, when crowded by invading languages, persisted only in geographically protected places; that they moved north and northwestward from the eastern Mediterranean; that they spread across racial and national lines; and that the freer the modern means of communication become, the greater are the resemblances between adjacent languages.

Religion. The early religions of Europe show the effects of geographic forces. The Greek religious ideas date furthest back of any that are historic. Out of their town and city type of social and political organization came the notion of city gods. At a similar time Romans were essentially rural and lived in very small groups or on farms and had farm and household gods, the *lares* and *penates*. Later, annoyed by enemies, they were driven to consolidate; then came the city and state religion with Mars, god of war, as the chief deity.

Nearly every primitive people, whether in Europe or not, had a god of fertility whose function was to make the soil productive or the cattle fertile. This seems to be a most logical deification for people to make in the stage of development when agriculture was beginning and when the acquisition of food was the most necessary and universal occupation. The Minoans had among others a goddess of fertility, and their history illustrates the belief that gods belong to specific regions. When the northern Greeks came about 1200 B.C., they brought Zeus, the sky-god, but as they came into Greece and Crete they adopted the native gods and made the Minoan goddess of fertility the mother of Zeus. The recognition that gods belonged with the lands and the place arose out of circumstances of topography, climate, seas, rivers, and forests.

The idea of resurrection after death came from lands where vegetation died down in the autumn and rose again in the spring, or died with drought and blossomed with the return of rain. Men's ideas of heaven and hell were quite reversed in extremes of climate. Northern tribes pictured the abode of the righteous as warm, dry, and sheltered, while evil-doers were consigned to the numbing, paralyzing effects of eternal cold and freezing; but the Hebrew heaven had shade and cool flowing waters for the good, while the bad were thrust into a dry, parched, hot place, as fatal to life as the worst desert. The Celts, harried by storm and pestilence, believed the dead had something to do with the mischief these misfortunes brought; hence they propitiated the dead with sacrifice and other rites.

It has often been noted that all three great monotheistic religions of the earth arose in the same locality and under similar, rather severe geographic conditions. Judaism first appeared in Palestine; Christianity followed, and not far away Moslemism had its origin. It is also pertinent that other religions which arose in that vicinity were swept away by these.

Christianity developed at a time of important and expanding commercial activities and spread rapidly. Its first general acceptance was promoted by three well-known factors: the comparative universality of one intellectual language (the Grecian) and of one supreme government (the Roman) and the ease of communication which such language and government afforded. The aid offered by such a material circumstance as the well-made, much-used Roman road must not be overlooked. Probably the purest interpretation and teaching of this religion centered in Rome and the western Empire. A less satisfactory form of Christianity developed in Istanbul and Greece, colored no doubt by the philosophy and life of the eastern people. The Western Catholic type spread northward and westward, as is proven by the memoirs of early missionaries and the ruins of chapels, abbeys, and monasteries scattered from Rome to Bergen. With the increase of power came corruption, which proved intolerable to some in the free atmosphere and energizing climate of southern Germany and Switzerland. Here arose the Reformation, which sent waves of Protestantism over all of northwestern Europe and to American shores. The virility of Christianity and its adaptability to human needs as compared with northern non-Christian religions are attested by its progress and acceptance in place of the native religions. This same Western Catholic Church, spreading to Spain, met there in those early days a people less thoughtful and inquiring than those in Germany. It was so far away from the Reformation centers that its corruption was not challenged, so the Spanish Catholic Church became noted for its intolerance and its Inquisition. The Eastern Church spread northward into Slavic teritory, where little ever happened to challenge its corruption and bigotry until recent times, after Church and State had become closely identified. By modern means of communication and transportation the Slavs were enabled to see the West prospering with its industrialization. Realizing that much of their economic, social, political, and religious machinery was antiquated, they decided to throw out all at once. There may be some excuse for the Communist characterization of religion as it was experienced in Russia.

Government. The earliest political units were probably based on kinship among nomadic people who had no territorial ties, and who must be in small groups for reasons of subsistence and personal protection. The most obvious tie for such a group is that of blood relationship. The ruler was the oldest man, or in war a valiant, more vigorous, younger man. This patriarchal or tribal form of government was a response to the geographic necessities. Where government and religion were combined, as among many early tribes, the chief claimed divine right to rule as well as the right due to age or valor. Units were small and well scattered, because subsistence depended not on intensive cultivation of crops but on foraging over natural preserves for berries, nuts, roots, leaves, birds, and beasts.

When domestication of animals began, groups could be larger and property rights required protection. Leadership required strength and wisdom enough to settle tribal difficulties. Because the tribe was still nomadic, it still remained relatively small. Except under favorable conditions, alliances and unions were ill-advised, lasted only a brief time, and were difficult to maintain. More often tribes divided because they had become too large, and united only under powerful leadership or against a common foe.

Homer described the political status of the tribal Greeks. At that time kingship was generally hereditary but might be changed as circumstances suggested; the people had a council of sub-chiefs and an assembly of all the citizens. The organization was not strong but was integrated under pressure of invasion, raid, and war. Later, when riches and commerce came, the people built prosperous cities and developed an intellectual life for the few, which promoted the intelligent study of governmental problems and the rise of a variety of governments. External pressure and common foes drove Greeks to unite and depend upon their unity of race, establishing a much larger group.

Tacitus, giving us the first picture of tribal government among the German tribes, says that at first the chieftainship was not hereditary. Cæsar adds in his writings that even in his day there was no kingship, and in time of peace no common magistracy. The situation seems to have been much the same as in early Greece, but looser and less permanent.

The beginning of fixed agriculture, planting and harvesting, required homes and introduced among the people the territorial tie and sovereignty for which a permanent chieftain was needed. In very early days coalitions, alliances, and unions arose for economic reasons, and today they seem to rely upon economic necessity more than upon anything else. Strong leadership has long been important in building up large political groups, but without economic, linguistic, racial, religious, or some other common interest, groups disintegrate when the powerful leader dies.

All changes in government should be looked upon as adjustments or attempts to adjust to changing conditions and expanding interests, and not interpreted as efforts to reach a fixed state or status. European political history has had a morphological unity; it has been a perpetual adaptation to growing or shifting connections and contacts with internal or external geographic conditions. New resources, new highways, or new uses for lands have been found; new neighbors have arisen or former ones have declined; therefore, peoples and nations have revised their own methods, boundaries, or activities and with these changes have come political changes in order the better to coördinate the new adjustments. The trend has been and still is toward larger unities and broader adjustments, toward a world state and a universal unity. Men should not try to realize this important coming event prematurely but work toward it continuously.

Cumulative culture. The time element is a factor in both civilization and culture. It takes more time for one people to make the same progress than for another under similar circumstances. No two tribes or peoples are exactly alike, nor are their environments the same, nor have the environments operated the same length of time in the various cases. Nor does one people forever move slowly in culture just because it once did. Perhaps the British people are a good example of long-arrested development followed by more rapid progress. The age in which one lives, as well as the nature of the environment, has much to do with the response one makes.

Through a lifetime one stores up his impressions, whether of landscapes, people, literature, or music, and matures the while. How much more fixed and potent they may become when stored through many generations of a tribe or people in the same locality! They are not stored alone in memory but in architecture, tools, methods of performing agricultural or industrial processes, ceremonies, and regulations, until, unless the tribe have external contacts, it is difficult to introduce new styles and methods.

With opportunity comes choice. That both environment, in a broad sense, and cultural antecedents color one's choices may be seen in many parts of Europe, but the nature of the antecedent culture has been cumulative and continually related to the geographic setting through the centuries. National and racial psychology has developed through long centuries of adjustment. Cultural contacts are important influences in conditioning choices and performance, and they too are results of both present environment and a long line of migrations, adjustments, and distributions. These distributions are a result of diffusions of civilization and culture, again a question of highways, means of communication, and contacts.

We look at Europe, a group of nations actuated by varying cultures which are the growth of ages, but forced into close physical proximity as time and space melt before the impact of modern invention. Will the instruments of an increasingly homogenous civilization bring these cultures into harmony?

QUESTIONS

1. If a geographic setting, lived in for a lifetime, deeply impresses the culture of an individual, what may well be our attitudes toward people who have long dwelt in a geographic landscape different from ours?

2. Under the same premise, what difference would travel make in one's culture? What point is there in living for a time in different environments?

3. Gibbins says, "The industrial factor is the most important in civilization." Discuss the truth of his statement. Why is it important?

4. Semple says, "Commerce is the great apostle of civilization." Discuss the truth of her statement. Compare the quotations in questions 3 and 4 and consider which has the greater significance, presenting your evidence.

5. Why, upon reading this chapter or the whole book, do we not all arrive at the same conclusions?

6. Discuss the problem of balance between birth-rate and death-rate as a factor in culture. Is it a factor in civilization? Why?

7. An art museum bears the inscription, "Art is a heritage from the past, a gift to the future." Discuss the truth of the statement as an item in culture. Is it reasonable to include an art collection as an element in one's environment? Why?

8. Discuss the relative value of some elements of culture as environmental factors in the development of other elements of culture.

BIBLIOGRAPHY

Artz, Frederick B., *The Intellectual History of Europe* (Boston, Ginn and Company, 1941).

Breasted, James H., *The Conquest of Civilization* (New York and London, Harper and Brothers, 1938).

Browne, Lewis, *This Believing World* (New York, The Macmillan Company, 1933).

CARVER, Thomas N., *The Essential Factors of Social Evolution* (Cambridge, Harvard University Press, 1935).

CHAPIN, F. Stuart, *Cultural Change* (New York, The Century Co., 1928).

CLARK, Grahame, *From Savagery to Civilization* (London, Cobbet Press, 1946).

DIXON, Roland B., *The Building of Cultures* (New York, Charles Scribner's Sons, 1928), the last chapter.

DUNNING, William A., *A History of Political Theories* (New York, The Macmillan Company, 1923).

ELIOT, T. S., *Notes Towards the Definition of Culture* (New York, Harcourt, Brace & Company, Inc., 1949).

ELLWOOD, Charles A., *Cultural Evolution* (New York, The Century Co., 1927).

EYRE, Edward, *European Civilization,* 7 vols. (London, Oxford University Press, Humphrey Milford, 1934-39).

FAIRGRIEVE, James, *Geography and World Power* (London, University of London Press, 1941).

FEIBLEMAN, James, *The Theory of Human Culture* (New York, Duell, Sloan, and Pearce, 1946).

GEIKIE, Archibald, *Scenery of Scotland* (London, The Macmillan Company, 1887).

GETTELL, Raymond G., *History of Political Thought* (New York, The Century Co., 1924).

GIBBINS, H. de B., *A History of Commerce in Europe* (New York, The Macmillan Company, 1891).

GRAVES, Frank P., *History of Education Before the Middle Ages* (New York, The Macmillan Company, 1911).

———, *History of Education during Middle Ages* (New York, The Macmillan Company, 1910).

———, *History of Education in Modern Times* (New York, The Macmillan Company, 1913).

HOCKING, William E., *Man and the State* (New Haven, Yale University Press, 1926).

———, *What Man Can Make of Man* (New York and London, Harper and Brothers, 1942).

HUNTINGTON, Ellsworth, *Civilization and Climate* (New Haven, Yale University Press, 1924).

———, *The Pulse of Progress* (New York, Charles Scribner's Sons, 1926).

———, *Mainsprings of Civilization* (New York, John Wiley & Sons, Inc., 1945).

HUXLEY, Aldous Leonard, *Science, Liberty and Peace* (New York and London, Harper and Brothers, 1946).

JEFFERSON, Mark S. W., "Culture of the Nations," *American Geographical Society Bulletin,* Vol. 41 (1911), pp. 241-265.

KROEBER, Alfred L., *Configurations of Culture Growth* (Berkeley and Los Angeles, University of California Press, 1944).

LOWIE, Robert H., *The Origin of the State* (New York, Harcourt, Brace & Company, Inc., 1927).

———, *An Introduction to Cultural Anthropology* (New York, Farrar and Rinehart, 1940).

MALINOWSKI, Bronislaw, *A Scientific Theory of Culture* (Chapel Hill, University of North Carolina Press, 1944).

MARTIN-CLARK, Daisy E., *Culture in Early Anglo-Saxon England* (Baltimore, Johns Hopkins Press, 1947).

MYRES, John L., *Mediterranean Culture* (Cambridge, England, Cambridge University Press, 1944).

PEAKE, Harold, and FLEURE, Herbert J., *The Corridors of Time,* 8 vols. (London, Oxford University Press, 1927).

POMFRET, John E., *The Geographic Pattern of Mankind* (New York, D. Appleton-Century Co., Inc., 1935).

POWYS, John Cowper, *The Meaning of Culture* (New York, W. W. Norton & Company, Inc., 1929).

ROBINSON, James Harvey, *"Civilization"* in *Encyclopedia Britannica,* 14th ed., Vol. 5 (New York and Chicago, Encyclopedia Britannica Co., Inc., 1937), pp. 735-741.

SEMPLE, Ellen C., *Geography of the Mediterranean Region* (New York, Henry Holt & Company, Inc., 1931).

SHAW, Charles G., *Trends of Civilization and Culture* (New York, American Book Company, 1932).

SMITH, Preserved, *A History of Modern Culture* (New York, Henry Holt & Company, Inc., 1934).

TOYNBEE, Arnold J., *Civilization on Trial* (New York, Oxford University Press, 1948).

TURNER, Ralph Edmund, *The Great Cultural Traditions* (New York, McGraw-Hill Book Company, Inc., 1941), esp. Chap. IX.

VIDAL DE LA BLACHE, Paul M. J., *Principles of Human Geography* (New York, Henry Holt & Company, Inc., 1926).

WALLIS, Wilson D., *Culture and Progress* (New York, McGraw-Hill Book Company, Inc., 1930).

WARE, Caroline F., *Cultural Approach to History* (New York, Columbia University Press, 1940).

WHITBECK, R. H., and THOMAS, Olive J., *The Geographic Factor* (New York, The Century Co., 1932).

WISSLER, Clark, *Man and Culture* (New York, Thomas Y. Crowell Company, 1923).

Index

(9)